W9-BIV-421

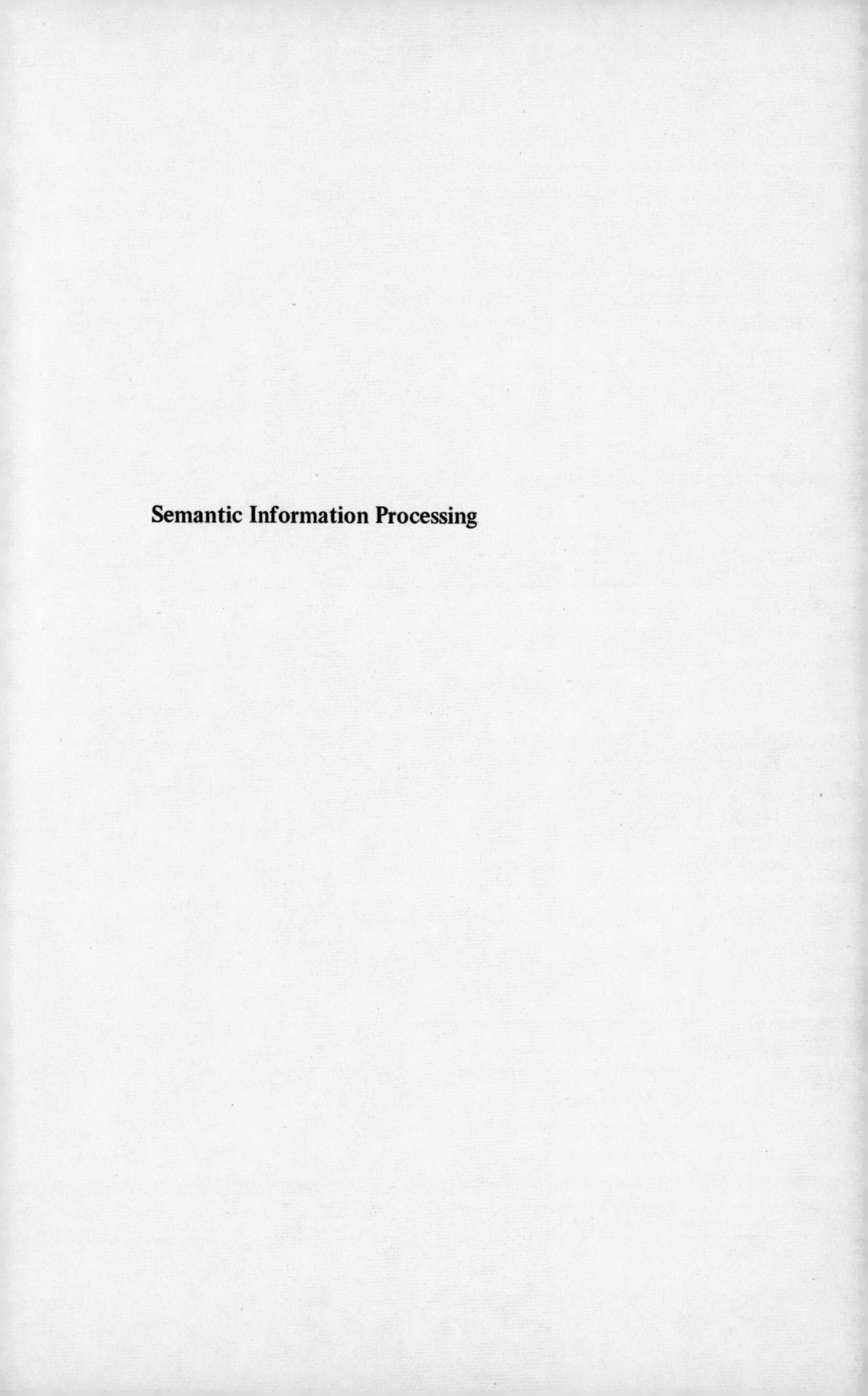

Semantic Information Processing

Semantic Information Processing

Marvin Minsky, Editor

The MIT Press
Massachusetts Institute of Technology
Cambridge, Massachusetts, and London, England

Set in IBM Press Roman. Printed and bound in the
United States of America by Publication Press, Inc.

Library of Congress catalog card number: 68-18239

Preface

How can one make machines understand things? This body is a collection of studies in *artificial intelligence,* the science of making machines do things that would require intelligence if done by men.

Most of the chapters are slightly edited Ph.D. theses, and the book is to serve two purposes: to make the results of these dissertations more available to scientists, and to exhibit the work to students searching for new problems in this area. Abbreviated versions of such studies, as usually presented in scientific journals, rarely suffice as a basis either for further work or for critical evaluation. Besides, the uncompressed original dissertations are usually easier to read and understand.

Each of the projects described in this book has already inspired more ambitious attacks. I hope to collect reports of those that succeed into a second volume within the next year or two.

In the long introduction that is Chapter 1, there are scattered remarks about contributors to this work. I want to acknowledge explicitly the influence of my own collaborators, John McCarthy and Seymour Papert, on the work that was done at M.I.T., and the support of that work, in its early years, by the M.I.T. Research Laboratory of Electronics and the M.I.T. Computation Center and, in recent years, by the Advanced Research Projects Agency through M.I.T.'s Project MAC. I want also to thank Edmund C. Berkeley for demanding and helping to get the papers collected and published.

Cambridge, Mass. Marvin Minsky
July 1968

Contents

1. Introduction

Marvin L. Minsky

1.1 Survey

This book presents a group of experiments directed toward making intelligent machines. Each of the computer programs described here demonstrates some aspects of behavior that everyone would agree require some intelligence.

Each program solves different kinds of problems. These include resolving ambiguities in word meanings, finding analogies between things, making logical and nonlogical inferences, resolving inconsistencies in information, engaging in coherent discourse with a person, and building internal models for representing newly acquired information. The programs are very limited in the range of situations they can handle. This survey will attempt a perspective for viewing these achievements and limitations.

Within the small domain in which each program operates, the performance is not too bad compared with some human activities. Thus Bobrow's STUDENT program (Chapter 3) rivals, within its algebraic scope, the average high-school student. Evans's ANALOGY program (Chapter 5) works also at this respectable level. The reasoning abilities of the programs of Black and Raphael (Chapters 6 and 2) could perhaps be compared with those of slightly younger children, and we simply do not know enough about how powerful Quillian's methods (Chapter 4) would be when provided with a more substantial knowledge bank. But much more important than what these particular experiments achieve are the methods they use to achieve what they do, *for each is a first trial of previously untested ideas.*

These programs work by setting up goals, trying to fit data into previously acquired patterns, forming and testing hypotheses, and so forth, often by using the meanings of statements that have been made to them.

Some readers may be disturbed by my deliberate use of psychological terms, such as "meaning," not usually employed so freely in describing the behavior of machines. But it is my opinion that these mentalist terms are not all superficial analogies. Indeed, the computer programs described here themselves confirm the validity and fertility of the intellectual revolution that came with the discovery that at least some mentalist descriptions of thought processes can be turned into specifications for the design of machines or, what is the same thing, the design of programs.

I will not waste the reader's time arguing the merits of this attitude: The level of the programs' performances speak for themselves. Instead, I wish merely to point out, for perspective, that there exists *no* other, competing family of experiments descending from the positivistic, behavioristic tradition in psychology whose rigid grip is just beginning to crumble. In that tradition we never dared speak about "meanings" or "goals" but only about input-output "observables." To be sure, there is no question about the initial stimulating effect of this hard-headed attitude that lead to the discoveries of many previously unsuspected facts about behavior (such as Skinner's demonstration that the contingencies of the occurrence of *reinforcement* could vary its effects by factors of hundreds). But in its more recent history, "behaviorism" has lead mainly to ineffectual, near-linear, statistically oriented theories. Originally intended to avoid the need for "meaning," these manage finally only to avoid the possibility of explaining it.

The practicality of the alternative–finding useful mechanistic interpretations of those mentalistic notions that have real value–is associated in its most elementary forms with what we call *cybernetics,* and in its advanced forms with what we call *artificial intelligence.* The public emergence of cybernetics can be dated rather sharply because of the nearly simultaneous appearance of three basic papers on the subject. Rosenblueth, Wiener, and Bigelow (16) showed how simple goals and purposes could be realized in feedback machines. McCulloch and Pitts (10) pointed out how some other logical categories and mental concepts could be represented in "neural" nets, and Craik (4) suggested a variety of ways by which machines might use models and analogies. To be sure, all of these had had their own intellectual ancestors, but here for the first time we see a sufficiently concrete (i.e., technical) foundation for the use of mentalistic language as a constructive and powerful tool for describing machines. It is ironic that these ideas descend more from the "idealistic" rather than from the "mechanistic" lines in metaphysical and psychological thought! For the mechanistic tradition was fatally dominated by the tightly limited stock of kinematic images that were available, and did not lead to models capable of adequate information processing. The idealists were better equipped (and more boldly prepared) to consider more sophisticated abstract structures and interactions, though they had no mechanical floor upon which to set them.

In the following decade these ideas were further developed, notably by Ashby (1), Hebb (7), and MacKay (8), both in theory and through experiments with mechanical and electronic devices. But it was not until general-purpose computers became available in the early 1950's that work on more complex organizations could proceed beyond philosophical speculation, for adequate theoretical mathematical techniques were not (and still are not) available. Intelligence surely can exist only within very intricate structures. Classical mathematical methods could deal with complicated systems only in very special situations; it was not possible to cope with but a few simultaneous nonlinear equations, to say nothing of a few dozen, or a few million. Under certain conditions mathematical analysis can mange complexity, e.g., when the situation gets complex in such a way that the parts of the system can be treated as individually and independently random; this is what happens in Statistical Thermodynamic theories. But this is just what does *not* happen when, as in a computation system, the structure has a more organized, purposeful structure. There simply is no reason to suppose that, as computations grow large, one will discover anything nontrivial by trying to "average out" the effects of many events. The effect of the computer's "conditional" is too strong to allow anything like a conservation concept to have a place in the theory.

Furthermore, the *general-purpose computer* had become necessary because theories of mental processes had become too complex and were evolving too rapidly to be built into ordinary machinery. Some of the processes we want to study make substantial changes in their own organization. The flexibility of computer programs makes experiments feasible that would be next to impossible in an "analogue" mechanical set-up.

1.2 Organization of the Book

Each chapter of the present book is a slightly edited but not revised version of an independent scientific paper. The chapters by Bobrow, Raphael, Black, Evans, and Quillian are essentially their doctoral theses. The editor has made a number of small stylistic changes, some deletions to reduce size, and has introduced a uniform section-numbering scheme to facilitate crossreferencing. None of the changes is meant to alter the intent of what is asserted; in particular, there was no attempt to "update" the content in view of subsequent results. The last few essays, by McCarthy and Minsky, were concerned with the same general questions in a slightly earlier period. The precise citations of the originals are given at the end of this introductory chapter.

Evans's chapter is concerned with the problem of *analogy.* To recognize analogies (or more important, since *some* comparisons can always be made between things—to construct, compare, contrast, and finally to choose the best of several analogies) he developed a system for describing complex objects in terms of certain relations between more primitive parts of the objects. Then, on a higher level, he constructed a system for comparing objects in terms of relations between their descriptions. Finally, on a still higher level, he goes on to a scheme for assessing the similarities and differences between the comparisons, and thus realizes a concept of analogical reasoning. The program has solved many problems taken directly from certain college-level intelligence tests. This kind of description-comparison appears to be of enormous importance, not just because it handles a concept of analogy or even because it shows that concepts like that of analogy can be so handled, but because through just some such technique we may in time be able to break the other problem-solving systems from their bonds of specialization. Then at last they will succeed in using knowledge gained in one area upon problems from other domains.

Raphael's chapter describes an attempt to build a memory structure that converts the information it receives into a systematic, efficient representation, or "model." The model takes the form of a network in which objects are interconnected by a variety of different relations; the system answers various kinds of questions by examining the network. Thus the system does not attack problems by applying logical deduction procedures directly to a stored library of statements it has received (as does Black's program). Instead, it works by *"understanding" the statements when they are made,* consolidating this understanding by adding to or modifying the network. (Indeed, the original sentences are lost, so far as the question-answering phase is concerned.) Ambiguities in the statements must be resolved when they are understood, and sometimes the system itself can do it on the basis of knowledge about how a relation has been used in the past. It is thus truly capable of using the context of "coherent discourse."

This program works very smoothly within the limitations of the relations the model is built to handle, but the model is highly preconstructed. In the last sections of his thesis, Raphael proposes extensions that would permit the system to understand statements describing new relations as well and thus using them to increase the variety of concepts representable in the network. This raises a number of serious technical points centering around the problem of functional abstraction (dealing with the same thing as a relation in one context and as an object in another) that have not yet been managed in efficient question-answering systems. Raphael and others are still working on such matters.

Two papers by McCarthy, consolidated into Chapter 7, deal with the problem of representing within a formal and logical system a variety of familiar ideas, such as causality and potentiality, that everyone "understands without effort" but that had never been suitably mechanized. One cannot imagine an intelligent being operating without powerful facilities for managing such concepts and, as Piaget and his associates (15) have demonstrated in many ways, the growth of "common sense" in small children is tightly entwined with the growth of the logical power required for reasoning with means-ends analysis. The second of these two papers, "Situations, Actions, and Causal Laws," has not been previously published but it has been fairly widely circulated among workers in the field. Because it is a direct continuation of "Programs with Common Sense" they have been joined together into a single chapter.

Fischer Black's paper on deductive question-answering is the least "semantic" paper in this collection, and it is included primarily for tutorial purposes. With great simplicity and clarity Black presents a system that formally realizes some of the goals of McCarthy's "advice-taker" proposal. Black's direct approach led to a number of practical problems as the collection of statements grew in size; since that time there have been a number of technical advances in theorem-proving systems that retard but do not completely put off the problems of recognizing loops and selecting relevant data. The solutions to these, I think, lie ultimately in the domain of good semantic structures. But one must be careful not to fall into what my colleague, Seymour Papert, calls the "superhuman human fallacy." The problems of looping and relevancy have been solved only to a degree, even in our own brains, for the solutions to difficult problems do not always come instantly to our minds!

Bobrow's chapter on solving algebra word problems is a demonstration *par excellence* of the power of using meaning to solve linguistic problems. By knowing in advance that a collection of sentences must describe some algebraic relations between some things, the program is able to make good guesses as to what are the relations and what are the things. The result is that, within certain limits, it can do the really hard part of school algebra: "setting-up" the equations from informal verbal statements. To be sure, the linguistic limitations are fairly severe but even so the performance of the system seems far beyond what could be obtained from any purely "syntactic" sentence-analyzer. Some readers might grumble that if one knows what a sentence is about, then parsing it correctly shouldn't be so difficult. But this is precisely Bobrow's point. For once the point is understood (and at the time this was not the fashion in linguistics), one can begin to divide one's efforts into classifying and recognizing the kinds of things sentences *could* be "about," discovering what special linguistic structures are customarily involved with each kind, and developing the machinery for managing the use of these linguistic conventions.

Quillian's paper is, on the surface, concerned with the problem of "ambiguous" words. A single word with two meanings gives no way to choose one of them, except perhaps simply to choose the "most probable" one. Two such ambiguous words might have four meanings, then, and a traditional theorist might now propose the use of a joint or conditional probability. Quillian instead builds a network of objects and relations, somewhat like Raphael's but less pre-figured, and this is able to compare the plausibilities of different interpretations by the strengths of the chains linking the various pairs of meanings. The result is, I believe, a step toward a linguistic mechanism, simpler yet more powerful than the generative, grammar-based syntactic analyzers. One still must account for grammatical phenomena, and the chief concern of Quillian's chapter is to show how a more sophisticated plan for understanding the relation between meaning and grammar might come from developing such network models.

In this development one can see the return to life of some of the basically sound concepts of association psychology that became frozen caricatures in a generation of premature linear and stochastic learning theories. Quillian's work derives from the environment of Newell and Simon's research project (14) on modeling human behavior. For reasons of space, the section of this paper dealing with analyses of human semantic behavior has been replaced by a brief summary that Quillian prepared at our request. This constitutes the only major change in any of the papers presented in this volume.

The final paper, "Matter, Mind, and Models," presents my own theory of why people are so unsatisfied by mechanistic explanations of their mental activities. Although this theory goes only a little way and I have found it hard to carry it further, it does have the virtue of explaining why it is difficult to understand such phenomena, and it gives us some suggestions about the kinds of technical advance that could help in this area.

1.3 Artificial Intelligence and its Cybernetic Background

Although each of the chapters is nominally independent, it will be easier to assess their significance if one knows something of the intellectual and experimental environment from which they come. While work on artificial intelligence draws upon methods from other fields, this is not a significantly interdisciplinary area; it has its own concepts, techniques, and jargon, and these are slowly growing to form an intricate, organized specialty. First we shall say a little about its background, then discuss some of the problems under attack, and finally try to relate its results to other avenues of the search for models of intellectual activity.

In the early 1950's the general-purpose computer first became available to the scientific community. By the middle of the decade, the power of the machine for simulation of complex non-numerical systems had been demonstrated by a few prototypical experiments with games, neural nets, picture transformations, and the like. The serious programming of "symbol-manipulation" processes had started with early experiments on language translation and (somewhat later) on symbolic machine-language compilations; such techniques first became generally available in a form suitable for use by non-specialists in computation with the publication of the IPL programming system in 1956 by Newell, Shaw, and Simon (13).

Up to that time, work on cybernetics had been restricted (with a few important exceptions) to theoretical attempts to formulate basic principles of behavior and learning. The experimental work was at best "paradigmatic"; small assemblies of simple "analogue" hardware convinced the skeptic that mechanical structures could indeed exhibit "conditioned" adaptive behaviors of various sorts. Mechanical mice, rats, and turtles appeared in every country.

The computer made it practical to be much more ambitious. As a result, cybernetics divided, in my view, into three chief avenues:

The first was the continuation of the search for simple basic principles—most clearly exemplified by the precise analyses of Ashby (1). This became transformed into the goal of discovering what we might call minimal Self-Organizing Systems. A paradigm of this approach is to find a large collection of generally similar components that, when arranged in a very weakly specified structure and placed in an appropriate environment, would gradually come to behave in an "adaptive" fashion. Eventually, it was hoped, intelligent behavior would emerge from the evolution of such a system. To date the experimental results of work along these lines have not been very fruitful, at least in regard to the "emergence" from such systems of recognizably higher cognitive activity, though much has been accomplished on the level of multivariable feedback-regulatory systems and of simple stimulus-response learning reactions. I include in this area most of the work alleged to be directed toward the simulation of biological (and particularly neurological) mechanisms. (Almost nothing is actually known about the physiology of higher behavior; at present there is no single outstanding physiological theory of memory! For this reason, the "biological models" are not in fact noticeably different from the synthetic self-organizing models.) Work in this area has been carried on throughout the world, and no particular center has emerged.

The second important avenue was an attempt to build working models of human behavior incorporating, or developing as needed, specific psychological theories. In requiring the machines' behaviors to match that of human subjects, one need be concerned only with over-all schematic strategy, for replication of complete individual details would make no more sense here than it would in psychology itself. Work in this area—Simulation of Human Thought—has focused rather sharply at the Carnegie Institute of Technology (Mellon University) where Quillian's work was done, in the group led by Newell and Simon.

The third approach, the one we call *Artificial Intelligence,* was an attempt to build intelligent machines without any prejudice toward making the system simple, biological, or humanoid. Workers taking this route regarded the self-organizing systems as unpromising or, perhaps, premature. Even if simplicity of initial structure was to be an ultimate goal, one might first need experience with working intelligent systems (based if necessary on *ad hoc* mechanisms) if one were eventually to be able to design more economical schemes. Besides, we have neither genetic nor physiological bases for assuming that human intelligence emerges from modest structural endowments, nor can we confidently estimate the amount of structure read-in from infantile *cultural* contacts. That the infant builds the better part of his mind by his own effort is widely and fondly believed, but there is less established basis for this theory than most people suppose. Much of the earlier work on artificial intelligence was done by the group at M.I.T., which gave rise to most of the papers in this collection.

The computer programs developed by this approach are usually called "heuristic programs," in recognition of the fact that their performances are based upon the incorporation of heuristic methods, i.e., features that improve the systems' problem-solving efficiency or range of capability. These range from *ad hoc* tricks for particular kinds of problems to very general principles of efficient administration and resource allocation.

It is worth noting that today there are still no very large differences, either in content or in organization, between the best results of work on artificial intelligence and work on simulation of human thought. In part this is because both are in fact using human problem-solving behavior as their most important model, in part because they have come to similar decisions about their program-administration methods, and in part because they have kept in rather close communication with one another. We expect substantial divergences to appear in the future, e.g., because of the power of certain logical and mathematical formalisms too alien to normal human thinking.

1.4 The Period between 1955 and 1962

The collection of papers reprinted in the book *Computers and Thought,* edited by E. Feigenbaum and J. Feldman, who did their graduate work in the Carnegie group (5), gives a good view of the state of affairs as it stood by about the end of 1961. At that time a number of heuristic programs could solve some respectably hard problems in certain particular areas. Most of these worked on fairly formal combinational problems, such as games, logic, or mathematics. Just to give the reader a rough picture of what had been accomplished, one can say that there was a program very good at playing checkers, and there were programs quite good at proving theorems in elementary geometry, calculus, trigonometry, logic, and the like; and many programs displayed various simple forms of learning. No programs had been demonstrated to do well at playing chess,[1] handling natural language, or developing higher-level concepts. In all cases the programs could handle only very narrow ranges in the format and content of the problems they could solve. Many critics made the simple but fatal mistake of explaining this pattern by proposing that, since a computer was basically a "logical" machine, it could work only at basically formal, logical problems.

It would be presumptuous to attempt a thorough historical perspective of what has happened since then, because not until we achieve a reasonably broad synthetic intelligence will we be in a position to say what were the main threads of its development. But one can try to pick out a few ideas that at this time seem important. The most central idea of the pre-1962 period was that of finding heuristic devices to control the breadth of a *trial-and-error search.* A close second preoccupation was with finding effective techniques for *learning.* In the post-1962 era the concern became less with "learning" and more with the problem of representation of knowledge (however acquired) and with the related problem of breaking through the formality and narrowness of the older systems. The problem of heuristic search efficiency remains as an underlying constraint, but it is no longer the problem one thinks about, for we are now immersed in more sophisticated subproblems, e.g., the representation and modification of *plans.* To explain the quality of this change I will have to make a few elementary remarks about heuristic problem-solving in general.

Many difficult problems can be solved, in principle, by trying all possible sequences of available actions. For example, one can consider all possible sequences of legal moves in chess, or all sequences of logical inferences for proving theorems in logic. But in practice these "exhaustive-search" methods cannot be used to solve hard problems, because of the unthinkably large numbers of combinations that have to be considered if the selection is to be indiscriminate. Consequently, a variety of techniques have been developed to replace blind trial-and-error methods.

In the earliest experiments with heuristic programs the amount of search was relatively large. This, coupled with the popular image of the computer as being fast but stupid, gave rise to a general impression that this is a characteristic feature of heuristic programs. This is quite incorrect so far as the better subsequent work is concerned, for the main concern soon became the careful, selective—one is tempted to say "thoughtful"—generation of a relatively few promising hypotheses, and often the problem is solved with the first of these. Thus even in the worst case reported by Evans only thirty-six rules were generated, usually far fewer. Bobrow's program uses very little search; it might need somewhat more if, for example, it attempted to handle several simultaneous idiomatic transformations. Raphael's program must often make extensive searches within the data network, but almost never at the top goal levels. Black's deduction system would indeed become fatally involved in large search trees if it were given a large "corpus" of factual data, and it remains a major research goal to combine such deductive structures with relevancy-oriented information-retrieval systems. Thus Black's proposal concerning "classifying" by main connective (his §6.2) would certainly help, and either Raphael's or Quillian's structures could do even more to make the deductive attempts restrict themselves to using only facts that are relevant to the problem under attack. Even the early (1961) integration program of Slagle (20), although clearly designed within the older goal-tree search framework, generated but a small fraction of irrelevant or nonachievable subgoals in the course of its solutions of college calculus problems. In other words, Slagle's hypothesis generators usually made sound first choices, and this led to very small search trees.[2]

A good way to see how the approach to search has changed is to compare the methods in the present volume with those used by the older-style game-playing machines. The outstanding example of this is the well-documented checker-playing program of Samuel (17) which, in its current version, is far above good amateur levels but not quite up to the highest master play.

The checker program, in deciding which move to make, explores thousands of possible board positions. This in itself requires great selectivity in choosing to explore only possibilities that are "plausible" in the view of subprograms containing some realistic knowledge about what is important in checkers; it does well without having to consider the countless zillions of moves that might be tried. On the other side there is every reason to suppose that good human players consider only dozens or, at most, hundreds of positions in any detail, but make a far more penetrating analysis of those.

I shall assume that the reader is familiar with the traditional minimax procedure by which a partial, incomplete analysis at terminal branches of the game tree is backed up to give a single numerical figure-of-merit for each available legal move. The incomplete terminal analysis, if applied only to the current position, would be quite inadequate for choosing the best move; but by combining this partial analysis of each available move with an attenuated search for some of its consequences the computer appears to act on the basis of a much deeper analysis—indeed, a better one than is presently available by any other route. The program contains a collection of rules for deciding when to continue the search and when to stop. When it stops, it assesses the merits of the current position in terms of rather simple factors concerning the numbers of men remaining on each side, their relative advancement, and other relations between them. Having more men is usually, but not always, an advantage: One might have two extra men but be about to lose three. However, if one considers many possible positions a few moves hence, and finds that an advantage is retained in all of them, then the analysis is more secure. Thus one can use search to compensate for incomplete analysis.

In the minimaxing process there is an ultraconservative operation—comparison of numerical scores—that decides that one variation or move is better than another. A human player does not do this. He looks at fewer positions but makes a more productive analysis of what he finds: "This position has a good defensive aspect but loses development time," he might say, or "That other position promises a good attack here but leaves some weakness in the corner. What kind of move could I make that might combine the virtues of both but eliminate the risks?"

It can be seen immediately how the opportunity for this is lost in the "minimaxing" analysis for, once a major branch of the tree has been explored, this exploration has to be "summarized" by a mere single number. The result of analyzing a second branch is compared to that of the first only through this number. But when exploration of several branches leads a good human player to the same general conclusion—say, that he is subject in each case to a certain kind of attack—he uses this information, not merely for *comparing the results* of exploring consequences of different moves, but for *generating a plan:* He will look particularly for moves that might plausibly lead to strengthening the appropriate defensive structure. This line of thought leads inexorably to the suggestion that what is needed for summarizing a search tree is not a numerical *utility-like* value good only for *comparison* but a *description-like* expression that can be used for *analysis.** We shall have more to say about descriptions a little further on.

1.5 Formality

One of the most popular misconceptions about artificial intelligence is that problem-solving by computer is confined to precisely defined "formal" problems. This is based in part on the dreadfully misleading set of concepts that people get when they are told (with the best intentions) that computers are nothing but assemblies of flip-flops; that their programs are really nothing but sequences of operations upon binary numbers, and so on. While this is one useful viewpoint, it is equally correct to say that the computer is nothing but an assembly of symbol-association and process-controlling elements and that programs are nothing but networks of interlocking goal-formulating and means-ends evaluating processes. This latter attitude is actually much healthier because it reduces one's egotistical tendency to assume total comprehension of all the possible future implications.

The false conception about formality is based also on a serious misinterpretation of the design goals of those early heuristic programs that were indeed concerned with very formal precise problems: I hope the reader will agree that problems like those attempted by Evans and Quillian are not sensibly of this character. To be sure, many experiments have been centered around

*This is not to say that a concept of a *currency* is undesirable, but it must be properly placed, i.e., for use when allocating conservative quantities.

formal problem areas like game-playing and theorem-proving, but closer examination will show that these choices are encouraged by an almost dialectically opposite quality. It is not that the games and mathematical problems are chosen because they are clear and simple; rather it is that *they give us, for the smallest initial structures, the greatest complexity,* so that one can engage some really formidable situations after a relatively minimal diversion into programming.

One must learn to be suspicious of arguments of the form "computers can prove theorems, but they cannot do well at (say) the art of music." For we are accustomed to setting a much higher standard on the latter activities, and most "ordinary" people would fail the same tests. It is premature to expect to find any special difficulties in these areas; there are already programs that write music which, although bad, is better than most people can write. To write really good music or draw highly meaningful pictures will of course require better *semantic* models in these areas. That these are not available is not so much a reflection on the state of heuristic programs as on the traditionally disgraceful state of analytic criticism in the arts—a cultural consequence of the fact that most esthetic analysts wax indignant when it is suggested that it might be possible to understand what they are trying to understand. In any case, the success of ANALOGY—so far as I know the first attempt of its kind—does not confirm the supposition that nonformality brings with it especially serious difficulties.

Returning to the general idea of heuristic search, one is tempted to go on from the idea of trying all sequences of moves or generating problem trees by applying combinations of an initially given set of methods to a higher level: using sequences of methods that generate new methods! This seems so natural that, as the experiments in this book do not go (on the surface) in that direction, we shall say a little about *why* they don't.

In discussing "intelligence," people are usually too concerned with the peaks of human creative innovation. First-rate creativity is not the most common nor the most essential quality of intelligence. Newton, Einstein, and Mozart, were very intelligent men, but we don't scorn other men as being "mere superpowered adding machines" because they don't routinely make monumental discoveries. The experiments described in this book are early attempts to use nontrivial concepts in contexts of modest complexity; we have to find how to represent and *use* concepts before we can work directly upon their invention. The following remarks on *Generality* and on *Learning* develop this idea further.

Eventually we shall have to deal with a higher level of concept discovery. The practical problems in doing this appear to be quite formidable, as evidenced by Newell's analysis (12) of the difficulties encountered in some of his attempts in this direction.

1.6 Generality

The critics who emphasized the fact that the older heuristic programs operated in very precise formal problem domains were off their mark, as already noted, in regarding this as a serious obstacle. Those who recognized that it was the narrowness of the content rather than of the form were pointing to a more real problem. By 1961 this became a matter of concern: Each program worked only on its restricted specialty, and there was no way to combine two different problem-solvers. (To be sure, no one even tried: Each project was initiated and completed nearly independently of others. The only notable exception was the Carnegie group's effort to extend the range of their GPS system, but even this tended to be in the direction of disjointly appending new and still separate problem domains.)

The programs described in this volume may still appear to have some of this character, but they are no longer ignoring the problem. In fact, their chief concern is finding methods of solving it! For the route toward generality must lie partly in more versatile organization of the knowledge-handling parts of the program's administration and partly in the representation of more and better kinds of knowledge. More about this later; the point to make here is again a dialectical one: The fact that the present batch of programs still appear to have narrow ranges of application does not indicate lack of progress toward generality. These programs are steps toward ways to handle knowledge. The dialectic is that the tools that will eventually give us generality are themselves rather sharply structured methods and must first be studied and debugged in the usual kind of well-understood (and hence narrowly defined) problem environment. Thus these programs, too, are independent experiments; they use different ways to represent information, and they cannot communicate

1.7 Learning

Another aspect of the situation, more disturbing to outsiders than to insiders, was the apparently small degree of "learning" in the programs; even less in the post- than in the pre-1961 periods. From a certain point of view, the new programs seem somewhat static; they solve the problems they were programmed to solve, but they do not *learn* how to solve them: The methods are built in. Of course, the matter is relative to one's goals: to make a machine with intelligence is not necessarily to make a machine that learns to be intelligent.

It is important to understand why the issue is not as simple as it might seem. The checker program is well-known for a certain degree of success at learning. (Learning, however, is not a major feature of the master-level version of the program.) The learning experiments reported by Samuel (17) are of two kinds. One is a *rote memorization* of the values of previously encountered board positions; the other is a correlation-like *computation* of the relative importance of a number of evaluation functions of board positions. Both improve the level of play, but neither gives anything like a new "concept" to build upon.*

On the other side, some people would not consider any of the programs in this book to be "learning" programs. Yet a most enormous "learning potential" is just below the surface. Consider the qualitative effect, upon the subsequent performance of Bobrow's STUDENT, of telling it that "*distance equals speed times time*"! That one experience alone enables it to handle a large new portion of high-school algebra: the physical position-velocity-time problems.† It is important not to fall into the habit, suggested by so much modern work in psychology, of concentrating only on the kinds of "learning" that appear as slow-improvement-attendant-upon sickeningly-often-repeated experience!

Bobrow's program does not have any cautious statistical devices that have to be told something over and over again, so its *learning* is too brilliant to be called so. In fact, there is no explicit use of probabilistic notions anywhere in this book: It seems that as we incorporate more and more sophisticated heuristic methods, the need for senseless sources of variation in behavior becomes less and less necessary. The same may turn out to hold in the case of making inferences from collections of experiences.

Of course I do not suggest that there is *no* use in having cautious evidence-assessing mechanisms. I only want to present a sufficiently positive view to set the negative view into perspective. Similarly, each fact added to Black's advice "corpus," each link on one of Quillian's networks, or each statement (to become a link) in Raphael's input can be treated as a high-level learning event. What about Evans's method? He has not programmed *any* carry-over from one problem to another. But *within* the course of solving each individual problem, one could make a case that it uses a form of learning more potent and more abstract than any of the others.

Thus, in "cases" 11 and 16, ANALOGY resolves [figure] and W into [figure] and △, and V and V respectively, rather than into (say) 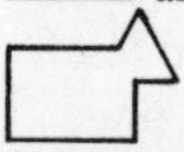 [figure] and ◻, and W and ᵛ, on the basis that the chosen subfigures occur elsewhere in the problem while the others do not. Thus the result of its inspection of figures "A" and "B" is to alter the primitive terms it will use to

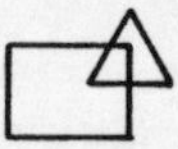

*These remarks do not apply to the nonlinear combinations of features studied in Samuel's more recent work (18). And there are a number of important concepts built into the checker program that are often overlooked when it is discussed purely in terms of learning.

†The usual objection is that "it didn't learn it; it was told." I hope the reader does not flatter himself by believing that he "figured out" the difference between energy and momentum. He was told; Newton figured it out, Galileo didn't, and there was no one to tell him.

describe the other figures in the scene. In psychological jargon, one could say that its visual perception of the objects is affected by their contextual relations.

Looking at it this way should clarify why we have come to feel that questions like "Why don't you put some *learning* into your program?" are much less sensible and straightforward than they may seem. In the early experiments in cybernetics the programs' abstract knowledge was very small and most decisions were based upon the values of simple explicit parameters. When things are done that way one could always build in a crude sort of adaptive behavior by using any of a number of correlation-like "reinforcement" schemes. There is no reason to suppose that anything like this is appropriate for "thinking." In thinking, the result of an intellectual experience is used, not simply to adjust a parameter but to construct a new way to represent something, or even to make a change in an administrative aspect of the problem-solving control system. Before it is profitable to attempt this, we need more experience with semantic representation experiments. It has taken some time to unlearn the false lesson of the success of parameter reinforcement in easy trial-and-error processes.[3]

Once we have achieved systems that at least partially analyze their own problem-solving experiences, we can expect to see rapid progress toward generality. One should not expect, however, to find problem-solving generality through the discovery of a single, magnificently general problem-solving method. Even humans do not have unfailing success in new areas; the acquisition of a new problem-solving method is a major event in our own cultural evolution. I think that in our present state it will be more productive to try to understand how people understand so well what they are told than to focus exclusively on what they discover for themselves; in the long run it may come to the same thing, but the two approaches lead to different research strategies.

All the experiments described in this book are concerned with the construction and manipulation of "descriptions" of situations. There are a number of roles we expect descriptions to play in the performance of the intelligent problem-solving machines of the future. At any point in the development of a heuristic program, one has at hand a variety of methods and techniques that can handle problems up to a certain level of complexity. To obtain greater problem-solving power, one can try either to improve the basic methods themselves or to improve the problem-solver's general ability to bring more difficult problems within the reach of the basic methods. The most natural way to achieve the latter kind of extension is to find ways to simplify problems by setting *subgoals,* i.e., to recognize when solving a simpler subproblem will facilitate the solution of the original problem. To do this, one must have ways (i.e., other kinds of methods) to break a problem apart, recognize relations between the parts, solve them, and combine the results to form a solution, or at least a plan or skeleton of a solution, for the original problem.

Whenever this is done, the key to a successful analysis seems to involve the use of some technique—a descriptive "language," as computer users always think of it—that makes it easy to dissect the problem in some useful way. Early programs worked by detecting several more or less independent features of a situation; today more powerful techniques are coming into use. The work of Evans is probably the best example to date of how descriptions can be used to invade an area of thought usually thought to be the exclusive province of the human mind: analogical reasoning.

Evans's goal was to construct a program to apprehend analogies between members of a loosely defined class of objects. The particular problem format selected was that of an intelligence-test technique called the Geometric Analogy Test. The test problems are widely regarded as requiring considerable intelligence and are used for college admission tests and similar purposes. Eight figures are presented in each test, and the reader is expected to answer the question: "*A* is to *B* as *C* is to which one of five 'answer' figures?" Obviously there is no "correct" solution to such a problem (in the sense that an algebra problem may have a unique numerical answer). Indeed, performance is not graded by a formalized rule but by comparison with other highly intelligent test takers.

To explain the spirit of this work, it is best to describe the program in mentalistic form. Given a set of figures, it constructs a set of hypotheses or theories as follows:

1. Based on the descriptions D(*A*) and D(*B*) of Figures *A* and *B,* there are many ways in which D(*A*) can be transformed into D(*B*); choose one of these.
2. There are also many ways in which the parts of *A* can be put into correspondence with the parts of *C:* Each such correspondence *suggests* a relation like that proposed in (1) but which now relates Figure *C* and some other figures.
3. It is unlikely that any of the relations found in (2) will apply perfectly to any of the answer figures. (If just one does, then that will be the program's answer.) For each answer figure, "weaken," i.e., generalize, each relation just enough so that it will apply to the figure.
4. Finally, the program measures how much it had to weaken each relation. It chooses the one that required the least change, and gives the corresponding answer figure as its answer.

By choosing that hypothesis which involved the least "weakening" of the original $A \rightarrow B$ transformation hypothesis, the program selects that explanation that contains the most information common to both the $A \rightarrow B$ and $C \rightarrow D$ relations. The details of the selection rules in steps (1), (2), (3), and (4) amount, in effect, to Evans's theory of human behavior in such situations. I feel sure that something of this general character is involved in any kind of analogical reasoning.

We next consider how this "mentalistic" sketch was turned into a "mechanistic" program. The technical device that was most helpful in closing the gap between these reasonable but complicated ideas, was the LISP programming language system designed by John McCarthy and developed by the M.I.T. group (9); it provides many automatic services for manipulating symbolic expressions and complicated "data structure." Without LISP ("List-Processor") or its predecessors, the "Information Processing Languages" of Newell, Shaw, and Simon (13), the work in artificial intelligence would have developed less rapidly because of the difficulty of writing such programs in machine-instructions, or in FORTRAN- or ALGOL-like systems. All the experiments described here were done with LISP except Quillian's, which used IPL-V.

Evans's thesis itself describes the technical details. What I want to emphasize is the small proportion of the effort it devotes to search as compared to that in its analysis of descriptions. The program considers only a very few hypotheses at the top level, and its inner search is concerned chiefly with choosing among the alternatives available for matching parts of figures with parts of descriptions. The "priorities" specified in its program make such good assignments in ambiguous cases that the total amount of trial and error remains quite small. Although there can be no factual basis for it, I suspect that human performance on such problems is not much more efficient.

1.8 Knowledge

Why do the heuristic programs solve much harder problems than do the self-organizing systems? Obviously, because they begin with methods appropriate to the classes of problems they are faced with, and because they are given enough specific factual knowledge about particular problems. They do not have to start from an unstructured basis to evolve everything they will need. But only to the extent that this "knowledge" is suitably represented can the program's use of it be intelligent, in the sense of appearing to *understand* the information, as opposed to merely being able to exploit it as part of a trying-all-combinations search. Thus questions about ownership and membership will be answered more efficiently by Raphael's SIR than by Black's QAS program, because of the direct predicate-links that, in SIR, almost physically chain together the immediate logical consequences of the given information.

It is important, although difficult, to find ways to distinguish various degrees of separation between problem-oriented factual information and general problem-solving heuristics. There is no particular distinction (for example) in Black's "Monkey problem" between specific information about monkeys and general information about causality. There *is* such a distinction in SIR, but it fades in the proposed SIR-1 which can deal with general advice about, say the properties of transitive predicates, on the same level as ordinary factual information. (To maintain efficiency that system would need some sort of recompilation procedure to convert the more general rules into noninterpreted programs for handling the less general information.)

STUDENT's efficacy reflects several levels of organized knowledge: On the lowest level, the algebra is carefully packaged within the function SOLVE, and without much search this device either solves the problem, declares it to be beyond its ability (in nonlinear cases, for example), or states that more information is needed. STUDENT could be made to handle some nonlinear problems simply by improving SOLVE. It is not quite true, however, to say that all the algebraic ability of STUDENT is in SOLVE. On the next higher level, the knowledge about how to achieve the goal of converting the pseudo-English input into suitable equations is partly algebraic in quality, and some possibly syntactic ambiguities in the input are decided on the over-all basis of algebraic consistency, using the SOLVE system if necessary.

At a still higher (though not particularly more complex) level we find in STUDENT some knowledge-classifying knowledge: The AGEPROBLEM information is used to detect a particular subclass of problems and to recruit the use of some special syntactic operations for input-conversion in such cases. A bright high-school student will soon work these out for himself; a dull one (like STUDENT) will have to be taught them. But we have agreed to set aside the problem of acquiring knowledge till we better understand how to represent and use it.

The problem I do *not* want to set aside is how to select the knowledge needed (at a particular moment) from all that is available. Each of the programs described here will work best when given exactly the necessary facts, and will bog down inexorably as the information files grow. In some sense this is inevitable (even in men); what is important is the rate and the quality of the degradation. For example, the degradation of the Raphael and Quillian models could be negligible for certain questions if the new facts are represented by direct links and if the question-answering processes choose them properly. Even in Black's system, if main-connective retrieval trees are used, huge files will cause little difficulty for some problems, but where multiple deductive chains must be discovered, large files will always cause trouble unless adequate models are developed to represent them.

In the field of theorem-proving by machine, the central problem is that of finding chains of logical inference, where some of the links depend on information, e.g., previously proved theorems, stored in files. Now, "theorem-proving" is a more comprehensive subject than one might think, because it is required not only in purely mathematical contexts but also in any situation requiring the discovering of specific logical implications from more general statements. (Thus for example, STUDENT doesn't do any logic, but one would surely want to extend it so that it could handle the kinds of logical inference that the programs of Black and Raphael do, in solving its "story problems.") SIR and QAS *are* theorem-proving programs.

To see how the problem grows, suppose one wants to know whether a certain proposition $[A \supset B]$ can be proved. One might first look to see whether it is not a particular instance of some more general, already known principle. If not, one looks for a chain: Suppose one knows already that $[A \supset C]$; then it would do to prove that $[C \supset B]$. For instance, I might want to find a proof for "Eagle ⊃ Fly." My files reveal that I know both "Eagle ⊃ Bird" and "Eagle ⊃ Animal." This proposes two alternative subproblems: "Bird ⊃ Fly," which is true, and "Animal ⊃ Fly," which isn't.

If neither subgoal can be immediately settled, one has a search problem, since the same, or worse, may also happen in working on each proposed link. Now semantic models can often help us reject branches in the search tree or at least put them in order of plausibility. One could reject "Animal ⊃ Fly" by exhibiting an animal that doesn't fly. (One might reject the other, too, by using an ostrich, unless the system properly represents "exceptions" at least as well as does Raphael's SIR system.)

An example of an area in which a good model *is* readily available, is Euclidean geometry. (Raphael's JRIGHT and JLEFT is perhaps the simplest possible example.) It is very difficult to find proofs for advanced high-school geometry theorems because of the problems of choosing a plan for constructions and of sensibly organizing the large amount of information usually available in the form of previously proven results. I think experiments would show that good students do not spend much time trying to prove false subtheorems; this is usually explained by talking about the "geometric intuition" that tells one, for example, that if two angle-bisecting segments inscribed in a triangle are equal then the triangle must be isosceles. (This is very hard to prove!) That kind of judgment (which reveals so little of its basis to consciousness) represents the activity of a massive complex of machinery in our minds; it uses visual and spatial representations that took years of childhood to build and quite probably rival our linguistic processes both in complexity and in temporal priority.

The "parsing" processes required for distinguishing the overlapping objects within a visual scene, for example, are surely more elaborate, at age 1, than those involved in linguistic activity. In any case, it is feasible to program a computer to use analytic methods to test the truth of a geometric proposition without even suggesting a way to *prove* the theorem; in other words, to *deduce* it within the Euclidean framework. In fact this is what was done with excellent results in the Gelernter-Rochester work (6).

The use of models to decide truth or falseness of propositions is a rather special application and, while it helps to eliminate wrong lines of speculation, it is not immediately valuable in the problem of large files of information. At the time of this writing the most promising approach to this seems to be through more active "semantic networks"; we shall return to the problems of relevance and contexts after a digression about language.

1.9 Grammar, Syntax, and Parsing Programs

The amount of "natural language" grammar in these experiments spans a wide range. Evans and Black use only logical predicate notation, while Raphael uses a few context-dependent constructions. Bobrow uses much more, and Quillian rather less in his program. Although Quillian goes into the matter rather deeply, particularly in Section 4.5, a few words about this aspect of the experiments may be useful here.

The recognition of regularities in linguistic activity dates from antiquity. Grammar had a renaissance in the middle 1950's with the elaboration of algebraic formalisms by Chomsky and his colleagues (3). This development meshed so closely with new requirements for the theory of automata and for the development of languages for algorithmic computation that it became a substantial branch of mathematics within a remarkably short time. It became clear that certain schemata (beginning with the "phrase-structure" formulations that resemble those of antiquity) give approximations to "sentence-structure," but that, as the approximations were sharpened, it became increasingly necessary to complicate the schemata in many ways. Every suitably flexible grammar leads to a great many "ambiguities"; an English sentence whose meaning seems perfectly clear at first sight is discovered to have a remarkably large number of possible "syntactic structures," many with quite different meanings. (This in itself must not be considered a defect of the analytic schema although, inexplicably, many have considered this to be the case because these are often *possible,* even if unlikely, meanings. Most written sentences have this character, when taken by themselves. To see this, simply read one several times, accenting each word in turn; and if that is not enough, try accenting *pairs* of words, etc. More serious are cases–see Quillian's Appendix 4.2–in which the principal "ordinary" meaning-structure is missed by the analysis.)

In natural language, the ambiguities arise not only from the variety of structural groupings the words could be given but also from the variety of meanings that can be assigned to each individual word. In STUDENT the strong semantic constraint (that the sentences express algebraic relations between the designated entities) keeps the situation more or less under control. Raphael performs some "disambiguation" by using a scheme that depends on a search through the semantic network; it employs the heuristic concept that an entity y that has participated in *being part of* something x in the past is more likely than not to participate in that kind of relation again. The understanding of the sentence "x has y" depends then on how "naturally" each of two proposed interpretations: (1) "x owns y," or (2) "y is part of x," meshes with the already developed semantic model. Raphael's criterion of "naturally" here would be to choose the injection into the model that introduces the fewest new predicates, overt or by implication, onto the property lists. The problem, when recognized, is transmitted to a part of the program that is able to review all that has happened before. This subprogram makes its decision on the following basis:

1. Is y already known to be part of some other thing? Or is y a member of some set whose members are known to be parts of something?
2. Is y known to be owned by something, or is it a member of some set whose members are known to be owned by something?
3. If exactly one of (1) and (2) is true, make the choice in the corresponding direction. If neither holds, give up and ask for more information. If both are true, then consider the further possibilities at (4) below. (Thus the program uses evidence about how previously acquired information has been incorporated into its "model" of the world.)
4. Once we get to this point, then y is already known to be involved in being part of something *and* in being owned, and we need a finer test.

Let u_1 and u_2 be the "something" or the "some set" that we know exists, respectively, in the answers to questions (1) and (2). These depend on y. We now ask, is x a member of or a subset of u_1, or of u_2? If neither, we give up. If one, we choose the corresponding result—"part of" or "owns." If both, we again give up and ask for more information. As Raphael says (Section 2.5.2):

These criteria are simple, yet they are sufficient to enable the program to make quite reasonable decisions about the intended purpose in various sentences of the ambiguous word "has." Of course, the program can be fooled into making mistakes, e.g., in case the sentence, "Dick has a chain," had been presented before the sentence "John owns a chain," in the . . . dialogue [cited] ; however, a human being exposed to a *new* word in a similar situation would make a similar error. The point here is that it is feasible to resolve ambiguities automatically in sentence meaning by referring to the descriptions of the words in the sentence, descriptions which can be created automatically through proper prior exposure to unambiguous sentences.

Thus, the program is instructed to attempt to search through its collection of prior knowledge, to find whether x and y are related, if at all, more closely in one or the other way. This "part" of the program is best conceived of as a little trial court or evidence-collecting-and-weighing procedure. It is good to think of it, not as a procedure directly within a prespecified sequence of problem-solving but rather as an appeal court which the main program consults when it encounters an inconsistency or ambiguity. When we write a large program, with many such courts, each capable of calling upon others for help, it becomes useless to think of the program as a "sequence of instructions." Even though the programmer himself has stated the "legal" principles that permit such "appeals," he will have only a very incomplete understanding of when and where in the course of the program's operation these procedures will call on each other. And for a particular "court," he may have only a sketchy idea of the circumstances that will cause it to be used. In short, one has to think of the parts of large heuristic programs as specifications for the individuals of little societies. Try as he may, the programmer will usually be unable to predict in advance all the details of their interactions. For that, after all, is why he needs the computer.

Within the "syntactic" development of linguistics, I have the impression that there was (at least until recently) a conscious attempt to avoid this sort of thing, and instead to complicate the "rules" or schemata in the hope of reducing ambiguity. Leaving aside the point that the ambiguity problem remains even if the "meaningless" options could be somehow syntactically eliminated—and one cannot really imagine how that could happen—one still wonders whether that approach would have much merit even if successful. For example, in connection with linguistic incidents exemplified by

"he filled the jars with water"

and

"he filled the jars with beads,"

one wants to account for the two forms of the plural. The standard solution is to invent a "grammatical category" for the names of those substances that do not hold their forms as permanent objects; therefore one proposes that there exist "mass nouns" whose plural forms are handled in such and such a manner.

While this is moderately successful in "explaining" some linguistic behavior, surely it is a step along a most treacherous path. For it is a sort of pun to represent a *physical* category ("material of fluid character") as a syntactic type! It can always be done so long as the pseudophysics is in itself primitive enough, but its success in simple cases encourages one to try the same in more complicated relational structures that cannot be represented so readily in a primitive set theory. I claim it will be much easier, in the long run, to build in a modest model of the elementary physics of a simplified real world. For example: to disambiguate the pronoun references in

"He put the box on the table. Because it wasn't level, it slid off."

requires but little "physics" to know that the table didn't slide off (because it's underneath) and the box wouldn't slide off just because *it* wasn't level, so probably it was the table that wasn't level. You *could* postulate "level nouns" but this doesn't really seem a good idea.

My point here is this: When one considers relations *one at a time* it is usually possible to represent them in a propositional calculus with something resembling a set-inclusion predicate. Thus one can usually build simple approximations of semantics into a grammar by inventing categories and special rules concerning them. But when one comes to deal with several interacting relations one will need a more powerful logic, but this won't be representable in anything like a simple set logic. The moral is to beware of concluding from any simple but disconnected "first steps" that there is a clear path in this direction.

I hope the reader does not conclude that I am "against" mass nouns. Linguistic phenomena must eventually be explained, and the use of the singular form for certain purposes here is a fairly regular phenomenon that involves certain words. But it is surely not a *grammatical* convention. Rather it must be a manifestation of a deeper convention concerning how one represents in words what one knows and wants to say. The assignment of the singular in this case is a property not of "water" but of water.

Another type of instance, which seems to have perplexed authorities on why machines can't do semantics is:

"The baby looked for his box. The box was in the pen."

How is the program to know that pen is "playpen"? Quillian points a way: the first sentence (understood in the course of reaching the second sentence) "activates" *baby.* The association-wave search, in dealing with the second sentence, is then biased toward accepting chains through *play-pen* (which is the disjunctive branch of *pen* that is most closely linked to *baby*). Now earlier associationists could, and probably did, make such suggestions, but Quillian (who is now working with Bobrow) is in the position of being able to form much more concrete proposals.

Quillian's models suggest a number of schemes to be explored, the simplest being to discount, in measuring chain lengths, those links that touch an activated node, so that the path to *play-pen* is preferred over the path to *fountain-pen.* (If, in understanding the first sentence, the program correctly interpreted "his box" as the baby's box, then *box* also gets disambiguated.) In any case, it would be a good idea to build into the semantic model enough common-sense geometrical physics to make it unlikely that the box is in the fountain-pen, or at least to use a Raphael-type search to find that it is unprecedented to have anything but ink in a fountain-pen.

It is probably bad psychological theory to imagine a sharp separation between a "parsing procedure" and a file of "grammatical rules." Much more plausible is the view that the rules are not *used by* the parsing program; they *are* the parsing program, or rather they are abstractions about the program's behavior and should be viewed as approximations to (or major divisions of) the program's flow chart. It is equally bad to think of the parser as entirely separate from the semantic model, as the word-to-word decisions and internal actions of the process undoubtedly depend on the immediate reactions of the activated parts of the semantic models involved. We have already referred to the technique used by Evans to resolve intersecting subfigures into parts, using their co-occurrence in other frames of the problem picture. It should be noted that this can be viewed quite concisely as a disambiguation procedure in which the overlapping substructures are selected on the basis of the activation of similar figures in the other frames.

1.10 Machine Translation of Languages

While on the general subject of natural language, let me refer to the problem of translation from one language to another. "Mechanical Translation," as it is usually called, has a peculiar relation both to the general subject of artificial intelligence and to the particular projects of this collection. For in the early and middle 1950's, mechanical-translation research was one of the very few well-financed non-numerical applications of computers, and hence represented the first serious sorties into the artificial-intelligence area. The immediate results in regard to actual useful translations were (it is generally agreed) not of sufficient quality to be of much use; yet there is no question about the great stimulus these projects gave to research on theoretical linguistics. In particular, the ambiguity problems that arise from word-by-word and sentence-by-sentence substitutions and transformations were seen to be more severe, I think, than had been expected on the basis of informal speculation. I have the impression that many of the participants in these first forays, preceding by a chronologically short but critical period the artificial intelligence projects of the late 1950's, became so disillusioned that they are today among those most skeptical of ever making intelligent machines.

In those early years, many people underestimated the amount of knowledge and structure that might be needed to think in a reasonably efficient fashion. The poor results in early translation attempts resulted from the hope that adequate syntactic analyses of *sentences* could be made without an apparatus for assessing the plausibility of proposed meanings. This gamble didn't pay off. It is now apparent that the meanings must be taken into account to resolve ambiguities even within coherent discourse in a single language, let alone in translating. One needs methods for representing the entities being discussed and the relations between them, as well as enough logical inference capacity to make common-sense deductions about consequences of these relations.

The quality required of these representations depends on the tolerances of the job to be done. An unintelligent or uneducated listener cannot be expected to catch delicate distinctions in a specialized context. As the power of the representations is improved, the variety of the ambiguities ought eventually to fall back to the level inherent in the text itself, that is, to the variety of interpretations that typical users of the language will make.

A mechanism performing "fully automatic high-quality translation" might very possibly need to contain structures that can represent situations as complex as those handled by an equivalent human translator. But this suggests only the need for work on the real problem of constructing a fairly general machine intelligence–the kind that could learn something about a subject by reading a book.

1.11 How Much Semantics?

How massive is this problem: Even ignoring the deeper problem of how it is to be structured, what is the magnitude of the mass of knowledge required for a humanoid intelligence? One aspect of the experiments in this book is the fact that there exists almost nothing that is common to the information in SIR and in STUDENT. Does this mean that when we fuse them together, there will be no condensation? Indeed, I rather think not: to fuse them will require some additional information! To casual observers this raises a dreadful specter: millions of topics, each having millions of facts, fusing in networks with trillions of vital links. Must the store of knowledge grow as the programs increase their versatility?

My first reply is a qualified affirmative. As knowledge grows, we open and explore new areas, and occasionally build up large bodies of knowledge substantially disjoint from those of other areas. The compensating processes of abstraction and condensation may never quite keep pace, and so the structure grows. No one today knows but a tiny fraction of our present technical information, and there isn't any reason to suppose that any human brain could. What, by the way, is the brain's capacity? We have all heard accounts of prodigious feats of memory, but I have never heard of any instance that seriously suggests that a person can hold many millions of independent facts. To be sure, we can find people who know, more or less, a whole Bible–but see if you can find one who knows a dozen. And if you hear someone claim to have a *physiological* estimate of memory capacity, you may be sure he is only bluffing, because there isn't any reasonably definitive current theory of memory at all, today.

The second reply is more optimistic. If we discount specialized knowledge and ask instead about the common, every-day structures–that which a person needs in order to have ordinary common sense–we will find first a collection of indispensable categories, each rather complex: geometrical and mechanical properties of things and of space; uses and properties of a few thousand objects;

hundreds of "facts" about hundreds of people, thousands of facts about tens of people, tens of facts about thousands of people; hundreds of facts, about hundreds of organizations.

As one tries to classify all his knowledge, the categories grow rapidly at first, but after a while one encounters more and more difficulty. My impression, for what it is worth, is that one can find fewer than ten areas, each with more than ten thousand "links." One can't find a hundred things that he knows a thousand things about. Or a thousand things, each with a full hundred new links. I therefore feel that a machine will quite critically need to acquire the order of a hundred thousand elements of knowledge in order to behave with reasonable sensibility in ordinary situations. A million, if properly organized, should be enough for a very great intelligence. If my argument does not convince you, multiply the figures by ten.

For comparison, let us take an informal look at the programs in this book. It is easy to be cynical about their ranges, for once you learn to operate them you discover ways to trick them into silly mistakes. But still one cannot help being astonished at how far they did get with their feeble semantic endowment. Raphael and Quillian have a few hundred facts buried in their programs; and perhaps the same magnitude in the explicit data structures we see in their examples. STUDENT is of the same order; Black's program less so–it uses more search. Evans's program also conceals no more than a few hundred geometrical assertions, relations, and priority assignments. These are all obviously going to grow rapidly in the near future, as we try to extend their powers. But somewhere, not too far away, we will find them beginning to condense, to find the growth of nonspecialized structure slowing down as the machines come to deal with ordinary new problems in common-sense ways.

1.12 Relevance and Structure

Let us return to the problems of dealing with very large bodies of information. It is clear that if many factual statements are filed with no orderly scheme, then a deduction system will have to use search to find chains, and the search effort will grow rapidly with the size of the files. An orderly system that supplies just the information needed for the immediate problem will suppress this growth completely, leaving only the cost of operating the retrieval system. But, as everyone knows, it is hard to find a knowledge-classifying system that works well for many different kinds of problems; it requires immense effort to build a plausible thesaurus that works even within one field. Furthermore, any particular retrieval structure is liable to entail commitments making it difficult to incorporate concepts that appear after the original structure is assembled. One is tempted to say: "It would be folly to base our intelligent machine upon some particular, elaborate, thesaurus-like classification of knowledge, some *ad hoc* syntopicon. Surely that is no road to 'general intelligence.' "

But we had better be cautious about this caution itself, for it exposes us to a far more deadly temptation: to seek a fountain of pure intelligence. I see no reason to believe that intelligence can exist apart from a highly organized body of knowledge, models, and processes. The habit of our culture has always been to suppose that intelligence resides in some separated crystalline element, call it *consciousness, apprehension, insight, gestalt,* or what you will, but this is merely to confound naming the problem with solving it. The problem-solving abilities of a highly intelligent person lies partly in his superior heuristics for managing his knowledge structure and partly in the structure itself; these are probably somewhat inseparable. In any case, there is no reason to suppose that you can be intelligent except through the use of an adequate, *particular* knowledge or model structure.

My thesis is simply that we must not try to evade the "thesaurus problem" just because we (rightly) can never be satisfied with any particular thesaurus. We must still learn how to build them, and find ways to make machines first to use them, then to modify them, and eventually to build for themselves new and better ones.

1.13 Practical Problems of Mechanizing Large Models

At each moment in the course of thinking about a problem, one is involved with a large collection of statements, definitions, associations, and so on, and a network of goals. One has to deal not only with facts about objects, relations between objects, and the like, but also facts about facts, classes of facts, relations between such classes, etc. The heuristic programs that, as we shall see, so neatly demonstrate principles when applied to small models will not work efficiently when applied to large ones. Problems like looping, branching, measuring progress, and generally keeping track of what is happening will come to require a disproportionate part of the computation time.

Even if one is working on a complex problem one usually has, at lower levels, simpler goals that require just a few hundred facts. Even assuming for the moment that these have somehow been isolated from the main store, it would be the exception to find that the fact one needs at the moment is at hand in exactly the required form. It is more usual to obtain it by "common sense": the ability to deduce "a sufficiently wide class of immediate consequences of anything it is told and what it already knows," as McCarthy puts it in Chapter 6. One acts as though he knows that 372 is larger than 265 without having the millions of such particular number facts stored as propositions. Now, it seems obvious that when one recognizes that an arithmetic problem is at hand, one brings to the surface the *general* knowledge concerning such problems, so that deductions can proceed without much lost effort in search.

This is easy, provided we recognize a clearly defined category. But what can we do when the classification system is not so clear? It is often suggested that "the trouble here is caused by the computers' serial processing; surely some sort of parallel associative memory will make the problem go away." Indeed, several of the systems presented in this book do lend themselves to substantial degrees of parallel processing, and I will conclude this chapter with a discussion of what seem to me to be the promises and the problems in doing this.

We have already proposed that when knowledge is neatly classified, one can "bring it out" and apply deductive programming methods. It is natural to ask why one should bother: Why not combine a network retrieval scheme like Raphael's or Quillian's with a reasoner like Black's or Bobrow's? Perhaps this could be developed along the lines sketched by Hebb (7), who suggests that thinking and learning could emerge from the construction and activation of links between concepts (or, rather, their physiological equivalents). The objection to this is that making intricate deductions requires intricate computations involving both particular facts and general principles. The former can be propagated to some extent by simple "activation" signals, but the latter can be applied only by making appropriate *bindings.* That is, one must transmit not just the rule to be used but also the assignments of particular values to symbols. These are needed to produce the required specializations of the general rules later in the course of deduction.

Such bindings—there are things like them, called association lists, in the IPL and LISP programming languages—can become quite complicated, and any serious proposal for deductive information retrieval within a parallel memory network must suggest a way to handle them. They would have to be transmitted along the paths in the net, and when they collide one must either perform some logic or compromise in some other way. To carry through without any compromise would seem to require that each node of the net be a rather substantial little computer, perhaps complete with a little push-down storage memory of its own. The binding problem is only one of the complications that arise; it therefore seems more productive to consider the compromises.

One possibility is to keep a single central association file and require all concurrent processes to use it. This would cause difficulty in certain kinds of deductions, but these would probably be kinds that are also troublesome in our own thinking (hence, presumably not incomparible with intelligent thinking). Another approach is the one we have hinted at all along: to use a simpler nonlogical activation-chain process to pre-select from all one's information a subset of probably relevant information. This in turn makes practical more intricate (and more serial) procedures that would be too lengthy to apply to the whole body of knowledge. It is easier to justify such a compromise if one is realistic about human performance. It takes a man a long time to solve a respectably hard problem. Similarly, when a fact is apparently not relevant to a problem, but some clever fellow finds that it really does apply, this is unusual enough to be applauded. Of course, any pre-selection carries with it the chance of missing a relevant fact, but before posing this as a critical objection to any such scheme for an intelligent machine, let the reader ask himself whether he himself never overlooks an obvious fact, let alone an obscure one.

Thus the binding problem, although serious, does not completely rule out a parallel memory. A parallel net, even while muddling its bindings, can probably be made to do rapid and useful low-quality reasoning with large bodies of knowledge. Many problems, perhaps including all those that can be solved by animals, might be of this kind. The results of such "low-level thought" could pre-select information, models, and structures to be used later by a more centralized high-level problem solver. Difficult problems are usually solved, I believe, by a process whose first stages are based on simplifying the situation. We then solve the simpler version by ignoring just the sorts of difficulties and conflicts we are discussing. Once this "planning stage" is over, we try to modify the proposed solution to fit the real situation, attending now to the conflicts and fine details. Thus, the lower-quality network activation schemes could mediate between the requirements for intricate logic on one side and for vast knowledge on the other, through their role in the act of planning. Once a plan is formulated, the information-retrieval problem becomes more specific and, presumably, easier.

Sources and Acknowledgments

Black, Fischer, *A Deductive Question-Answering System,* Ph.D. dissertation, Harvard, June 1964, 172 pp.

The Project MAC* time-shared computer system was used in Black's program development. He mentions J. McCarthy, M. Minsky (thesis advisor), P. Fischer, T. Marill, F. Safier, A. Wolf, D. Bobrow, B. Raphael, and W. Teitelman in his acknowledgments.

Bobrow, Daniel G., *Natural Language Input For a Computer Problem-Solving System,* Ph.D. dissertation, M.I.T., September 1964, 128 pp. Appeared as Report TR-1, Project MAC*, M.I.T. A brief digest was published under the title "A Question-Answering System for High-School Algebra Word Problems" in *Proceedings of AFIPS Fall Joint Computer Conference,* 1964, pp. 591-614.

Bobrow acknowledges the support of the M.I.T. Computation Center and Project MAC, and earlier support by the Systems Development Corporation and by Bolt, Beranek and Newman, Inc. He also mentions M. Minsky (thesis advisor), V. Yngve, M. Eden, H. Simon, N. Chomsky, and S. Papert in his acknowledgments.

Evans, Thomas G., *A Heuristic Program to Solve Geometric-Analogy Problems,* Ph.D. dissertation, M.I.T., June 1963, 199 pp. A brief digest was published under the same title in the *Proceedings of the Spring Joint Computer Conference,* 1964, pp. 327-338. The thesis has also appeared in the form of a report of the Air Force Cambridge Research Laboratories under the title "A Program for the Solution of a Class of Geometric-Analogy Intelligence-Test Questions."

Evans wishes to acknowledge the permission of the Educational Testing Service, Princeton, N.J., for use and reproduction of test items, and Educations Records Bureau, New York, for the data pertaining to human performance on the tests. Most of the computation used the M.I.T. Computation Center facilities. He also acknowledges help from M. Minsky (thesis advisor), O. Selfridge, and V. Yngve.

McCarthy, John, "Programs with Common Sense," in *Mechanization of Thought Processes,* Her Majesty's Stationery Office, London, 1959, pp. 75-84.

Also, "Situations, Actions and Causal Laws," Stanford Artificial Intelligence Project Memo No. 2, July 1963. This work was supported by ARPA**, under contract SD-183.

Minsky, Marvin, "Descriptive Languages and Problem-Solving," in *Proceedings of the Western Joint Computer Conference,* 1961, pp. 215-218.

Also, "Matter, Mind, and Models," in *Proceedings of the IFIP Congress,* 1965, pp. 45-49.

Quillian, M. Ross, *Semantic Memory,* Ph.D. dissertation, Carnegie Institute of Technology (now Carnegie-Mellon University), October 1966, 222 pp. Appeared as Report AFCRL-66-189.

Quillian wishes to acknowledge the support of NIH grant MH-07722, the Systems Development Corporation, and the Advanced Research Projects Agency** (P.R. CRI-561-76, ARPA Order No. 627). He also mentions H. Simon (thesis advisor), B. Green, A. Newell, W. Reitman, G. Baylor, D. Bobrow, and R. Simmons.

Raphael, Bertram, *SIR: A Computer Program for Semantic Information Retrieval,* Ph.D. dissertation, M.I.T., June 1964, 169 pp. Appeared as Report TR-2, Project MAC*, M.I.T. A brief digest was published under the title: "A Computer Program Which 'Understands'," in *Proceedings of AFIPS Fall Joint Computer Conference,* 1964, pp. 577-589.

Raphael wishes to acknowledge the support of the M.I.T. Computation Center and Project MAC*, and earlier support by the RAND Corporation and by Bolt, Beranek and Newman, Inc. He also mentions M. Minsky (thesis advisor), V. Yngve, and H. Rogers, Jr., in his acknowledgments.

Bibliography

1. Ashby, W. Ross, *An Introduction to Cybernetics,* John Wiley & Sons, New York, 1956.
2. Berkeley, E. C., and Bobrow, D. G., *The Programming Language LISP,* Information International, Inc., Cambridge, Mass., Nov. 1964.
3. Chomsky, N., *Syntactic Structures,* Mouton and Co., The Hague, 1957.
4. Craik, K. J. W., *The Nature of Explanation,* Cambridge University Press, 1943.
5. Feigenbaum, E. A., and Feldman, J. (eds.), *Computers and Thought,* McGraw-Hill, New York, 1963
6. Gelernter, H., Hansen, J. R., and Loveland, D. W., "Empirical Explorations of the Geometry-Theorem Proving Machine," in *Proc. of the Western Joint Computer Conference,* 1960, 143.
7. Hebb, D. O., *The Organization of Behavior,* John Wiley & Sons, New York, 1949.
8. MacKay, D. M., "The Informational Analysis of Questions and Commands," in *Proc. of 4th London Symposium on Information Theory,* Academic Press, New York, 1961.
9. McCarthy, J., et al., *LISP 1.5 Programmer's Manual,* The M.I.T. Press, Cambridge, Mass., 1963.
10. McCulloch, W. S., and Pitts, W., "A Logical Calculus of the Ideas Immanent in Nervous Activity," *Bull. Math.-Biophysics 5,* 1943, 115. Also in *Embodiments of Mind,* The M.I.T. Press, Cambridge, Mass., 1966.
11. Minsky, M., "Why Programming is a Good Medium for Expressing Poorly Understood and Sloppily Formulated Ideas," *Design Quarterly,* Fall 1967, 117.
12. Newell, A., "The Search for Generality," in *Proc. IFIP Congress* 1965, Spartan Books, 17.
13. Newell, A., Shaw, J. C., and Simon, H. A., *Information Processing Language V Manual,* Prentice-Hall, Englewood Cliffs, N.J., 1961.
14. Newell, A., and Simon, H. A., "The Simulation of Human Thought," in *Current Trends in Psychological Theory,* University of Pittsburgh Press, 1961.
15. Piaget, J., *The Construction of Reality in the Child,* Basic Books, Inc., New York, 1954.
16. Rosenblueth, A., Wiener, N., and Bigelow, J., "Behavior, Purpose and Teleology," *Philosophy of Science, 10,* 1943, 18.
17. Samuel, A. L., "Some Studies in Machine Learning Using the Game of Checkers," *IBM J. of Research and Development 3,* No. 3, 1959, 210.
18. Samuel, A. L., "Some Studies in Machine Learning Using the Game of Checkers, II–Recent Progress," *IBM J. of Research and Development 11,* No. 6, 1967, 601.
19. Skinner, B. F., *Cumulative Record,* Appleton-Century-Crofts, New York, 1961.
20. Slagle, J., "A Computer Program for Solving Problems in Freshman Calculus," *J. ACM.,* 1964; also doctoral dissertation, Mathematics Department, M.I.T., May 1961.

Added in proof

1. A recently developed program plays tournament-quality chess; under regular competition clock conditions, it is considered to be in the middle amateur ranks.
   Greenblatt, R. D., Eastlake, D. E., and Crocker, S. D., "The Greenblatt Chess Program," *Proc. Fall Joint Computer Conference*, 1967, pp. 801–810, Thompson Books, Washington, D.C.
2. A recently developed integration program solves a wide range of textbook integration programs with practically no wrong attempts at all.
   Moses, J., *Symbolic Integration*, Ph.D. dissertation, M.I.T. Mathematics Department, September 1967.
3. A very detailed analysis of a class of "adaptive" machines will be found in:
   Minsky, M., and Papert, S., *Perceptrons,* M.I.T. Press, 1968.

2. SIR: Semantic Information Retrieval

Bertram Raphael

2.1 Introduction

2.1.1 The Problem

This chapter discusses the problem of developing a computer* which "understands." The method of study involved the construction of a computer system having certain cognitive abilities and exhibiting some humanlike conversational behavior.

This computer system is called "SIR"–Semantic Information Retriever. The conversation presented in Fig. 2-1 between a person (identified by "***.") and SIR illustrates some of the system's capabilities. Although it is capable of "understanding" statements dealing with set relations, part-whole relations, ownership, and certain spatial relations, SIR has no initial built-in associations for nouns like "John," "boy," and "table."

"Understanding" is difficult to define precisely. The present study makes the following specific assumptions and observations:

i) "Understanding" can be demonstrated by dialogue, which requires the participants to indicate an awareness of the meaning of their subject matter. Therefore a computer should be considered able to "understand" if it can converse intelligently, i.e., if it can remember what it is told, answer questions, and make responses which a human observer considers reasonable.†

*The term "computer" refers to the combination of digital computer hardware and operating computer program.

†I am concerned here with the computer's internal information representation and retrieval techniques. For this purpose I assume that abstract "words" are the basic signal unit. There is no need to be concerned with speech recognition, sensory receptors, or other problems involving the physical nature of the communication channel and signals.

```
(***.    EVERY BOY IS A PERSON)

(I UNDERSTAND)

(***.    A FINGER IS PART OF A HAND)

(I UNDERSTAND)

(***.    EACH PERSON HAS TWO HANDS)

(THE ABOVE SENTENCE IS AMBIGUOUS ** PLEASE RE-PHRASE IT)

(***.    THERE ARE TWO HANDS ON EACH PERSON)

(I UNDERSTAND)

(***.    HOW MANY FINGERS DOES JOHN HAVE Q)

(THE ABOVE SENTENCE IS AMBIGUOUS ** BUT I ASSUME (HAS) MEANS (HAS AS PARTS))
(I DON*T KNOW WHETHER FINGER IS PART OF JOHN)

(***.    JOHN IS A BOY)

(I UNDERSTAND)

(***.    HOW MANY FINGERS DOES JOHN HAVE Q)

(THE ABOVE SENTENCE IS AMBIGUOUS ** BUT I ASSUME (HAS) MEANS (HAS AS PARTS))
((HOW MANY FINGER PER HAND Q))

(***.    EVERY HAND HAS 5 FINGERS)

(THE ABOVE SENTENCE IS AMBIGUOUS ** BUT I ASSUME (HAS) MEANS (HAS AS PARTS))
(I UNDERSTAND)

(***.    HOW MANY FINGERS DOES JOHN HAVE Q)

(THE ABOVE SENTENCE IS AMBIGUOUS ** BUT I ASSUME (HAS) MEANS (HAS AS PARTS))
(THE ANSWER IS 10)

(***.    HOW MANY AUTOMOBILES DOES JOHN HAVE Q)

(THE ABOVE SENTENCE IS AMBIGUOUS ** PLEASE RE-PHRASE IT)

(***.    WHO IS PRESIDENT OF THE UNITED STATES Q)

(STATEMENT FORM NOT RECOGNIZED)

(***.    THE BOY IS JUST TO THE LEFT OF THE TABLE)

(G02840 IS A TABLE)
(I UNDERSTAND)

(***.    THE LAMP IS JUST TO THE LEFT OF THE TABLE)

(G02841 IS A LAMP)
(THE ABOVE STATEMENT IS IMPOSSIBLE)

(***.    THE TABLE IS TO THE RIGHT OF THE CHAIR)

(G02842 IS A CHAIR)
(I UNDERSTAND)

(***.    WHAT IS THE RELATIVE POSITION OF A PERSON Q)

(THE LEFT-TO-RIGHT ORDER IS AS FOLLOWS)
(CHAIR (BOY TABLE))
```

Figure 2-1. Sample Conversation

ii) In addition to echoing, upon request, the facts it has been given, a machine which "understands" must be able to recognize the logical implications of those facts. It also must be able to identify (from a large data store) facts which are relevant to a particular question.

iii) The most important prerequisite for the ability to "understand" is a suitable internal representation, or model, for stored information. This model should be structured so that information relevant for question-answering is easily accessible. Direct storage of English text is not suitable since the structure of an English statement generally is not a good representation of the meaning of the statement. On the other hand, models which are direct representations of certain kinds of relational information usually are unsuited for use with other relations. A general-purpose "understanding" machine should utilize a model which can represent semantic content for a wide variety of subject areas.

SIR is a prototype of an "understanding" machine. It demonstrates how these conversational and deductive abilities can be obtained through use of a suitable model. Later sections will describe the model and the SIR program, how they were developed, how they are used, and how they can be extended for future applications.

2.1.2 Where the Problem Arises

The need for computers which "understand" arises in several areas of computer research. Some examples follow.

1. *Information retrieval:* The high speeds and huge memory capacities of present computers could be of great aid in scanning scientific literature. Unfortunately, high-speed search is useless unless the searcher is capable of recognizing what is being searched for; and existing computer systems for information retrieval use techniques that are too crude for specifying and identifying the objects of the search.

Information-retrieval systems generally provide either *document* retrieval or *fact* retrieval. *Document* retrieval programs usually depend upon a human preassignment of "descriptors" to the documents. A user of the system may know the list of descriptors but cannot know precisely what the descriptors meant to the cataloguer. It is difficult for the user to determine what the semantic interactions between the descriptors are and how these interactions help determine the content of the documents obtained.

Fact retrieval systems usually require that the information to be retrieved first be placed in a rigid form designed for a particular subject area. This rigid representation for the data, and the corresponding rigid formulation of the retrieval requests, could be produced automatically by a computer which "understands" statements expressed in a form more natural to the human user. Further, if the computer could "understand" information expressed in some general manner, specialized formal representations would be unnecessary.

In order to make a computer serve as a reference librarian, it is not sufficient simply to store in it a large volume of information. The computer must also have the ability to find and retrieve information in response to flexible descriptive commands. Further, the computer should be able to modify both the information in storage and the requests it is receiving, and it should be able to describe its actions and to request clarifying information. The most useful information retrieval system will be one which can "converse" with its users, to make sure that each request is well-defined and correctly "understood."

2. *Mechanical translation:* Researchers in the area of mechanical translation of natural language have been disappointed to discover how difficult their task is. First word-to-word translations, and then word-to-word translations coupled with grammatical analysis, rearrangement, and context-dependent restrictions, have proven inadequate for achieving good translations. The vital feature missing from present computer translating systems is the ability of human translators to "understand" what they read in one language, and then "say the same thing" in another. The SIR computer system can store facts, make logical deductions, answer questions, and exhibit other features of human conversational behavior, and therefore appears to have some such "understanding" ability. The mechanisms which help it to "understand" are likely to help also in solving the mechanical translation problem.

3. *General computer applications:* During the past decade there has been a tremendous growth in the amount of computer utilization and in the variety of computer applications. However, before each new problem can be tackled by a computer, someone must perform the arduous task of "programming" a solution, i.e., encoding the problem into a form acceptable to a computer.

Various "problem-oriented" computer languages have been developed to ease this encoding problem. Unfortunately, such languages are useful only when programs ("compilers" or "interpreters") are available to translate automatically from the problem-oriented language to the basic "order-code" of the computer. At present all such problem-oriented languages are very rigid systems. This means that the problem domain must be one which lends itself to rigorous, complete, formal definition, e.g., algebraic manipulations, accounting procedures, or machine-tool operations.

Many interesting problems are not sufficiently well defined or clearly understood to be expressed in any of the conventional computer programming languages. Still, people are able to describe these problems to each other and to assist one another in making the problems more precise and in solving them. In order to utilize the high speed and large memory capacities of computers while working on such ill-defined problems, people need some useful way to communicate incomplete information to the computer; some way which will make the computer "aware" of facts and enable it to "understand" the nature of the problems which are described to it. SIR is a prototype of a computer system which captures some measure of the "meaning" of the information presented to it and can act upon its stored body of knowledge in an "intelligent" manner.

2.2 Semantic Information Retrieval Systems

The word "semantic" is used in the title of this chapter for two reasons: First, the actual information extracted from text and stored by the program is intended to approximate the linguistic "semantic content" or "meaning" of the material. Second, the computer representation of information used in SIR (cf. Section 2.3.4) is derived from the "semantic" model structures of formal mathematical logic. "Information retrieval" refers to the fact that the systems discussed operate on collections of statements, retrieving facts in response to questions. Question-answering was chosen because it is a straightforward context in which to experiment with the understanding and communicative ability of a computer.

The SIR system utilizes results from two major research areas: the study of the semantics of natural language, and the study of previously developed computer programming techniques for solving various specific question-answering problems.

2.2.1 Semantics

Semantics is generally studied from one of two viewpoints: pure and descriptive. *Pure* semantics, as studied by Carnap (5), deals with the properties of artificially constructed formal systems (which may or may not have analogues in the real world), with respect to rules for sentence formation and designation of formal models and truth values. I shall rather be concerned with *descriptive* semantics, an empirical search for rules governing truth and meaningfulness of sentences in natural language.

1. *Semantics and meaning:* When discussing meaning, one quickly encounters difficulties in having to use words with which to discuss the meaning of words, especially that of the word "meaning." Therefore one finds it difficult to distinguish between object-language and meta-language. A common device is to define "meaning" in a very specialized sense or to deny that it can be defined at all. Quine, tongue in cheek, recognizes this difficulty in the following paragraph (33):

> One must remember that an expression's meaning (if we are to admit such things as meanings) is not to be confused with the object, if any, that the expression designates. Sentences do not designate at all . . . , though words in them may; sentences are simply not singular terms. But sentences still have meanings (if we admit such things as meanings); and the meaning of an eternal sentence is the object designated by the singular term found by bracketing the sentence.

That singular term will have a meaning in turn (if we are prodigal enough with meanings), but it will presumably be something further. Under this approach the meaning (if such there be) of the non-eternal sentence "The door is open" is not a proposition. . . .

Quine continues that the elusive meaning of "The door is open" is some complete intuitive set of circumstances surrounding a particular occasion on which the statement "The door is open" was uttered. Clearly this kind of concept does not lend itself to computer usage. In order to construct a computer system which behaves as if it understands the meaning of a statement, one must find specific words and relations which can be represented within the computer's memory, yet which somehow capture the significance of the statement they represent.

Ziff (47) is more precise in making the following distinction: Words may have meaning, but not significance; utterances (phrases, sentences) may have significance, but not meaning. However, he states that an analysis of the *significance* of a whole utterance cannot be completed without an analysis of the *meanings* of the words in the utterance. I find Ziff's distinction between word meaning and utterance significance a useful distinction, although the terminology is poor since both concepts contribute to what is commonly called "meaning." Since Ziff does not present any further explanation or representation of "meaning" and "significance," let us proceed to the similar but more complete discussion by Ullmann (44).

Ullmann considers a word as the smallest significant unit with isolated "content," whereas phrases and sentences express *relations* between the things which are symbolized by individual words. Here "meaning" is defined as "a reciprocal relationship between the name and the sense, which enables the one to call up the other." By "sense" is meant the thought or reference to an object or association which is represented by the word. Note that meaning here relates word with thought about object, not necessarily with object itself. Now, "thought about object" is too vague an idea for computer formalization. However, we *can* work with a verbalization of a thought; namely, the *words* which name objects and features associated with the thought.

We may consider the meaning of a word which names an object or class of objects to be either the thing named or, after Ullmann, the most common thoughts people have in connection with the thing named. In either case, in the SIR system I *approximate* the meaning of the word by building up, in the computer, a *description* of the object or class. This description, itself composed of words, presents properties of the described entity and names other objects and classes to which that entity is related. The meaning of an *utterance* can then be represented in a natural way by particular entries in the descriptions of the objects named in the utterance.

Walpole (45) points out similarly that a word may be defined (i.e., the meaning of a word may be explained) by any kind of association, connection, or characteristic, and these features of a word are usually described verbally. Thus such features can be part of the computer's description of the word being defined.

> Words do not live in isolation in a language system. They enter into all kinds of groupings held together by a complex, unstable and highly subjective network of associations; associations between the names and the senses, associations based on similarity or some other relation. It is by their effects that these associative connections make themselves felt; . . . . The sum total of these associative networks is the *vocabulary*. (45)

SIR uses an approximation to those associative networks as its basic data store.

Walpole also notes that some word relationships, such as part to whole, or class to subclass, determine partial orderings of large classes of nouns and thus can be represented by tree structures. This fact leads to certain search procedures which are useful in our computer system. However, the class of abstract nouns ("fictions"), which do not name any object in any specific sense-experience, do not lend themselves to such ordering and hence are omitted from early versions of computer representations for semantic information.

2. *Grammar and meaning:* Thus far I have discussed meaning (semantics) while ignoring the grammar (syntax) of language. However, grammar is important since I would like the computer program to take advantage of whatever useful information is available in the grammatical structure of its input. Also, at least one school of thought (to be discussed under the next heading) holds that syntactic analysis is an adequate method for obtaining semantic classification. Therefore let us consider the nature of grammar.

A "grammar" is usually defined as a set of rules defining which strings of alphabetic characters are "sentences" of the language and which are not. Deriving a grammar for a natural language is an empirical process, since the ultimate test of whether a statement is grammatical or not is to ask a native speaker. Considering only the functions of words in sentences (their "parts of speech") but not their meanings in any sense, Chomsky (9) develops various kinds of English grammars. *Phrase structure* is a simple concept and works for a small part of the language, but it is frequently inadequate. *Transformational grammar* schemes are probably adequate but are complicated and difficult to complete or test.

Although syntactic procedures are generally supposed to ignore meaning, the boundary between syntactics and semantics is hazy. For example, some linguists classify the so-called "mass nouns" (e.g., "water") as a separate grammatical group because they do not take the article. However, the distinction between "I want meat" and "I want a steak" seems to be basically a semantic one.

Ziff defines meaningfulness in terms of rigidity of grammatical structure.

Words that are necessary in a particular grammatical configuration, such as frequent occurrences of "to," "do," "the," and the like, are said to have no meaning. On the other hand, words which could be replaced by a large number of alternatives within a given grammatical context are considered very meaningful. Simmons (38) makes this distinction between *function* words and *content* words even more sharp, as we shall see later (paragraph 3 of Part 2.2.3). I have used these ideas to the extent that only words which are names of objects or classes, or of properties of objects or classes, appear in the internal representation used in SIR. The frequently occurring "meaningless" words of Ziff are used as indicators of relations between other "meaningful" words appearing in the same sentences (cf. Part 2.4.2).

3. *Formalizing meaning:* The intelligent computer has to understand and remember the meaning of what it is told; therefore it needs some precise internal representation for these meanings. Let us now examine some of the formal representations of meaning which have been proposed and see which ideas from those representations might be useful in a computer representation.

One way to deal with the problem of semantics is to avoid it by translating ordinary language into a formal system which could be handled syntactically (1). Thus far, attempts to encode all of natural English formally seem to introduce a mass of detailed notation which obscures the real problem, for the problem of representing meaning must be solved in order to develop a good translation scheme. At first view, Freudenthal's LINCOS (15) may seem like a formal system for describing human behavior. Actually the LINCOS system is not practical, since it assumes far greater abilities for inductive inference of rules and situations on the part of the receiver than is expected of the usual language student.

Another approach, used for example by Klein (19), is to increase the number and kinds of categories in the usual syntactic analysis systems until the semantic properties are automatically included. Although some of the results are promising, it seems to me that this approach will eventually obtain the same ultimate system of word associations that can be approached more simply by considering and representing directly the "meaningful" relations between words.

Quillian (32) attempts to represent the semantic content of words as sets of "concepts," which can be combined to represent the meanings of phrases and sentences. With the basic premise that learning a new word involves measuring its values on a set of basic scales, he is trying to build up a repertoire of suitable coordinate scales. Each word is represented by a set of values which are generally intuitive, unidimensional coordinates, such as length, time, and hue. Quillian also permits defining words in terms of predefined words as coordinates. My feeling is that the relations *between* words are more important than the conceptual meaning of *individual* words, and therefore a simpler approach which ignores "basic" meanings would be more immediately fruitful.

Sommers (42) is more concerned with permissible word combinations than with the meanings of individual words. He first describes a hierarchy of sentence types: 1) ungrammatical; 2) grammatical but nonsense; 3) sensible but false; 4) true. He then argues that the crucial semantic distinction lies between the grammatical declarative sentences which are nonsense and those which are significant (but may be true or false). Any pair of monadic predicates P_1, P_2 are said by Sommers to have a sense value $U(P_1,P_2)$ if there exists *any* significant sentence conjoining them. Otherwise they have value $\sim U=N(P_1,P_2)$. The U-relation is symmetric and is preserved under certain logical operations on its arguments, but it is not transitive. A stronger relation $Q \leftarrow P$ is true if "of (what is) P, it can be significantly said that it is Q . . . , e.g., P=Prime minister, Q=quick." This permits the arrangement of these "monadic predicates" into a simple tree, where all words in the same meaning class, e.g., all colors, or all words describing weight, occupy the same node.

My main objection to this work is in where the important distinctions lie. Sommers would argue that "The idea is always green" is nonsense, but "The yellow sky is always green" is sensible (since sky may have color, "The sky is blue" and "The sky is not blue" are significant), although false. Note that "Ideas cannot be green" would be considered nonsense rather than true, by Sommers. I feel the distinction between "nonsense" and "sensible but not true of the real world" is not precise enough to be a basis for a computer representation of a semantic system. SIR is concerned with deductions of consequences from a given body of statements, rather than judgments of "nonsense" or "sensible."

In summary, many schemes have been developed in the literature for formally describing the semantic properties of language. Some of these are here described. Most of the schemes are vague, and although Klein's and Quillian's, among others, are being programmed for computers, none of the presently available semantic systems has been developed to the point where they could provide a useful basis for computer "understanding." However, I have used some of the ideas from the above systems in developing SIR. The idea of representing meaning by word associations is particularly important for the information representation used in SIR.

2.2.2 Models

The SIR system uses a special data structure which I call the "model." The program refers to this "model" whenever it must store or retrieve semantic information. The purpose of this section is to explain what I mean by the term "model" in general and to define the SIR model in particular.

1. *Definition:* The term "model" has been grossly overworked, and it does not seem to have any generally agreed-upon definition (18). For purposes of this paper, I present the following definition:

A *model* for an entity x has the following properties:

a. Certain features of the model correspond in some well-defined way to certain features of x.

b. Changes in the model represent, in some well-defined way, corresponding changes in x.

c. There is some distinct advantage to studying the model and effects of changes upon it in order to learn about x, rather than studying x directly.

The term x may be any of a wide class of entities, such as an object, a statement in English, or a mathematical concept.

2. *Examples of models:*

i) A small-scale wind-tunnel test section for part of an airplane is a *model* for the actual part because aerodynamicists understand how air flow around the test section is related to air flow around an actual airplane part (whose shape corresponds to the shape of the test section in a well-defined way). An obvious advantage of such a model is its convenient size.

ii) A verbal statement of a plane-geometry problem usually includes statements about line segments, connections, shapes, etc. The usual *model* is a pencil or chalk diagram which has the geometric features described in the statement. The advantage of the model is that it is conceptually easier for people to interpret geometric relationships from a diagram than from a verbal statement, which is really an encoding of the geometric information into a linear string of words.

iii) Problem-solving ability in human beings has been modeled by a computer program developed by Newell, Shaw, and Simon (28). The model can be improved by modifying the program so that its external behavior corresponds more closely to the behavior of people working on the same problems. The advantage of this model for behavior is that its internal workings are observable and hence provide a hypothesis for the corresponding mechanisms involved at the information-processing level in human problem solving.

iv) Logicians develop and study formal systems. Occasionally these have no significance other than their syntactic structures. Sometimes, however, systems are developed in order to study the properties of external (usually mathematical) relationships. On these occasions one says that statements in the formal system correspond "under standard interpretation" to facts about the relationships. The *model* for such a formal (syntactic) system usually consists of sets of objects which satisfy our intuitive notions of the "meaning" of the original relationships, yet whose properties correspond to certain features of the syntactic statements. Thus one may study the abstract formal system by manipulating a model which has intuitive significance. Semantics, in mathematical logic, refers to the study of such models (6).

There may not always be a clear-cut distinction between entities which are *models* and those which are not really representations of something else. For example, Newell, Shaw, and Simon's problem-solving program discussed in (iii) above is truly a *model,* in the sense defined earlier, only insofar as it is intended to represent human behavior. Otherwise the program would have to be treated just on its merits as an independent problem-solving machine.

3. *Question-answering model:* In designing a question-answering system one is concerned with providing a store of information, or a mechanism for developing such a store, and a procedure for extracting appropriate information from that store when presented with a question. The store may be built up on the basis of information presented in the form of simple declarative English sentences, as it is in SIR, or it may be a prepared data structure. In either case, it generally contains information which people would normally communicate to each other in English sentences. I consider the store of information which is the basis of any question-answering system as a *model* for any set of English sentences which contains the same information. Of course, "information contained" refers here to the semantic content, not the number of information-theoretic bits. Note that, due to the present vague state of semantic analysis in natural language, the most effective way of discovering this information content of a question-answering system's store of information is to ask the system some questions and make subjective inferences from its performance.

The information store of a system is a model for a set of English sentences, because the information which can be extracted from the store corresponds in a well-defined way, and in fact should be identical, to at least some of the information available in the sentences. The principal advantage of such a model is that it is easier to identify and extract desired information from the model than it would be from the complete English sentences. Question-answering systems have been developed which use various kinds of models and which have achieved varying degrees of success. The best-known examples of such systems are discussed in the following paragraphs. The structure of the model used in my new question-answering system will be dealt with in Section 2.3.

2.2.3 Some Existing Question-Answering Systems

Several computer programs have been written whose aims and results are somewhat related to those of SIR. None of these "question-answering" systems uses a model for storing arbitrary semantic information, and none of them deals with the same general kind of subject matter as SIR. However, each has certain interesting features, some of which have influenced the design of SIR.

1. *"Baseball: An Automatic Question-Answerer."* This program (17), written in the IPL-V (25) programming language, answers most reasonable verbal English questions about a set of baseball games. Example:

input: "How many teams played in 8 places in July?"
output: MONTH = JULY
$\text{PLACE}_{\text{number of}} = 8$
$\text{TEAM}_{\text{number of}} = 3$: YANKEES, TIGERS, RED SOX.

The stored information (model) consists of a list-structure containing all the relevant baseball-game results arranged according to a preselected hierarchical format. There is no provision for automatically modifying this model. Each question is translated into a specification-list with the desired information represented by blanks. This specification-list is then matched against the model, the blanks filled, and the entire final specification-list printed out. No attempt is made to respond in grammatical English.

The bulk of the program is devoted to the task of translating a question sentence into a specification-list. This requires looking up words in a dictionary, identifying idioms, performing grammatical analyses, resolving ambiguities, etc. The dictionary consists of a set of entries for each word, such as its part of speech, whether the word is part of an idiom, and its "meaning." "Meaning," which only appears for certain words, refers to a canonical translation of the word within the context of the program; e.g., the meaning of "who" is "Team = ?" Thus the specialized nature of the subject matter enables simple, *ad hoc* procedures to solve what would otherwise be very difficult problems. The model consists of a fixed structure of information arranged to facilitate the process of filling blanks in specification-lists.

The "Baseball" system gives the illusion of intelligent behavior because it can respond to a wide variety of English question forms. However, a limited amount of information about a specific subject must be prearranged in a fixed data structure, and the data must lend themselves to hierarchical ordering. Such a scheme cannot be generalized conveniently to handle the larger variety of information necessary for a truly "intelligent" system.

2. *Phillips' "Question-Answering Routine."* This program (31), written in the LISP programming language (23), can correctly answer certain simple English questions on the basis of a corpus of simple English sentences. Example:

input: ((AT SCHOOL JOHNNY MEETS THE TEACHER)
(THE TEACHER READS BOOKS IN THE CLASSROOM))
(WHERE DOES THE TEACHER READ BOOKS)
output: (IN THE CLASSROOM)

The model for a sentence is a list of up to five elements: subject, verb, object, place, and time. This model is constructed for each sentence in the corpus and for the question (where a special symbol in the question-list identifies the unknown item). The question-list is matched against each sentence-list and, if an appropriately matching sentence is found, the correct reply is extracted from the corresponding sentence in the original corpus.

This is a primitive system in several obvious respects: any information in a sentence other than the five "basic" elements, and any sentence which cannot be analyzed, is ignored; the words in the question must be exactly the same as those in a corpus sentence; a question must be answerable on the basis of a single sentence from the corpus; and the model for the entire corpus must be searched linearly for the answer to each question. However, the idea of a model which is created and extended automatically as new sentences are added and which serves as an intermediary form to assist in finding answers to questions is an essential feature of an intelligent, humanlike system; this is the important contribution of Phillips' work.

3. *"SYNTHEX."* This program (38), written in the JOVIAL programming language (37), can answer a wide variety of questions about information contained in a large corpus of simple natural English such as the *Golden Book Encyclopedia.* Example:

input: "What do birds eat?"
(somewhere in the encyclopedia): "Worms are eaten by birds."
output: "Birds eat worms."

The program classifies all words as either *function* words, which have structural (syntactic) significance (e.g., the, is, do, what), and *content* words, which have semantic significance (in practice, content words are any words which have not been chosen as function words). Initially the corpus (the encyclopedia) is indexed with respect to all occurrences of all content words. This index occupies about the same amount of space as the corpus itself. When a question is asked, the system selects those sentences from the corpus which have the greatest number of content words in common with the question. At this point elaborate grammatical analyses are used to determine whether *any* of the selected sentences provides an answer to the question.

This system doesn't use a model at all; the complete corpus is kept in its original form and referred to, when necessary, through the use of an index. Since the information is not preprocessed into a more usable form, the grammatical analysis required at the time the question is answered is quite complex. Related work by Klein (19) indicates that some of the rules of the grammar can be developed automatically from the corpus, and information from several sentences may be combined by use of syntactic methods to help answer questions.

My feeling is that the word-relations being developed by these "dependency grammar" methods can be discovered more easily by means of *semantic* analysis, and they would then be more intuitively meaningful. A model based on such semantic relations would significantly simplify the question-answering procedure. SIR illustrates the feasibility of directly storing and using semantic relations.

4. *Lindsay's "SAD-SAM: Sentence Appraiser and Diagrammer, and Semantic Analyzing Machine."* This program (21), written in the IPL-V (26) programming language, accepts as input any sentence in Basic English (30), extracts from it any information concerning kinship, and adds this information to a "family tree." Example:

input: "John, Mary's brother, went home."
effect: John and Mary are assigned a common set of parents, i.e., they are

represented as descendants of a common node in the family tree. The grammar is sufficient to handle a considerable portion of natural English in recognizing family relationships. Although the author does not consider question-answering in detail, it is clear that the family relation information is immediately available in the tree model and specific requests could be answered almost trivially.

This system illustrates the effectiveness of a model designed for a very specific task. Lindsay decided in advance that only family relationships were of interest and observed that there is a natural model for family relationships. Then whatever relevant information was received was processed into this model, leaving practically nothing to be done at question-answering time.

Unfortunately, different forms of "natural" models are needed for different kinds of information. In a more general system, it might be possible to use the best available model to represent information for each subject area, e.g., trees for family relations, Cartesian coordinates for spatial relations, perhaps just the original text in areas for which there is no obviously better representation; but this would be a confused system with tremendous organizational problems. The SIR system is based on a single model which captures some of the advantages of various specific models while permitting uniform processing procedures as well as the storage and retrieval of arbitrary facts which arise in human conversation.

5. *Darlington's program for the translation of restricted English into the notation of symbolic logic.* This program (12), written in the COMIT (34) programming language, translates certain English riddles into a logical form which may then be tested for validity by another program, written by the same author, which applies the Davis-Putnam proof procedure (13) for statements in the propositional calculus. Example:

input: "If the butler was present, then the butler would have been seen, and if the butler was seen, then the butler would have been questioned. If the butler had been questioned, then the butler would have replied, and if the butler had replied, then the butler would have been heard. The butler was not heard. If the butler was neither seen nor heard, then the butler must have been on duty, and if the butler was on duty, then the butler must have been present. Therefore the butler was questioned."

output: $[[L \Rightarrow M] \wedge [M \Rightarrow N] \wedge [N \Rightarrow P] \wedge [P \Rightarrow Q] \wedge \sim Q \wedge [[\sim M \wedge \sim Q] \Rightarrow R] \wedge [R \Rightarrow L]] \Rightarrow N]$

The input is typical of a type of problem which appears in elementary logic texts. It has been pre-edited to perform certain clarifications including removal of most pronouns and insertion of necessary marker words such as "then." The program translates this input, by means of dictionary references and grammatical analysis, into the model, which is a statement in mathematical logic having the same truth value as the original English statement. The "question" in these problems is understood to be, "Is this argument valid (i.e., necessarily true)?" The answer can be obtained by applying established methods to the logical model.

As in Lindsay's kinship system, Darlington's program takes advantage of a model ideally suited to the type of problem involved and advance knowledge of the only possible question. If one considers the possibility of questions such as, "What was the occupation of the suspect who was questioned?" or "What was done to the butler?," then the complicated process of translating the corpus into logical terms would not be of any aid in finding answers. Only a small part of the information needed for intelligent behavior can be expressed in the propositional calculus. As will be discussed in Section 2.6, even a version of the quantificational calculus is not sufficient to formalize the conversational ability of SIR; a procedural language is also necessary.

6. *Bennett's computer program for word relations.* This program (3), written in the COMIT programming language, will accept information and answer questions framed in a small number of fixed formats. Example:

input: DOG IS ALWAYS MAMMAL.
MAMMAL IS ALWAYS ANIMAL.
WHAT IS ALWAYS ANIMAL Q.
output: MAMMAL IS ALWAYS ANIMAL.

The input sentences must be in one of five formats (e.g., "*X* IS ALWAYS *Y*", "*X* MAY BE *Y*", etc.), and only one occurrence of each format may be held true at one time for any one item *X*. This input information is translated into the model, which has associated with every item *X* each corresponding item *Y* and an identifying number for the format which set up the correspondence. (The model actually consists of linear strings of tagged entries, as is required by the COMIT language.) Similarly, there is a small number of allowable question formats, each associated with one of the input formats and resulting in a particular class of entries being retrieved from the model.

The major feature of this system, which is also the basic feature of SIR, is that the information kept in the model identifies particular kinds of semantic relations between particular words. Questions are analyzed with respect to, and answered by referring to the model for information about, these same relations. Principal shortcomings of Bennett's system, which I have overcome in SIR, include the following:

a. Relations are identified with particular formats rather than with their intended interpretations.

b. Logical implications based on the meanings of the relations are ignored.

c. Interactions between different relations are ignored.

d. Its string representation makes processing the model more difficult than necessary.

e. The user must know the form and content of the model in order to make changes to it.

In summary, several computer question-answering systems have been developed to solve special problems or illustrate special abilities. *None* of them constitutes a direct approach to providing intelligent "understanding" behavior for the computer. Although various forms of models are used in the existing systems, none represents semantic relations in an intuitive, *general,* and usable way. The SIR model described in the following section provides the basis for a system that is more powerful than any developed thus far. This system can store and retrieve information about arbitrary subjects, make logical deductions, account for interactions between stored relations, resolve certain ambiguities, and perform other tasks that are necessary prerequisites for an understanding machine.

2.3 Representations for Semantic Information

The SIR model is the collection of data to which the SIR programs can refer in the course of question-answering. It is a *dynamic* model, in the sense that new information can cause automatic additions or changes to the data. In addition, it is a *semantic* model, in the sense that the data are organized in a structure which represents the *meanings* of the English sentences upon which the model is based. The purpose of this section is to describe this semantic organization, which is responsible for convenient accessibility of relevant information and therefore for efficient question-answering.

Many kinds of "semantic" models are possible. The precise form of the SIR model evolved from studies of possible word-association models and of the semantic systems of mathematical logic. Its implementation was influenced by the features of available computer programming languages. It is only capable of representing a particular group of semantic relations. These factors are discussed in the following paragraphs. Section 2.6 will present a proposal for future expansion and formalization of this model and its associated programs.

2.3.1 Symbol-Manipulating Computer Languages

Programming the SIR system or any other elaborate question-answering system would have been almost impossible if not for the availability of symbol-manipulating computer languages (4). By taking care of much of the necessary encoding and bookkeeping, these languages permit a programmer to concentrate on the more significant aspects of organization and representation necessary for problem-solving. Since the choice of a symbol-manipulating language was an important step in the development of SIR, it seems worthwhile to discuss this class of languages in some detail.

Historically, the data used in computers have been numerical, in the form of either numbers or fixed-size vectors and arrays of numbers. Question-answering and other areas of recent computer research require the use of symbolic as well as numeric data, and it is frequently desirable to transmit information by means of the relational structure as well as the symbolic content of the data. The "symbol-manipulating" or "list-processing" computer languages have been developed to handle these special processing needs. An important feature of these languages is that computer memory space for data structures need not be preassigned; storage for each structure is allocated automatically as it is needed. Thus a symbol-manipulating language gives a programmer a powerful set of tools for describing processes which create, modify, search, or otherwise operate on arbitrary amounts of symbolic data without being concerned with the inherent limitations or basic numerical operations of the computer being used.

The most widely used symbol-manipulating computer languages are IPL (25), COMIT (35), and LISP (23).* IPL, used in the "Baseball" and "SAD-SAM" question-answering systems described in the preceding section, is one of the oldest symbol-manipulating languages. The basic units of data used in IPL are list structures composed of IPL symbols. An IPL program describes symbol manipulation at a very basic level, leaving the programmer with the problems of keeping track of storage used, symbols assigned, etc. On the other hand, it is quite easy in IPL to build up elaborate programs out of simpler processes and to manipulate arbitrarily complex list structures.

COMIT, originally designed to be a convenient system in which to process natural language, was used in two of the question-answering systems here described. Although COMIT is a general-purpose symbol manipulation system, it is best suited to problems involving string manipulation, i.e., problems in which the data can be represented in the form of strings of symbols without introducing undue complication into the processing algorithms. The COMIT system provides a simple yet powerful formalism for describing string manipulations, which can be extremely useful for describing procedures, such as parsing, which operate on sentences of natural language.

*See reference (4) for definitions of list-processing terms and more detailed descriptions and comparisons of these languages.

LISP, the language used in one of the above question-answerers and the one chosen for programming SIR, was originally designed to be a formalism useful for studying the mathematical properties of functions of symbolic expressions and also useful in a practical programming system. LISP programs consist of *functions* rather than sequences of instructions or descriptions of data forms. These functions map symbolic expressions into symbolic expressions; the basic form of a LISP symbolic expression is a binary tree which can easily be used to represent list structures when necessary. The organization of LISP programs into functions enables one to describe elaborate recursive tree-searching and list-structure-building operations simply and concisely. Reasons for choosing LISP as the language for programming SIR include the following:

a. Unlike IPL, LISP offers several significant programming conveniences, such as the use of mnemonic symbols and the automatic maintenances of available storage.

b. Unlike COMIT, complex trees and list structures, which frequently arise in the chosen representation for the model (see Part 2.3.4), can be represented directly as LISP data.

c. The LISP formalism is particularly well suited for describing the recursive tree-searching procedures which are an important part of the system (see Section 2.5).

In an earlier version of SIR, COMIT was used as a preprocessor to translate from English sentences into a function form better suited for LISP input. However, since the simple format-matching input procedures finally chosen (see Section 2.4) could just as easily be handled in LISP, the problems of a hybrid system were avoided by converting everything to the LISP language.

2.3.2 Word Association Models

The variety of existing question-answering systems discussed in Section 2.2 demonstrates that many different kinds of models for representing the information in English text are possible. One can develop question-answering systems that vary widely in approach. At one extreme are systems, such as Lindsay's kinship program, which immediately process the text into a form from which anticipated questions can be answered trivially but which thereby ignore much of the information in the input. At the other extreme are systems, such as the SYNTHEX system, which simply store the raw text and perform all necessary computations after each question is received, thereby becoming embroiled in complex grammatical analysis.

I feel that a system capable of intelligent, humanlike behavior must lie between these two extremes. Accordingly, the design requirements for the model in SIR included the following:

i) The model organization should be general enough to be useful in a wide variety of subject areas, yet the stored information should be specific enough to be of real assistance in the question-answering process.
ii) The effort involved in the question-answering procedure should be divided between the job of encoding input into the model and that of retrieving answers from the model. Neither job must be prohibitively complicated or time consuming.

Models based upon words and word associations are the best candidates for meeting these requirements.

Words are the basic symbols in most natural languages. Certain words, usually verbs and prepositions, denote *relationships* between real objects. In the SIR model I shall use words themselves to represent the objects or classes denoted by the words, and specific kinds of associations between words to represent relations between those objects or classes.

Before describing the kinds of associations actually used in the SIR model, let us consider a simpler word-association model structured solely by class-inclusion ("$\subset$") and class-membership ("$\in$") relations. It is structured as follows: Let X and Y be words which denote the objects or classes represented by x and y, respectively. All such words are arranged in a tree, i.e., partially ordered, according to the following rule: $X<Y$ if either $x \subset y$ or $x \in y$. In addition to this primary ordering, various kinds of secondary associations can be indicated by special additional links. Similarly, some verbs can be partially ordered.

For example, if x and y denote the subject and object, respectively, of a verb in a sentence $x\alpha y$, we shall order verbs by the criterion: $\alpha < \beta$ if, for all objects x and y, $x\alpha y$ implies $x\beta y$. For intransitive verbs, the criterion is $\alpha < \beta$ if $x\alpha$ implies $x\beta$. Figure 2-2 shows such trees for some words from a first-grade reader (29). The parenthesized words were not in the vocabulary of the text but are included to motivate the organization of the tree.

Having defined the tree of nouns and the tree of verbs, I must now complete the model by defining connections between these two trees. Although a formal notation for such crosslinks could be defined, for present purposes I shall simply give the following examples of statements describing crosslinkages (with respect to the node-labeling in Fig. 2-2):

i) Any noun below node 1 is a suitable subject for any verb below node 1′.
ii) Any noun below node 2 is a suitable subject for any verb above node 2′.
iii) Only nouns below nodes 3 or 4 may be subjects for verbs below node 3′.

The complete model, composed of tree structures and statements about their possible connections, is a representation for the class of all possible events. In other words, it represents the computer's knowledge of the world. We now have a mechanism for testing the "coherence" or "meaningfulness" of new samples of text. As information is fed into a system which uses this model, the

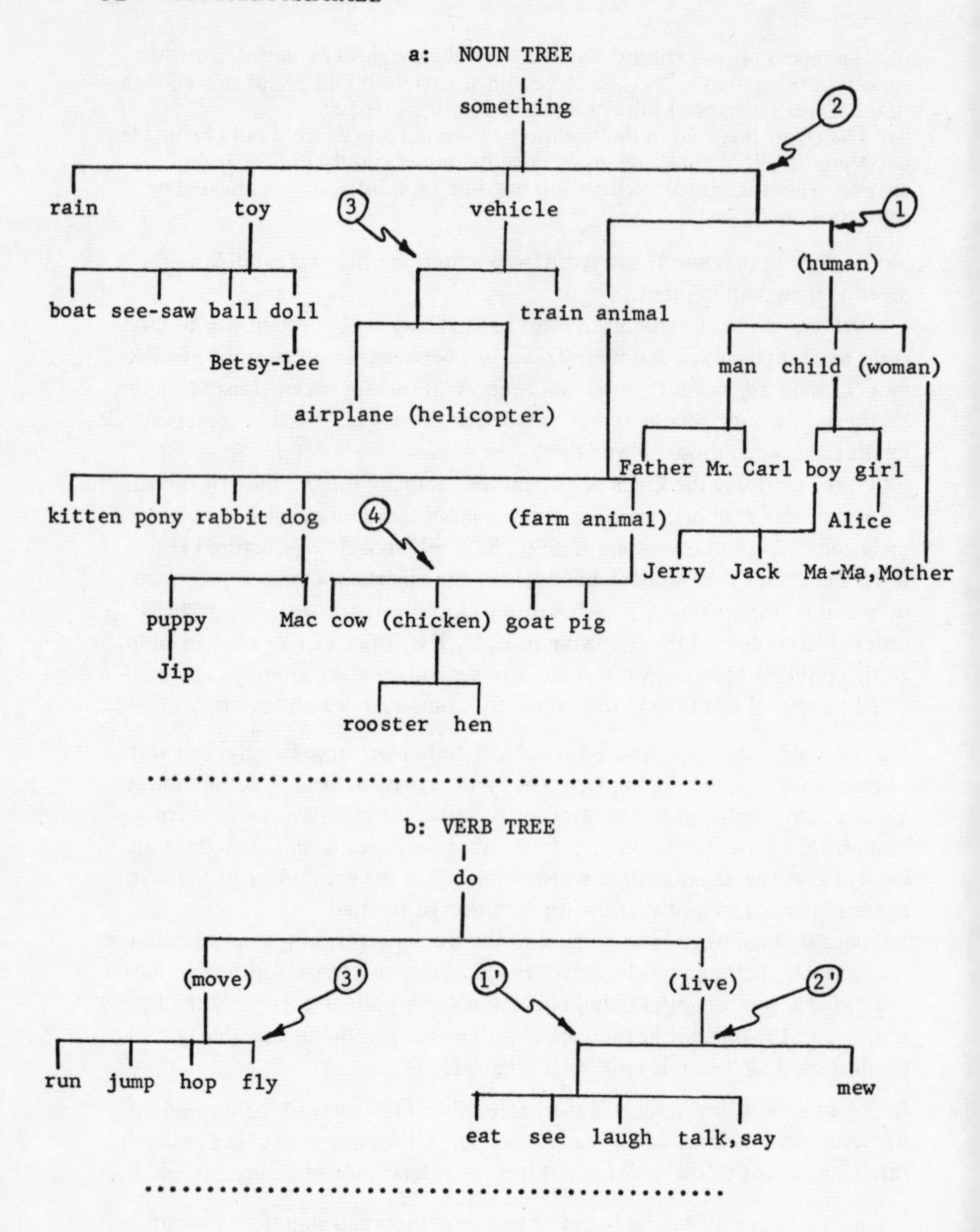

Figure 2-2. A Word Association Model

program would simply have to insert a "thread" of special connections into the model. The thread would distinguish those events which actually happened from those which are just "conceivable" to the computer. Questions about the input statements could then be answered by referring to the model to see which way the thread passed. Such a model would be useful in a pragmatic system such as Abelson's (7), to test the credibility of what it is told. It could identify sources of its factual knowledge by their threads, and compare the reliabilities of the various sources.

Unfortunately, the model described has several drawbacks which prevent its use in a general semantic information retrieval system. It is extremely difficult to construct a useful model, of the form described, for a significant amount of information; writing a program which *automatically* would add information to the model is out of the question. The "$\subset$" and "$\in$" relations are not sufficient to describe many useful groupings of nouns, but the introduction of a few additional relations would confuse the structural organization of the model and force the crosslink statements to be much more complicated. The verb groupings, in order to be useful, must be carefully selected according to the ill-defined restriction that the resulting configuration allow simple and useful crosslink statements. This may not always be possible and certainly becomes more difficult as the number of relations considered increases.

The model used in SIR is a word-association model similar in some respects to the one just described. However, the words are linked in a general manner so that no particular relations are more significant than others. The model is constructed, on the basis of input sentences, completely automatically. Descriptions of the behavior of particular relations, which roughly correspond to the crosslink statements in the above system, are programmed into SIR rather than being part of the model. Part 2.3.4 describes the actual model used in SIR.

2.3.3 Semantics and Logic

The structure of the SIR model was partly motivated by the structure of models in mathematical logic. These logical models represent the "meanings" of logical statements and thereby help the mathematician "think" about his problems, in the same way that the SIR model is supposed to represent the "meaning" of English input, and thereby help the program obtain answers to questions. Let us take a more detailed look at logical models.

The "semantics" of mathematical logic is the study of models for logical systems (6). Such a model consists of a set of individuals (corresponding to the domain of the logical variables), and, for each logical predicate or relation, a set of ordered *n*-tuples of individuals. A relation is true of certain individuals if and only if, in the model, the ordered *n*-tuple of those individuals is an element of the set corresponding to the relation. For example, a model for a logical system dealing with the natural ordering of the integers might have as its model the set of integers (as the domain of individual variables) and a set of ordered pairs of integers corresponding to the "$<$" (less-than) relation. This latter set would contain all pairs $\langle a, b \rangle$ for which integer a is truly less than integer b, i.e., for which the statement $a<b$ is true.

These semantic models are particularly useful in logic for studying certain properties, such as consistency and completeness, of the associated formal systems. They are not generally as useful as aids in proving particular theorems or in studying the possible interactions between various relations. The SIR model organization must be better suited to these latter problems, which are of major interest in developing a question-answering system.

The idea of representing a relation by a set of ordered n-tuples is a good starting point for a question-answering system model. However, certain modifications are necessary. Since we are interested in the conversational ability in the computer, the "relations" in our model should represent concepts which commonly occur in human conversation, such as set-inclusion and spatial relationships, rather than abstract mathematical properties. Furthermore, unlike a logical model, the system should have built-in provisions for determining restrictions, extensions, or inconsistencies in the model, based on properties of the relations involved. For example, if "$\subset$" indicates set-inclusion, and if $a \subset b$ and $b \subset c$ are both in the model, the system should deduce that $a \subset c$ should also be in the model (or, equivalently, that $a \subset c$ is a true statement) from the built-in knowledge that set-inclusion is transitive. Finally, for reasons of computational efficiency, a subject never considered in formal logic but of prime importance in a practical computer system, information about relations must be more easily accessible than it would be if it consisted simply of unordered sets of n-tuples of objects. These considerations led to a choice of the description-list organization for the actual word association model used in SIR and described in Part 2.3.4.

Although some ideas were borrowed from logical semantic systems, SIR is not directly dependent upon any formal logical mechanism. Instead, the model and the programs that utilize it were designed according to informal heuristic principles of reasoning, which I believe to be the most convenient ones for a first, experimental system for intelligent conversation between machines and human beings. Once a working system has been developed, one can try to extract from it a logical basis for a more advanced system. Such an extension is the subject of Section 2.6.

2.3.4 The SIR Model

The SIR model consists of words associated with each other through particular relations. These associations are represented by "description-list" entries. In this part I shall discuss the description-list structure, the relations used in SIR, and the precise representations for those relations.

1. *Description-lists:* The model in SIR is based largely upon the use of *description-lists.* A description-list is a sequence of pairs of elements, and the entire list is associated with a particular object. The first element of each pair is the name of an *attribute* applicable to a class of objects, and the second is the *value* of that attribute for the object described. For example, if the object is the number "3," its description-list might contain the following sequence of attributes (underlined) and associated values:

SUCCESSOR, 4, ODD, YES, SHAPE, CURVY, ...

The fact that "3" is an odd number could have been indicated simply by the presence of the attribute "ODD," with *any* associated value or no value at all, provided the system using the description-lists is capable of recognizing such a "flag," i.e., valueless attribute.

The class of "cats" might be described by the list:

SOUND, MEW, COLOR, (BLACK, WHITE, YELLOW, BROWN),
LEGGEDNESS, 4, ...

Note that, since the color of cats is not unique, the value associated with COLOR is a list of possible cat colors. Its enclosure in parentheses indicates that the entire list of colors is a single element of the description-list.

I can illustrate the way description-lists may be used by considering their place in the IPL programming system (25). By convention, every IPL data list has an associated description-list. The attributes on IPL description-lists are IPL symbols, and the values are symbols which may name arbitrarily complex IPL list structures. Basic IPL operations can add pairs to description-lists; others retrieve the second element of a pair (a value) on the description-list, given the first element (the attribute) and the name of the main data list. An attribute can only occur once on any one description-list, and the order of the attributes on a description-list is ignored. Thus, description-list operations simulate an associative memory containing arbitrary descriptive information for the described object.

The LISP system (23) utilizes "property-lists" which are used in much the same ways as IPL description-lists. In LISP, the described objects are individual words, or "atomic symbols," rather than lists. LISP associates with each unique atomic symbol a property-list which is a description-list allowing the use of flags as well as attribute-value pairs. Although originally provided to facilitate the internal operations of the LISP system, property-lists may be searched and modified by the programmer. The model in SIR depends upon the use of property-lists.

2. *Model organization and development:* The purpose of the model is to assist the computer in understanding and communicating with a person in English sentences. SIR works only with simple sentences that consist of words which denote real objects or classes of objects and words which express particular relationships between the objects and classes. If one considers the objects

and classes as the individual elements in a formal system, then these relationships between objects and classes are analogous to the relations of formal logic (described in 2.3.3). "Understanding the meaning" of a sentence is interpreted as the process of recognizing the objects in the sentence and of placing them in a specified relation to one another. The proper relation to use is frequently determined by the verbs and prepositions in the sentence, and the way in which to place the objects into the relation is determined by the form of the sentence. For example, the verb "is" usually determines a set relation. The form "Every x is a y" determines that class x is a subset of class y.

In the computer representation the basic objects as well as the names of relations are simply *words.* The intended interpretation of this representation is as follows: Suppose word x is associated in the model with word y by means of relation R. Then this represents a statement which "means" that the object or class denoted by x is associated with the object or class denoted by y by means of the relation named R.

The procedure for developing the form of the model and the associated storage and retrieval programs was approximately as follows: A single relation – set inclusion – was chosen because it is an easy concept to recognize from English text and is also (intuitively) important to the "meaning" of simple sentences. An internal computer representation was then found which adequately represented the relational information, seemed general enough to model many other kinds of relations, and also had connectivity and accessibility properties which make it useful for question-answering. Programs were then developed for recognizing sentences which deal with the given relation by their syntactic forms (see Section 3.4); selecting relevant word tokens from the sentences; and adding to, modifying, or searching the model according to the results of the recognition process. The search programs are designed to "know" the peculiar properties of the relation being searched, e.g., transitivity or reflexivity. Therefore a special set of search programs had to be written for each relation. Each time a new concept or relation was added to the system, the above steps were repeated. That is, the basic model structure was generalized, if necessary; new syntactic recognition forms were introduced, and existing ones modified if any ambiguities had been introduced; and search and response programs for the new relation were written. Search programs designed for relations already available in the system were modified when the old and new relations "interacted."*

The relations included in SIR were chosen because they demonstrate various aspects of the information normally conveyed in human conversation. They were introduced in the following order and for the reasons stated:

*"Interactions" between relations, and the structure of a modified system which is easier to expand, are discussed in Section 2.6.

a. Set-inclusion, because it is one of the most basic relations of which people are aware.

b. Part-whole relationship, because, although it differs significantly from, it interacts strongly with, the set-inclusion relation and has several common properties with it permitting the use of common subroutines.

c. Numeric quantity associated with the part-whole relation, since it is not a new relation but rather consists of special descriptive information which must be carried along with relational information.

d. Set membership, because it is closely related to set inclusion but requires attention to properties of individual objects as well as classes.

e. Left-to-right spatial relations, to see how the chosen model works for a different kind of relation for which there is a different, more natural-appearing, model.

f. Ownership, since it is quite different from the existing part-whole relation, and yet frequently is specified by the same verb ("to have"). It is therefore a suitable subject for an experiment in resolving ambiguities.

3. *Model structure:* The basic objects in the model are the words which denote real objects and classes. If an English statement is interpreted by the sentence-form recognition program as asserting that relation R holds between objects or classes named x and y, then this relationship is represented by placing attribute-value pairs on the property-lists of both x and y. Each attribute specifies a relation, and the value of the attribute indicates which other objects are related to the described object by means of the specified relation.

Since in general relations are not symmetric, relation R must be factored into two relations $R1$ and $R2$ so that if relation R holds between x and y (in logic terms, if $\langle x,y \rangle \in R$), then one can say that y stands in relation $R1$ to x and x stands in the inverse relation $R2$ to y. One may think of $R1$ and $R2$ as mappings from individuals into sets such that $\langle x,y \rangle \in R$ if and only if $y \in R1(x)$ and $x \in R2(y)$. For example, if R is the set-inclusion relation, $R1$ is the subset relation and $R2$ the superset relation. $R1$ and $R2$ may be named by the symbols SUBSET and SUPERSET. In general, the symbols naming $R1$ and $R2$ are used as attributes on the property lists of x and y, respectively. Note that if R is a symmetric relation then only one mapping, which may itself be named R, is necessary; for $y \in R(x)$ implies $x \in R(y)$, and vice versa.

If one and only one object can be in relation $R1$ to any word x, then the value of attribute $R1$ of x can be simply the name of that object. In this case I say that a *type*-1 link exists from x to y following (or, by means of) the attribute $R1$. An example of the use of type-1 links is in spatial relations, where only one object can be "just-to-the-right" of another. If the system learns that "The lamp is just to the right of the chair," then the attribute-value pair (JRIGHT, LAMP) is added to the property-list of CHAIR, and the inverse relation is indicated by adding the pair (JLEFT, CHAIR) to the property-list of LAMP.

If R holds between x and y and also between x and z, type-1 links are inadequate, since there can only be one value corresponding to a given attribute on a given property-list. However, this value may be a *list* of object-names instead of just a single object-name. In particular, we can make the value of $R1$ a list of the objects related to x by relation R. For example, in the set-inclusion relation we may learn independently that every boy is a person, every girl is a person, and every MIT student is a person. The value of the attribute SUBSET on the property-list of PERSON would then be the list (BOY, GIRL, MIT-STUDENT). This type of linkage is called a *type*-2 link.

Occasionally descriptive information pertinent to a particular occurrence of a relation must be represented, in addition to the basic fact that the relation exists. For example, "A person has two hands" implies not only that a hand is part of every person, but also that in the case of "hands" there are exactly two such parts. This relation can be handled by using *type*-3 links, where the value of an attribute is a list of items, each of which is itself a property-list. The first item on such sub-property-lists is the flag PLIST, which indicates that a property-list follows. NAME is an attribute on each sub-property-list whose type-1 value is the principal object on the list. For example, after the system learns that "A person has two hands" and also "A finger is part of a person," the property-list of PERSON would contain the attribute-value pair:

(SUBPART, ((PLIST, NAME, HAND, NUMBER, 2) (PLIST, NAME, FINGER))).

In the interest of generality and uniformity, type-3 links are the predominant mechanism for structuring the model.

2.4 SIR Treatment of Restricted Natural Language

SIR must communicate with people; therefore the input and response languages of the SIR system should both be reasonably close to natural English. Since SIR utilizes a relational model, we are faced with the difficult problem of extracting relational information from natural language text.

I am primarily interested in the ability of a computer to store and utilize relational information in order to produce intelligent behavior. Although the linguistic problem of transforming natural language input into a usable form will have to be solved before we obtain a general semantic information retrieval system, it is independent of the representation and retrieval problems and therefore is considered beyond the scope of this chapter.

In this section I shall describe briefly the background for the linguistic problem and the devices which SIR uses to bypass it while still utilizing understandable English-like input and output.

2.4.1 Background

In the past ten to fifteen years much research has been done on the structure of natural languages, including English, for automatic processing by computer. In virtually every case, the form of the original text is restricted or preprocessed in some way to make it more amenable to automatic processing. Some of these studies were mentioned in Section 2.2 in connection with existing question-answering systems. A paper by Bobrow (3) surveys various approaches and catalogues existing computer programs that automatically parse English text.

The object of most of these systems is to identify the classical grammatical structures of the sentences for purposes of linguistic analysis, mechanical translation, or information retrieval. Large dictionaries of parts of speech and grammatical rules are generally employed, and usually no consideration is given to the meanings (in any acceptable sense of the term "meaning") of the words and phrases involved.

One exception is the work at the National Bureau of Standards dealing with a "picture language machine" (10). Here the object is to determine whether a given English statement is a correct assertion about geometrical relationships in a given picture; therefore the "meaning" of the sentence is critical. The procedure used is to translate the English sentence into a logical statement involving geometric predicates, and then to test the truth of the logical statement by determining whether the relations specified by the predicates hold for the given picture.

In the SIR search and retrieval programs I am concerned with a problem similar to that of the picture language machine: namely, translating from English to a relational statement and then determining how the relational statement affects the model. However, the SIR model is a data structure automatically built up on the basis of input relational statements, rather than an independently provided "picture." In the NBS system, the process of translating from English to the logical statement involves using a complete phrase-structure grammar for a fragment of English associated with picture descriptions. This seems like an extravagant approach, although it may turn out to be the one best capable of generalization. In the present version of SIR I am not concerned with constructing a formal logical statement of the relations recognized from the English sentence. Instead, the recognition programs directly invoke the appropriate storage or retrieval programs to deal with the relations recognized. I call the process of extracting relational information from English text "semantic parsing." The NBS work cited points to one rather expensive approach for obtaining this relational information. Charney (8) has studied the relation between sentence form and word meanings. Reichenbach (34) and Fries (16) also discuss the semantic parsing problem, and other approaches will undoubtedly be developed by linguists in the near future. It seems significant, although somewhat surprising, that the simple format-matching approach used in SIR and discussed in Part 2.4.2 is as effective as it is.

2.4.2 Input Sentence Recognition

SIR solves the semantic parsing problem by recognizing only a small number of sentence forms, each of which corresponds in specific ways to particular relations. The allowable input language is defined by a list of *rules,* each of which recognizes and operates upon a particular form of English sentence. Each sentence presented to SIR is tested by each rule in the list. The first rule applicable to the sentence determines the action taken by the system and immediately invokes a program to perform the action. If no rule is applicable, the sentence is ignored, except that the system makes an appropriate response (see 2.4.3). A new rule may be added to the system, and thus the class of recognizable sentences may be enlarged, by executing the LISP function "addrule [x]" where *x* is the rule to be added. Let us consider the use of these rules in detail.

1. *Format-matching procedure:* The four components of a *rule* are a *format,* a list of the *variables* appearing in the format, a list of *applicability tests,* and an *"action"* list specifying the actions to be taken if the sentence satisfies all the tests. The format is simply a string of symbols which may be words. The list of variables contains those symbols that appear in the format, which should be treated as variables. All other symbols in the format are constants. The first step in trying to apply a rule to a sentence is a "similarity test" between the sentence and the format of the rule to see whether the constants in the format all appear, in the same order, in the sentence. If they don't, the rule is rejected. If the sentence *is* similar to the format, the variables in the format are identified with their corresponding substrings in the sentence.

The applicability tests are then applied, one to each substring matched by a variable. Each of these tests is the evaluation of a specified function of one argument, the corresponding substring. If the value of any of these function evaluations is the special LISP symbol "NIL," the substring is considered unsuitable and the entire rule is rejected. Otherwise, the system composes a list of the results of the applicability tests and communicates this list to the last part of the rule, the "action" list.

The first element of the action list is the name of a function which will act on the model to perform the operation required by the English sentence: create a link, test whether a particular relation holds by checking the existence of certain chains of links, or extract certain information from the model. The remaining elements of the action list are functions which, when applied to the list resulting from the applicability tests, produce arguments for the main action function.

For example, the semantic parsing of the sentence, "(A BOY IS A PERSON)" would be performed by a rule such as

((X IS A Y) (X Y) (ART ART) (SETR CAR CADR))

The format "(X IS A Y)" is indeed similar to the sentence "(A BOY IS A PERSON)" because the constants "IS" and "A" appear in the same order in both. Therefore the variable *X* is associated with the string "A BOY" and *Y* with "A PERSON". "ART" is the name of a function which tests whether its argument is a string of two symbols, the first of which is an indefinite article. If so, the value of "ART" is the second symbol in the string. Otherwise, the value of "ART" is "NIL". In this case, the same applicability test function, "ART", is used for both matched substrings "A BOY" and "A PERSON". In both cases the results of the test are positive; thus the values of the two evaluations of "ART" are "BOY" and "PERSON," respectively. The system then composes the list of these values "(BOY, PERSON)", and proceeds to the "action" list. Here "SETR" is the SIR function which creates links indicating the existence of a set-inclusion relation between its two arguments. "CAR" and "CADR" are functions which obtain the arguments for "SETR" by extracting the first and second elements, respectively, from the value list "(BOY, PERSON)". After this final function "setr [BOY; PERSON] " is executed, the model will contain the relational information which the rule extracted from the sentence "(A BOY IS A PERSON)". The recognition scheme does not distinguish between declarative sentences and questions; they each have their own formats and corresponding action functions. Of course, the effects of the action functions for questions are usually quite different from the effects of declarative-sentence functions. All action functions, as well as applicability tests, are programs which must be provided to the system along with each new rule.

Figure 2-3 is a listing of all the rules included in the present version of SIR. The symbol "Q" is to be read as a question mark. The significance of the "classify" function is explained in the following paragraph.

2. *Ambiguities:* The translation from English sentence to action function can work only if a desired action is uniquely determined by each format. This is not really the case with many of the formats used for one of two reasons, which I call *format ambiguity* and *semantic ambiguity.*

Format ambiguity is a programming device rather than a true ambiguity. It occurs when a single format (and rule) is used in order to save space and processing effort, even though several formats would be necessary to determine the required action uniquely. For example, the sentence "Every boy is

```
((X IS W)  (X  W) (CLASSIFY  CLASSIFY)  (SETR-SELECT  CAR  CADR))
((IS X Q)  (X)  (DECOMPOSE)  (SETRQ-SELECT  CAAR  CDAR))
((X OWNS Y) (X Y) (CLASSIFY  CLASSIFY)  (OWN-SELECT CADR  CAR))
((DOES X OWN Y Q) (X Y) (CLASSIFY CLASSIFY)  (OWN-SELECT CADR CAR))
((HOW MANY Y DOES X OWN Q) (Y X)(SING CLASSIFY) (OWN-SELECT CAR CADR))
((X IS Y PART OF Z)  (X Y Z)  (CLASSIFY A- CLASSIFY)
     (PARTR-SELECT  CAR  CADDR))
((X HAS AS A PART ONE Y)  (X Y)  (CLASSIFY  IDEN-1)
     (PARTRN-SELECT  CAR  CADR))
((THERE ARE Y ON X) (Y X) (NUM-Y CLASSIFY) (PARTRN-SELECT CADR CAR))
((THERE IS ONE Y ON X)  (Y  X)  (IDEN1  CLASSIFY)
     (PARTRN-SELECT  CADR  CAR))
((IS X PART OF Y Q)  (X Y)  ((LAMBDA  (J)  (CLASSIFY  (ALAST  J)))
     CLASSIFY)  (PARTRQ-SELECT  CAR  CADR))
((HOW MANY Y ARE TH ON X Q) (Y TH X) (SING THERE- CLASSIFY)
     (PARTRNQ-SELECT  CAR  CADDR))
((HOW MANY Y ARE PARTS OF X Q)  (Y X)  (SING  CLASSIFY)
     (PARTRNQ-SELECT  CAR  CADR))
((X HAS Y)  (X Y)  (CLASSIFY CLASSIFY)  (HAS-RESOLVE  CADR  CAR))
((X HAS W)  (X W)  (CLASSIFY  NUM-Y)  (HASN-RESOLVE  CADR  CAR))
((HOW MANY X DOES Y HAVE Q)  (X  Y)  (SING  CLASSIFY)
     (HAVE-RESOLVE  CAR  CADR)))
((X IS JUST TO THE RIGHT OF, Y)  (X  Y)  (CLASSIFY  CLASSIFY)
     (JRIGHT-SELECT  CAR  CADR))
((X IS JUST TO THE LEFT OF Y)  (X  Y)  (CLASSIFY  CLASSIFY)
  (JRIGHT-SELECT  CADR  CAR)  )
((X IS TO THE RIGHT OF Y)  (X  Y) . (CLASSIFY  CLASSIFY)
  (RIGHT-SELECT  CAR  CADR)  )
((X IS TO THE LEFT OF Y)  (X  Y)  (CLASSIFY  CLASSIFY)
  (RIGHT-SELECT  CADR  CAR)  )
((IS X JUST TO THE RIGHT OF Y Q)  (X  Y)  (CLASSIFY  CLASSIFY)
  (JRIGHTQ-SELECT  CAR  CADR)  )
((IS X JUST TO THE LEFT OF Y Q)  (X  Y)  (CLASSIFY  CLASSIFY)
  (JRIGHTQ-SELECT  CADR  CAR)  )
((IS X TO THE RIGHT OF Y Q)  (X  Y)  (CLASSIFY  CLASSIFY)
  (RIGHTQ-SELECT CAR  CADR)  )
((IS X TO THE LEFT OF Y Q)  (X  Y)  (CLASSIFY  CLASSIFY)
  (RIGHTQ-SELECT  CADR  CAR)  )
((WHERE IS X Q)  (X)  (CLASSIFY)  (WHERE-SELECT  CAR))
((WHAT IS THE X OF Y Q)  (X Y)  (LOC CLASSIFY) (LOC-SELECT CADR))
```

Figure 2-3. Sentence Recognition Rules

a person" specifies that the set "boy" is included in the set "person," while "The boy is a person" specifies that some particular element of the set "boy" is also an element of the set "person." These two types of sentences could be uniquely recognized by the formats "Every *x* is a *y*" and "The *x* is a *y.*" Instead, SIR uses a single format of the form "*z* is a *y.*" In the rule containing this format, the "action" function cannot be one which directly creates either a set-inclusion link corresponding to the first of the above interpretations or a set-membership link corresponding to the second interpretation. Instead, the applicability test is the "classify" function which transmits to the action function an indicator of the nature of the article in the string matched by variable *z,* as well as the noun in the string. The action function then used is a "select" type of function which resolves the format ambiguity by examining the indicator supplied by "classify" and then invoking the correct action as a subroutine.

A more interesting case is that of semantic ambiguity, in which the ambiguity in desired action is due to the meanings of the words involved. Such an ambiguity cannot be resolved by using more detailed formats. The example implemented in SIR involves the verb "to have," which may mean either "to have attached as parts" or "to own;" e.g., "John has ten fingers" versus "John has three marbles." In a case of semantic ambiguity the "action" function is a "resolve" type function which once again has the task of resolving the ambiguity and selecting the appropriate subroutine rather than performing any action on the model directly. However, the ambiguity cannot be resolved on the basis of any information available in the original sentence. Instead, the ambiguity resolution depends upon word associations in the model which were created on the basis of previous, unambiguous sentences. Part 2.5.2 contains some examples and a discussion of the processes used, and further discussion of ambiguity can be found in Part 2.7.4.

2.4.3 Output: Formation and Importance of Responses

As with the input language, SIR avoids the problems of natural language processing in its responses. The response mechanism involves a set of built-in response formats. Although some generative grammar would probably be needed in a larger system, these response formats are adequate to demonstrate the use of the model and the ability of the present system to produce intelligible conversation.

Some of the responses are complete prepared statements, such as are frequently used as diagnostic comments in modern programming systems; e.g., the comment "The above statement is not recognized by the present system," which is printed if no rule is found to be applicable to the input sentence. Other responses must be completed by the programs which use them before being printed; e.g., the form, "I don't know whether** is part of**," which is printed, after the **'s are appropriately replaced, in response to certain questions about part-whole relations.

One principle used in programming this system was that SIR should always make easily understandable reports of its actions. In particular, it should never fail to act on a new input sentence without presenting a reasonable explanation for its failure. Implementing this principle turned out to be easier than expected, for there always seemed to be only a small number of possible reasons for the failure of any one search procedure, and thus it was only necessary to provide a few response formats (and programs to use them). These responses, in turn, not only improved the conversational ability and thus the apparent intelligence of the system but also greatly aided in debugging. SIR, in effect, frequently told me what it was doing wrong.

The conversation shown in Fig. 2-1 was produced by operating in an abbreviated-response mode in which SIR only prints directly relevant responses. The program can also operate in a mode in which SIR provides a running commentary of its activities, identifying functions used and commenting on every link created. Although less readable, this full-response mode was a significant program-debugging aid. Figure 2-4 shows the output for the dialogue of Fig. 2-4 in the alternate full-response mode.

2.5 Behavior and Operation of SIR

In this section I shall give examples of typical conversations with SIR and explain the mechanisms which enable SIR to carry on its end of a conversation. These examples can frequently best be presented with the aid of logical notation; formal symbols will therefore be used when necessary. Explanations of the standard logical symbols are given in Appendix 2.1.

Some knowledge of the LISP (21) programming language might be of aid in understanding the following pages. However, it should be sufficient for the reader to know that "fcn [a;b]" indicates that the function named "fcn" is to be applied to the symbols or symbolic expressions named "a" and "b" as arguments. This function of these arguments will have a *value* which is itself a symbolic expression, although the evaluation process may have side effects such as changing the model structure or printing comments. In more conventional programming terms, one may think of "fcn" as naming a subroutine, and "fcn[a;b]" representing the execution of the subroutine with "a" and "b" as input data. The creation of a single symbolic expression called the *value* is the principal result of the execution. This value of a function, which is a symbolic expression resulting from a computation, should not be confused with the value of an attribute, which is the entry following the attribute on a property-list.

```
(THE NEXT SENTENCE IS . .)
(EVERY BOY IS A PERSON)

(THE FUNCTION USED IS . .)
SETR-SELECT
((GENERIC . BOY) (GENERIC . PERSON))
(THE REPLY . .)
(THE SUB-FUNCTION USED IS . .)
SETR
(BOY PERSON)
(ITS REPLY . .)
(I UNDERSTAND THE SUPERSET RELATION BETWEEN PERSON AND BOY)
(I UNDERSTAND THE SUBSET RELATION BETWEEN BOY AND PERSON)


(THE NEXT SENTENCE IS . .)
(A FINGER IS PART OF A HAND)

(THE FUNCTION USED IS . .)
PARTR-SELECT
((GENERIC . FINGER) (GENERIC . HAND))
(THE REPLY . .)
(THE SUB-FUNCTION USED IS . .)
PARTR
(FINGER HAND)

(ITS REPLY . .)
(I UNDERSTAND THE SUBPART-OF-EACH RELATION BETWEEN FINGER AND HAND)
(I UNDERSTAND THE SUPERPART-OF-EACH RELATION BETWEEN HAND AND FINGER)


(THE NEXT SENTENCE IS . .)
(EACH PERSON HAS TWO HANDS)

(THE FUNCTION USED IS . .)
HASN-RESOLVE
((2 . HAND) (GENERIC . PERSON))
(THE REPLY . .)
(THE ABOVE SENTENCE IS AMBIGUOUS ** PLEASE RE-PHRASE IT)


(THE NEXT SENTENCE IS . .)
(THERE ARE TWO HANDS ON EACH PERSON)

(THE FUNCTION USED IS . .)
PARTRN-SELECT
((GENERIC . PERSON) (2 . HAND))
(THE REPLY . .)
(I UNDERSTAND THE SUPERPART-OF-EACH RELATION BETWEEN PERSON AND HAND)
(I REALIZE THE NUMBER RELATION BETWEEN 2 AND (PLIST NAME PERSON))
(I UNDERSTAND THE SUBPART-OF-EACH RELATION BETWEEN HAND AND PERSON)
(I REALIZE THE NUMBER RELATION BETWEEN 2 AND (PLIST NAME HAND))


(THE NEXT SENTENCE IS . .)
(HOW MANY FINGERS DOES JOHN HAVE Q)

(THE FUNCTION USED IS . .)
HAVE-RESOLVE
(FINGER (UNIQUE . JOHN))
(THE REPLY . .)
(THE ABOVE SENTENCE IS AMBIGUOUS ** BUT I ASSUME (HAS) MEANS (HAS AS PARTS))
(I DON*T KNOW WHETHER FINGER IS PART OF JOHN)


(THE NEXT SENTENCE IS . .)
(JOHN IS A BOY)

(THE FUNCTION USED IS . .)
SETR-SELECT
((UNIQUE . JOHN) (GENERIC . BOY))
(THE REPLY . .)
(THE SUB-FUNCTION USED IS . .)
SETRS
(JOHN BOY)
(ITS REPLY . .)
(I UNDERSTAND THE ELEMENTS RELATION BETWEEN JOHN AND BOY)
(I UNDERSTAND THE MEMBER RELATION BETWEEN BOY AND JOHN)


(THE NEXT SENTENCE IS . .)
(HOW MANY FINGERS DOES JOHN HAVE Q)

(THE FUNCTION USED IS . .)
HAVE-RESOLVE
(FINGER (UNIQUE . JOHN))


(THE REPLY . .)
(THE ABOVE SENTENCE IS AMBIGUOUS ** BUT I ASSUME (HAS) MEANS (HAS AS PARTS))
(I KNOW THE SUPERPART-OF-EACH RELATION BETWEEN HAND AND FINGER)
((HOW MANY FINGER PER HAND Q))


(THE NEXT SENTENCE IS . .)
(EVERY HAND HAS 5 FINGERS)

(THE FUNCTION USED IS . .)
HASN-RESOLVE
((5 . FINGER) (GENERIC . HAND))
(THE REPLY . .)
(THE ABOVE SENTENCE IS AMBIGUOUS ** BUT I ASSUME (HAS) MEANS (HAS AS PARTS))
```

Figure 2-4. Sample Conversation in Full-Response Mode

```
(I KNOW THE SUPERPART-OF-EACH RELATION BETWEEN HAND AND FINGER)
(I REALIZE THE NUMBER RELATION BETWEEN 5 AND (PLIST NAME HAND))
(I KNOW THE SUBPART-OF-EACH RELATION BETWEEN FINGER AND HAND)
(I REALIZE THE NUMBER RELATION BETWEEN 5 AND (PLIST NAME FINGER))


(THE NEXT SENTENCE IS . .)
(HOW MANY FINGERS DOES JOHN HAVE Q)

(THE FUNCTION USED IS . .)
HAVE-RESOLVE
(FINGER (UNIQUE . JOHN))
(THE REPLY . .)
(THE ABOVE SENTENCE IS AMBIGUOUS ** BUT I ASSUME (HAS) MEANS (HAS AS PARTS))
(I KNOW THE SUPERPART-OF-EACH RELATION BETWEEN HAND AND FINGER)
(I KNOW THE SUPERPART-OF-EACH RELATION BETWEEN PERSON AND HAND)
(THE ANSWER IS 10)


(THE NEXT SENTENCE IS . .)
(HOW MANY AUTOMOBILES DOES JOHN HAVE Q)

(THE FUNCTION USED IS . .)
HAVE-RESOLVE
(AUTOMOBILE (UNIQUE . JOHN))
(THE REPLY . .)
(THE ABOVE SENTENCE IS AMBIGUOUS ** PLEASE RE-PHRASE IT)


(THE NEXT SENTENCE IS . .)
(WHO IS PRESIDENT OF THE UNITED STATES Q)

(STATEMENT FORM NOT RECOGNIZED)


(THE NEXT SENTENCE IS . .)
(THE BOY IS JUST TO THE LEFT OF THE TABLE)

(THE FUNCTION USED IS . .)
JRIGHT-SELECT
((SPECIFIC . TABLE) (SPECIFIC . BOY))
(THE REPLY . .)
(THE SUB-FUNCTION USED IS . .)
JRIGHT
(TABLE BOY)
(ITS REPLY . .)
(G02840 IS A TABLE)
(I UNDERSTAND THE ELEMENTS RELATION BETWEEN G02840 AND TABLE)
(I UNDERSTAND THE MEMBER RELATION BETWEEN TABLE AND G02840)
(I REALIZE THE JRIGHT RELATION BETWEEN TABLE AND BOY)
(I REALIZE THE JLEFT RELATION BETWEEN BOY AND TABLE)


(THE NEXT SENTENCE IS . .)
(THE LAMP IS JUST TO THE LEFT OF THE TABLE)

(THE FUNCTION USED IS . .)
JRIGHT-SELECT
((SPECIFIC . TABLE) (SPECIFIC . LAMP))
(THE REPLY . .)
(THE SUB-FUNCTION USED IS . .)
JRIGHT
(TABLE LAMP)
(ITS REPLY . .)
(G02841 IS A LAMP)
(I UNDERSTAND THE ELEMENTS RELATION BETWEEN G02841 AND LAMP)
(I UNDERSTAND THE MEMBER RELATION BETWEEN LAMP AND G02841)
(THE ABOVE STATEMENT IS IMPOSSIBLE)


(THE NEXT SENTENCE IS . .)
(THE TABLE IS TO THE RIGHT OF THE CHAIR)

(THE FUNCTION USED IS . .)
RIGHT-SELECT
((SPECIFIC . TABLE) (SPECIFIC . CHAIR))
(THE REPLY . .)
(THE SUB-FUNCTION USED IS . .)
RIGHT
(TABLE CHAIR)
(ITS REPLY . .)
(G02842 IS A CHAIR)
(I UNDERSTAND THE ELEMENTS RELATION BETWEEN G02842 AND CHAIR)
(I UNDERSTAND THE MEMBER RELATION BETWEEN CHAIR AND G02842)
(I UNDERSTAND THE RIGHT RELATION BETWEEN TABLE AND CHAIR)
(I UNDERSTAND THE LEFT RELATION BETWEEN CHAIR AND TABLE)


(THE NEXT SENTENCE IS . .)
(WHAT IS THE RELATIVE POSITION OF A PERSON Q)

(THE FUNCTION USED IS . .)
LOC-SELECT
((GENERIC . PERSON))
(THE REPLY . .)
(THE SUB-FUNCTION USED IS . .)
LOCATEG
(PERSON)
(ITS REPLY . .)
(THE LEFT-TO-RIGHT ORDER IS AS FOLLOWS)
(CHAIR (BOY TABLE))
```

Figure 2-4. *(Continued)*

2.5.1 Relations and Functions

Each part of Fig. 2-5 is a conversation between a person and SIR, presented in the abbreviated-response mode described at the end of Part 2.4.3. Each example illustrates the use of a different group of relations and their associated LISP functions in the SIR system. With minor exceptions, the examples are cumulative, i.e., later ones freely use functions introduced earlier but not conversely. These conversations are presented again as Appendix 2.3 in the full-response mode which identifies the functions used. In Fig. 2-5, the symbol "***." prefixes the input sentences; all other remarks are SIR responses.

The following pages present descriptions of all the significant functions mentioned in Appendix 2.3 in the order in which they are needed for the conversations. The functions are presented in groups which correspond to the various parts of Fig. 2-5, and which are identified by the principal attribute-links manipulated by the functions in the group.

Each function description consists of three parts: a *purpose,* a *method,* and a *procedure.* The *purpose* is a brief statement of the effect the function is designed to have. The *method* is an intuitive description of how the purpose should be achieved, and is usually presented in a mixture of English and logical notation for maximum clarity. Finally, the *procedure* is a description of how the method is implemented, and may be considered a rough flow-chart of the actual program. Notice that the relational structure of the model is the key internal feature of SIR which enables the *procedures* to implement the *methods* in a direct and efficient manner. These *methods,* in turn, determine the degree of SIR's ability to store facts and answer questions. Section 2.6 will discuss how SIR's model, methods, and procedures could be generalized to produce a more powerful semantic information retrieval system.

Operation of functions:

a. Attributes: SUBSET, SUPERSET

1. setr[$x;y$]

purpose: To specify in the model that set x is included in set y.

method: Create a type-3 link between x and y which indicates set-inclusion.

procedure:

a. Add "(PLIST NAME x)" to the value list of attribute "SUBSET" of y.

b. Add "(PLIST NAME y)" to the value list of attribute "SUPERSET" of x.

c. Respond "(I UNDERSTAND)"

2. setrq[$x;y$]

purpose: To reply as to whether an arbitrary element of set x is an element of set y.

method: A member of x is considered to be a member of y if the sets x and y are identical; or if there is a chain of explicit set-inclusion links proving that

a. SET-INCLUSION

```
(***.   EVERY KEYPUNCH-OPERATOR IS A GIRL)
(I UNDERSTAND)

(***.   ANY GIRL IS AN EXAMPLE OF A PERSON)
(I UNDERSTAND)

(***.   IS A KEYPUNCH-OPERATOR A PERSON Q)
YES

(***.   IS A PERSON A PERSON Q)
YES

(***.   IS A PERSON A GIRL Q)
SOMETIMES

(***.   IS A MONKEY A KEYPUNCH-OPERATOR Q)
(INSUFFICIENT INFORMATION)
```

b. SET-MEMBERSHIP

```
(***.   MAX IS AN IBM-7094)
(I UNDERSTAND)

(***.   AN IBM-7094 IS A COMPUTER)
(I UNDERSTAND)

(***.   IS MAX A COMPUTER Q)
YES

(***.   THE BOY IS AN MIT-STUDENT)
(G02840 IS A BOY)
(I UNDERSTAND)

(***.   EVERY MIT-STUDENT IS A BRIGHT-PERSON)
(I UNDERSTAND)

(***.   IS THE BOY A BRIGHT-PERSON Q)
YES

(***.   JOHN IS A BOY)
(I UNDERSTAND)

(***.   IS THE BOY A BRIGHT-PERSON Q)
(WHICH BOY . . (G02840 JOHN))
```

c. EQUIVALENCE

```
(***.   THE MAN IS A JERK)
(G02840 IS A MAN)
(I UNDERSTAND)

(***.   JACK IS A DOPE)
(I UNDERSTAND)

(***.   JOHN IS JACK)
(I UNDERSTAND)

(***.   IS JOHN A DOPE Q)
YES

(***.   IS THE MAN A DOPE Q)
(INSUFFICIENT INFORMATION)

(***.   JOHN IS THE MAN)
(I UNDERSTAND)

(***.   IS THE MAN A DOPE Q)
YES

(***.   JIM IS A MAN)
(I UNDERSTAND)

(***.   IS THE MAN A DOPE Q)
(WHICH MAN . . (G02840 JIM))
```

Figure 2-5. Selected Conversations

d. OWNERSHIP, GENERAL

```
(***.     EVERY FIREMAN OWNS A PAIR-OF-RED-SUSPENDERS)
(I UNDERSTAND)

(***.     DOES A PAIR-OF-RED-SUSPENDERS OWN A PAIR-OF-RED-SUSPENDERS Q)
(NO ** THEY ARE THE SAME)

(***.     DOES A DOCTOR OWN A PAIR-OF-RED-SUSPENDERS Q)
(INSUFFICIENT INFORMATION)

(***.     A FIRECHIEF IS A FIREMAN)
(I UNDERSTAND)

(***.     DOES A FIRECHIEF OWN A PAIR-OF-RED-SUSPENDERS Q)
YES
```

e. OWNERSHIP, SPECIFIC

```
(***.     ALFRED OWNS A LOG-LOG-DECITRIG)
(I UNDERSTAND)

(***.     A LOG-LOG-DECITRIG IS A SLIDE-RULE)
(I UNDERSTAND)

(***.     DOES ALFRED OWN A SLIDE-RULE Q)
YES

(***.     EVERY ENGINEERING-STUDENT OWNS A SLIDE-RULE)
(I UNDERSTAND)

(***.     VERNON IS A TECH-MAN)
(I UNDERSTAND)

(***.     A TECH-MAN IS AN ENGINEERING-STUDENT)
(I UNDERSTAND)

(***.     DOES VERNON OWN A SLIDE-RULE Q)
YES

(***.     DOES AN ENGINEERING-STUDENT OWN THE LOG-LOG-DECITRIG Q)
(G02840 IS A LOG-LOG-DECITRIG)
(INSUFFICIENT INFORMATION)

(***.     ALFRED IS A TECH-MAN)
(I UNDERSTAND)

(***.     DOES AN ENGINEERING-STUDENT OWN THE LOG-LOG-DECITRIG Q)
YES
```

Figure 2-5. *(Continued)*

f. PART-WHOLE, GENERAL

```
(***.     A NOSE IS PART OF A PERSON)
(I UNDERSTAND)

(***.     A NOSTRIL IS A PART OF A NOSE)
(I UNDERSTAND)

(***.     A PROFESSOR IS A TEACHER)
(I UNDERSTAND)

(***.     A TEACHER IS A PERSON)
(I UNDERSTAND)

(***.     IS A NOSTRIL PART OF A PROFESSOR Q)
YES

(***.     IS A NOSE PART OF A NOSE Q)
(NO , PART MEANS PROPER SUBPART)

(***.     A PERSON IS A LIVING-CREATURE)
(I UNDERSTAND)

(***.     IS A NOSTRIL PART OF A LIVING-CREATURE Q)
SOMETIMES

(***.     IS A LIVING-CREATURE PART OF A NOSE Q)
(NO , NOSE IS SOMETIMES PART OF LIVING-CREATURE)
```

g. PART-WHOLE, SPECIFIC

```
(***.     A VAN-DYKE IS PART OF FERREN)
(I UNDERSTAND)

(***.     A VAN-DYKE IS A BEARD)
(I UNDERSTAND)

(***.     IS A BEARD PART OF FERREN Q)
YES

(***.     A CRT IS A DISPLAY-DEVICE)
(I UNDERSTAND)

(***.     A CRT IS PART OF THE PDP-1)
(G02840 IS A PDP-1)
(I UNDERSTAND)

(***.     SAM IS THE PDP-1)
(I UNDERSTAND)

(***.     A SCREEN IS PART OF EVERY DISPLAY-DEVICE)
(I UNDERSTAND)

(***.     IS A SCREEN PART OF SAM Q)
YES

(***.     A BEARD IS PART OF A BEATNIK)
(I UNDERSTAND)

(***.     EVERY COFFEE-HOUSE-CUSTOMER IS A BEATNIK)
(I UNDERSTAND)

(***.     BUZZ IS A COFFEE-HOUSE-CUSTOMER)
(I UNDERSTAND)

(***.     IS A BEARD PART OF BUZZ Q)
YES
```

Figure 2-5. *(Continued)*

h. NUMBER

```
(***.     A BOY IS A PERSON)

(I UNDERSTAND)

(***.     JOHN IS A BOY)

(I UNDERSTAND)

(***.     A FINGER IS PART OF A HAND)

(I UNDERSTAND)

(***.     HOW MANY FINGERS DOES JOHN HAVE Q)

(THE ABOVE SENTENCE IS AMBIGUOUS ** BUT I ASSUME (HAS) MEANS (HAS AS PARTS))
(I DON*T KNOW WHETHER FINGER IS PART OF JOHN)

(***.     THERE IS ONE HAND ON EACH ARM)

(I UNDERSTAND)

(***.     THERE ARE TWO ARMS ON A PERSON)

(I UNDERSTAND)

(***.     HOW MANY FINGERS DOES JOHN HAVE Q)

(THE ABOVE SENTENCE IS AMBIGUOUS ** BUT I ASSUME (HAS) MEANS (HAS AS PARTS))
((HOW MANY FINGER PER HAND Q))

(***.     A HAND HAS 5 FINGERS)


(THE ABOVE SENTENCE IS AMBIGUOUS ** BUT I ASSUME (HAS) MEANS (HAS AS PARTS))
(I UNDERSTAND)

(***.     HOW MANY FINGERS DOES JOHN HAVE Q)

(THE ABOVE SENTENCE IS AMBIGUOUS ** BUT I ASSUME (HAS) MEANS (HAS AS PARTS))
(THE ANSWER IS 10)
```

Figure 2-5. *(Continued)*

i. LEFT-TO-RIGHT POSITION

```
(•••.      THE TELEPHONE IS JUST TO THE RIGHT OF THE BOOK)

(G02840 IS A TELEPHONE)
(G02841 IS A BOOK)
(I UNDERSTAND)

(•••.      THE TELEPHONE IS JUST TO THE LEFT OF THE PAD)

(G02842 IS A PAD)
(I UNDERSTAND)

(•••.      IS THE PAD JUST TO THE RIGHT OF THE BOOK Q)

NO

(•••.      IS THE BOOK TO THE LEFT OF THE PAD Q)

YES

(•••.      THE PAD IS TO THE RIGHT OF THE TELEPHONE)

(THE ABOVE STATEMENT IS ALREADY KNOWN)

(•••.      THE PAD IS TO THE LEFT OF THE TELEPHONE)

(THE ABOVE STATEMENT IS IMPOSSIBLE)

(•••.      THE ASH-TRAY IS TO THE LEFT OF THE BOOK)

(G02843 IS A ASH-TRAY)
(I UNDERSTAND)

(•••.      THE PENCIL IS TO THE LEFT OF THE PAD)

(G02844 IS A PENCIL)
(I UNDERSTAND)

(•••.      THE PAPER IS TO THE RIGHT OF THE TELEPHONE)

(G02845 IS A PAPER)
(I UNDERSTAND)

(•••.      WHERE IS THE PAD Q)

(JUST TO THE RIGHT OF THE TELEPHONE)
(SOMEWHERE TO THE RIGHT OF THE FOLLOWING . . (PENCIL))

(•••.      WHAT IS THE POSITION OF THE PAD Q)

(THE LEFT-TO-RIGHT ORDER IS AS FOLLOWS)
(ASH-TRAY (BOOK TELEPHONE PAD) PAPER)
(TO FURTHER SPECIFY THE POSITIONS YOU MUST INDICATE WHERE THE PENCIL IS WITH RESPECT TO THE ASH-TRA

(•••.      THE BOOK IS JUST TO THE RIGHT OF THE ASH-TRAY)

(I UNDERSTAND)

(•••.      WHAT IS THE POSITION OF THE PAD Q)

(THE LEFT-TO-RIGHT ORDER IS AS FOLLOWS)
(PENCIL (ASH-TRAY BOOK TELEPHONE PAD) PAPER)

(•••.      A TELEPHONE IS AN AUDIO-TRANSDUCER)

(I UNDERSTAND)

(•••.      A DIAPHRAGM IS PART OF AN AUDIO-TRANSDUCER)

(I UNDERSTAND)

(•••.      WHERE IS A DIAPHRAGM Q)

(JUST TO THE LEFT OF THE PAD)
(JUST TO THE RIGHT OF THE BOOK)
(SOMEWHERE TO THE LEFT OF THE FOLLOWING . . (PAPER))
```

Figure 2-5. *(Continued)*

x is a subset of y, i.e., if there exists a (possibly empty) sequence of sets $v, w, \ldots z$ such that $x \subset v \wedge v \subset w \wedge \ldots \wedge z \subset y$.
A member of x is "sometimes" in y if there is a chain of explicit set-inclusion links proving that y is a subset of x.
procedure:

a. If $x = y$, respond "YES".

b. If there is a path from x to y through type-3 links following the attribute "SUPERSET", respond "YES".

c. If there is a path from y to x through type-3 links following the attribute "SUPERSET", respond "SOMETIMES".

d. Otherwise, respond "(INSUFFICIENT INFORMATION)".

b. Attributes: MEMBER, ELEMENTS

1. setrs$[x;y]$

purpose: To specify in the model that x is a member of the set y.
method: Create a type-3 link between x and y which indicates set-membership.
procedure:

a. Add "(PLIST NAME y)" to the value list of attribute "MEMBER" of x.

b. Add "(PLIST NAME x)" to the value list of attribute "ELEMENTS" of y.

c. Respond "(I UNDERSTAND)".

2. setrsq$[x;y]$

purpose: To reply as to whether x is a member of the set y.
method: Reply "YES" if the following is true:

$(\exists u)[[u=x \vee [u$ is equivalent* to $x]] \wedge$
$[[$there is a link indicating that u is a member of $y] \vee$
$[(\exists z)[[$there is a link indicating that u is a member of $z] \wedge$
$[$any member of set z is a member of set $y]]]]]$

procedure:

a. Make a list of the items connected to x by a type-3 link following the attribute "MEMBER".

b. If y is on the list, respond "YES".

c. If, for any member z of the list, setrsq$[z;y]$=YES, respond "YES".

d. Repeat steps (a) through (c) with x replaced by each item equivalent* to x (if any) until a "YES" response is made.

e. Otherwise respond "(INSUFFICIENT INFORMATION)".

3. setrsl$[x;y]$

purpose: To specify in the model that the unique element (if any) of the set x is also an element of the set y.
method: Create a type-3 link from the unique element of x to y which indicates set-membership. If x has more than one element, do not set up any link.

*See part (c), page 74, for an explanation of "equivalent."

procedure:

a. Compute u = specify[x].

b. If u = NIL, terminate.

c. Otherwise execute setrs[u,y].

4. specify[x]

purpose: To determine the unique element, if any, of the set x.

method: If x has one element, find its name. If x has no elements, create one and give it a name. If x has more than one element, ask which one and indicate failure.

procedure:

a. Get the value list of the attribute "ELEMENTS" of x.

b. If there is no list, create a new symbol u, respond "(u IS A x)", execute setrs[u,x], and return u as the value of specify[x].

c. If there is just one element named on the list, or if all the elements are equivalent, return the name of the first element as the value of specify[x].

d. Otherwise respond "(WHICH x . . v)", where v is a list of names of the elements, and return "NIL" as the value of specify[x].

5. setrslq[x,y]

purpose: To reply as to whether the unique element, if any, of the set x, is a member of the set y.

method: Determine the element referred to and apply *setrsq*.

procedure:

a. Compute u = specify[x].

b. If u = NIL, terminate.

c. Execute setrsq[u,y].

c. Attribute: EQUIV

1. equiv[x,y]

purpose: To specify in the model that x and y are equivalent.

method: Create a type-2 link between x and y which indicates equivalence.

procedure:

a. Add x to the value list of attribute "EQUIV" of y.

b. Add y to the value list of attribute "EQUIV" of x.

c. Respond "(I UNDERSTAND)".

2. equivl[x,y]

purpose: To specify in the model that x is equivalent to the unique element of the set y.

method: Determine the element referred to and apply *equiv*.

procedure:

a. Compute u = specify[y].

b. If u = NIL, terminate.

c. Execute equiv[x,u].

d. Attributes: OWNED-BY-EACH, POSSESS-BY-EACH

1. ownr[x,y]

purpose: To specify in the model that every member of set y owns some member of set x.
method: Create a type-3 link between x and y which indicates the ownership relation between their members.
procedure:

a. Add "(PLIST NAME y)" to the value list of attribute "OWNED-BY-EACH" of x.

b. Add "(PLIST NAME x)" to the value list of attribute "POSSESS-BY-EACH" of y.

c. Respond "(I UNDERSTAND)".

2. ownrq[x,y]

purpose: To reply as to whether an arbitrary member of set y owns some member of set x.
method: The answer is "YES" if $x \neq y$, and

$(\exists z)[y=z \vee [y$ is a subset of $z]] \wedge$
[there exists the appropriate ownership link between x and z]]

procedure:

a. If $x = y$, respond "(NO ** THEY ARE THE SAME)".

b. Create the list l containing y and all sets u for which there is a path from y to u through type-3 links following the attribute "SUPERSET".

c. If any element of l contains a type-3 link to x following the attribute "POSSESS-BY-EACH", respond "YES".

d. Otherwise respond "(INSUFFICIENT INFORMATION)".

e. Attributes: OWNED, POSSESS

1. ownrgu[x,y]

purpose: To specify in the model that y owns a member of the set x.
method: Create a type-3 link between x and y which indicates the intended ownership relation.
procedure:

a. Add "(PLIST NAME x)" to the value list of attribute "POSSESS" of y.

b. Add "(PLIST NAME y)" to the value list of attribute "OWNED" of x.

c. Respond "(I UNDERSTAND)".

2. ownrguq[x,y]

purpose: To reply as to whether y owns a member of set x.
method: The reply is "YES" if there is a link indicating that y owns a member of x or of some subset of x; or if

$(\exists z)[[y$ is a member of $z] \wedge (\exists u)[[u=z \vee z \subset u] \wedge$
[there is a link indicating that every member of set u owns a member of set x]]]

procedure:

a. If there is a link indicating an x is owned by y, respond "YES".

b. Consider each set z for which there is a link indicating that y owns a member of z. If, for any z, setrq[z;x] = YES, respond "YES".

c. Consider each set z such that there is a link indicating y is an element of z.

d. For each z, construct a list l containing every set u for which setrq[z;u] = YES.

e. Compute m = the list of all sets v such that there is a type-3 link from x to v following the attribute "OWNED-BY-EACH".

f. If, for some z, the intersection of l and m is non-empty, respond "YES".

g. Otherwise, respond "(INSUFFICIENT INFORMATION)".

3. ownrsgq[x;y]

purpose: To reply as to whether the unique element of the set x is owned by some element of the set y.

method: Determine that a unique element of x exists. Then, the reply is "YES" if

$(\exists z)$[[there is a link indicating that a member of set x is owned by z] $\wedge$
$(\exists v)$[[$v=z \vee$ [v is equivalent to z]] $\wedge$
$(\exists w)$[[there is a link indicating that y is an element of w] $\wedge$
[there are links indicating that w is a subset of y]]]]

procedure:

a. Compute u = specify[x]

b. If u = NIL, terminate.

c. Generate the individuals w which are linked to x as type-3 values of the attribute "OWNED".

d. For each w, generate the sets z which w, and any individual equivalent to w, is a member of.

e. If, for some z, setrq[z;y] = YES, respond "YES".

f. Otherwise respond "(INSUFFICIENT INFORMATION)".

f. Attributes: SUPERPART-OF-EACH, SUBPART-OF-EACH

1. partr[x;y].

purpose: To specify in the model that every element of set x is part of some element of set y.

method: Create a type-3 link between x and y which indicates the part-whole relation between their members.

procedure:

a. Add "(PLIST NAME y)" to the value list of attribute "SUPERPART-OF-EACH" of x.

b. Add "(PLIST NAME x)" to the value list of attribute "SUBPART-OF-EACH" of y.

c. Respond "(I UNDERSTAND)".

2. partrq[x;y].

purpose: To reply as to whether an arbitrary member of set x is a part of some member of set y.

method: No element may be part of itself. Reply "YES" if

$(\exists w)$[[there is a chain of links indicating that an arbitrary member of set x is part of some member of w] $\wedge$ [[y=w $\vee$
[there is a chain of links indicating that y is a subset of w]]].

Reply "SOMETIMES" if

$(\exists w)$[[there is a chain of links indicating that an arbitrary member of set x is part of some member of w] $\wedge$
[there is a chain of links indicating that w is a subset of y]].

Reply "NO" if an arbitrary member of set y is always or sometimes a part of some member of set x.

procedure:

a. If $x = y$, respond "(NO, THEY ARE THE SAME)".

b. Generate those sets w which can be reached from x through a chain of of type-3 links following the attribute "SUPERPART-OF-EACH".

c. If, for some w. setrq[y;w] = YES or SOMETIMES, respond "YES" or "SOMETIMES", respectively.

d. If the response for partrq[y;x] would be YES or SOMETIMES, respond "(NO, y IS PART OF x)" or "(NO, y IS SOMETIMES PART OF x)", respectively.

e. Otherwise respond "(INSUFFICIENT INFORMATION)".

g. Attributes: SUBPART, SUPERPART

1. partrgu[x;y]

purpose: To specify in the model that some element of set x is a part of the individual y.

method: Create a type-3 link between x and y which indicates the appropriate part-whole relation.

procedure:

a. Add "(PLIST NAME x)" to the value list of attribute "SUBPART" of y.

b. Add "(PLIST NAME y)" to the value list of attribute "SUPERPART" of x.

c. Respond "(I UNDERSTAND)".

2. partrgs[x;y]

purpose: To specify in the model that some element of set x is a part of the unique element, if any, of the set y.

method: Determine z, the unique element of y. Then specify that some element of x is part of z.

procedure:

a. Compute z = specify [y].

b. If z = NIL, terminate.

c. Else, compute partrgu[x;z].

3. partrguq[x;y]

purpose: To reply as to whether some element of set x is part of the individual y.

method: A member of x is a part of y if

$(\exists u)[[u=y \vee [u$ is equivalent to $y]] \wedge$
$[(\exists w)[[$there is a link indicating that an element of w is a subpart of $u] \wedge$
$[[w=x \vee [$there are links indicating that w is a subset of $x] \vee$
$(\exists z)[[$there are links indicating that every element of z has some element of x as a part$] \wedge$
$[w=z \vee [$there are links indicating that w is a subset of $z]]]] \vee$
$[(\exists z)[[u$ is an element of set $z] \wedge$
$[(\exists v)[$there are links indicating that z is a subset of $v]]]]]]]]$

procedure:

a. Generate those nodes w which can be reached from y, or from any node equivalent to y, by a chain of type-3 links following the attribute "SUBPART."

b. If, for any w, setrq[w;x]=YES, respond "YES".

c. Otherwise, generate those nodes z which can be reached from x by a chain of type-3 links following the attribute "SUPERPART-OF-EACH".

d. If, for any z and any w, setrq[w;z]=YES respond "YES".

e. Otherwise, compute the list l of sets for which there is a type-3 link from y, or any node equivalent to y, following the attribute "MEMBER".

f. Generate the nodes v which can be reached by a chain of type-3 links from x following the attribute, "SUPERPART-OF-EACH".

g. If, for any v and any u in l, setrq[u,v]=YES, respond "YES".

h. Otherwise, respond "(INSUFFICIENT INFORMATION)".

4. partrss[x;y]

purpose: To specify in the model that the unique element, if any, of set x is part of the unique element, if any, of set y.

method: Identify the unique elements u and v of sets x and y, respectively. Specify that some element of set x is part of the individual v. Then create a type-2 link from the appropriate type-3 link from x to u, specifying which element of x is involved.

procedure:

a. Compute v=specify [b], and u=specify [a].

b. If u or v = NIL, terminate.

c. Execute partrgu[x,v].

d. Add u to the value list of attribute "ELEMENTS" on that member of the "SUPERPART" value list of x which refers to y.

e. Respond "(I UNDERSTAND)".

5. partrsgq[x;y]

purpose: To reply as to whether the unique element of set x is part of some element of set y.

method: The answer is "YES" if there exists a unique element z of set x and if

$(\exists w)$[[there is a link indicating that some x is part of w] $\wedge$
$(\exists u)$[[u=$w \vee u$ is equivalent to w] $\wedge$
$(\exists v)$[[there is a link indicating that u is an element of v] $\wedge$
[[y=v] $\vee$ [there are links indicating that y is a subset of v] $\wedge$
$(\exists q)$[[there are links indicating that every y is part of some q] $\wedge$ [[v=q] $\vee$
[there are links indicating that v is a subset of q]]]]]]]

procedure:

a. Compute z = specify[x].

b. If z = NIL, terminate.

c. Generate those nodes w which can be reached from x by a type-3 link following the attribute "SUPERPART".

d. For each w compute the list l of those sets of which w, or any set equivalent to w, is a member.

e. If y is in l, respond "YES".

f. If, for any $v \in l$, setrq[y;v] = YES, respond "YES".

g. Otherwise, generate those nodes q which can be reached from y by a type-3 link following the attribute "SUPERPART-OF-EACH".

h. If, for any q, setrq[v;q] = YES, respond "YES".

i. Otherwise respond "(INSUFFICIENT INFORMATION)".

h. Attribute: NUMBER

1. partrn[x;y;n]

purpose: To specify in the model that there are n elements of the set x which are parts of every element of set y.

method: Create a type-3 link between x and y specifying that an element of x is part of some element of y. Create type-1 links associating the number n with that type-3 link.

procedure:

a. Execute partr[x;y].

b. Add "(NUMBER n)" to both the list which was added to the value list of attribute "SUBPART-OF-EACH" of y, and the list which was added to the value list of attribute "SUPERPART-OF-EACH" of x.

2. partrnu[x;y;n]

purpose: To specify in the model that there are n elements of set x which are parts of individual y.

method: Create a type-3 link between x and y which indicates that some

element of set x is part of y. Create type-1 links associating the number n with that type-3 link.
procedure:

a. Execute partrgu[x;y].

b. Add "(NUMBER n)" to both the list which was added to the value list of attribute "SUBPART" of y, and the list which was added to the value list of attribute "SUPERPART" of x.

3. partrnuq[x;y]

purpose: to reply as to how many elements of the set x are parts of the individual y.
method: If

$(\exists u)$[[there is a link indicating that an element of u is part of y] $\wedge$
[[u=x] $\vee$ $(\exists v)$[[there is a chain of links indicating that a v is part of every u] $\wedge$ [[x=v] $\vee$
[there is a chain of links indicating x is a subset of v]]]]] $\vee$
$(\exists u)$[[there is a link indicating that y is an element of set u]
$(\exists v)$[[there is a chain of links indicating that a v is a part of every u] $\wedge$ [[x=v] $\vee$
[there is a chain of links indicating that x is a subset of v]]]],

then the answer is the product of the values of the type-1 links following the attribute "NUMBER", associated with each type-3 link used in proving the required part relation. If any such "NUMBER" attribute is missing, the reply should explicitly request it. If the part-whole relation cannot be established, the reply indicates that fact.
procedure:

a. Follow the procedure of partrguq[x;y] until links are found which warrant a "YES" response. Save a list l of all required links which follow the attribute "SUBPART" or "SUPERPART-OF-EACH".

b. If no such list can be found, respond
"(I DON*T KNOW WHETHER x IS PART OF y)".

c. For each element α of l, where α specifies a "SUPERPART-OF-EACH" link from u to v, get the value of the attribute "NUMBER" of α. If, for some α, no such value exists, respond "(HOW MANY u PER v Q)".

d. Compute z = the product of the numbers obtained above.
Respond "(THE ANSWER IS z)".

i. Attributes: LEFT, RIGHT, JLEFT, JRIGHT

1. jright[x;y]

purpose: To specify in the model that the unique element of set x is located just to the right of the unique element of set y.
method: Check whether the statement is consistent with existing knowledge; *i.e.*, that nothing is known to be between x and y and that y is not known to

be to the right of x. If it is not consistent, complain. Otherwise, create a type-1 link indicating the positional relation.
procedure:

a. If specify$[x]$ or specify$[y]$ = NIL, terminate.

b. If there is already a type-1 link from y to x following the attribute "JRIGHT", respond "(THE ABOVE STATEMENT IS ALREADY KNOWN)".

c. If it can be proven that y is to the right of x, *i.e.*, if rightp$[y;x]$=T; or if there is any type-1 link from y following the attribute "JRIGHT"; or if there is any type-1 link from x following the attribute "JLEFT"; then respond "(THE ABOVE STATEMENT IS IMPOSSIBLE)".

d. If rightp$[x;y]$=T, and there does not exist a direct type-2 link from y to x following the attribute "RIGHT", respond "(THE ABOVE STATEMENT IS IMPOSSIBLE)".

e. Otherwise, create a type-1 link from y to x following the attribute "JRIGHT"; create a type-1 link from x to y following the attribute "JLEFT"; and respond "(I UNDERSTAND)".

2. rightp$[x;y]$

purpose: To test whether it is known that the x is located to the right of the y.

method: "rightp$[x;y]$" is defined recursively as follows: If there is no type-1 link from y following the attribute "JRIGHT", and no type-2 link from y following the attribute "RIGHT", the value of "rightp$[x;y]$" is NIL; if either of the above links exists and links to x, the value is T. Otherwise the value is the disjunction of the values of "rightp$[x;y]$" for all u which are linked to y by one of the above links.
procedure:

a. Compute u, the value of the type-1 link from y following the attribute "JRIGHT".

b. If u=x, value is T; if there is no u, go to step *d.*

c. If rightp$[x,u]$ = T, the value is T.

d. Compute l, the value of the type-2 link from y following the attribute "RIGHT".

e. If x is a member of list l, the value is T; if there is no l, the value is NIL.

f. If, for any $v \in l$, rightp$[x;v]$ = T, the value is T; otherwise the value is NIL.

Note: "T" and "NIL" are special LISP symbols standing for "true" and "false," respectively.

3. right$[x;y]$

purpose: To specify in the model that the unique element of set x is located to the right of the unique element of set y.

method: Check whether the statement is consistent with existing knowledge. If so, create a type-2 link indicating the positional relation. Otherwise, complain.
procedure:

a. If specify[*x*]=NIL or specify [*y*]=NIL, terminate.

b. If rightp[*x*,*y*]=T, respond "(THE ABOVE STATEMENT IS ALREADY KNOWN)".

c. If rightp[*y*,*x*]=T, respond "(THE ABOVE STATEMENT IS IMPOSSIBLE)".

d. Otherwise, create a type-2 link from *y* to *x* following the attribute "RIGHT"; create a type-2 link from *x* to *y* following the attribute "LEFT"; and respond "(I UNDERSTAND)".

4. jrightssq[*x*;*y*]

purpose: To reply as to whether the *x* is located just to the right of the *y*.
method: Determine whether the links in the model indicate that *x* is just to the right of *y*, *x* cannot be just to the right of *y*, or neither.
procedure:

a. If specify[*x*]=NIL or specify[*y*]=NIL, terminate.

b. If there is a type-1 link from *y* to *x* following the attribute "JRIGHT", respond "YES".

c. If rightp[*x*;*x*]=T; or if there is any type-1 link from y following the attribute "JRIGHT"; or if there is any type-1 link from *x* following the attribute "JLEFT"; then respond "NO".

d. If rightp[*x*;*y*]=T and there does not exist a direct type-2 link from *y* to *x* following the attribute "RIGHT", respond "NO".

e. Otherwise, respond "(INSUFFICIENT INFORMATION)".

5. rightssq[*x*;*y*]

purpose: To reply as to whether the *x* is located to the right of the *y*.
method: Determine whether the links in the model indicate that *x* is to the right of *y*, to the left of *y*, or neither.
procedure:

a. If specify[*x*]=NIL or specify[*y*]=NIL, terminate.

b. If rightp[*x*;*y*]=T, respond "YES".

c. If rightp[*y*;*x*]=T, respond "NO".

d. Otherwise, respond "(INSUFFICIENT INFORMATION)".

6. wheres[*x*]

purpose: To determine the locations of those objects which have been positioned with respect to the unique element of the set *x*.
method: Reply with the information provided by each positional link associated with *x*.
procedure:

a. If specify[*x*]=NIL, terminate.

b. Compute *u* = the value of the type-1 link from *x* following the attribute "JLEFT"; *v* = the value of the type-1 link from *x* following the attribute "JRIGHT"; *l* = the value of the type-2 link from *x* following the attribute "LEFT"; and *m* = the value of the type-2 link from *x* following the attribute "RIGHT".

c. If *u, v, l,* and *m* all do not exist, respond "(NO POSITION IS KNOWN)".

d. If *u* does not exist, go to step (f).

e. Respond, "(JUST TO THE RIGHT OF THE *u*)", and go to the next step.

f. If *v* does not exist, go to step (h).

g. Respond, "(JUST TO THE LEFT OF THE *v*)", and go to the next step.

h. If *l* does not exist, go to step (j).

i. Respond, "(SOMEWHERE TO THE RIGHT OF THE FOLLOWING . . *l*)", and go to the next step.

j. If *m* does not exist, terminate.

k. Respond, "(SOMEWHERE TO THE LEFT OF THE FOLLOWING . . *m*)".

7. locates[*x*]

purpose: To determine the location of the unique element of set *x* with respect to as many other objects as possible.

method: Construct a diagram of the left-to-right order of objects by searching through all chains of positional links starting from *x* and proceeding recursively. The form of the diagram is a list, with objects known to be adjacent appearing in sublists. If no positional links from *x* exist or if a well-ordering cannot be determined, make an appropriate comment.

procedure:

a. If specify[*x*]=NIL, terminate.

b. Set the initial diagram g="(*x*)".

c. Compute *u* = the value of the type-1 link from *x* following the attribute "JRIGHT". If no *u* exists or if *u* is already in *g,* go to step *f.*

d. Insert *u* just to the right of *x* in *g, i.e.,* insert *u* right after *x* in a sublist of *g.*

e. Replace *g* by the result of executing this procedure starting from step (c), with the current value of *u* replacing the argument *x* and the current value of *g* as the diagram.

f. Repeat step c, for the attribute "JLEFT". In case of failure, go to step (i).

g. Insert *u* just to the left of *x* in *g.*

h. Repeat step (e).

i. Compute *l* = the value of the type-2 link from *x* following the attribute "RIGHT". If no *l* exists, go to step *l.*

j. For each *m*∈*l:* If *m* is already in the current *g,* ignore it; if there exists a *v* in *g* which is the object (or first object on a sublist) following *x* (or a sublist containing *x*), go to step *k.* Otherwise insert *m* after *x* (or the sublist containing *x*) in *g,* and repeat step (e), with the current value of *m* replacing *x.* When all *m*∈*l* have been treated go to step (1).

k. If rightp[*v;m*] =T, insert *m* after *x* and continue with the next *m* in step *j.* If rightp[*m,v*] =T, then just for this value of *m* replace *x* by *v* and continue as in step (j). Otherwise, respond

"(THE LEFT-TO-RIGHT ORDER IS)
g
(TO FURTHER SPECIFY THE POSITIONS YOU MUST INDICATE
WHERE THE *m* IS WITH RESPECT TO THE *v*)".

l. Perform operations analogous to *i, j,* and *k* for the attribute "LEFT" of *x*.

m. If the current *g*="(*x*)", respond "(NO RELATIVE POSITION IS KNOWN)".

n. Otherwise respond, "(THE LEFT-TO-RIGHT ORDER IS) *g*".

8. whereg[*x*]

purpose: To determine the locations of those objects which have been positioned with respect to some element of set *x*.

method: Find an object *u* of which an *x* is an example or a part, and which has positional links. Then find the locations of those objects which have been positioned with respect to *u.*

procedure:

a. If *x* has any positional links, *i.e.,* if the attributes "JRIGHT", "JLEFT", "RIGHT", and "LEFT" of *x* are not all missing, execute wheres[*x*].

b. If
(∃u)[[there is a sequence of links following the attribute
"SUPERPART-OF-EACH" from *x* to *u*]∧
[*u* has at least one positional link]],
then execute wheres[*u*].

c. If the hypotheses of step(b) hold for the attribute "SUBSET", execute wheres[*u*].

d. If
(∃u)[[there is a sequence of links following the attribute
"SUPERPART-OF-EACH" from *x* to *u*]∧
(∃w)[[there is a sequence of links following the attribute
"SUBSET" from *u* to *w*]∧
[*w* has at least one positional link]]],
then execute wheres[*w*].

e. Otherwise respond "(NO RELATIVE POSITION IS KNOWN)".

2.5.2 Special Features

This part discusses the sample conversations for Fig. 2-6 which illustrate three special features of the SIR system. The first two – the *exception principle* and *resolving ambiguities* – illustrate how SIR can be used to simulate various aspects of human linguistic behavior. The third feature – *streamlining* – demonstrates one way in which SIR can automatically modify its model structure in order to save computer memory space.

a. *Exception principle:* General information about "all the elements" of a set is considered to apply to particular elements only in the absence of more specific information about those elements. Thus it is not necessarily contradictory to learn that "mammals are land animals" and yet "a whale is a mammal which always lives in water." In the program, this idea is implemented by always referring for desired information to the property-list of the individual concerned *before* looking at the descriptions of sets to which the individual belongs.

The justification for this departure from the no-exception principles of Aristotelian logic is that this precedence of specific facts over background knowledge seems to be the way people operate, and I wish the computer to communicate with people as naturally as possible.

The present program does not experience the uncomfortable feeling people frequently get when they must face facts like "a whale is a mammal which lives in water although mammals as a rule live on land." However, minor programming additions to the present system could require it to identify those instances in which specific information and general information differ; the program could then express its amusement at such paradoxes.

b. *Resolving ambiguities:* The criteria used by the program to decide whether "has," in the format "x has y," should be interpreted "has as parts" or "owns" are the following:

1. Let P be the proposition "Either y is known to be part of something, or y is an element of some set whose elements are known to be parts of something."

2. Let N be the proposition "Either y is known to be owned by something, or y is an element of some set whose elements are known to be owned by something."

3. If $P \wedge \sim N$, assume "has" means "has as parts."
   If $\sim P \wedge N$, assume "has" means "owns."
   If $\sim P \wedge \sim N$, give up and ask for rephrasing.

4. Let P′ be the proposition
   $(\exists u)[[[y$ is known to be part of $u] \vee [y$ is an element of some set whose elements are known to be parts of the elements of $u]] \wedge (\exists w)[[u \in w \vee u \subset w] \wedge [x \in w \vee x \subset w]]]$.

a. EXCEPTION PRINCIPLE

```
(***.     THERE ARE 5 FINGERS ON EVERY HAND)
(I UNDERSTAND)

(***.     THERE ARE TWO HANDS ON A PERSON)
(I UNDERSTAND)

(***.     A BOY IS A PERSON)
(I UNDERSTAND)

(***.     TOM IS A BOY)
(I UNDERSTAND)

(***.     DICK IS A BOY)
(I UNDERSTAND)

(***.     HARRY IS A BOY)
(I UNDERSTAND)

(***.     TOM HAS NINE FINGERS)
(THE ABOVE SENTENCE IS AMBIGUUUS ** BUT I ASSUME (HAS) MEANS (HAS AS PARTS))
(I UNDERSTAND)

(***.     DICK HAS ONE HAND)
(THE ABOVE SENTENCE IS AMBIGUUUS ** BUT I ASSUME (HAS) MEANS (HAS AS PARTS))
(I UNDERSTAND)

(***.     HOW MANY FINGERS DOES TOM HAVE Q)
(THE ABOVE SENTENCE IS AMBIGUOUS ** BUT I ASSUME (HAS) MEANS (HAS AS PARTS))
(THE ANSWER IS 9)

(***.     HOW MANY FINGERS DOES DICK HAVE Q)
(THE ABOVE SENTENCE IS AMBIGUOUS ** BUT I ASSUME (HAS) MEANS (HAS AS PARTS))
(THE ANSWER IS 5)

(***.     HOW MANY FINGERS DOES HARRY HAVE Q)
(THE ABOVE SENTENCE IS AMBIGUOUS ** BUT I ASSUME (HAS) MEANS (HAS AS PARTS))
(THE ANSWER IS 10)

(***.     HOW MANY FINGERS DOES JOE HAVE Q)
(THE ABOVE SENTENCE IS AMBIGUOUS ** BUT I ASSUME (HAS) MEANS (HAS AS PARTS))
(I DON*T KNOW WHETHER FINGER IS PART OF JOE)
```

Figure 2-6. Special Features

b. RESOLVING AMBIGUITIES

```
(***.     JOHN IS A PERSON)

(I UNDERSTAND)

(***.     DICK IS A PERSON)

(I UNDERSTAND)

(***.     A CHAIN IS PART OF A BICYCLE)

(I UNDERSTAND)

(***.     THE POWER-SAW HAS A CHAIN)

(THE ABOVE SENTENCE IS AMBIGUOUS ** BUT I ASSUME (HAS) MEANS (HAS AS PARTS))
(G02840 IS A POWER-SAW)
(I UNDERSTAND)

(***.     JOHN OWNS A CHAIN)

(I UNDERSTAND)

(***.     DICK HAS A CHAIN)

(THE ABOVE SENTENCE IS AMBIGUOUS ** BUT I ASSUME (HAS) MEANS (OWNS))
(I UNDERSTAND)

(***.     THE CUCKOO-CLOCK HAS A CHAIN)

(THE ABOVE SENTENCE IS AMBIGUOUS ** PLEASE RE-PHRASE IT)
```

Figure 2-6. *(Continued)*

c. STREAMLINING LINKAGES

```
(•••.     JOHN IS A PERSON)

(I UNDERSTAND)

(•••.     JOHN IS A TECH-MAN)

(I UNDERSTAND)

(•••.     JOHN IS A BOY)

(I UNDERSTAND)

(•••.     JOHN IS A STUDENT)

(I UNDERSTAND)

(•••.     JOHN IS A BRIGHT-PERSON)

(I UNDERSTAND)

(•••.     EVERY BOY IS A PERSON)

(I UNDERSTAND)

(•••.     EVERY TECH-MAN IS A PERSON)

(I UNDERSTAND)

(•••.     EVERY TECH-MAN IS A BRIGHT-PERSON)

(I UNDERSTAND)

(•••.     EVERY TECH-MAN IS A STUDENT)

(I UNDERSTAND)

(•••.     EVERY BRIGHT-PERSON IS A PERSON)

(I UNDERSTAND)

(•••.     EVERY STUDENT IS A BRIGHT-PERSON)

(I UNDERSTAND)

(•••.     EVERY STUDENT IS A PERSON)

(I UNDERSTAND)

END OF EVALQUOTE, VALUE IS ..
(NO MORE INPUT SENTENCES)


 FUNCTION   EVALQUOTE   HAS BEEN ENTERED, ARGUMENTS..
STREAMLINE
(JOHN)

(I FORGET THE MEMBER-ELEMENTS RELATIONS BETWEEN PERSON AND JOHN)
(I FORGET THE MEMBER-ELEMENTS RELATIONS BETWEEN STUDENT AND JOHN)
(I FORGET THE MEMBER-ELEMENTS RELATIONS BETWEEN BRIGHT-PERSON AND JOHN)
(I FORGET THE SET-INCLUSION RELATION BETWEEN PERSON AND TECH-MAN)
(I FORGET THE SET-INCLUSION RELATION BETWEEN BRIGHT-PERSON AND TECH-MAN)
(I FORGET THE SET-INCLUSION RELATION BETWEEN PERSON AND STUDENT)

END OF EVALQUOTE, VALUE IS ..
NIL
```

Figure 2-6. *(Continued)*

5. Let N′ be the proposition
$(\exists u)[[[y$ is known to be owned by $u] \vee [y$ is an element of some set whose elements are known to be owned by the elements of $u]] \wedge (\exists w)[[u \in w \vee u \subset w] \wedge [x \in w \vee x \subset w]]]$.
6. If $P' \wedge \sim N'$, assume "has" means "has as parts."
If $\sim P' \wedge N'$, assume "has" means "owns."
Otherwise, give up and ask for rephrasing.

These criteria are simple, yet they are sufficient to enable the program to make quite reasonable decisions about the intended purpose in various sentences of the ambiguous word "has." Of course, the program can be fooled into making mistakes, e.g., in case the sentence, "Dick has a chain," had been presented before the sentence "John owns a chain," in Fig. 2-6b; however, a human being exposed to a *new* word in a similar situation would make a similar error. The point here is that it is feasible to resolve ambiguities automatically in sentence meaning by referring to the descriptions of the words in the sentence, descriptions which can be created automatically through proper prior exposure to unambiguous sentences.

c. *Streamlining linkages:* All question-answering (model-searching) functions which involve references to set-inclusion or set-membership relations must "know" about the basic properties of those relations, i.e., those functions must have built into them the ability to apply theorems like

$x \subset y \wedge y \subset z \Rightarrow x \subset z$ and

$\alpha \in x \wedge x \subset y \Rightarrow \alpha \in y$;

otherwise the functions would not be able to make full use of the usually limited information available in the form of explicit links. On the other hand, since the functions involved will be "aware" of these theorems, then the set of questions which can be answered is independent of the presence or absence of explicit links which provide the information to the right of the "⇒," provided the information to the left of the "⇒" is available.

The "STREAMLINE" operation starts with the object x which is its argument, and considers all objects linked to x, directly or indirectly, through set inclusion or set membership. All explicit links among these objects which can also be deduced by use of the known theorems are deleted. A response of the form "(I FORGET THE SET-INCLUSION RELATION BETWEEN y AND z)" indicates that whatever links were created by some sentence of a form similar to "(EVERY z IS A y)" are being deleted, and the space they occupied is being made available for other use.

In this example, the STREAMLINE operation deleted more than half the existing links, at no reduction in the question-answering power of the system. However, the *time* required to obtain answers to certain questions was significantly increased.

2.6 Formalization and Generalization of SIR

The present version of the SIR system not only demonstrates the *possibility* of designing a computer that "understands;" it also points the way toward more general, *practical* systems by providing a useful data representation (the model) and by suggesting useful general information retrieval mechanisms.

SIR's abilities were illustrated by Fig. 2-1 and, in greater detail, by the conversations of Fig. 2-5. Unfortunately, the system is quite limited in the number of semantic relations it can "understand" and in the depth of its apparent understanding of any one relation. Moreover, the present system has some basic features which make these limitations extremely difficult to overcome.

The purposes of this section are to identify those features which make SIR difficult to extend; to point out how those difficulties arose and how they may be overcome; and to propose a formalism and a computer implementation for a more general semantic information retrieval system which has most of the advantages of SIR but few of its limitations.

The SIR treatment of restricted natural language was discussed at length in Section 2.4 and is not of concern here. Here we deal only with the action of SIR on relational statements which precisely define the desired information storage or retrieval operations.

2.6.1 Properties and Problems of SIR

Let us now examine the present structure and mode of operation of SIR. In particular, we are interested in learning why SIR cannot be extended in simple ways to handle a greater quantity and complexity of information.

1. *Program organization:* The present computer implementation of SIR is an interdependent collection of specially designed subprograms. Each different information storage or retrieval operation is controlled by a different subprogram.

Such a diffuse program structure has a certain advantage for producing early results with a new experimental system. SIR was primarily developed as an experimental vehicle through which one may learn the best forms of information representation and the best storage and retrieval procedures. As an experimental device, SIR must be easily amenable to changes in its structure and modes of operation. The programmer must be able to learn the most useful interpretations of relational statements and the most useful responses the system should make. This learning takes place as he tries, by means of *ad hoc* changes to the program, different interpretations, and different response modes. These program changes are easiest to make if the program consists of many separate subprograms without much over-all structure.

As such a system grows more complicated, each change in a subprogram may affect more of the other subprograms. The structure becomes more awkward and more difficult to generalize as its size increases. Finally, the system may become too unwieldy for further experimentation. (SIR is presently close to this point of diminishing returns.)

However, by the time this barrier is reached many fruitful results may have been attained. *Ad hoc* features may coalesce into general principles. Desirable features may be discovered, and uniform methods may emerge for handling problems which originally seemed quite different from each other. In particular, my experiences in developing SIR to its present state have enabled me to specify the more uniform, more general, more powerful system proposed in 2.6.2 and 2.6.3.

2. *The model:* The model is a flexible body of data whose content and organization are crucial factors in SIR's learning and question-answering abilities. SIR's "knowledge" is derived from two sources: facts represented in the model, and procedures embodied in the program. Basic procedures in the program provide for automatic revision of the model, if necessary, whenever new information is presented to the system. No such automatic procedures exist for revising the program itself.

The greater the variety of information which can be stored in the model, the more flexible the resulting system; the more specific requirements and restrictions are built into the program, the more rigid and less general the overall system. It seems desirable, then, to store in the model a great variety of information, including facts about objects, relations, and the operation of the program itself. The program would then consist simply of storage procedures which would modify the model, and retrieval procedures whose actions would be controlled by data in the model. The user could then simply "tell" the system how to change its retrieval procedures whenever such changes are desired.

Such a flexible system, whose program is "driven" by the model, is an ultimate objective of this research. Unfortunately, this objective must be approached by successive approximations. A model-controlled system cannot be designed at the outset for the following reasons:

a. In order to store all the significant, controlling information in the model, we must first discover what *constitutes* the significant information in a semantic information retrieval system. After developing *any* workable program-plus-model system we are in a better position to recognize truly important features and to transfer control of them to the model.
b. The value and efficiency of the system depend upon the *structure* of the model and the manner in which the program and model interact. One should limit the complexity of the model until the organization of the model and of the over-all system have been proved feasible.
c. The problem of how to *express* controlling information which we wish to add to the model, e.g., how best to describe search and deduction procedures, must be solved along with the problems of representing and utilizing

that information once it is in the model. Formalisms for describing such control procedures are easier to devise after some experience has been gained in the use of similar procedures. This experience, in turn, is easy to develop through experimentation with the *program* portion of simplified semantic information retrieval systems.

In SIR the model consists only of descriptions of objects and of classes. The number, kind, and interpretation of the descriptors (attributes) in the model are determined by the program. The information about how the meanings of certain attributes are related to each other is incorporated in the subprograms which identify those attributes, rather than in the model.

Although SIR is approaching its limit in usefulness, experience with the system has brough me to the point where I can confidently propose an improved, generalized system. The system proposed in 2.6.2 and 2.6.3 keeps the now proven description-list organization for the model; it increases the variety of data to be stored in the model; it transfers some of the information about the attributes from the program to the model; and it provides the user with a simplified method for experimenting with the deductive procedures of the system.

3. *Question-answering method:* In order to describe how SIR's question-answering behavior has been achieved and how it can be improved, I must first introduce some notation. As described in Part 3 of Section 2.3.4, each relation in the SIR system is a dyadic relation and hence is represented in the model by two attribute links. Table 2-1 gives the correspondence between relation names and attribute names, and a typical English interpretation for each relation. Note that I use the familiar infixes "⊂" and "∈" for set-

Table 2-1. Relational Notation

Relation	Attribute on property-list of x	Attribute on property-list of y	Typical English interpretation
$x \subset y$	SUPERSET	SUBSET	An x is a y.
$x \in y$	MEMBER	ELEMENT	x is a y.
equiv[$x;y$]	EQUIV	EQUIV	x and y name the same object.
owng[$x;y$]	OWNED-BY-EACH	POSSESS-BY-EACH	Every y owns an x.
own[$x;y$]	OWNED	POSSESS	y owns an x.
partg[$x;y$]	SUPERPART-OF-EACH	SUBPART-OF-EACH	An x is part of a y.
part[$x;y$]	SUPERPART	SUBPART	An x is part of y.
right[$x;y$]	LEFT	RIGHT	The x is to the right of the y.
jright[$x;y$]	JLEFT	JRIGHT	The x is just to the right of the y.

inclusion and set membership, respectively, although functional notation, such as "equiv[x,y]," is used for all other relations. Also, the usual symbols of mathematical logic, which are defined in Appendix 2.1, will be used when convenient.

A relation "holds" for specified arguments, i.e., a relation with specified arguments (called a *predicate*) is "true," if and only if any reasonable English interpretation of the relational statement is a true English statement. An English interpretation should be considered "reasonable" only if the natural-language processing part of the system would translate it into the given relational statement. A relation with specified objects as arguments clearly is true if the objects are linked in the model by the attributes which correspond to the relation. However, frequently such a predicate is "true" even when its arguments are *not* directly linked. In such cases the truth of the predicate can be determined indirectly from other information available in the model or in the program.

SIR contains a separate subprogram for determining "truth" for each relation in the system. These are the subprograms responsible for answering "yes-or-no" questions. For example, the answer to the question "Is the chair to the right of the table?" would be found by a subprogram called "rightq" which deals with the truth of the "right" relation. "Chair" and "table" would be the inputs to the "rightq" program, which would then search the model and make an appropriate response.

During the development of SIR, procedures for establishing the truth of relations had to be explored independently for each relation; therefore a separate program was written for each relation. The detailed operation of these subprograms was described in Section 2.5. Now, as we consider how to generalize the system, the time has come to look for common features of these subprograms. Such common features could serve as the basis for a simpler, more unified program structure. Indeed, such common features *have* been found, and they are exploited in the general system to be described in 2.6.2 and 2.6.3.

The first step in trying to simplify the truth-testing procedures is to express them in such a way that their operations can be easily compared and understood. In practice each of the truth-testing subprograms operates by searching the model, looking for certain combinations of attribute links. However, since the existence of an attribute link implies the truth of a corresponding predicate, we may consider the subprogram as deducing the truth of a predicate from the fact that certain other predicates are true. Such deduction procedures are conveniently expressible in the first-order predicate calculus (the "quantificational calculus").

Frequently the truth of a predicate depends upon the fact that the *relation* involved has a special property, e.g., transitivity. These properties of relations may conveniently be described by "definition" statements in which a bound variable stands for the name of some unspecified relation. These definitions are simply abbreviations which will become ordinary quantificational calculus statements when the bound variables are replaced by particular relation names.

The properties defined below are useful for describing some of the SIR relations:

Symmetry: $\mathfrak{S}(P) = df\,(\forall x)(\forall y)[P[x;y] \Rightarrow P[y;x]]$

Reflexivity: $\mathfrak{R}(P) = df\,(\forall x)[P[x;x]]$

Transitivity: $\mathfrak{T}(P) = df\,(\forall x)(\forall y)(\forall z)[P[x;y] \wedge P[y;z] \Rightarrow P[x;z]]$

The following logical sentences hold throughout SIR and represent basic properties of the "equiv" relation:

$(\forall P)(\forall x)(\forall y)(\forall z)[P[x;y] \wedge \text{equiv}[x;z] \Rightarrow P[z;y]]$

$(\forall P)(\forall x)(\forall y)(\mathsf{A}\, z)[P[x;y] \wedge \text{equiv}[y;z] \Rightarrow P[x;z]]$

Table 2-2 lists predicate calculus statements corresponding to the deduction procedures actually used in the SIR subprograms for truth-testing. These statements were obtained by studying the SIR subprograms, and they accurately represent the operation of those subprograms, except for the following:

a. All quantifiers range over only the finite universe of objects, classes, and relations represented in the model.
b. Each subprogram contains built-in mechanisms for searching the model in the course of trying to apply one of the deduction procedures. The linkage structure of the model allows the programs to make direct, exhaustive searches through just the relevant portions of the model.
c. When alternative deduction procedures are available for testing a predicate, each subprogram specifies the order in which the procedures should be attempted. As is illustrated by the "Exception Principle" (Part 1 of 2.5.2), the use of alternate deduction procedures may result in different answers to a question. This means that, from a purely predicate-calculus point of view, the deduction procedures together with the information stored in the model may form an inconsistent system. Therefore the order in which deduction procedures are used influences the answers obtained. In the present form of SIR the ordering rule has been that those procedures dealing with indirect links are to be used only if no answer can be obtained by using those procedures dealing with more direct links.
d. Each subprogram is independent and contains complete programs for its deduction procedures. Since some of the deduction procedures in different subprograms are similar, some program segments appear several times in the SIR system. For example, programs which test whether a particular class-inclusion relation holds appear in most of the truth-testing subprograms. This program redundancy results from the independent subprogram organization of SIR and should be removed in a more uniform system.

Thus far I have been discussing only those programs which answer "yes-or-no" questions. More complex questions, such as "Where is the table?" or "How many fingers does John have?", require different question-answering procedures. SIR contains an additional subprogram for each of these complex

Table 2-2. Deduction Procedures in SIR Subprograms

Relation being tested	Deduction Procedures*
$\subset$	1. $\mathfrak{T}[\subset]$
	2. $x=y \Rightarrow x \subset y$
	3. equiv$[x;y] \Rightarrow x \subset y$
$\in$	4. $\alpha \in x \wedge x \subset y \Rightarrow \alpha \in y$
equiv	5.,6.,7. $\mathfrak{T}$[equiv], $\mathfrak{R}$[equiv], $\mathfrak{S}$[equiv]
owng	8. $\sim$owng$[x;x]$
	9. owng$[x;y] \wedge z \subset y \Rightarrow$ owng$[x;z]$
	10. owng$[x;y] \wedge x \subset z \Rightarrow$ owng$[z;y]$
own	11. own$[x;y] \wedge x \subset z \Rightarrow$ own$[z;y]$
	12. owng$[x;y] \wedge z \in y \Rightarrow$ own$[x;z]$
partg	13. $\sim$partg$[x;x]$
	14. partg$[x;y] \wedge z \subset y \Rightarrow$ partg$[x;z]$
part	15. part$[x;y] \wedge x \subset z \Rightarrow$ part$[z;y]$
	16. part$[x;y] \wedge$ partg$[z;x] \Rightarrow$ part$[z;y]$
	17. partg$[x;y] \wedge z \in y \Rightarrow$ part$[x;z]$
right, jright	18. right$[x;y] \Rightarrow \sim$right$[y;x]$
	19. $\mathfrak{T}$[right]
	20. jright$[x;y] \Rightarrow$ right$[x;y]$
	21. jright$[z;y] \wedge z \neq x \Rightarrow \sim$jright$[x;y]$
	22. jright$[x;z] \wedge z \neq y \Rightarrow \sim$jright$[x;y]$
	23. right$[x;y] \wedge$ right$[y;z] \Rightarrow \sim$jright$[x;z]$

*Universal quantification over all free variables is assumed.

question forms. These subprograms will be discussed further in Part 3 of 2.6.3.

2.6.2 Formalism for a General System.

With a suitable formal system, a separate truth-testing subprogram for each relation in the SIR system is not necessary. Instead, a single "proof-procedure" program can serve for answering all "yes-or-no" questions.

The deduction procedures of Table 2-2 could be used as the axioms of such a formal system. However, the study of those "axioms" has suggested an alternative system which is more concise, more intuitively meaningful, and easier to extend to new relations. This alternative formal system is the subject of this section.

1. *Interactions:* Two relations "interact" if, in order to test the truth of a predicate involving one of the relations, it is necessary first to test the truth of some predicate involving the other. Whenever two or more relations appear in the same deduction-procedure statement in Table 2-2, we may say that those relations interact.

Interactions may be classified informally as follows:

a. Interactions between the $\in$ or $\subset$ relation and some other relation.
b. Interactions between relations whose meanings are similar to each other. (This "similarity" will be defined more precisely in Section 2.)
c. Interactions which arise principally because of some peculiarity of *one* of the relations involved.
d. Other interactions.

Interactions are of interest because they create the biggest obstacle to generalizing the SIR system. Whenever a new relation is added to the system, the programmer must identify all the relations in the system which interact with the new relation, and modify the system to allow for the interactions. With the present system, this means modifying each of the question-answering subprograms associated with the interacting relations. This formidable reprogramming task accounts for the fact that the deduction schemes in the present version of SIR do not allow for *all* the intuitively necessary interactions between relations in the system. For example, if SIR is told that an x is part of every y and that z owns a y, it cannot deduce that z owns an x. To perform this and similar deductions SIR would have to "know" about additional interactions among the relations part, partg, own, owng, $\underline{\in}$, and $\underline{\subset}$.

Almost all the interactions accounted for in the present system and in the deduction procedures of Table 2-2 are of type "*a*," "*b*," or "*c*," according to the above classification scheme; i.e., they involve the relations $\in$ or $\subset$, relations whose meanings are similar, or relations with individual peculiar properties. The formal system to be described below will eliminate the need for explicitly considering *any* interactions of these three types. Once a new relation is properly described according to simple, intuitive rules, any type "*a*," "*b*," or "*c*" interactions between it and other relations will automatically be accounted for by the logical system. Although other interactions may still exist, they will be easy to describe and modify. For example, a single simple statement will be sufficient to make the system "aware" of the interaction between part-whole and ownership relations illustrated in the previous paragraph.

2. *SIR-1: A proposed formal system for truth-testing:* The formal system called "SIR-1" to be proposed here will consist of: definitions of certain terms, including terms which describe strings of symbols; a standard interpretation for the symbols; and a logical method for determining whether certain strings called "sentences" of SIR-1 are "true." The significance of the system is that all "yes-or-no" questions which can be answered by SIR, and a great many which cannot, are expressible as sentences in SIR-1; i.e., the standard interpretation of a formal sentence is its corresponding English question. Further, if a sentence is "true" in SIR-1, then the answer to its corresponding question is "yes." These points will be illustrated by examples. A computer implementation of SIR-1 will be discussed in 2.6.3.

a. Definitions:

basic object $=_{df}$ any object which is described in the model and which has the following property: No object described in the model may be related to a basic object by being a member or a subset of it.

basic relation $=_{df}$ a symbol which names a relation whose arguments must all be basic objects.

variable $=_{df}$ a symbol used in place of the name of some unspecified object described in the model. The standard interpretation of the name of an object is, of course, the object itself.

basic predicate $=_{df}$ a basic relation written as a function of the names of basic objects or of variables which stand for the names of basic objects. The standard interpretation of a predicate is that the specified relation holds between the specified objects.

$\in$*-quantifier* $=_{df}$ either of the symbols "$(\forall \nu_1 \in \nu_2)$" or "$(\exists \nu_1 \in \nu_2)$," where ν_1 is any variable and ν_2 is any variable, any object name, or the special symbol "M" which stands for "model." These $\in$-quantifiers are related in the first-order predicate calculus as follows:

$$\begin{aligned} (\forall \alpha \in x)\,[R[\alpha]] &=_{df} (\forall\ \alpha \in M)\,[\alpha \in x \Rightarrow R[\alpha]] \\ (\exists \alpha \in x)\,[R[\alpha]] &=_{df} (\exists\ \alpha \in M)\,[\alpha \in x \wedge R[\alpha]] \end{aligned} \qquad (2.1)$$

where $(\forall \alpha \in M)$ and $(\exists \alpha \in M)$ are the usual universal and existential quantifiers of mathematical logic, respectively, except for an explicit reminder that they range over only the finite universe of objects described in the model; and $R[\alpha]$ is any predicate, although it usually contains at least one occurrence of the symbol α among its arguments.

An $\in$*-quantification* of a string S is the string "Q[S]" where Q is any $\in$-quantifier. The first variable in Q is then called *bound* by the $\in$-quantification of S for all its occurrences in Q and in S, including occurrences as the second variable of other $\in$-quantifiers.

A *link-predicate* is defined recursively as follows:

i) A basic predicate is a link-predicate.

ii) The strings "$\nu_1 \in \nu_2$" and "$\nu_1 = \nu_2$," where ν_1 and ν_2 are any object-names or variables, are link-predicates.

iii) An $\in$-quantification of a link-predicate is a link-predicate. Link-predicates may be used to represent most of the relations which are represented by attribute links in the present version of SIR.

A well-formed-formula (wff) is defined recursively as follows:

i) A link-predicate is a wff.

ii) Any propositional function of wff's is a wff.

iii) Any $\in$-quantification of a wff is a wff.

An occurrence of a variable in a wff is called *free* if the occurrence is not bound by an $\in$-quantification of some string containing that occurrence.

A *sentence* $=_{df}$ a wff which contains no free variables.

An *object-predicate* $=_{df}$ a wff which contains exactly one free variable.

b. Logical system:

The *axioms* of SIR-1 are sentences which, under standard interpretation, describe properties of individual basic relations and specify type-"*d*" interactions between basic relations.

Any sentence in SIR-1 can be transformed into a sentence in the standard first-order predicate calculus (the "quantificational calculus") by putting each $\in$-quantifier into its "$\in$M" form by use of the equations 2.1, and then omitting the "$\in$M." All the usual deduction procedures of the quantificational calculus are acceptable deduction procedures in SIR-1. Therefore, any theorem provable from SIR-1 axioms in the quantificational calculus is also a theorem of SIR-1; i.e., it is a "true" sentence of SIR-1, provided "$\in$M's" are inserted into all quantifiers, regardless of the state of the current model. In other words, SIR-1 is *reducible* to the quantificational calculus. This reducibility provides us with methods – namely the methods of quantificational calculus, such as Subordinate Proof Derivation ("Natural Deduction") as others–for proving whether sentences of SIR-1 are *theorems*. However, we need different, more direct methods for testing the truth of SIR-1 sentences which depend on the model. These truth-testing methods must be implemented on the computer, for they constitute the basic question-answering mechanism of the generalized semantic information retrieval system. However, I shall first describe a totally impractical truth-testing method which demonstrates that a decision procedure exists for testing "truthhood" of SIR-1 sentences with respect to a particular SIR-1 model. A more efficient, heuristic approach will be described in Part 2.6.3.

The SIR-1 model is quite similar to the SIR model. It consists of a finite number of object names, each of which is "described" by a finite list of attribute-value pairs. Each attribute may name an object-predicate which is true of the described object, or it may be a link which relates the described object to another object. This latter object is named in the value corresponding to be given attribute. In 2.6.3 I shall describe the nature of SIR-1 attributes more precisely. For present purposes it is sufficient to assume that the information carried by each attribute on a property-list in the SIR-1 model can be expressed in some well-defined way as a SIR-1 sentence.

A SIR-1 sentence is considered "true" if the sentence can be deduced from the SIR-1 axioms and the information in the SIR-1 model.

A decision procedure for this deduction follows:

i) For each attribute in the model, write the SIR-1 sentence which expresses the same thing.

ii) Let A = the conjunction of all the sentences found in i) and of all the SIR-1 axioms. Consider the sentence

$$A \Rightarrow S \qquad (2.2)$$

where S is the sentence being tested.

iii) Put all ∈-quantifiers in equation 2.2 into the "∈M" form by using equation 2.1.

iv) Let $o_1, o_2, \ldots, o_n$ be the names of the objects described in the model. Eliminate the quantifiers in equation 2.2 by replacing each string of the form $(\forall \nu \in M)\,[R[\nu]]$, where ν is any variable and R is any predicate possibly depending on ν, with the finite conjunction

$$R[o_1] \wedge R[o_2] \wedge \cdots \wedge R[o_n];$$

and by replacing each string of the form $(\exists \nu \in M)[R[\nu]]$ with the disjunction

$$R[o_1] \vee R[o_2] \vee \ldots \vee R[o_n].$$

v) Test the resulting expression by a decision procedure for the propositional calculus, e.g., by truth-table analysis. *S* is true with respect to the model, and the question corresponding to *S* should be answered "YES ," if and only if this final expression is a theorem of the propositional calculus.

c. Examples and comments:

i) *Object-predicates:* As defined above, an object-predicate is a SIR-1 wff which contains exactly one free variable. If that free variable is replaced by an object-name, the object-predicate becomes a SIR-1 sentence. The standard interpretation of an object-predicate applied to an object in the SIR-1 model is that the sentence obtained by replacing the free variable in the predicate by the object-name is a true sentence. This resulting sentence may then be used as an additional axiom in any SIR-1 logical deduction procedure.

Object-predicates may be placed on the property-list of any object in the SIR-1 model. Their purposes are to describe those properties of the object which cannot easily be expressed, in terms of link-predicates, as specific associations with other objects.

ii) *Basic relations:* The "∈" relation occupies a special place in SIR-1 because of its connection with ∈-quantifiers, and is treated in the formalism as if it were a basic relation. The identity relation "=" is also treated as a basic relation because identity is a useful feature to have in a logical system based on the quantificational calculus. The SIR relation "equiv" was simply an equivalence relation used to identify when different object-names referred to the same object. In SIR-1 it is sufficient to subsume the function of "equiv" under the "=" sign; i.e., the formal statement "x=y" is considered to be true if either *x* and *y* are the same symbol, or if "equiv[*x*;*y*] " is a true predicate in the SIR model.

The predicates in Table 2-3.1 show the basic relations and the object-predicate needed by SIR-1 in order to deal with all the relations covered by SIR programs.

iii) *Connections between SIR and SIR-1 relations:* Table 2-3.2 lists a SIR-1 expression which should be used in place of each SIR predicate. Corresponding expressions have exactly the same interpretations; the SIR-1 statements are more complicated, but they utilize fewer basic symbols, and they show more logical structure than their SIR counterparts.

The SIR-1 link-predicate corresponding to "partg[x;y]" in Table c_2 has the interpretation, "Some x is part of every y." Although this is the interpretation used in most SIR question-answering subprograms, "partg[x;y]" might equally well be interpreted, "Every x is part of some y," in which case the SIR-1 link-predicate $(\forall\alpha\in x)(\exists\beta\in y)[\text{partb}[\alpha;\beta]]$ should be used. Actually the interpretation of "partg[x;y]" suggested in Table 2-1: "An x is part of a y," is ambiguous. This ambiguity occurs because the natural-language input system in the present version of SIR cannot discover the finer meanings of "An x is part of a y." Perhaps the most suitable representation for this latter sentence is a conjunction of two SIR-1 link-predicates

$$(\forall\beta\in y)(\exists\alpha\in x)[\text{partb}[\alpha;\beta]]\wedge(\forall\alpha\in x)(\exists\beta\in y)[\text{partb}[\alpha;\beta]]$$

Table 2-3.1. Basic Relations of SIR-1

Predicate	Standard Interpretation
$x\in y$	x is a member of the set y.
$x=y$	Either x and y are identical, or they are two names for the same object.
ownb[x;y]	x is owned by y.
partb[x;y]	x is part of y.
rightb[x;y]	x is to the right of y.
jrightb[x;y]	x is just to the right of y.
single[x]	$(\exists\alpha\in M)[\alpha\in x\wedge(\forall\beta\in M)[\beta\in x\Rightarrow\beta=\alpha]]$ (interpretation: x has exactly one member.)

Table 2-3.2. SIR Predicates Expressed in SIR-1

SIR predicate	SIR-1 expression
$x\subset y$	$(\forall\alpha\in x)[\alpha\in y]$
$x\in y$	$x\in y$
equiv[x;y]	$x=y$
owng[x;y]	$(\forall\beta\in y)(\exists\alpha\in x)[\text{ownb}[\alpha;\beta]]$
own[x;y]	$(\exists\alpha\in x)[\text{ownb}[\alpha;y]$
partg[x;y]	$(\forall\beta\in y)(\exists\alpha\in x)[\text{partb}[\alpha;\beta]]$
part[x;y]	$(\text{E}\alpha\in x)[\text{partb}[\alpha;y]]$
right[x;y]	$(\exists\alpha\in x)(\exists\beta\in y)[\text{rightb}[\alpha;\beta]]\wedge\text{single}[x]\wedge\text{single}[y]$
jright[x;y]	$(\exists\alpha\in x)(\exists\beta\in y)[\text{jrightb}[\alpha;\beta]]\wedge\text{single}[x]\wedge\text{single}[y]$

The SIR predicate "right[x;y]" was interpreted as "The x is to the right of the y." This English sentence implies first that x and y are each sets containing unique elements, and secondly that those elements bear a certain positional relationship to each other. In SIR the special subprogram "specify" was used to determine the nature of the sets involved, before the positional information was considered. Similarly, the SIR-1 expression must be the conjunction of the object-predicates "single[x]" and "single[y]" to describe the special nature of x and y, and the link-predicate whose interpretation is, "an x is to the right of a y." Similarly, object-predicates, as well as a link-predicate, are needed to represent the SIR "jright" relation.

iv) *Axioms of SIR-1:* Some useful properties of SIR-1 relations are defined as follows:

P is symmetric:

$\mathcal{S}(P) =df (\forall x \in M)(\forall y \in M)[P[x;y] \Rightarrow P[y;x]]$

P is asymmetric:

$\overline{\mathcal{S}}(P) =df (\forall x \in M)(\forall y \in M)[P[x;y] \Rightarrow \sim P[y;x]]$

P is reflexive:

$\mathcal{R}(P) =df (\forall x \in M)[P[x;x]]$

P is set-nonreflexive:

$\overline{\mathcal{R}}(P) =df (\forall x \in M) \sim (\forall \beta \in x)(\exists \alpha \in x)[P[\alpha;\beta]]$

P is transitive:

$\mathcal{T}(P) = df (\forall x \in M)(\forall y \in M)(\forall z \in M)[P[x;y] \wedge P[y;z] \Rightarrow P[x;z]]$

P is uniquely linked:

$\mathcal{U}(P) =df (\forall x \in M)(\forall y \in M)[P[x;y] \Rightarrow (\forall \alpha \in M)[[\alpha \neq y \Rightarrow \sim P[x;\alpha]] \wedge [\alpha \neq x \Rightarrow \sim P[\alpha;y]]]]$

Notice that these properties will be expressed by ordinary SIR-1 sentences when the bound variable "P" is replaced by the name of a SIR-1 relation.

Table 2-4 is a list of all the axioms necessary to give SIR-1 at least the question-answering ability of the SIR deduction procedures in Table 2-2, except for the "axioms" derived from object-predicates on the property-lists of particular objects. In Table 2-2, deduction procedures No. 1-4, 9-11, 14, and 15 all represent interactions with the "$\in$" or "$\subset$" relations, i.e., type "a" interactions. Corresponding axioms are not needed in SIR-1 because of the way "$\subset$" is defined (see Table 2-3.2) and the way $\in$-quantifiers are used. Table 2-2, Nos. 12 and 17 are interactions between "similar" relations, i.e., type "b" interactions. "Similar" relations are those which are defined in terms of a single basic relation in SIR-1. Additional axioms are not needed because information about interactions between "similar" relations are implicit in their definitions as link-predicates. Procedure No. 16 is really a statement of the transitivity of the basic part-whole relation (a type "c" interaction), somewhat obscured by a statement of the interaction between the similar "part" and "partg" relations (a type "b" interaction).

Table 2-4. SIR-1 Axioms

Axioms	Discussion
$\mathfrak{R}$ (=) $\mathfrak{T}$ (=) $\mathfrak{S}$ (=)	This fact that "=" is an equivalence relation is not strictly necessary in the axioms, since it is built into the logical system.
$\overline{\mathfrak{R}}$ (ownb) $\overline{\mathfrak{R}}$ (partb)	cf. Nos. 8 and 13, Table 2-2. These are "experimental" axioms, which should be dropped from the system if too many exceptions turn up.
$\mathfrak{T}$ (partb)	cf. No. 16, Table 2-2.
$\overline{\mathfrak{S}}$ (rightb)	cf. No. 18, Table 2-2.
$\mathfrak{T}$ (rightb)	cf. No. 19, Table 2-2.
$\mathfrak{U}$ (jrightb)	Nos. 21 and 22, Table 2-2, were needed because this property was missing.
$(\forall x \in M)\ (\forall y \in M)\ [\text{jrightb}[x;y] \Rightarrow \text{rightb}[x;y]]$	cf. No. 20, Table 2-2.
$(\forall x \in M)\ (\forall y \in M)\ (\forall z \in M)\ [\text{rightb}[x;y] \wedge \text{rightb}[y;z] \Rightarrow \sim \text{jrightb}[x;z]]$	cf. No. 21, Table 2-2.
	The last two axioms represent true type "d" interactions between *rightb* and *jrightb.*

Interactions 21 and 22 of Table 2-2 are of type "c," for they are due solely to the peculiar property of "jright" which is expressed in SIR-1 by $\mathfrak{U}$ (jrightb). Finally, Nos. 20 and 23 of Table 2-2 are true type "d" interactions, and corresponding axioms are necessary in SIR-1.

Let me now make this discussion more precise. The deductive systems of SIR and SIR-1 are both based on the quantificational calculus. The only difference between them is that the SIR deduction procedures in Table 2-2 are a description of the operation principles of an existing computer program. SIR-1 is a formally developed system which may eventually contribute to the specification for a computer program. If the SIR-1 system with its short list of axioms (Table 2-4) is already as effective a "yes-or-no" question-answerer as the programs described by the SIR procedures in Table 2-2, then adding those procedure rules to SIR-1 cannot increase the power of SIR-1. In other words, SIR-1 must already contain all the information available in the rules of Table 2-2. To prove that this is indeed the case, I have shown that SIR-1 sentences corresponding to each of the rules of Table 2-2 are *theorems* in SIR-1. The method used was to reduce the SIR-1 axioms and sentences to the quantificational calculus and then to prove the theorems by Subordinate Proof Derivations (Appendix 2.1). The details are given in Appendix 2.2.

v) *∈-quantifiers:* The most obvious difference between SIR-1 and the quantificational calculus is the occurrence in SIR-1 of ∈-quantifiers. These new symbols serve three functions, the most obvious but least important of which is notational conciseness. Since the value of any notational device depends upon its understandability, ∈-quantifiers are valuable because they indicate the intended interpretation of SIR-1 sentences to the user or reader. Finally, ∈-quantifiers are important for the computer implementation of SIR-1. They are indicators which relate the formal system to particular model search-procedures. Details of a proposed implementation scheme are presented in 2.6.3.

2.6.3 Implementation of the General Question-Answering System

A semantic information retrieval system which can be as effective as SIR and yet have the uniformity and generality of the SIR-1 formalism must have the following components:

i) a *model* patterned after the SIR model but containing more complete information in its linkages and containing a larger class of describable objects.
ii) a *theorem-proving program* which can determine whether certain assertions are true, on the basis of axioms of SIR-1 and current information in the model.
iii) a *programming language* for specifying question-answering procedures which are more complex than truth-testing.

In addition, these components must be designed to work together to form a compact, efficient system. A detailed description of each of these components of the proposed system will follow shortly.

A program to translate natural or restricted English into formal relational terms and a program to annex new relational information to the model are also necessary components of any semantic question-answering system. The latter annexing program is straightforward, and all the basic mechanisms are already available in SIR. English translation is a linguistic problem whose detailed study is beyond the scope of this paper. The trivial format-matching solution (Section 2.4) may be used until something better becomes available. In any case, I shall assume the availability of *some* mechanism for accepting new information in a form convenient to the human user and then inserting corresponding relational information into the model.

1. *The model:* As discussed in 2.1.2, one objective of this research is to find ways of using information stored in the model to control the operation of the system, since that information can be modified most easily. Since the operation of any theorem-proving program is "controlled" by the axioms of

the formal system involved, the axioms for SIR-1 should be stored in the model.

The SIR model consists of objects and associated property-lists. The advantage of this model structure is that the program using the model can obtain all the information about an object, such as how it is related to other objects simply by referring to the object itself. The SIR-1 axioms of Table 2-4 all describe either properties of SIR-1 basic relations or interactions between basic relations. These axioms should be stored, then, on the property-lists of the basic relations which they affect. In this way the theorem-proving program will be able to find relevant axioms by looking at the property-lists of the basic relations with which it is concerned, and the human user or programmer will be able to modify the axiom set by "telling" the system to modify its model, with no reprogramming necessary. Object-predicates define additional axioms which apply to particular objects. Therefore, they should be stored on the property-lists of the objects involved.

In SIR, a relation between objects is represented in the model by attribute-links on the property-lists of the objects. Each relation is uniquely represented by particular attributes. Simple (types "*a*" and "*b*") interactions between relations cannot be represented in the model; rather they have to be "known" by the program.

As has been shown, the class of SIR relations roughly corresponds to the class of relations represented in SIR-1 by link-predicates. Each link-predicate, in turn, is defined in terms of a SIR-1 basic relation. We must now decide how to represent relational information in the SIR-1 model.

Each basic relation could be uniquely represented by particular attributes. However, these attributes would not be sufficient to represent all the facts which were representable in SIR. For example, the sentence, "Every hand is part of a person," could be represented in SIR-1 by locating every object in the system which is a member of the set "hand," and linking each of them to some member of the set "person" with the attributes corresponding to the *partb* basic relation. However, it is not clear which hands should be parts of which persons; and the *general* fact concerning hands and persons would be unavailable for future deductions, e.g., when a new individual "person" is introduced into the model.

Alternatively, one could represent each possible link-predicate by a different attribute. The disadvantages of such a scheme would be twofold: First, much of the flexibility introduced by the definition and use of link-predicates would be lost, since special symbols would have to be assigned as attributes for each link-predicate actually used in a model; second, the important structure of the link-predicate, i.e., the basic predicate and $\in$-quantifiers of which it is composed, would be undiscoverable except by means of some table look-up or other decoding procedure.

I propose that, corresponding to the attribute-links of SIR, SIR-1 should use *descriptions* of the link-predicates involved. The *attribute* on the property-list of an object should itself be a property-list. This subproperty-list would contain special attributes whose values were the basic relation involved and the string of ∈-quantifiers which produce the link-predicate from that basic relation. An additional item on the subproperty-list could identify the argument-position of the described object, thus eliminating the need for more than one symbol (corresponding to the attribute-link symbols of SIR) for each basic relation. With this representation no special symbol assignment or other anticipatory action is necessary in order to add new link-predicates to the model. Any link-predicate recognized by the input program and based on an available basic relation is representable.

The names of object-predicates should be another kind of attribute which may appear on SIR-1 property-lists. The object-predicates should themselves by SIR-1 objects whose property-lists contain their definitions as SIR-1 wff's. In this way object-predicates may easily be defined or applied to new objects.

In summary, the basic objects in the SIR-1 model are the words which denote: individuals, classes, basic relations, and object-predicates. A property-list is associated with each basic object. Attributes in the descriptions of individuals and classes are either the names of object-predicates, or themselves property-lists which describe link-predicates. In lists describing link-predicates, the values corresponding to those attributes give the other objects associated with the described object through the described link-predicate. The property-lists of basic relations contain the axioms which specify properties of the described relations. The property-lists of object-predicates contain the definitions of the object-predicates in terms of SIR-1 wff's.

2. *The theorem-prover:* Part 2.2.2 presented a decision procedure for testing the truth of any SIR-1 sentence with respect to a given SIR-1 model. Unfortunately, that procedure is impractical, since it requires the enumeration of every object and every link in the model as well as the consideration of every known logical truth in the course of each truth-test. Clearly these procedures would involve an inordinate amount of time. Also, I have gone to great lengths to develop a model structure which enables the system to save time by having information organized and accessible in a convenient way; the decision procedure completely ignores the structure of the model.

Instead of an impractical decision procedure, I propose that SIR-1 use a heuristic Theorem-Proving program ("TP") for its truth-testing. TP will start its truth-testing with the most relevant axioms and model linkages, introducing additional facts only when needed. The model structure will dictate what constitutes "most relevant," as will be explained below.

The best example of a heuristic theorem-proving program is Newell and Simon's "Logic Theorist" (LT) (27), a program which proves theorems in the propositional calculus. Since TP will be modeled somewhat after LT, let us consider the general behavior of LT. LT must be given a list of true theorems or axioms and a statement (the "problem") whose proof is desired. The system tries to prove the test-statement by showing that it, or some statement from which it can easily be deduced, is a substitution instance of a true statement. The true statement must be either a theorem or a statement whose proof is easily obtained from the list of theorems. LT has several methods – the principal ones being called *chaining, detachment,* and *replacement* – for creating statements from which the problem statement can be deduced, and for selecting "relevant" theorems from the theorem list. LT also contains special devices for keeping track of sub-problems and keeping out of "loops."

LT was designed largely as a model of the behavior of naive students of logic and is reasonably successful as such. It has not been a very effective theorem-prover, partly because its methods and selection heuristics are not powerful enough, and partly because the problem domain, the propositional calculus, has a simple decision procedure (46) which makes any alternative approach seem weak. TP must deal with a problem domain more complicated than that of LT. It is concerned with a domain containing a possibly large, although finite, number of objects, relations, and axioms. Also, the objects and relations as well as the axioms may be changed from problem to problem. However, the actual proofs of SIR-1 sentences by TP will, on the average, be shorter and simpler than typical LT proofs. After all, TP parallels the human mechanisms for recalling facts in memory and doing some simple reasoning, not for solving formal mathematical problems. Development of elaborate logical ability in a computer must come after the achievement of our present goal: a mechanism for simple, human-like communication. Deductive methods similar to those of LT should be adequate for TP, provided we can furnish a mechanism for selecting the "most relevant" true facts from which to start each deduction; and of course the central information organizational device of SIR and SIR-1 – the model – is just such a mechanism.

I therefore propose that TP contain the same deductive methods as LT and in general be patterned after LT, with the following important exceptions:

a. In trying to apply its methods, LT always scans the complete list of true theorems. TP should initially attempt a proof with a small list of "most relevant" truths extracted from the model. If the proof methods fail, the list of truths should be gradually expanded until the "relevant" portion of the model is exhausted; or, more commonly, until the specified time or effort limits have been reached. One method of generating "relevant" truths for the proof of a SIR-1 sentence S is the following:

i) Let B= the set of all basic relations which appear in S. Let F= the set of all object-names in the model which appear in S as arguments of members of B.

ii) Construct a truth list consisting of three parts: those axioms which appear on the description lists of the basic relations in B, those link-predicates which involve relations in B and which are described by attributes of objects in F, and those axioms obtained from object-predicates which appear on the property-lists of objects in F.

If a proof cannot be found, the initial truth list can be expanded by enlarging B or F in any of the following ways, and then repeating step ii):

iii) Add the "∈" relation to B. This relation is important for deductions which involve transforming or removing ∈-quantifiers.
iv) Add to B any new basic relations which appear in the current truth list. Whenever basic relations interact, an axiom on the property-list of one will name the other, thereby introducing it into the system. Also, axioms from object-predicates may introduce new basic relations.
v) Add to F all object-names which appear in *values* of those attributes of objects already named in F, which involve relations already named in B.

Each iteration of step iv) or v) and step ii) will add facts to the truth list which are more indirectly related to the test sentence than any facts previously available. When no new facts can be added in this way, the truth list will contain all the information in the model which may be relevant for the desired proof. However, I expect that in most cases true sentences will be provable from a truth list obtained in very few iterations.

b. SIR-1 is concerned with the truth of relational statements *with respect to the model*, whereas LT is concerned with the *universal truth* of logical propositions. The ultimate test of the truth of a sentence in LT is whether or not the sentence is a substitution instance of a known sentence. The corresponding ultimate test of the truth of most SIR-1 sentences is whether or not certain links exist in the model. Every SIR-1 sentence is a propositional function of link-predicates. A link-predicate is true of the model if it exists as an explicit link in the model, or if it can be deduced from axioms or higher-order link-predicates explicit in the model. Therefore, for the ultimate test of the truth of a link-predicate, TP must contain subprograms for eliminating ∈-quantifiers. For example, $(\forall\alpha\in x)\ [P[\alpha]]$ is true of the model if $P[\mu]$ is true of the model, for every object μ such that $\mu\in x$ is true of the model. Thus, the ∈-quantifier structure of SIR-1 sentences serves as an important guide for the theorem-proving program.

c. The problem of implementing the "Exception Principle," discussed in Part 3.c of 2.6.1 for SIR, is still with us in SIR-1. This means that the use of different sets of "truths" extracted from the model may lead to different answers to the same question. The solution to this problem is simply to be very careful in building and expanding the list of "truths" used by TP. I believe the iteration described in (a) above is adequate, since it introduces the most closely related facts first. However, some experimentation in this area, once a working TP system is developed, will certainly be of interest.

In summary, an English question should be answered "yes" by the generalized semantic information retrieval system if and only if TP can prove the truth, with respect to the model, of the SIR-1 sentence which corresponds to the question. TP attempts to prove the truth of sentences by going through the following steps:

i) Test whether the sentence is immediately implied by direct links in the model.
ii) Create a list of the axioms and link-predicates in the model which are most closely related to the sentence. Attempt to deduce the truth of the sentence from this list of truths, using both logical transformation methods such as those of LT, and model-dependent methods such as elimination of ∈-quantifiers.
iii) After a reasonable amount of effort, add to the list of truths the axioms and link-predicates which are next-most-closely related to the sentence.
Repeat steps ii) and iii) until proof is completed or abandoned.

Note that TP operates in the finite domain of the propositional calculus. No provision has been make for true quantificational deductions, such as proving in general

$$(\exists y)(\forall x)\,P[x,y] \Rightarrow (\forall x)(\exists y)\,P[x,y]$$

Therefore TP could not, for example, perform the derivations of Appendix 2.2 which relate SIR and SIR-1. The problem which TP *does* attack is that of selecting relevant information from a large (although finite) store in order to construct proofs efficiently. Of course, a similar program for quantificational deduction would be a welcome addition to TP.

3. *Complex question-answering:* Some of the questions which SIR can answer require the system to perform more elaborate information retrieval tasks than simply testing the truth of an assertion. The answers to questions like, "How many fingers does John have?" and "Where is the book?" must be computed by searching and manipulating the data stored in the model in order to *create* appropriate responses.

Let us define a "question type" as a class of questions whose answers are found by following the same computational procedure. Questions of the same type generally differ from each other by referring to different objects in the model; those object-names are inputs to the computational procedure. In the previous sections we have considered the special type of all "yes-or-no" questions. In SIR, this class of questions was considered to be made up of many different question types – one for each SIR relation – and there was a corresponding multiplicity of computational procedures. In SIR-1, the computational procedure for all "yes-or-no" questions is simply TP. However, TP requires as an input not just the names of objects but rather the complete SIR-1 sentence which corresponds to the question.

Unfortunately, no other SIR question types can be combined easily for a more general system. Each question type requires a different procedure for searching through the network of links, identifying useful information when it is found, and manipulating the information to produce the answer. Computer programming languages are well suited for specifying computational procedures and, for reasons described in 2.3.1, the LISP language was quite convenient for specifying the complex question-answering procedures of SIR. However, as one attempts to enlarge and generalize SIR it becomes obvious that these programs should be made easier to write and easier to understand wherever possible. The full generality of LISP must be kept available, since new question types may require, in the answering process, unanticipated kinds of data manipulation; but the devices described below may be used to simplify the construction of question-answering programs.

In LISP, the flow of control within a program is normally determined by special functions called "predicates." The LISP system evaluates each predicate according to built-in or separately provided evaluation procedures, and chooses the next operation to be performed according to whether the value of the predicate is "T" or "NIL" (corresponding to "true" or "false"). The SIR-1 procedure-specification language should be similar to LISP, but should also allow the use of an additional class of predicates: namely, statements whose LISP values are "T" if a particular SIR-1 sentence is true with respect to the model, and "NIL" otherwise. The procedure for evaluating these additional predicates would be just the procedure ordinarily used by SIR for determining the truth of SIR-1 sentences, namely TP. Thus the full power of the SIR "yes-or-no" type of question-answering procedure could automatically be used within the procedure for answering a more complex type of question. Suppose that in the course of the procedure for answering the question, "What is the relative position of x?" it is determined that y is to the right of x and also that a z is to the right of x. The procedure could then contain the statement:

if $(\exists \alpha \in z)[\text{rightb}[\alpha;x] \wedge \text{rightb}[y;\alpha]]$ *then* go A *else* go B where A and B are locations of appropriate further instructions in the procedure. The procedure writer need not consider how to answer the question, "Is a z between x and y?" for TP will do that for him.

As a special application of this method for procedure-writing, let us consider how to obtain "no" or "sometimes" answers to questions of the "yes-or-no" type. The existence of separate programs for each relation in SIR permitted the consideration of special properties of the relation in determining an appropriate reply. In our generalized system, TP can reply "yes" if the SIR-1 sentence S corresponding to the question is provable; otherwise the reply must be "insufficient information." Although a "no" answer cannot be obtained by TP directly, we *can* build into TP the ability to make a negative reply if it determines that the sentence $\sim$S is provable; but no general change to TP can account for special properties of individual relations. However, this flexibility of SIR is recovered in the generalized system, without relinquishing any of the uniformity and generality of the SIR-1 formalism and the TP program, by the use of simple procedures written in the LISP-plus-TP specification language. For example, the procedure for answering the question, "Is an x a y?" might be as follows:

if $(\forall\alpha\in x)[\alpha\in y]$ *then* YES;
else if $(\forall\alpha\in x)[\sim\alpha\in y]$ *then* NO;
else if $(\forall\alpha\in y)[\alpha\in x]$ *then* SOMETIMES;
else (INSUFFICIENT INFORMATION)

There remains the problem of implementing the specification language on a computer. When TP is available, it will be a simple matter to design an interpreter which would route control between TP and the LISP interpreter. Whether a compiler for these procedures is feasible depends on many factors, including the precise form of the TP system. The point here is that implementation of this procedure-specification language, a key part of the generalized semantic question-answerer, *is* feasible at the present state of the programming art.

In summary, a simple formalism has been presented which adds to LISP the truth-testing power of TP. This procedure-specification language, together with the SIR-1 formalism, a corresponding word-association model structure, and the TP truth-testing program, constitute the basis for a "generalized" semantic information retrieval system. On the basis of information gleaned from the development of SIR, I have been able to describe this "generalized" system which has all the question-answering ability of SIR and accepts a much larger class of questions. More importantly, new relations can be added to the "generalized" system, the axioms of its proof procedure can be modified without any reprogramming, and question-answering procedures can be introduced and modified much more easily than they can be in SIR.

2.7 Conclusions

2.7.1 Results

1. *Question-answering effectiveness:* Section 2.1 described how question-answering behavior is a measure of a computer system's ability to "understand." SIR represents "meanings" in the form of a word-association, property-list model. As a result SIR is more general, more powerful, and, judging from its conversational ability, more "intelligent" than any other existing question-answering system. With respect to the fundamental problems of the other systems discussed in Section 2.2:

a) SIR is not limited to a rigid prepared data structure and corresponding programs with specific, built-in, *ad hoc* definitions of "meanings" as is the

"Baseball" program. Rather, it constructs its data structure as information is presented to it, and interprets "meanings" from "learned" word associations.
b) SIR is not restricted to the sentence-by-sentence matching of Phillips' "Question-Answering Routine" (31). Instead, the SIR model provides access to *relevant* stored facts in a direct, natural way.
c) SIR, unlike SYNTHEX, does not require grammatical analyses which be-become more detailed and more complicated as the system expands. Instead, question-answering is based on *semantic* relationships, and the program structure can be *simplified* while enlarging the scope of the system in the manner described in Section 2.6.
d) The SIR model is not tailored for a single concept like the family relationships of SAD-SAM. However, the property-list structure of the model can easily be used to represent various special-purpose models and thus take advantage of their benefits, while permitting the storage of *any* relational information.
e) The SIR system is not restricted to testing the universal truth of a complete statement, regardless of the meanings of its components, as is Darlington's program (12). Rather, SIR procedures can be devised to answer any form of question, and the answers are based on SIR's current "knowledge" as determined by word associations in the model.
f) Although conceptually similar to Bennett's word relation system (2), SIR represents a vast improvement in that its list-structure model permits a direct representation for arbitrary word relations; the system contains programs for handling several different relations and their interactions; and both input formats and program logic may easily be modified.

2. *Communication language:* SIR provides a framework for reasonably natural communication between people and computers. Although somewhat stilted, both the input and the response languages used by SIR are sufficiently close to natural English to be easily understood by an untrained human. The input format recognition process used in SIR (Part 2.4.2) illustrates how far one may go toward "understanding" natural language, in the sense of recognizing word associations, without reference to grammatical structure. Of course, such a scheme cannot be generalized to cover any large portion of a natural language. It was used here simply as a device to get past the input phase and into the problems of representation and retrieval. However, this format matching process can easily be expanded to handle any sufficiently small portion of English.

Even in its present primitive state the process is not excessively restrictive to the untrained user. With the present system, the user could be instructed to present in complete English sentences simple facts and questions and not to use any sentences with subordinate clauses, adjectives, conjunctions, or commas. These sentences may be about class relations, part-whole relations (possibly involving numbers), possessions, and left-to-right ordering relations. When used in a time-sharing environment (11) in which each sentence receives an immediate response, the system would have the effect of a "teaching machine" in training its user to restrict himself to recognizable sentence forms.

After a few trial runs the programmer can easily add any new sentence forms which frequently arise, thus improving the chances of success for the next user. If this training process is too slow, the new user could study sample conversations from previous tests or refer to an outline of available formats before composing new statements to SIR. These processes are much simpler than learning a "programming" language. A sorted list of formats and more sophisticated similarity tests in the matching procedure would allow the addition of many more formats to the system with no corresponding increase in time required for recognition.

At the output end, the system demonstrates that "intelligent" responses are frequently possible without an elaborate generative grammar, as long as one can anticipate the classes of responses and frame each class in a suitable format.

3. *The model:* An important feature of SIR is the flexibility of the property-list structure of the model. Independent or related facts can automatically be added to or extracted from the system, and the same data may be expressed in more than one way.

Several existing computer systems, e.g., airline reservation systems, permit dynamic fact storage and retrieval. However, they depend upon the use of fixed, unique representations for the information involved. In SIR, there can be many representations which are equally effective in providing correct answers. For example, the system "knows" that the statement, "A finger is part of John" is true if (a) there is an explicit part-whole link from FINGER to JOHN; or if (b) there are links by means of which the retrieval programs can deduce that a finger is part of a person and John is a person; or if (c) there are links by means of which the retrieval programs can deduce that a finger is part of a hand, and a hand is part of John; and so on. In addition, the system can automatically translate from one representation to another having some advantages. For example, the "streamline" operation described in Part 2.5.2, reduces storage-space requirements by removing redundancy in the representation without making any changes in the system.

The property-list model turns out to have advantages even when another form of model seems more natural. For example, left-to-right spatial relations seem most easily represented by a linear ordering; i.e., "x is to the left of y" could be modeled by placing x ahead of y in a left-to-right list. However, incomplete information can cause trouble for such a model. If it is known that "x is to the left of y" and "z is to the left of y," the linear ordering system cannot uniquely model the relative positions of x, y, and z. The property-list system, on the other hand, represents exactly the relations which are known; and the linear ordering of the objects can be *deduced* from the property-list model, as is done in SIR by the "locate" function, if the data is sufficiently complete.

4. *Present state:* The processing time per statement for the SIR system

with a standard LISP configuration on an IBM 7094 computer with 32K words of memory was about one second. All the examples prepared for Figs. 2-1 and 2-5, including loading and compiling all programs, took about 6 minutes of computer time. The SIR system, with all the relations, processing programs, and language formats described in this chapter utilizes almost the full capacity of the computer.

It must be remembered that the SIR system was not designed to solve any particular practical question-answering problem. It consists of a collection of relations which were introduced, as described in Part 2.3.4, in order to investigate the various features and possibilities of the model. These relations do not necessarily bear any other useful or logical relationships to each other.

Although cramped for memory space, the present system has been successful in the sense that it has demonstrated the usefulness of the word-association, property-list model, and it has suggested the more general system described in Section 2.6, which extends the uses of the same model.

The scope of the present system indicates that it *would* be feasible to use the SIR model and present program organization in a practical information retrieval system for an IBM 7090 size computer, provided the system involves a reasonably small number of relations whose interactions are clearly understood. One possible application is a retrieval system which has been proposed at the RAND Corporation for information about documents in Soviet cybernetics (24). In that system the users will be interested in indirect relationships and implications, as well as the storage and retrieval of specific facts concerning authors and subjects of technical papers.

5. *Question-answering details:* The following points, although obvious in hindsight, did not become apparent until the program was fairly well developed:

a) A question-answering system cannot give definite negative replies without special information about the completeness and consistency of its data. The fact that SIR does not have such information accounts for frequent occurrences of the "INSUFFICIENT INFORMATION" response in places where a clearcut "NO" would be preferred.

b) If x stands in relation R to y, then a one-way link, e.g., from x to y through attribute $R1$ on the property-list of x, may be sufficient for most question-answering applications. However, in the course of expanding the system the reverse link, from y to x through attribute $R2$ on the y property-list may be much more convenient. To allow for any eventuality in a general system, both links should be furnished from the start. Two-way links also provide the accessibility needed to experiment with various tree-searching procedures.

c) It is frequently possible for search procedures, even when unsuccessful, to provide extremely useful information to the user or programmer by specifying *why* they were unsuccessful. This point is discussed further in Part 2.4.3.

2.7.2 Extensions of SIR.

1. *Adding relations:* Two major obstacles, in addition to computer memory size, stand in the way of extending a SIR-like system by adding new relations and their associated programs: (a) the problem of interaction between a new relation and those already in the system, requiring modifications throughout the system for even minor additions; and (b) the problem of the time required to search through trees of words linked by relations. This time apparently must grow exponentially as the number of relations increases.

The problem of interactions can best be overcome by replacing SIR with a generalized system. As discussed in Section 2.6, this change would greatly reduce the interaction problem and simplify the introduction of new relations. In addition, the programs would probably be significantly smaller in the generalized system. Not only would all "yes-or-no" type question-answering programs be replaced by a single, "theorem-proving" program; in addition, the procedure-specification language of the generalized system would result in more compact as well as more readable programs.

The other obstacle to the expansion of a semantic information retrieval system is the same one which occurs in programs for theorem proving, game playing, and other areas of artificial intelligence: the problem of searching through an exponentially growing space of possible solutions. Here there is no basic transformation that can be made to avoid the mathematical fact that the number of possible interconnections between elements is an exponential function of the number of elements involved. This means that in SIR the time required to search for certain relational links increases very rapidly with both the number of individual elements which can be linked and the number of different relations which can do the linking. However, many of the heuristics for reducing search effort which have been suggested in other areas concerned with tree-structured data can be applied here.

In the first place, relations seem to be divided into independent (non-interacting) groups; e.g., spatial relations are quite independent of temporal relations. The search space affected by a new relation is really just the space of *interacting* relations, which may be a very small subset of the total space of relations. The axioms of the generalized system can be used to identify the groups of interacting relations. Secondly, the existence of two-way links permits the search for a path between two points in the data structure to proceed from either end (whichever is likely to produce a more efficient search), or possibly from both ends simultaneously, toward an unknown common point. Finally, semantic information in the model might be useful in suggesting intermediate points to use as "stepping stones" in a larger tree search, thus greatly reducing the search effort. I believe that the use of these and similar heuristic devices, along with expected increases in computer speed and memory size and the introduction of parallel processing computer hardware, will make a large-scale semantic information retrieval system practical.

2. *Adjectives and n-ary relations:* All the relations in the present system are binary relations. The model can be extended to handle arbitrary *n*-ary relations as follows:

a. Unary operators could be simply flags on the property-lists of the objects to which they apply. Or, if for purposes of uniformity we forbid the use of flags, then they could be attributes whose values are always a dummy symbol which indicates that the attribute is to be interpreted as a unary operator. In handling adjectives, the following decision would have to be made: Should an adjective be modeled by a unary operator, or should it be the value of some attribute? For example, "little red schoolhouse" could be represented in the model in any of the following ways:

i) An object which is an element of the set "SCHOOLHOUSE", and which has on its property list the flags "LITTLE" and "RED".
ii) The same object, which has on its property list the attribute "MODIFIERS" with associated value "(LITTLE, RED)".
iii) The same object, which has on its property list the attribute-value pairs "(SIZE, LITTLE)" and "(COLOR, RED)".
The second representation is equivalent to the first but avoids the need for unary operators. The third representation contains the most information and is most consistent with the present form of the SIR model, but it has the disadvantage that it requires the use of a dictionary to establish appropriate classifications of adjectives. The "best" representation to use would have to be determined by experimentation and would depend upon the organization of the information retrieval programs which use the model.

b. Trinary (e.g., those involving transitive verbs) and higher order relations could be represented in various ways analogous to the treatment of binary relations. For example, the *n*-ary relation *R* can be factored into *n* relations *R1, R2, . . . , Rn,* such that

$$\langle x_1, x_2, \ldots, x_n \rangle \in \mathrm{R} \text{ if and only if}$$
$$\langle x_2, \ldots, x_n \rangle = \mathrm{R1}[x_1] \wedge \langle x_1, x_3, \ldots, x_n \rangle = \mathrm{R2}[x_2] \wedge$$
$$\cdots \wedge \langle x_1, x_2, \ldots, x_{n-1} \rangle = \mathrm{Rn}[x_n]$$

where the value of the attribute *Rj* on the property list of *xj* would be the ordered sequence $\langle x_1, \ldots, x_{j-1}, x_{j+1}, \ldots, x_n \rangle$. More specifically, the trinary relation established by the statement, "John gave a book to Jim" could be factored into the three relations "GIVER", "GIVEN", and "GETTER". The property-list of "JOHN" would have the pair "(GIVER, (BOOK, JIM))", the property-list describing "BOOK" would contain "(GIVEN, (JOHN, JIM))", and "(GETTER, (JOHN, BOOK))" would be placed on "JIM's" property-list. Once again, the practicality and efficiency of such a representation can only be discovered by developing and experimenting with working computer programs.

3. *Next steps:* The present SIR system, and its generalized version discussed in Section 2.6, are only first steps toward a true "understanding" machine. Eventually we must solve the "advice-taker" problem (22), which involves controlling the operation of the machine merely by "advising" it, in a suitable English-like language, of the desired procedures or results.

One approach to the "advice-taker" is to develop programs which can produce other programs in accordance with simple instructions. Such program-writing programs could be an outgrowth of current work on computer language "compilers," if the input and output forms are sufficiently well-defined. Simon (39) is working on this approach by developing a system which accepts a broad range of English statements as input to such a program-writing program.

SIR suggests an alternative approach. Rather than developing a program which writes other programs to do specified tasks, I propose we develop a single, general program which can do any task provided the program is properly controlled by information in its model. "Giving advice" would then require only the relatively simple process of inserting appropriate control information into the model. The SIR model provides its programs with information about the truth of particular relations between specific objects. The model in the generalized system also provides the "theorem-prover" program with axioms which describe properties of relations and interactions between relations. The next generalization should involve adding to the model information which will specify and control theorem-proving and model-searching procedures for the program.

After these two approaches to an "understanding" machine have been developed independently, they should be synthesized. The program-writing program should be incorporated into the general program of the model-dependent system. The resulting system would then be able to construct arbitrary procedure specifications, in accordance with simple instructions which had been placed in its model.

Ultimately, the "intelligent" machine will have to be able to abstract from the information in its model, "realize" the necessity for additional action, and create the necessary instructions for itself. The design of such an "artificial intelligence" awaits the development of automatic concept formation and inductive inference systems (20, 41) as well as the generalizations of SIR described.

2.7.3 Programming

1. *Value of programming:* Many of the results and conclusions written

after the development of a large computer program such as SIR frequently appear as if they could have been established without the tedious effort of programming. This is rarely true, and in fact, new systems which are described as complete "except for the programming" usually require fundamental modifications if and when they are translated into operating programs. The reasons for the importance of actually writing the program include the following:

a. Without a program it is extremely difficult to tell whether the specifications for a system are really complete and consistent. Crucial decisions may be considered minor details, and contradictions may go unnoticed, until one is compelled to build an operating system.
b. The process of programming not only turns up fallacies in the specifications for a system, but also generally suggests ways for avoiding them and improving the system. Thus programming can be much more valuable than just searching for errors in the original specification. A completed "debugged" programmed system usually turns out to be a compromise between the system as it was originally specified, a simpler system which was more feasible to actually construct, and a more elaborate system whose new features were thought of during the programming process. This resulting system is frequently as useful and certainly more reliable than the originally specified system; in addition it may suggest the design of even more advanced systems. With SIR, for example, methods for implementing the "exception principle" and resolution of ambiguities arose from the design of the basic question-answerer, and the specifications for the generalized system of Section 2.6 are based largely on properties of the final, working SIR system.
c. The programming process frequently turns up insights which might not otherwise be discovered (see for example paragraph 5 in 2.7.1).
d. Finally, the resulting program provides at the same time a demonstration of the feasibility of the ideas upon which it is based, a measure of the practicality of the system in terms of time and space requirements, and an experimental device for testing variations in the original specifications.

2. *Uniformity of representation:* A uniform tree linkage and search procedure would simplify coding and allow the programmer to concentrate on the more important problems of program organization and search strategies. Such a standard representation would have to be flexible enough to handle the most complicated cases. In SIR, the uniform use of only type-3 links or all property-lists and only type-1 links on all sub-property-lists would probably achieve the desired result. An alternative, somewhat more complicated (but more economical of storage) way to achieve the same result of freeing the programmer from concern for details, would be to allow several kinds of linkages to be used wherever they were best suited (e.g., type-1, -2, and -3 links), but require all retrieval programs to be able to recognize the type of a link and treat each one appropriately.

If this alternative of allowing the use of several types of linkages were used in the generalized system, the nature of the links appropriate for particular relations could be stored in the model on the property-lists of the relations. In this way the type-identification would be readily available to the retrieval programs.

3. *Programming tree search:* In order to handle some of the retrieval processes I had to develop some general tree-tracing functions. The facility in the LISP language for defining functions of functional arguments permitted the design of programs providing a powerful ability to specify complex search procedures. For example, one of the most useful functions was "find [start; link; test] ," where "start" can be any word in the model structure, "link" specifies which attribute to use to find succeeding words, and "test" is the name of a function to be applied in turn to each word reachable from "start" along the kind of path specified by "link." If the value of "test" applied to a word is the special symbol "NIL," the search continues; otherwise the value of "find" itself. For example, in testing whether every A is part of some B, we may contain the word which satisfied the test and the successful path, i.e., the list of words which link "start" to the selected word in the desired way. Note that the function "find" can be cascaded, i.e., "test" can be another application of "find" itself. For example, in testing whether every A is part of some B, we may wish to test whether there is a class *u* such that every A is a *u* and every *u* is part of some B. This test is carried out simply by executing the following function (given in LISP metalanguage notation) and testing whether or not its value is "NIL":

find[A; SUPERSET; λ[[*u*] [find [*u*; SUPERPART-OF-EACH; λ[[*v*] [*v*=B]] ;B]]]].

If a uniform representation (as described in paragraph 2) had been used throughout SIR, then it would have been easy to develop a complete set of general network-tracing functions like "find." Such a set of functions could be the basis for a language which makes programming tree- and network-searching systems much simpler than it is now. Such a language might thus contribute to research in the areas of pattern recognition, game-playing (36), and network analysis as well as of semantics and information retrieval. Note that the success or failure of an application of the function "find" depends only on the connectivity of the network; the *order* in which nodes are generated and tested, and therefore the efficiency of the system for various kinds of networks must be decided in advance and built into the definition of the function.

4. *Program simplification:* The "procedures" presented in Part 2.5.1 which were described as "rough flow charts" for the retrieval programs may seem unnecessarily complicated. This is true for the following reasons:

a. Each procedure was written as an explanation of how a particular program operates, and the place of these programs in the over-all program structure was de-emphasized to avoid confusion. There is much more hierarchical structure and use of common subroutines in the actual SIR program than is indicated in those procedures.
b. As with most programming tasks, many possible simplifications occur to the programmer as after thoughts. If I started over now, I could certainly construct a neater, more compact SIR system, especially by incorporating some of the ideas discussed in paragraphs 2 and 3. However, I would be more inclined to ignore SIR altogether and instead start programming the generalized system of Section 2.6.
c. Unfortunately, many of the "simple" reasoning procedures the program must go through really *are* complicated. It was surprising to me how many possible routes one may take to deduce a simple fact, like "A is part of B."

2.7.4 Subjects for Future Experiments

1. *Search procedures:* The relative merits of different tree-searching procedures should be investigated, since any device which significantly reduced search effort would be a valuable contribution to the practicality of SIR-like systems. In seeking a path between two nodes, for example, one might compare the procedure of alternately moving one ply from each end and looking for a common node, with the procedure of continually branching out from one node and searching for the other. Even this latter procedure can be performed in either a "breadth first" or a more naturally recursive "depth first" manner. While the first procedure cuts the effective depth of a successful search in half, it also introduces matching problems in recognizing success and makes it more difficult to discover the complete successful path. Which of the various procedures is "best" will depend on the size of the networks, the relative frequency of success, the average length of successful paths, and so on. Therefore the best way to determine the most efficient methods is to experiment on an operating system, preferably with respect to a particular problem area.

2. *Linkage structure:* The optimum number of explicit links needed should be investigated. One might expect a trade-off here between space and time; i.e., that a removal of redundant links, for instance by "streamlining" operations, should save storage at the expense of increasing the average question-answering time, while introducing redundant links, for instance by adding as explicit links all question-answers which are successfully obtained, should use up space but speed up the question-answering process. However, this trade-off is not strictly necessary. Explicit links save time only when they provide correct answers; otherwise they use time by requiring spurious parts of the network to be searched. Which redundant links to weed out, as

well as which search procedure to use, depends on the characteristics of the model and questions in a particular application and must be determined by experimentation.

Another structuring problem to be considered is that of consistency. At present SIR tries to test the consistency of each input sentence with the information it already has stored, before adding the new relations to the model. It might be more efficient to blindly accept each input sentence independently, and then check the consistency of the model from time to time, say between input sentences, "complaining" if problems occur. This procedure would give later information equal precedence with earlier inputs, which might be a preferred arrangement for some applications.

3. *Ambiguity in language:* A system similar to SIR could be used as a basis for a study of ambiguity in language. The example given above in Part 2.5.2 shows how SIR can resolve an ambiguous word meaning on the basis of related word meanings. Similarly an expanded version of SIR might be able to resolve ambiguous sentence structure on the basis of the meanings (or, more precisely, the contents of the property-lists) of the words in the sentence. Thus the system could be as effective as people in recognizing the structural difference between sentences like, "Bring me the bottle of milk which is sour," and "Bring me the bottle of milk which is cracked." Such a study might contribute to our knowledge of the use of language and of how people resolve ambiguities. It could investigate how much semantic or contextual information is needed to resolve ambiguities which give people trouble, such as "They are flying planes."

4. *Simulation:* The behavior of SIR in answering questions and resolving ambiguities suggests that the program "understands the meanings" of the words in its model. The information SIR associates with a word by means of the property-list of the word is analogous to the information a person associates with an object by means of a "mental image" of the object. Perhaps we can carry this analogy further and say that, since certain aspects of the behavior of SIR are similar to human behavior, the representation and manipulation of data within SIR is similar (at the information processing level) to the representation and manipulation procedures a person carries out when "thinking."

Psychologists have simulated on a computer human problem-solving behavior (28) and the process of memorizing nonsense syllables (14). Perhaps SIR can be considered a simulation of the human process of learning and thinking about coherent facts. Psychological experiments would have to be devised to test this theory by testing more precisely the similarity of SIR's behavior to human behavior. In the process we might obtain valuable ideas for both improving the model and understanding human cognitive processes.

Appendix 2.1 Notation

A.2.1.1 Basic Symbols

The purpose of this section is to present some of the formal logical terminology used in this chapter. In the following list, the use of various symbols will be explained by means of definitions, examples, or statements of interpretation.

Symbol	*Explanation*
$\ldots$	and so forth
A,B,C, . . .	meta-symbols standing for any logical formulas
$\sim \wedge \vee \Rightarrow \Leftrightarrow$	the propositional connectives
$\sim$A	not A; A is false
A$\wedge$B	A and B (are both true)
A$\vee$B	A or B or both
A$\Rightarrow$B	A implies B
A$\Leftrightarrow$B	A if and only if B
$x,y,z,\ldots$	variables; names of unknown objects or sets
$\alpha,\beta,\gamma,\ldots$	constants; names of particular objects or sets
$\alpha\in x$	α is a member of the set x
$x\subset y$	set x is contained in set y
$\alpha\in x$	$\sim[\alpha\in x]$; α is not a member of the set x
$x=y$	x and y are the same object or set
$x\neq y$	$\sim[x=y]$
$\forall$	universal quantifier symbol
$(\forall x)$	universal quantifier
$(\forall x)$A	A is true for all values of x
$\exists$	existential quantifier symbol
$(\exists x)$	existential quantifier
$(\exists x)$A	there exists an x such that A is true
$\{\alpha,\beta,\gamma,\ldots\zeta\}$	an unordered set of the objects named
$<\alpha,\beta>$	the ordered pair of the objects named
$=df$	equals by definition; is defined to be

A.2.1.2 Subordinate Proof Derivation

"Subordinate proof" is a method for proving logical deductions in the first-order predicate calculus ("the quantificational calculus"). The formulation outlined here is due to Prof. Hartley Rogers, Jr. It is similar to the system of "general inference" described by Suppes (43).

Definition: Subordinate Proof Derivation of a formula B from a finite (possibly empty) set of formulas $\mathcal{A}$ is defined to be an arrangement of formulas and long brackets satisfying the conditions:

1) The first k lines of the derivation consist of the formulas of $\mathcal{A}$.
2) Given n lines of the derivation, the $n+1^{st}$ line may consist of any formula whatever, if a new long bracket is begun to the left of that formula inside all existing brackets not previously terminated.
Definition: In a Subordinate Proof Derivation, line j is called an *ancestor* of line l if $j<l$ and line j occurs inside no long brackets other than those containing line l.
3) Given n lines of a derivation, the $n+1^{st}$ line may consist of a formula A (without a new long bracket) if
i) A is a known true theorem,
ii) A is implied, in the propositional calculus, by any set of formulas in ancestor lines to the $n+1^{st}$ line, or
iii) A can be obtained from a formula in an ancestor line by an allowable use of the method of US, UG, ES, EG, I1, or I2.
Definitions: Let A be any formula, and let $\underline{\alpha}$ and $\underline{\beta}$ be terms.
$A^{\alpha}_{\beta} = df$ of the formula obtained from A by substituting $\underline{\beta}$ for every *free* occurrence of $\underline{\alpha}$ in A, *i.e.*, for every occurrence of $\underline{\alpha}$ not within the scope of a quantifier containing $\underline{\alpha}$.
US $=df$ Universal Specification, by which $(\forall\alpha)A$ becomes A^{α}_{β}.
UG $=df$ Universal Generalization, by which A becomes $(\forall\alpha)A$.
ES $=df$ Existential Specification, by which $(\exists\alpha)A$ becomes A^{α}_{γ}.
EG $=df$ Existential Generalization, by which A becomes $(\exists\beta)A^{\alpha}_{\beta}$.
I1 $=df$ A rule which allows insertion of a formula of the form $\alpha=\alpha$.
I2 $=df$ A rule by which $\{\alpha=\beta, A\}$ leads to A^{α}_{β}.
Certain conditions restrict the allowable usage of most of these quantifier transformation methods. These conditions, which relate to conflicts between variable interpretations and dependencies between constants, are too involved to present in this outline.
4) An innermost long bracket may be terminated at (and including) the nth line if we write as the $n+1^{st}$ line $[A \Rightarrow C]$ where A and C are, respectively, the first and last formulas in the long bracket in question.
5) An innermost long bracket may be terminated at the nth line if that bracket begins with a formula $\sim A$ and has for its last two lines C and $\sim C$, for some formula C, if we write A as the $n+1^{st}$ line.
6) The last line has no long brackets and is the formula B.
Main Theorem (given here without proof): If there is a Subordinate proof Derivation of B from $\mathcal{A}$, then B is quantificationally deducible from $\mathcal{A}$.

Appendix 2.2 Derivations of SIR Deduction Procedures

Each of the 23 deduction procedures listed in Table 2-2 is a theorem of the SIR-1 formal system. The proofs presented below generally consist of four statements:

i) The SIR deduction procedure, as stated in Table 2-2.
ii) A corresponding SIR-1 wff, obtained through use of the correspondences of Table 2-3.
iii) The quantificational calculus statement obtained from the formula in ii) by eliminating ϵ-quantifiers as described in Part 2.6.2.
iv) The outline of a Subordinate Proof Derivation for the statement in iii). These proofs are "outlines" in the sense that occasionally several steps are combined into one, line numbers are used as meta-symbols to stand for lengthy expressions, and derived rules of inference such as "modes ponens" are used when convenient. However, enough detail and explanation are presented so that complete formal "SPD's" can easily be constructed if desired.

The axioms of SIR-1, as given in Table 2-4 and its associated definitions, are introduced into the Subordinate Proofs as "true" theorems whenever necessary. Universal quantification over all free variables in the initial and final statements in the following proofs is assumed.

In some cases, the proofs of SIR deduction procedures follow immediately from SIR-1 axioms or definitions, so that "SPD's" are unnecessary.

1. $\mathfrak{T}(\subset)$

$x \subset y \wedge y \subset z \Rightarrow x \subset z$

$(\forall\alpha)[\alpha\epsilon x \Rightarrow \alpha\epsilon y] \wedge (\forall\alpha)[\alpha\epsilon y \Rightarrow \alpha\epsilon z] \Rightarrow (\forall\alpha)[\alpha\epsilon x \Rightarrow \alpha\epsilon z]$

1.	$(\forall\alpha)[\alpha\epsilon x \Rightarrow \alpha\epsilon y] \wedge (\forall\alpha)[\alpha\epsilon y \Rightarrow \alpha\epsilon z]$	
2.	$\beta\epsilon x \Rightarrow \beta\epsilon y$	US1 (by US in line 1)
3.	$\beta\epsilon y \Rightarrow \beta\epsilon z$	US1
4.	$\quad\beta\epsilon x$	
5.	$\quad\beta\epsilon y$	4,2
6.	$\quad\beta\epsilon z$	5,3
7.	$\beta\epsilon x \Rightarrow \beta\epsilon z$	
8.	$(\forall\alpha)[\alpha\epsilon x \Rightarrow \alpha\epsilon z]$	UG7

1. ⇒8. qed.

2. $x = y \Rightarrow x \subset y$

$x = y \Rightarrow (\forall\alpha\epsilon x)[\alpha\epsilon y]$

$x = y \Rightarrow (\forall\alpha)[\alpha\epsilon x \Rightarrow \alpha\epsilon y]$

1.	$x=y$	
2.	$\sim(\forall\alpha)[\alpha\epsilon x\Rightarrow\alpha\epsilon y]$	
3.	$(\exists\alpha)\sim[\alpha\epsilon x\Rightarrow\alpha\epsilon y]$	2
4.	$\sim[\beta\epsilon x\Rightarrow\beta\epsilon y]$	ES3
5.	$\beta\epsilon x\wedge\sim\beta\epsilon y$	
6.	$\beta\epsilon y$	I2-1,5
7.	$\sim\beta\epsilon y$	5
8.	$(\forall\alpha)[\alpha\epsilon x\Rightarrow\alpha\epsilon y]$	

1. $\Rightarrow$ 8. qed.

3. $\text{equiv}[x,y]\Rightarrow x\subset y$

$x=y\Rightarrow(\forall\alpha\epsilon x)[\alpha\epsilon y]$ same as 2).

4. $\alpha\epsilon x\wedge x\subset y\Rightarrow\alpha\epsilon y$

$\alpha\epsilon x\wedge(\forall\beta\epsilon x)[\beta\epsilon y]\Rightarrow\alpha\epsilon y$

$\alpha\epsilon x\wedge(\forall\beta)[\beta\epsilon x\Rightarrow\beta\epsilon y]\Rightarrow\alpha\epsilon y$

1.	$\alpha\epsilon x\wedge(\forall\beta)[\beta\epsilon x\Rightarrow\beta\epsilon y]$	
2.	$\alpha\epsilon x\Rightarrow\alpha\epsilon y$	US1
3.	$\alpha\epsilon y$	1,3

1. $\Rightarrow$ 3. qed.

5. $\mathfrak{T}(\text{equiv})$

$\mathfrak{T}(=)$ axiom.

6. $\mathfrak{R}(\text{equiv})$

$\mathfrak{R}(=)$ axiom.

7. $\mathfrak{S}(\text{equiv})$

$\mathfrak{S}(=)$ axiom.

8. $\sim$owng$[x;x]$

$\sim(\forall\alpha\epsilon x)(\exists\beta\epsilon x)[\text{ownb}[\alpha;\beta]]$
$\overline{\mathcal{R}}(\text{ownb})$ axiom.

9. owng$[x;y]\wedge z\subset y\Rightarrow$owng$[x;z]$

$(\forall\beta\epsilon y)(\exists\alpha\epsilon x)[\text{ownb}[\alpha;\beta]]\wedge(\forall\alpha\epsilon z)[\alpha\epsilon y]\Rightarrow(\forall\beta\epsilon z)(\exists\alpha\epsilon x)[\text{ownb}[\alpha;\beta]]$

$(\forall\beta)[\beta\epsilon y\Rightarrow(\exists\alpha)[\alpha\epsilon x\wedge\text{ownb}[\alpha;\beta]]]\wedge(\forall\alpha)[\alpha\epsilon z\Rightarrow\alpha\epsilon y]$
$\Rightarrow(\forall\beta)[\beta\epsilon z\Rightarrow(\exists\alpha)[\alpha\epsilon x\wedge\text{ownb}[\alpha;\beta]]]$

1. $(\forall\beta)[\beta\epsilon y\Rightarrow(\exists\alpha)[\alpha\epsilon x\wedge\text{ownb}[\alpha;\beta]]]\wedge(\forall\alpha)[\alpha\epsilon z\Rightarrow\alpha\epsilon y]$
2. $\gamma\epsilon y\Rightarrow(\exists\alpha)[\alpha\epsilon x\wedge\text{ownb}[\alpha;\gamma]]$ US1
3. $\gamma\epsilon z\Rightarrow\gamma\epsilon y$ US1
4. $\gamma\epsilon z\Rightarrow(\exists\alpha)[\alpha\epsilon x\wedge\text{ownb}[\alpha;\gamma]]$ 3,2
5. $(\forall\beta)[\beta\epsilon z\Rightarrow(\exists\alpha)[\alpha\epsilon x\wedge\text{ownb}[\alpha;\beta]]]$ UG4

1. $\Rightarrow$5. qed.

10. owng$[x;y]\wedge x\subset z\Rightarrow$owng$[z;y]$

$(\forall\beta\epsilon y)(\exists\alpha\epsilon x)[\text{ownb}[\alpha;\beta]]\wedge(\forall\alpha\epsilon x)[\alpha\epsilon z]\Rightarrow(\forall\beta\epsilon y)(\exists\alpha\epsilon z)[\text{ownb}[\alpha;\beta]]$

$(\forall\beta)[\beta\epsilon y\Rightarrow(\exists\alpha)[\alpha\epsilon x\wedge\text{ownb}[\alpha;\beta]]]\wedge(\forall\alpha)[\alpha\epsilon x\Rightarrow\alpha\epsilon z]$
$\Rightarrow(\forall\beta)[\beta\epsilon y\Rightarrow(\exists\alpha)[\alpha\epsilon z\wedge\text{ownb}[\alpha;\beta]]]$

1. $(\forall\beta)[\beta\epsilon y\Rightarrow(\exists\alpha)[\alpha\epsilon x\wedge\text{ownb}[\alpha;\beta]]]\wedge(\forall\alpha)[\alpha\epsilon x\Rightarrow\alpha\epsilon z]$
2. $\gamma\epsilon y\Rightarrow(\exists\alpha)[\alpha\epsilon x\wedge\text{ownb}[\alpha;\gamma]]$ US1
3. $\gamma\epsilon y$
4. $(\exists\alpha)[\alpha\epsilon x\wedge\text{ownb}[\alpha;\gamma]]$ 3,2
5. $\mu\epsilon x\wedge\text{ownb}[\mu;\gamma]$ ES4
6. $\mu\epsilon x\Rightarrow\mu\epsilon z$ US1
7. $\mu\epsilon z\wedge\text{ownb}[\mu;\gamma]$ 5,6
8. $(\exists\alpha)[\alpha\epsilon z\wedge\text{ownb}[\alpha;\gamma]]$ EG7
9. 3. $\Rightarrow$8.
10. $(\forall\beta)[\beta\epsilon y\Rightarrow(\exists\alpha)[\alpha\epsilon x\wedge\text{ownb}[\alpha;\beta]]]$ UG9

1. $\Rightarrow$10. qed.

11. $\text{own}[x;y] \wedge x \subset z \Rightarrow \text{own}[z;y]$

$(\exists \alpha \epsilon x)[\text{ownb}[\alpha;y]] \wedge (\forall \alpha \epsilon x)[\alpha \epsilon z] \Rightarrow (\exists \alpha \epsilon z)[\text{ownb}[\alpha;y]]$

$(\exists \alpha)[\alpha \epsilon x \wedge \text{ownb}[\alpha;y]] \wedge (\forall \alpha)[\alpha \epsilon x \Rightarrow \alpha \epsilon z] \Rightarrow (\exists \alpha)[\alpha \epsilon z \wedge \text{ownb}[\alpha;y]]$

1.	$(\exists \alpha)[\alpha \epsilon x \wedge \text{ownb}[\alpha;y]] \wedge (\forall \alpha)[\alpha \epsilon x \Rightarrow \alpha \epsilon z]$	
2.	$\beta \epsilon x \wedge \text{ownb}[\beta;y]$	ES1
3.	$\beta \epsilon x \Rightarrow \beta \epsilon z$	US1
4.	$\beta \epsilon z \wedge \text{ownb}[\beta;y]$	2,3
5.	$(\exists \alpha)[\alpha \epsilon z \wedge \text{ownb}[\alpha;y]]$	EG4

1. ⇒ 5. qed.

12. $\text{owng}[x;y] \wedge z \epsilon y \Rightarrow \text{own}[x;z]$

$(\forall \beta \epsilon y)(\exists \alpha \epsilon x)[\text{ownb}[\alpha;\beta]] \wedge z \epsilon y \Rightarrow (\exists \alpha \epsilon x)[\text{ownb}[\alpha;z]]$

$(\forall \beta)[\beta \epsilon y \Rightarrow (\exists \alpha)[\alpha \epsilon x \wedge \text{ownb}[\alpha;\beta]] \wedge z \epsilon y \Rightarrow (\exists \alpha)[\alpha \epsilon x \wedge \text{ownb}[\alpha;z]]$

1.	$(\forall \beta)[\beta \epsilon y \Rightarrow (\exists \alpha)[\alpha \epsilon x \wedge \text{ownb}[\alpha;\beta]] \wedge z \epsilon y$	
2.	$z \epsilon y \Rightarrow (\exists \alpha)[\alpha \epsilon x \wedge \text{ownb}[\alpha;z]]$	US1
3.	$(\exists \alpha)[\alpha \epsilon x \wedge \text{ownb}[\alpha;z]]$	1,2

1. ⇒ 3. qed.

13. $\sim \text{partg}[x;x]$

$\underline{\sim}(\forall \alpha \epsilon x)(\exists \beta \epsilon x)[\text{partb}[\alpha;\beta]]$
$\mathfrak{R}(\text{partb})$ axiom.

14. $\text{partg}[x;y] \wedge z \subset y \Rightarrow \text{partg}[x;z]$

$(\forall \beta \epsilon y)(\exists \alpha \epsilon x)[\text{partb}[\alpha;\beta]] \wedge (\forall \alpha \epsilon z)[\alpha \epsilon y] \Rightarrow (\forall \beta \epsilon z)(\exists \alpha \epsilon x)[\text{partb}[\alpha;\beta]]$

Proof is the same as proof of (9), with "ownb" replaced by "partb."

15. $\text{part}[x;y] \wedge x \subset z \Rightarrow \text{part}[z;y]$

$(\exists \alpha \epsilon x)[\text{partb}[\alpha;y]] \wedge (\forall \alpha \epsilon x)[\alpha \epsilon z] \Rightarrow (\exists \alpha \epsilon z[\text{partb}[\alpha;y]]$

Proof is the same as proof of (11) with "ownb" replaced by "partb."

16. $\text{part}[x;y] \wedge \text{partg}[z;x] \Rightarrow \text{part}[z;y]$

$$(\exists \alpha \epsilon x)[\text{partb}[\alpha;y]] \wedge (\forall \beta \epsilon x)(\exists \alpha \epsilon z)[\text{partb}[\alpha;\beta]] \Rightarrow (\exists \alpha \epsilon z)[\text{partb}[\alpha;y]]$$

$$(\exists \alpha)[\alpha \epsilon x \wedge \text{partb}[\alpha;y]] \wedge (\forall \beta)[\beta \epsilon x \Rightarrow (\exists \alpha)[\alpha \epsilon z \wedge \text{partb}[\alpha;\beta]]]$$
$$\Rightarrow (\exists \alpha)[\alpha \epsilon z \wedge \text{partb}[\alpha;y]]$$

1.	$(\exists \alpha)[\alpha \epsilon x \wedge \text{partb}[\alpha;y]] \wedge (\forall \beta)[\beta \epsilon x \Rightarrow (\exists \alpha)[\alpha \epsilon z \wedge \text{partb}[\alpha;\beta]]]$	
2.	$\gamma \epsilon x \wedge \text{partb}[\gamma;y]$	ES1
3.	$\gamma \epsilon x \Rightarrow (\exists \alpha)[\alpha \epsilon z \wedge \text{partb}[\alpha;\gamma]]$	US1
4.	$(\exists \alpha)[\alpha \epsilon z \wedge \text{partb}[\alpha;\gamma]]$	2,3
5.	$\mu \epsilon z \wedge \text{partb}[\mu;\gamma]$	ES5
6.	$\mathfrak{T}(\text{partp})$	Axiom
7.	$\text{partb}[u;\gamma] \wedge \text{partb}[\gamma;y] \Rightarrow \text{partb}[u;y]$	US6
8.	$\mu \epsilon z \wedge \text{partb}[\mu;y]$	5,2,7
9.	$(\exists \alpha)[\alpha \epsilon z \wedge \text{partb}[\alpha;y]]$	EG8

1. ⇒9. qed.

17. $\text{partg}[x;y] \wedge z \epsilon y \Rightarrow \text{part}[x;z]$

$$(\forall \beta \epsilon y)(\exists \alpha \epsilon x)[\text{partb}[\alpha;\beta]] \wedge z \epsilon y \Rightarrow (\exists \alpha \epsilon x)[\text{partb}[\alpha;z]]$$

Proof is the same as proof of (12) with "ownb" replaced by "partb."

Lemma 1: $(\forall \alpha)(\forall \beta)(\forall x)[\text{single}[x] \wedge \alpha \epsilon x \wedge \beta \epsilon x \Rightarrow \alpha = \beta]$

1.	$\text{single}[x] \wedge \text{a} \epsilon x \wedge \text{b} \epsilon x$	
2.	$(\exists \alpha)[\alpha \epsilon x \wedge (\forall \beta)[\beta \epsilon x \Rightarrow \beta = \alpha]]$	1,def. of *single*
3.	$\gamma \epsilon x \wedge (\forall \beta)[\beta \epsilon x \Rightarrow \beta = \gamma]$	ES2
4.	$a \epsilon x \Rightarrow a = \gamma$	US3
5.	$a = \gamma$	1,4
6.	$b \epsilon x \Rightarrow b = \gamma$	US3
7.	$b = \gamma$	1,6
8.	$a = b$	I2-5,7
9.	1. ⇒ 8.	

$(\forall \alpha)(\forall \beta)(\forall x)[\text{single}[x] \wedge \alpha \epsilon x \wedge \beta \epsilon x \Rightarrow \alpha = \beta]$ qed. UG9

18. $\text{right}[x;y] \Rightarrow \sim\text{right}[y;x]$

$$(\exists\alpha\epsilon x)(\exists\beta\epsilon y)[\text{rightb}[\alpha;\beta]] \wedge \text{single}[x] \wedge \text{single}[y] \Rightarrow \sim[(\alpha y)(\beta x)[\text{rightb}[\alpha;\beta]] \wedge \text{single}[y] \wedge \text{single}[x]$$

$$(\exists\alpha)[\alpha\epsilon x \wedge (\exists\beta)[\beta\epsilon y \wedge \text{rightb}[\alpha;\beta]]] \wedge \text{single}[x] \wedge \text{single}[y] \Rightarrow \sim[(\exists\alpha)[\alpha\epsilon y \wedge (\exists\beta)[\beta\epsilon x \wedge \text{rightb}[\alpha;\beta]]] \wedge \text{single}[y] \wedge \text{single}[x]$$

1.	$(\exists\alpha)[\alpha\epsilon x \wedge (\exists\beta)[\beta\epsilon y \wedge \text{rightb}[\alpha;\beta]]] \wedge \text{single}[x] \wedge \text{single}[y]$	
2.	$\gamma\epsilon x \wedge (\exists\beta)[\beta\epsilon y \wedge \text{rightb}[\gamma;\beta]]$	ES1
3.	$\mu\epsilon y \wedge \text{rightb}[\gamma;\mu]$	ES2
4.	$(\exists\alpha)[\alpha\epsilon y \wedge (\exists\beta)[\beta\epsilon x \wedge \text{rightb}[\alpha;\beta]]]$	
5.	$\omega\epsilon y \wedge (\exists\beta)[\beta\epsilon x \wedge \text{rightb}[\omega;\beta]]$	ES4
6.	$\lambda\epsilon x \wedge \text{rightb}[\omega;\lambda]$	ES5
7.	$\text{single}[x] \wedge \gamma\epsilon x \wedge \lambda\epsilon x \Rightarrow \gamma=\lambda$	US-Lem.1
8.	$\gamma=\lambda$	1,2,6,7
9.	$\text{single}[y] \wedge \mu\epsilon y \wedge \omega\epsilon y \Rightarrow \mu=\omega$	US-Lem.1
10.	$\mu=\omega$	1,3,5,9
11.	$\text{rightb}[\lambda;\omega]$	3,8,10,I2
12.	$\mathfrak{S}(\text{rightb})$	Axiom
13.	$\text{rightb}[\lambda;\omega] \Rightarrow \sim\text{rightb}[\omega;\lambda]$	US12
14.	$\sim\text{rightb}[\omega;\lambda]$	11,13
15.	$\text{rightb}[\omega;\lambda]$	6
16.	$\sim 4.$	
17.	$\sim[4. \wedge \text{single}[y] \wedge \text{single}[x]]$	16

1. $\Rightarrow 17.$ qed.

19. $\mathfrak{T}(\text{right})$

$$(\exists\alpha\epsilon x)(\exists\beta\epsilon y)[\text{rightb}[\alpha;\beta]] \wedge (\exists\alpha\epsilon y)(\exists\beta\epsilon z)[\text{rightb}[\alpha;\beta]] \wedge \text{single}[x] \wedge \text{single}[y] \wedge \text{single}[z] \Rightarrow (\exists\alpha\epsilon x)(\exists\beta\epsilon z)[\text{rightb}[\alpha;\beta] \wedge \text{single}[x] \wedge \text{single}[z]$$

$$(\exists\alpha)[\alpha\epsilon x \wedge (\exists\beta)[\beta\epsilon y \wedge \text{rightb}[\alpha;\beta]]] \wedge (\exists\alpha)[\alpha\epsilon y \wedge (\exists\beta)[\beta\epsilon z \wedge \text{rightb}[\alpha;\beta]]] \wedge \text{single}[x] \wedge \text{single}[y] \wedge \text{single}[z] \Rightarrow (\exists\alpha)[\alpha\epsilon x \wedge (\exists\beta)[\beta\epsilon z \wedge \text{rightb}[\alpha;\beta]]] \wedge \text{single}[x] \wedge \text{single}[z]$$

1.	$(\exists\alpha)\,[\alpha\epsilon x \wedge (\exists\beta)\,[\beta\epsilon y \wedge \text{rightb}[\alpha;\beta]]] \wedge (\exists\alpha)[\alpha\epsilon y \wedge (\exists\beta)\,[\beta\epsilon z \wedge \text{rightb}[\alpha;\beta]]] \wedge \text{single}[y]$	
2.	$\gamma\epsilon x \wedge (\exists\beta)\,[\beta\epsilon y \wedge \text{rightb}[\gamma;\beta]]$	ES1
3.	$\mu\epsilon y \wedge \text{rightb}\,[\gamma;\mu]$	ES2
4.	$\omega\epsilon y \wedge (\exists\beta)\,[\beta\epsilon z \wedge \text{rightb}[\omega;\beta]]$	ES1
5.	$\lambda\epsilon y \wedge \text{rightb}[\omega;\beta]$	ES4
6.	$\text{single}[y] \wedge \mu\epsilon y \wedge \omega\epsilon y \Rightarrow \mu=\omega$	US-Lem.1
7.	$\mu=\omega$	1,3,4,6
8.	$\text{rightb}[\gamma;\omega]$	3,7,I2
9.	$\mathfrak{T}(\text{rightb})$	Axiom
10.	$\text{rightb}[\gamma;\omega] \wedge \text{rightb}[\omega;\lambda] \Rightarrow \text{rightb}[\gamma;\lambda]$	US9
11.	$\lambda\epsilon z \wedge \text{rightb}[\gamma;\lambda]$	8,5,10
12.	$(\exists\beta)\,[\beta\epsilon z \wedge \text{rightb}[\gamma;\beta]]$	EG11
13.	$\gamma\epsilon x \wedge 12.$	2,12
14.	$(\exists\alpha)\,[\alpha\epsilon x \wedge (\exists\beta)\,[\beta\epsilon z \wedge \text{rightb}[\alpha;\beta]]]$	EG13
15.	$1. \Rightarrow 14.$	
	$1. \wedge \text{single}[x] \wedge \text{single}[z] \Rightarrow 14. \wedge \text{single}[x] \wedge \text{single}[z]$ qed.	15

20. $\text{jright}[x;y] \Rightarrow \text{right}[x;y]$

$$(\exists\alpha\epsilon x)\,(\exists\beta\epsilon y)\,[\text{jrightb}[\alpha;\beta]] \wedge \text{single}[x] \wedge \text{single}[y]$$
$$\Rightarrow (\exists\alpha\epsilon x)\,(\exists\beta\epsilon y)\,[\text{rightb}[\alpha;\beta]] \wedge \text{single}[x] \wedge \text{single}[y]$$

$$(\exists\alpha)\,[\alpha\epsilon x \wedge (\exists\beta)\,[\beta\epsilon y \wedge \text{jrightb}[\alpha;\beta]]] \wedge \text{single}[x] \wedge \text{single}[y]$$
$$\Rightarrow (\exists\alpha)\,[\alpha\epsilon x \wedge [\exists\beta)\,[\beta\epsilon y \wedge \text{rightb}\,[\alpha;\beta]]] \wedge \text{single}[x] \wedge \text{single}[y]$$

1.	$(\exists\alpha)\,[\alpha\epsilon x \wedge (\exists\beta)\,[\beta\epsilon y \wedge \text{jrightb}[\alpha;\beta]]]$	
2.	$\gamma\epsilon x \wedge (\exists\beta)\,[\beta\epsilon y \wedge \text{jrightb}[\gamma;\beta]]$	ES1
3.	$\mu\epsilon y \wedge \text{jrightb}[\gamma;\mu]$	ESβ
4.	$(\forall x)\,(\forall y)\,[\text{jrightb}[x;y] \Rightarrow \text{rightb}[x;y]]$	Axiom
5.	$\text{jrightb}[\gamma;\mu] \Rightarrow \text{rightb}[\gamma;\mu]$	US4
6.	$\mu\epsilon y \wedge \text{rightb}[\gamma;\mu]$	3,5
7.	$(\exists\beta)\,[\beta\epsilon y \wedge \text{rightb}[\gamma;\beta]]$	EG6
8.	$\gamma\epsilon x \wedge 7.$	2,7
9.	$(\exists\alpha)\,[\alpha\epsilon x \wedge (\exists\beta)\,[\beta\epsilon y \wedge \text{rightb}[\alpha;\beta]]]$	EG8
10.	$1. \Rightarrow 9.$	
	$1. \wedge \text{single}[x] \wedge \text{single}[y] \Rightarrow 9. \wedge \text{single}[x] \wedge \text{single}[y]$ qed. 10	

21. jright$[x;y] \wedge z \neq y \Rightarrow \sim$jright$[x;z]$

Note: The SIR programs assumed that "$z \neq y$" was equivalent to the assertion, "the z is not the y." This latter preferred interpetation can be expressed directly in the SIR-1 formalism by

$$\text{single}[z] \wedge \text{single}[y] \wedge (\forall \alpha \in z)\ [\alpha \notin y].$$

Therefore the appropriate SIR-1 statement corresponding to 21) is:

$$(\exists \alpha \epsilon x)(\exists \beta \epsilon y)\ [\text{jrightb}[\alpha;\beta]] \wedge \text{single}[x] \wedge \text{single}[y] \wedge \text{single}[z]$$
$$\wedge (\forall \alpha \epsilon z)\ [\alpha \notin y]$$
$$\Rightarrow \sim [(\exists \alpha \epsilon x)(\exists \beta \epsilon z)\ [\text{jrightb}[\alpha;\beta]] \wedge \text{single}[x] \wedge \text{single}[z]]$$

$$(\exists \alpha)\ [\alpha \epsilon x \wedge (\exists \beta)\ [\beta \epsilon y \wedge \text{jrightb}[\alpha;\beta]]] \wedge \text{single}[x] \wedge \text{single}[y] \wedge \text{single}[z]$$
$$\wedge (\forall \alpha)\ [\alpha \epsilon z \Rightarrow \alpha \notin y]$$
$$\Rightarrow \sim [(\exists \alpha)\ [\alpha \epsilon x \wedge (\exists \beta)\ [\beta \epsilon z \wedge \text{jrightb}[\alpha;\beta]]] \wedge \text{single}[x] \wedge \text{single}[z]]$$

Proof is in the proof of (22).

22. jright$[x;y] \wedge z \neq x \Rightarrow \sim$jright$[z;y]$

As discussed in the above note, the appropriate SIR-1 statement is:

$$(\exists \alpha \epsilon x)(\ \ \beta \epsilon y)[\text{jrightb}[\alpha;\beta]] \wedge \text{single}[x] \wedge \text{single}[y] \wedge \text{single}[z]$$
$$\wedge (\forall \alpha \epsilon z)\ [\alpha \notin x]$$
$$\Rightarrow \sim [(\exists \alpha \epsilon z)(\exists \beta \epsilon y)\ [\text{jrightb}[\alpha;\beta]] \wedge \text{single}[z] \wedge \text{single}[y]]$$

$$(\exists \alpha)\ [\alpha \epsilon x \wedge (\exists \beta)\ [\beta \epsilon y \wedge \text{jrightb}[\alpha;\beta]]] \wedge \text{single}[x] \wedge \text{single}[y] \wedge \text{single}[z]$$
$$\wedge (\forall \alpha)\ [\alpha \epsilon z \Rightarrow \alpha \notin x]$$
$$\Rightarrow \sim [(\exists \alpha]\ [\alpha \epsilon z \wedge (\exists \beta)\ [\beta \epsilon y \wedge \text{jrightb}[\alpha;\beta]]] \wedge \text{single}[z] \wedge \text{single}[y]]$$

1.	$(\exists\alpha)\ [\alpha\epsilon x \wedge (\exists\beta)\ [\beta\epsilon y \wedge \text{jrightb}[\alpha;\beta]\,]\,] \wedge \text{single}[x] \wedge \text{single}[y]$	
2.	$\lambda\epsilon x \wedge (\exists\beta)\ [\beta\epsilon y \wedge \text{jrightb}[\lambda;\beta]\,]$	ES1
3.	$\omega\epsilon y \wedge \text{jrightb}[\lambda;\omega]$	ES2
4.	$\mathfrak{U}(\text{jrightb})$	Axiom
5.	$\text{jrightb}[\lambda;\omega] \Rightarrow (\forall\alpha)[[\alpha\neq\omega \Rightarrow \sim\text{jrightb}[\lambda;\alpha]\,]$ $\wedge\ [\alpha\neq\lambda \Rightarrow \sim\text{jrightb}[\alpha;\omega]\,]\,]$	US4
6.	$(\forall\alpha)\,[[\alpha\neq\omega \Rightarrow \sim\text{jrightb}[\lambda;\alpha]\,] \wedge [\alpha\neq\lambda \Rightarrow \sim\text{jrightb}[\alpha;\omega]\,]\,]$	3,5
7.	$\text{single}[z] \wedge \text{single}[y] \wedge (\forall\alpha)\ [\alpha\epsilon z \Rightarrow \alpha\notin y]$	
8.	$(\exists\alpha)\ [\alpha\epsilon x \wedge (\exists\beta)\ [\beta\epsilon z \wedge \text{jrightb}[\alpha;\beta]\,]\,]$	
9.	$\lambda\epsilon x\ \wedge (\exists\beta)\ [\beta\epsilon z \wedge \text{jrightb}[\gamma;\beta]\,]$	ES8
10.	$\mu\epsilon z \wedge \text{jrightb}[\gamma;\mu]$	ES9
11.	$\text{single}[x] \wedge \lambda\epsilon x \wedge \gamma\epsilon x \Rightarrow \gamma=\lambda$	US-Lem.1
12.	$\gamma=\lambda$	1,2,9,11
13.	$\mu\epsilon z \Rightarrow \mu\notin y$	US7
14.	$\mu=\omega$	
15.	$\mu\notin y$	10,13
16.	$\mu\epsilon y$	3,14,I2
17.	$\mu\neq\omega$	
18.	$\mu\neq\omega \Rightarrow \sim\text{jrightb}[\lambda;\mu]$	US6
19.	$\sim\text{jrightb}[\lambda;\mu]$	17,18
20.	$\text{jrightb}[\lambda;\mu]$	10,12,I2
21.	$\sim$8.	
22.	$\sim [8. \wedge \text{single}[x] \wedge \text{single}[z]\,]$	21,1,7
23.	7.$\Rightarrow$22.	
24.	$\text{single}[z] \wedge \text{single}[x] \wedge (\forall\alpha)\ [\alpha\epsilon z \Rightarrow \alpha\notin x]$	
25.	$(\exists\alpha)\ [\alpha\epsilon z \wedge (\exists\beta)\ [\beta\epsilon y \wedge \text{jrightb}[\alpha;\beta]\,]\,]$	
26.	$a\epsilon z \wedge (\exists\beta)\ [\beta\epsilon y \wedge \text{jrightb}[a;\beta]\,]$	ES25
27.	$b\epsilon y \wedge \text{jrightb}[a;b]$	ES26
28.	$\text{single}[y] \wedge b\epsilon y \wedge \omega\epsilon y \Rightarrow b=\omega$	US-Lem.1
29.	$b=\omega$	1,27,3,28
30.	$a\epsilon z \Rightarrow a\notin x$	US24
31.	$a=\lambda$	
32.	$a\notin x$	26,30
33.	$a\epsilon x$	2,31,I2
34.	$a\neq\lambda$	
35.	$a\neq\lambda \Rightarrow \sim\text{jrightb}[a;\omega]$	US6
36.	$\sim\text{jrightb}[a;\omega]$	34,35
37.	$\text{jrightb}[a;\omega]$	26,29,12
38.	$\sim$25.	
39.	$\sim [25. \wedge \text{single}[z] \wedge \text{single}[y]\,]$	38,24,1
40.	24.$\Rightarrow$39.	
41.	[7.$\Rightarrow$22.] $\wedge$ [24.$\Rightarrow$39.]]	23,40
42.	1.$\Rightarrow$ [[7.$\Rightarrow$22.] $\wedge$ [24.$\Rightarrow$39.]]	
43.	[1.$\Rightarrow$ [7.$\Rightarrow$22.]] $\wedge$ [1$\Rightarrow$ [24.$\Rightarrow$39.]]	42
	1.$\wedge$7.$\Rightarrow$22. qed 21).	43
	1.$\wedge$24.$\Rightarrow$39. qed 23).	43

23. $\text{right}[z,y] \wedge \text{right}[y,z] \Rightarrow \sim \text{jright}[x;z]$

$$(\exists \alpha \epsilon x)(\exists \beta \epsilon y)[\text{rightb}[\alpha;\beta]] \wedge (\exists \alpha \epsilon y)(\exists \beta \epsilon z)\ [\text{rightb}[\alpha;\beta] \wedge \text{single}[x] \wedge \text{single}[y] \wedge \text{single}[z] \Rightarrow \sim [\,(\exists \alpha \epsilon x)(\exists \beta \epsilon z)\ [\text{jrightb}[x;z]] \wedge \text{single}[x] \wedge \text{single}[z]\,]$$

$$(\exists \alpha)\ [\alpha \epsilon x \wedge (\exists \beta)\ [\beta \epsilon y \wedge \text{rightb}[\alpha;\beta]]] \wedge (\exists \alpha)\ [\alpha \epsilon y \wedge (\exists \beta)\ [\beta \epsilon z \wedge \text{rightb}[\alpha;\beta]]] \wedge \text{single}[x] \wedge \text{single}[y] \wedge \text{single}[z] \Rightarrow \sim [\,(\exists \alpha)\ [\alpha \epsilon x \wedge (\exists \beta)\ [\beta \epsilon z \wedge \text{jrightb}[\alpha;\beta]]] \wedge \text{single}[x] \wedge \text{single}[z]\,]$$

1.	$(\exists \alpha)\ [\alpha \epsilon x \wedge (\exists \beta)\ [\beta \epsilon y \wedge \text{rightb}[\alpha;\beta]]] \wedge (\exists \alpha)\ [\alpha \epsilon y \wedge (\exists \beta)\ [\beta \epsilon z \wedge \text{rightb}[\alpha;\beta]]] \wedge \text{single}[x] \wedge \text{single}[y] \wedge \text{single}[z]$	
2.	$\mu \epsilon x \wedge (\exists \beta)\ [\beta \epsilon y \wedge \text{rightb}[\mu;\beta]]$	ES1
3.	$\omega \epsilon y \wedge \text{rightb}[\mu;\omega]$	ES2
4.	$\gamma \epsilon y \wedge (\exists \beta)\ [\beta \epsilon z \wedge \text{rightb}[\gamma;\beta]]$	ES1
5.	$\lambda \epsilon z \wedge \text{rightb}\ [\gamma;\lambda]]$	ES4
6.	$\text{single}[y] \wedge \omega \epsilon y \wedge \gamma \epsilon y \Rightarrow \omega = \gamma$	US-Lem.1
7.	$\omega = \gamma$	1,3,4,6
8.	$\text{rightb}[\omega;\lambda]$	5,7,I2
9.	$(\forall x)(\forall y)(\forall z)\ [\text{rightb}[x,y] \wedge \text{rightb}[y,z] \Rightarrow \sim \text{jrightb}[x,z]]$	Axiom
10.	$\text{rightb}[\mu;\omega] \wedge \text{rightb}[\omega;\lambda] \Rightarrow \sim \text{jrightb}[\mu;\lambda]$	US9
11.	$(\exists \alpha)\ [\alpha \epsilon x \wedge (\exists \beta)\ [\beta \epsilon z \wedge \text{jrightb}[\alpha;\beta]]]$	
12.	$a \epsilon x \wedge (\exists \beta)\ [\beta \epsilon z \wedge \text{jrightb}[a;\beta]]$	ES11
13.	$\text{b} \epsilon z \wedge \text{jrightb}[a;\text{b}]$	ES12
14.	$\text{single}[x] \wedge \mu \epsilon x \wedge a \epsilon x \Rightarrow \mu = a$	US-Lem.1
15.	$\mu = a$	1,2,12,14
16.	$\text{single}[z] \wedge \lambda \epsilon z \wedge \text{b} \epsilon z \Rightarrow \lambda = b$	US-Lem.1
17.	$\lambda = b$	1,5,13,16
18.	$\text{jrightb}[\mu;\lambda]$	13,15,17,I2
19.	$\sim \text{jrightb}[\mu;\lambda]$	3,8,10
20.	$\sim 11.$	
21.	$\sim [11. \wedge \text{single}[x] \wedge \text{single}[z]]$	20

$1. \Rightarrow 21.$ qed.

During the four years since the work described in this chapter, powerful proof procedures for the first-order predicate calculus have emerged. These procedures, based upon the *resolution principle* by J. A. Robinson, give us new hope for a practical theorem-proving component in a general question-answering system; they are already superior to the "TP" system described in the discussion of a hypothetical SIR-1.

At Stanford Research Institute we are currently implementing a general question answerer that uses a *resolution* theorem prover and already have an operating system that dominates SIR in several respects. This work is reported in a paper, "The Use of Theorem-Proving Techniques in Question-Answering Systems" by C. Cordell Green and the present author, submitted for presentation at the 1968 ACM National Conference.

Appendix 2.3. Full-Response Output for Fig. 2-5.

A.2.3.1. Set Inclusion

```
(THE NEXT SENTENCE IS . .)
(EVERY KEYPUNCH-OPERATOR IS A GIRL)

(THE FUNCTION USED IS . .)
SETR-SELECT
((GENERIC . KEYPUNCH-OPERATOR) (GENERIC . GIRL))
(THE REPLY . .)
(THE SUB-FUNCTION USED IS . .)
SETR
(KEYPUNCH-OPERATOR GIRL)
(ITS REPLY . .)
(I UNDERSTAND THE SUPERSET RELATION BETWEEN GIRL AND KEYPUNCH-OPERATOR)
(I UNDERSTAND THE SUBSET RELATION BETWEEN KEYPUNCH-OPERATOR AND GIRL)


(THE NEXT SENTENCE IS . .)
(ANY GIRL IS AN EXAMPLE OF A PERSON)

(THE FUNCTION USED IS . .)
SETR-SELECT
((GENERIC . GIRL) (GENERIC . PERSON))
(THE REPLY . .)
(THE SUB-FUNCTION USED IS . .)
SETR
(GIRL PERSON)
(ITS REPLY . .)
(I UNDERSTAND THE SUPERSET RELATION BETWEEN PERSON AND GIRL)
(I UNDERSTAND THE SUBSET RELATION BETWEEN GIRL AND PERSON)


(THE NEXT SENTENCE IS . .)
(IS A KEYPUNCH-OPERATOR A PERSON Q)

(THE FUNCTION USED IS . .)
SETRQ-SELECT
((GENERIC . KEYPUNCH-OPERATOR) (GENERIC . PERSON))
(THE REPLY . .)
(THE SUB-FUNCTION USED IS . .)
SETRQ


(KEYPUNCH-OPERATOR PERSON)
(ITS REPLY . .)
YES


(THE NEXT SENTENCE IS . .)
(IS A PERSON A PERSON Q)

(THE FUNCTION USED IS . .)
SETRQ-SELECT
((GENERIC . PERSON) (GENERIC . PERSON))
(THE REPLY . .)
(THE SUB-FUNCTION USED IS . .)
SETRQ
(PERSON PERSON)
(ITS REPLY . .)
YES


(THE NEXT SENTENCE IS . .)
(IS A PERSON A GIRL Q)

(THE FUNCTION USED IS . .)
SETRQ-SELECT
((GENERIC . PERSON) (GENERIC . GIRL))
(THE REPLY . .)
(THE SUB-FUNCTION USED IS . .)
SETRQ
(PERSON GIRL)
(ITS REPLY . .)
SOMETIMES


(THE NEXT SENTENCE IS . .)
(IS A MONKEY A KEYPUNCH-OPERATOR Q)

(THE FUNCTION USED IS . .)
SETRQ-SELECT
((GENERIC . MONKEY) (GENERIC . KEYPUNCH-OPERATOR))
(THE REPLY . .)
(THE SUB-FUNCTION USED IS . .)
SETRQ
(MONKEY KEYPUNCH-OPERATOR)
(ITS REPLY . .)
(INSUFFICIENT INFORMATION)
```

A.2.3.2. Set Membership

```
(THE NEXT SENTENCE IS . .)
(MAX IS AN IBM-7094)

(THE FUNCTION USED IS . .)
SETR-SELECT
((UNIQUE . MAX) (GENERIC . IBM-7094))
(THE REPLY . .)
(THE SUB-FUNCTION USED IS . .)
SETRS
(MAX IBM-7094)
(ITS REPLY . .)
(I UNDERSTAND THE ELEMENTS RELATION BETWEEN MAX AND IBM-7094)
(I UNDERSTAND THE MEMBER RELATION BETWEEN IBM-7094 AND MAX)


(THE NEXT SENTENCE IS . .)
(AN IBM-7094 IS A COMPUTER)

(THE FUNCTION USED IS . .)
SETR-SELECT
((GENERIC . IBM-7094) (GENERIC . COMPUTER))
(THE REPLY . .)
(THE SUB-FUNCTION USED IS . .)
SETR
(IBM-7094 COMPUTER)
(ITS REPLY . .)
(I UNDERSTAND THE SUPERSET RELATION BETWEEN COMPUTER AND IBM-7094)
(I UNDERSTAND THE SUBSET RELATION BETWEEN IBM-7094 AND COMPUTER)


(THE NEXT SENTENCE IS . .)
(IS MAX A COMPUTER Q)

(THE FUNCTION USED IS . .)
SETRQ-SELECT
((UNIQUE . MAX) (GENERIC . COMPUTER))
(THE REPLY . .)
(THE SUB-FUNCTION USED IS . .)
SETRSQ



(MAX COMPUTER)
(ITS REPLY . .)
YES


(THE NEXT SENTENCE IS . .)
(THE BOY IS AN MIT-STUDENT)

(THE FUNCTION USED IS . .)
SETR-SELECT
((SPECIFIC . BOY) (GENERIC . MIT-STUDENT))
(THE REPLY . .)
(THE SUB-FUNCTION USED IS . .)
SETRS1
(BOY MIT-STUDENT)
(ITS REPLY . .)
(G02840 IS A BOY)
(I UNDERSTAND THE ELEMENTS RELATION BETWEEN G02840 AND BOY)
(I UNDERSTAND THE MEMBER RELATION BETWEEN BOY AND G02840)
(I UNDERSTAND THE ELEMENTS RELATION BETWEEN G02840 AND MIT-STUDENT)
(I UNDERSTAND THE MEMBER RELATION BETWEEN MIT-STUDENT AND G02840)
```

```
(THE NEXT SENTENCE IS . .)
(EVERY MIT-STUDENT IS A BRIGHT-PERSON)

(THE FUNCTION USED IS . .)
SETR-SELECT
((GENERIC . MIT-STUDENT) (GENERIC . BRIGHT-PERSON))
(THE REPLY . .)
(THE SUB-FUNCTION USED IS . .)
SETR
(MIT-STUDENT BRIGHT-PERSON)
(ITS REPLY . .)
(I UNDERSTAND THE SUPERSET RELATION BETWEEN BRIGHT-PERSON AND MIT-STUDENT)
(I UNDERSTAND THE SUBSET RELATION BETWEEN MIT-STUDENT AND BRIGHT-PERSON)


(THE NEXT SENTENCE IS . .)
(IS THE BOY A BRIGHT-PERSON Q)

(THE FUNCTION USED IS . .)
SETRQ-SELECT
((SPECIFIC . BOY) (GENERIC . BRIGHT-PERSON))
(THE REPLY . .)
(THE SUB-FUNCTION USED IS . .)
SETRS1Q
(BOY BRIGHT-PERSON)
(ITS REPLY . .)
YES


(THE NEXT SENTENCE IS . .)
(JOHN IS A BOY)

(THE FUNCTION USED IS . .)
SETR-SELECT
((UNIQUE . JOHN) (GENERIC . BOY))
(THE REPLY . .)
(THE SUB-FUNCTION USED IS . .)
SETRS


(JOHN BOY)
(ITS REPLY . .)
(I UNDERSTAND THE ELEMENTS RELATION BETWEEN JOHN AND BOY)
(I UNDERSTAND THE MEMBER RELATION BETWEEN BOY AND JOHN)


(THE NEXT SENTENCE IS . .)
(IS THE BOY A BRIGHT-PERSON Q)

(THE FUNCTION USED IS . .)
SETRQ-SELECT
((SPECIFIC . BOY) (GENERIC . BRIGHT-PERSON))
(THE REPLY . .)
(THE SUB-FUNCTION USED IS . .)
SETRS1Q
(BOY BRIGHT-PERSON)
(ITS REPLY . .)
(WHICH BOY . . (G02840 JOHN))
```

A.2.3.3. Equivalence

```
(THE NEXT SENTENCE IS . .)
(THE MAN IS A JERK)

(THE FUNCTION USED IS . .)
SETR-SELECT
((SPECIFIC . MAN) (GENERIC . JERK))
(THE REPLY . .)
(THE SUB-FUNCTION USED IS . .)
SETRS1
(MAN JERK)
(ITS REPLY . .)
(G02840 IS A MAN)
(I UNDERSTAND THE ELEMENTS RELATION BETWEEN G02840 AND MAN)
(I UNDERSTAND THE MEMBER RELATION BETWEEN MAN AND G02840)
(I UNDERSTAND THE ELEMENTS RELATION BETWEEN G02840 AND JERK)
(I UNDERSTAND THE MEMBER RELATION BETWEEN JERK AND G02840)


(THE NEXT SENTENCE IS . .)
(JACK IS A DOPE)

(THE FUNCTION USED IS . .)
SETR-SELECT
((UNIQUE . JACK) (GENERIC . DOPE))
(THE REPLY . .)
(THE SUB-FUNCTION USED IS . .)
SETRS
(JACK DOPE)
(ITS REPLY . .)
(I UNDERSTAND THE ELEMENTS RELATION BETWEEN JACK AND DOPE)
(I UNDERSTAND THE MEMBER RELATION BETWEEN DOPE AND JACK)


(THE NEXT SENTENCE IS . .)
(JOHN IS JACK)

(THE FUNCTION USED IS . .)
SETR-SELECT
((UNIQUE . JOHN) (UNIQUE . JACK))
(THE REPLY . .)
(THE SUB-FUNCTION USED IS . .)
EQUIV
(JOHN JACK)
(ITS REPLY . .)
(I UNDERSTAND THE EQUIV RELATION BETWEEN JOHN AND JACK)
(I UNDERSTAND THE EQUIV RELATION BETWEEN JACK AND JOHN)


(THE NEXT SENTENCE IS . .)
(IS JOHN A DOPE Q)

(THE FUNCTION USED IS . .)
SETRQ-SELECT
((UNIQUE . JOHN) (GENERIC . DOPE))
(THE REPLY . .)
(THE SUB-FUNCTION USED IS . .)
SETRSQ
(JOHN DOPE)
(ITS REPLY . .)
YES
```

```
(IS THE MAN A DOPE Q)

(THE FUNCTION USED IS . .)
SETRQ-SELECT
((SPECIFIC . MAN) (GENERIC . DOPE))
(THE REPLY . .)
(THE SUB-FUNCTION USED IS . .)
SETRS1Q
(MAN DOPE)
(ITS REPLY . .)
(INSUFFICIENT INFORMATION)


(THE NEXT SENTENCE IS . .)
(JOHN IS THE MAN)

(THE FUNCTION USED IS . .)
SETR-SELECT
((UNIQUE . JOHN) (SPECIFIC . MAN))
(THE REPLY . .)
(THE SUB-FUNCTION USED IS . .)
EQUIV1
(JOHN MAN)
(ITS REPLY . .)
(I UNDERSTAND THE EQUIV RELATION BETWEEN JOHN AND G02840)
(I UNDERSTAND THE EQUIV RELATION BETWEEN G02840 AND JOHN)


(THE NEXT SENTENCE IS . .)
(IS THE MAN A DOPE Q)

(THE FUNCTION USED IS . .)
SETRQ-SELECT
((SPECIFIC . MAN) (GENERIC . DOPE))
(THE REPLY . .)
(THE SUB-FUNCTION USED IS . .)
SETRS1Q
(MAN DOPE)
(ITS REPLY . .)
YES


(THE NEXT SENTENCE IS . .)
(JIM IS A MAN)

(THE FUNCTION USED IS . .)
SETR-SELECT
((UNIQUE . JIM) (GENERIC . MAN))
(THE REPLY . .)
(THE SUB-FUNCTION USED IS . .)
SETRS
(JIM MAN)
(ITS REPLY . .)
(I UNDERSTAND THE ELEMENTS RELATION BETWEEN JIM AND MAN)
(I UNDERSTAND THE MEMBER RELATION BETWEEN MAN AND JIM)


(THE NEXT SENTENCE IS . .)
(IS THE MAN A DOPE Q)

(THE FUNCTION USED IS . .)
SETRQ-SELECT
((SPECIFIC . MAN) (GENERIC . DOPE))
(THE REPLY . .)
(THE SUB-FUNCTION USED IS . .)
SETRS1Q
(MAN DOPE)
(ITS REPLY . .)
(WHICH MAN . . (G02840 JIM))
```

A.2.3.4. Ownership, General.

```
(THE NEXT SENTENCE IS . .)
(EVERY FIREMAN OWNS A PAIR-OF-RED-SUSPENDERS)

(THE FUNCTION USED IS . .)
OWN-SELECT
((GENERIC . PAIR-OF-RED-SUSPENDERS) (GENERIC . FIREMAN))
(THE REPLY . .)
(THE SUB-FUNCTION USED IS . .)
OWNR
(PAIR-OF-RED-SUSPENDERS FIREMAN)
(ITS REPLY . .)
(I UNDERSTAND THE POSSESS-BY-EACH RELATION BETWEEN PAIR-OF-RED-SUSPENDERS AND FIREMAN)
(I UNDERSTAND THE OWNED-BY-EACH RELATION BETWEEN FIREMAN AND PAIR-OF-RED-SUSPENDERS)


(THE NEXT SENTENCE IS . .)
(DOES A PAIR-OF-RED-SUSPENDERS OWN A PAIR-OF-RED-SUSPENDERS Q)

(THE FUNCTION USED IS . .)
OWNQ-SELECT
((GENERIC . PAIR-OF-RED-SUSPENDERS) (GENERIC . PAIR-OF-RED-SUSPENDERS))
(THE REPLY . .)
(THE SUB-FUNCTION USED IS . .)
OWNRQ
(PAIR-OF-RED-SUSPENDERS PAIR-OF-RED-SUSPENDERS)
(ITS REPLY . .)
(NO ** THEY ARE THE SAME)


(THE NEXT SENTENCE IS . .)
(DOES A DOCTOR OWN A PAIR-OF-RED-SUSPENDERS Q)

(THE FUNCTION USED IS . .)
OWNQ-SELECT
((GENERIC . PAIR-OF-RED-SUSPENDERS) (GENERIC . DOCTOR))
(THE REPLY . .)
(THE SUB-FUNCTION USED IS . .)
OWNRQ
(PAIR-OF-RED-SUSPENDERS DOCTOR)
(ITS REPLY . .)
(INSUFFICIENT INFORMATION)


(THE NEXT SENTENCE IS . .)
(A FIRECHIEF IS A FIREMAN)

(THE FUNCTION USED IS . .)
SETR-SELECT
((GENERIC . FIRECHIEF) (GENERIC . FIREMAN))
(THE REPLY . .)
(THE SUB-FUNCTION USED IS . .)
SETR
(FIRECHIEF FIREMAN)
(ITS REPLY . .)
(I UNDERSTAND THE SUPERSET RELATION BETWEEN FIREMAN AND FIRECHIEF)
(I UNDERSTAND THE SUBSET RELATION BETWEEN FIRECHIEF AND FIREMAN)


(THE NEXT SENTENCE IS . .)
(DOES A FIRECHIEF OWN A PAIR-OF-RED-SUSPENDERS Q)

(THE FUNCTION USED IS . .)
OWNQ-SELECT
((GENERIC . PAIR-OF-RED-SUSPENDERS) (GENERIC . FIRECHIEF))
(THE REPLY . .)
(THE SUB-FUNCTION USED IS . .)
OWNRQ
(PAIR-OF-RED-SUSPENDERS FIRECHIEF)
(ITS REPLY . .)
YES
```

A.2.3.5. *Ownership, Specific.*

```
(THE FUNCTION USED IS . .)
OWN-SELECT
((GENERIC . LOG-LOG-DECITRIG) (UNIQUE . ALFRED))
(THE REPLY . .)
(THE SUB-FUNCTION USED IS . .)
OWNRGU
(LOG-LOG-DECITRIG ALFRED)
(ITS REPLY . .)
(I UNDERSTAND THE POSSESS RELATION BETWEEN LOG-LOG-DECITRIG AND ALFRED)
(I UNDERSTAND THE OWNED RELATION BETWEEN ALFRED AND LOG-LOG-DECITRIG)

(THE NEXT SENTENCE IS . .)
(A LOG-LOG-DECITRIG IS A SLIDE-RULE)

(THE FUNCTION USED IS . .)
SETR-SELECT
((GENERIC . LOG-LOG-DECITRIG) (GENERIC . SLIDE-RULE))
(THE REPLY . .)
(THE SUB-FUNCTION USED IS . .)
SETR
(LOG-LOG-DECITRIG SLIDE-RULE)
(ITS REPLY . .)
(I UNDERSTAND THE SUPERSET RELATION BETWEEN SLIDE-RULE AND LOG-LOG-DECITRIG)
(I UNDERSTAND THE SUBSET RELATION BETWEEN LOG-LOG-DECITRIG AND SLIDE-RULE)

(THE NEXT SENTENCE IS . .)
(DOES ALFRED OWN A SLIDE-RULE Q)

(THE FUNCTION USED IS . .)
OWNQ-SELECT
((GENERIC . SLIDE-RULE) (UNIQUE . ALFRED))
(THE REPLY . .)
(THE SUB-FUNCTION USED IS . .)
OWNRGUQ
(SLIDE-RULE ALFRED)
(ITS REPLY . .)
YES

(THE NEXT SENTENCE IS . .)
(EVERY ENGINEERING-STUDENT OWNS A SLIDE-RULE)

(THE FUNCTION USED IS . .)
OWN-SELECT
((GENERIC . SLIDE-RULE) (GENERIC . ENGINEERING-STUDENT))
(THE REPLY . .)
(THE SUB-FUNCTION USED IS . .)
OWNR
(SLIDE-RULE ENGINEERING-STUDENT)
(ITS REPLY . .)
(I UNDERSTAND THE POSSESS-BY-EACH RELATION BETWEEN SLIDE-RULE AND ENGINEERING-STUDENT)
(I UNDERSTAND THE OWNED-BY-EACH RELATION BETWEEN ENGINEERING-STUDENT AND SLIDE-RULE)

(THE NEXT SENTENCE IS . .)
(VERNON IS A TECH-MAN)

(THE FUNCTION USED IS . .)
SETR-SELECT
((UNIQUE . VERNON) (GENERIC . TECH-MAN))
(THE REPLY . .)
(THE SUB-FUNCTION USED IS . .)
SETRS
(VERNON TECH-MAN)
(ITS REPLY . .)
(I UNDERSTAND THE ELEMENTS RELATION BETWEEN VERNON AND TECH-MAN)
(I UNDERSTAND THE MEMBER RELATION BETWEEN TECH-MAN AND VERNON)
```

```
(THE FUNCTION USED IS . .)
SETR-SELECT
((GENERIC . TECH-MAN) (GENERIC . ENGINEERING-STUDENT))
(THE REPLY . .)
(THE SUB-FUNCTION USED IS . .)
SETR
(TECH-MAN ENGINEERING-STUDENT)
(ITS REPLY . .)
(I UNDERSTAND THE SUPERSET RELATION BETWEEN ENGINEERING-STUDENT AND TECH-MAN)
(I UNDERSTAND THE SUBSET RELATION BETWEEN TECH-MAN AND ENGINEERING-STUDENT)

(THE NEXT SENTENCE IS . .)
(DOES VERNON OWN A SLIDE-RULE Q)

(THE FUNCTION USED IS . .)
OWNQ-SELECT
((GENERIC . SLIDE-RULE) (UNIQUE . VERNON))
(THE REPLY . .)
(THE SUB-FUNCTION USED IS . .)
OWNRGUQ
(SLIDE-RULE VERNON)
(ITS REPLY . .)
YES

(THE NEXT SENTENCE IS . .)
(DOES AN ENGINEERING-STUDENT OWN THE LOG-LOG-DECITRIG Q)

(THE FUNCTION USED IS . .)
OWNQ-SELECT
((SPECIFIC . LOG-LOG-DECITRIG) (GENERIC . ENGINEERING-STUDENT))
(THE REPLY . .)
(THE SUB-FUNCTION USED IS . .)
OWNRSGQ
(LOG-LOG-DECITRIG ENGINEERING-STUDENT)
(ITS REPLY . .)
(G02840 IS A LOG-LOG-DECITRIG)
(I UNDERSTAND THE ELEMENTS RELATION BETWEEN G02840 AND LOG-LOG-DECITRIG)
(I UNDERSTAND THE MEMBER RELATION BETWEEN LOG-LOG-DECITRIG AND G02840)
(INSUFFICIENT INFORMATION)

(THE NEXT SENTENCE IS . .)
(ALFRED IS A TECH-MAN)

(THE FUNCTION USED IS . .)
SETR-SELECT
((UNIQUE . ALFRED) (GENERIC . TECH-MAN))
(THE REPLY . .)
(THE SUB-FUNCTION USED IS . .)
SETRS
(ALFRED TECH-MAN)
(ITS REPLY . .)
(I UNDERSTAND THE ELEMENTS RELATION BETWEEN ALFRED AND TECH-MAN)
(I UNDERSTAND THE MEMBER RELATION BETWEEN TECH-MAN AND ALFRED)

(THE NEXT SENTENCE IS . .)
(DOES AN ENGINEERING-STUDENT OWN THE LOG-LOG-DECITRIG Q)

(THE FUNCTION USED IS . .)
OWNQ-SELECT
((SPECIFIC . LOG-LOG-DECITRIG) (GENERIC . ENGINEERING-STUDENT))
(THE REPLY . .)
(THE SUB-FUNCTION USED IS . .)
OWNRSGQ
(LOG-LOG-DECITRIG ENGINEERING-STUDENT)
(ITS REPLY . .)
YES
```

A.2.3.6. Part-Whole, General.

```
(THE NEXT SENTENCE IS . .)
(A NOSE IS PART OF A PERSON)

(THE FUNCTION USED IS . .)
PARTR-SELECT
((GENERIC . NOSE) (GENERIC . PERSON))
(THE REPLY . .)
(THE SUB-FUNCTION USED IS . .)
PARTR
(NOSE PERSON)
(ITS REPLY . .)
(I UNDERSTAND THE SUBPART-OF-EACH RELATION BETWEEN NOSE AND PERSON)
(I UNDERSTAND THE SUPERPART-OF-EACH RELATION BETWEEN PERSON AND NOSE)


(THE NEXT SENTENCE IS . .)
(A NOSTRIL IS A PART OF A NOSE)

(THE FUNCTION USED IS . .)
PARTR-SELECT
((GENERIC . NOSTRIL) (GENERIC . NOSE))
(THE REPLY . .)
(THE SUB-FUNCTION USED IS . .)
PARTR
(NOSTRIL NOSE)
(ITS REPLY . .)
(I UNDERSTAND THE SUBPART-OF-EACH RELATION BETWEEN NOSTRIL AND NOSE)
(I UNDERSTAND THE SUPERPART-OF-EACH RELATION BETWEEN NOSE AND NOSTRIL)


(THE NEXT SENTENCE IS . .)
(A PROFESSOR IS A TEACHER)

(THE FUNCTION USED IS . .)
SETR-SELECT
((GENERIC . PROFESSOR) (GENERIC . TEACHER))
(THE REPLY . .)
(THE SUB-FUNCTION USED IS . .)
SETR


(PROFESSOR TEACHER)
(ITS REPLY . .)
(I UNDERSTAND THE SUPERSET RELATION BETWEEN TEACHER AND PROFESSOR)
(I UNDERSTAND THE SUBSET RELATION BETWEEN PROFESSOR AND TEACHER)

(THE NEXT SENTENCE IS . .)
(A TEACHER IS A PERSON)

(THE FUNCTION USED IS . .)
SETR-SELECT
((GENERIC . TEACHER) (GENERIC . PERSON))
(THE REPLY . .)
(THE SUB-FUNCTION USED IS . .)
SETR
(TEACHER PERSON)
(ITS REPLY . .)
(I UNDERSTAND THE SUPERSET RELATION BETWEEN PERSON AND TEACHER)
(I UNDERSTAND THE SUBSET RELATION BETWEEN TEACHER AND PERSON)
```

```
(THE NEXT SENTENCE IS . .)
(IS A NOSTRIL PART OF A PROFESSOR Q)

(THE FUNCTION USED IS . .)
PARTRQ-SELECT
((GENERIC . NOSTRIL) (GENERIC . PROFESSOR))
(THE REPLY . .)
(THE SUB-FUNCTION USED IS . .)
PARTRQ
(NOSTRIL PROFESSOR)
(ITS REPLY . .)
YES


(THE NEXT SENTENCE IS . .)
(IS A NOSE PART OF A NOSE Q)

(THE FUNCTION USED IS . .)
PARTRQ-SELECT
((GENERIC . NOSE) (GENERIC . NOSE))
(THE REPLY . .)
(THE SUB-FUNCTION USED IS . .)
PARTRQ
(NOSE NOSE)
(ITS REPLY . .)
(NO , PART MEANS PROPER SUBPART)


(THE NEXT SENTENCE IS . .)
(A PERSON IS A LIVING-CREATURE)

(THE FUNCTION USED IS . .)
SETR-SELECT
((GENERIC . PERSON) (GENERIC . LIVING-CREATURE))
(THE REPLY . .)
(THE SUB-FUNCTION USED IS . .)
SETR
(PERSON LIVING-CREATURE)
(ITS REPLY . .)
(I UNDERSTAND THE SUPERSET RELATION BETWEEN LIVING-CREATURE AND PERSON)
(I UNDERSTAND THE SUBSET RELATION BETWEEN PERSON AND LIVING-CREATURE)


(THE NEXT SENTENCE IS . .)
(IS A NOSTRIL PART OF A LIVING-CREATURE Q)

(THE FUNCTION USED IS . .)
PARTRQ-SELECT
((GENERIC . NOSTRIL) (GENERIC . LIVING-CREATURE))
(THE REPLY . .)
(THE SUB-FUNCTION USED IS . .)
PARTRQ
(NOSTRIL LIVING-CREATURE)
(ITS REPLY . .)
SOMETIMES


(THE NEXT SENTENCE IS . .)
(IS A LIVING-CREATURE PART OF A NOSE Q)

(THE FUNCTION USED IS . .)
PARTRQ-SELECT
((GENERIC . LIVING-CREATURE) (GENERIC . NOSE))
(THE REPLY . .)
(THE SUB-FUNCTION USED IS . .)
PARTRQ
(LIVING-CREATURE NOSE)
(ITS REPLY . .)
(NO , NOSE IS SOMETIMES PART OF LIVING-CREATURE)
```

A.2.3.7. Part-Whole, Specific.

```
(THE NEXT SENTENCE IS . .)
(A VAN-DYKE IS PART OF FERREN)

(THE FUNCTION USED IS . .)
PARTR-SELECT
((GENERIC . VAN-DYKE) (UNIQUE . FERREN))
(THE REPLY . .)
(THE SUB-FUNCTION USED IS . .)
PARTRGU
(VAN-DYKE FERREN)
(ITS REPLY . .)
(I UNDERSTAND THE SUBPART RELATION BETWEEN VAN-DYKE AND FERREN)
(I UNDERSTAND THE SUPERPART RELATION BETWEEN FERREN AND VAN-DYKE)

(THE NEXT SENTENCE IS . .)
(A VAN-DYKE IS A BEARD)

(THE FUNCTION USED IS . .)
SETR-SELECT
((GENERIC . VAN-DYKE) (GENERIC . BEARD))
(THE REPLY . .)
(THE SUB-FUNCTION USED IS . .)
SETR
(VAN-DYKE BEARD)
(ITS REPLY . .)
(I UNDERSTAND THE SUPERSET RELATION BETWEEN BEARD AND VAN-DYKE)
(I UNDERSTAND THE SUBSET RELATION BETWEEN VAN-DYKE AND BEARD)


(THE NEXT SENTENCE IS . .)
(IS A BEARD PART OF FERREN Q)

(THE FUNCTION USED IS . .)
PARTRQ-SELECT
((GENERIC . BEARD) (UNIQUE . FERREN))
(THE REPLY . .)
(THE SUB-FUNCTION USED IS . .)


PARTRGUQ
(BEARD FERREN)
(ITS REPLY . .)
YES


(THE NEXT SENTENCE IS . .)
(A CRT IS A DISPLAY-DEVICE)

(THE FUNCTION USED IS . .)
SETR-SELECT
((GENERIC . CRT) (GENERIC . DISPLAY-DEVICE))
(THE REPLY . .)
(THE SUB-FUNCTION USED IS . .)
SETR
(CRT DISPLAY-DEVICE)
(ITS REPLY . .)
(I UNDERSTAND THE SUPERSET RELATION BETWEEN DISPLAY-DEVICE AND CRT)
(I UNDERSTAND THE SUBSET RELATION BETWEEN CRT AND DISPLAY-DEVICE)

(THE NEXT SENTENCE IS . .)
(A CRT IS PART OF THE PDP-1)

(THE FUNCTION USED IS . .)
PARTR-SELECT
((GENERIC . CRT) (SPECIFIC . PDP-1))
(THE REPLY . .)
(THE SUB-FUNCTION USED IS . .)
PARTRGS
(CRT PDP-1)
(ITS REPLY . .)
(G02840 IS A PDP-1)
(I UNDERSTAND THE ELEMENTS RELATION BETWEEN G02840 AND PDP-1)
(I UNDERSTAND THE MEMBER RELATION BETWEEN PDP-1 AND G02840)
(I UNDERSTAND THE SUBPART RELATION BETWEEN CRT AND G02840)
(I UNDERSTAND THE SUPERPART RELATION BETWEEN G02840 AND CRT)


(THE NEXT SENTENCE IS . .)
(SAM IS THE PDP-1)

(THE FUNCTION USED IS . .)
SETR-SELECT
((UNIQUE . SAM) (SPECIFIC . PDP-1))
(THE REPLY . .)
(THE SUB-FUNCTION USED IS . .)
EQUIVL
(SAM PDP-1)
(ITS REPLY . .)
(I UNDERSTAND THE EQUIV RELATION BETWEEN SAM AND G02840)
(I UNDERSTAND THE EQUIV RELATION BETWEEN G02840 AND SAM)
```

```
(THE NEXT SENTENCE IS . .)
(A SCREEN IS PART OF EVERY DISPLAY-DEVICE)

(THE FUNCTION USED IS . .)
PARTR-SELECT
((GENERIC . SCREEN) (GENERIC . DISPLAY-DEVICE))
(THE REPLY . .)




(THE SUB-FUNCTION USED IS . .)
PARTR
(SCREEN DISPLAY-DEVICE)
(ITS REPLY . .)
(I UNDERSTAND THE SUBPART-OF-EACH RELATION BETWEEN SCREEN AND DISPLAY-DEVICE)
(I UNDERSTAND THE SUPERPART-OF-EACH RELATION BETWEEN DISPLAY-DEVICE AND SCREEN)


(THE NEXT SENTENCE IS . .)
(IS A SCREEN PART OF SAM Q)

(THE FUNCTION USED IS . .)
PARTRQ-SELECT
((GENERIC . SCREEN) (UNIQUE . SAM))
(THE REPLY . .)
(THE SUB-FUNCTION USED IS . .)
PARTRGUQ
(SCREEN SAM)
(ITS REPLY . .)
YES


(THE NEXT SENTENCE IS . .)
(A BEARD IS PART OF A BEATNIK)

(THE FUNCTION USED IS . .)
PARTR-SELECT
((GENERIC . BEARD) (GENERIC . BEATNIK))
(THE REPLY . .)
(THE SUB-FUNCTION USED IS . .)
PARTR
(BEARD BEATNIK)
(ITS REPLY . .)
(I UNDERSTAND THE SUBPART-OF-EACH RELATION BETWEEN BEARD AND BEATNIK)
(I UNDERSTAND THE SUPERPART-OF-EACH RELATION BETWEEN BEATNIK AND BEARD)


(THE NEXT SENTENCE IS . .)
(EVERY COFFEE-HOUSE-CUSTOMER IS A BEATNIK)

(THE FUNCTION USED IS . .)
SETR-SELECT
((GENERIC . COFFEE-HOUSE-CUSTOMER) (GENERIC . BEATNIK))
(THE REPLY . .)
(THE SUB-FUNCTION USED IS . .)
SETR
(COFFEE-HOUSE-CUSTOMER BEATNIK)
(ITS REPLY . .)
(I UNDERSTAND THE SUPERSET RELATION BETWEEN BEATNIK AND COFFEE-HOUSE-CUSTOMER)
(I UNDERSTAND THE SUBSET RELATION BETWEEN COFFEE-HOUSE-CUSTOMER AND BEATNIK)


(THE NEXT SENTENCE IS . .)
(BUZZ IS A COFFEE-HOUSE-CUSTOMER)

(THE FUNCTION USED IS . .)
SETR-SELECT
((UNIQUE . BUZZ) (GENERIC . COFFEE-HOUSE-CUSTOMER))
(THE REPLY . .)
(THE SUB-FUNCTION USED IS . .)
SETRS




(BUZZ COFFEE-HOUSE-CUSTOMER)
(ITS REPLY . .)
(I UNDERSTAND THE ELEMENTS RELATION BETWEEN BUZZ AND COFFEE-HOUSE-CUSTOMER)
(I UNDERSTAND THE MEMBER RELATION BETWEEN COFFEE-HOUSE-CUSTOMER AND BUZZ)


(THE NEXT SENTENCE IS . .)
(IS A BEARD PART OF BUZZ Q)

(THE FUNCTION USED IS . .)
PARTRQ-SELECT
((GENERIC . BEARD) (UNIQUE . BUZZ))
(THE REPLY . .)
(THE SUB-FUNCTION USED IS . .)
PARTRGUQ
(BEARD BUZZ)
(ITS REPLY . .)
YES
```

A.2.3.8. Number

```
(THE NEXT SENTENCE IS . .)
(A BOY IS A PERSON)

(THE FUNCTION USED IS . .)
SETR-SELECT
((GENERIC . BOY) (GENERIC . PERSON))
(THE REPLY . .)
(THE SUB-FUNCTION USED IS . .)
SETR
(BOY PERSON)
(ITS REPLY . .)
(I UNDERSTAND THE SUPERSET RELATION BETWEEN PERSON AND BOY)
(I UNDERSTAND THE SUBSET RELATION BETWEEN BOY AND PERSON)


(THE NEXT SENTENCE IS . .)
(JOHN IS A BOY)

(THE FUNCTION USED IS . .)
SETR-SELECT
((UNIQUE . JOHN) (GENERIC . BOY))
(THE REPLY . .)
(THE SUB-FUNCTION USED IS . .)
SETRS
(JOHN BOY)
(ITS REPLY . .)
(I UNDERSTAND THE ELEMENTS RELATION BETWEEN JOHN AND BOY)
(I UNDERSTAND THE MEMBER RELATION BETWEEN BOY AND JOHN)


(THE NEXT SENTENCE IS . .)
(A FINGER IS PART OF A HAND)

(THE FUNCTION USED IS . .)
PARTR-SELECT
((GENERIC . FINGER) (GENERIC . HAND))
(THE REPLY . .)
(THE SUB-FUNCTION USED IS . .)



PARTR
(FINGER HAND)
(ITS REPLY . .)
(I UNDERSTAND THE SUBPART-OF-EACH RELATION BETWEEN FINGER AND HAND)
(I UNDERSTAND THE SUPERPART-OF-EACH RELATION BETWEEN HAND AND FINGER)


(THE NEXT SENTENCE IS . .)
(HOW MANY FINGERS DOES JOHN HAVE Q)

(THE FUNCTION USED IS . .)
HAVE-RESOLVE
(FINGER (UNIQUE . JOHN))
(THE REPLY . .)
(THE ABOVE SENTENCE IS AMBIGUOUS ** BUT I ASSUME (HAS) MEANS (HAS AS PARTS))
(I DON*T KNOW WHETHER FINGER IS PART OF JOHN)

(THE NEXT SENTENCE IS . .)
(THERE IS ONE HAND ON EACH ARM)

(THE FUNCTION USED IS . .)
PARTRN-SELECT
((GENERIC . ARM) (1 . HAND))
(THE REPLY . .)
(I UNDERSTAND THE SUPERPART-OF-EACH RELATION BETWEEN ARM AND HAND)
(I REALIZE THE NUMBER RELATION BETWEEN 1 AND (PLIST NAME ARM))
(I UNDERSTAND THE SUBPART-OF-EACH RELATION BETWEEN HAND AND ARM)
(I REALIZE THE NUMBER RELATION BETWEEN 1 AND (PLIST NAME HAND))


(THE NEXT SENTENCE IS . .)
(THERE ARE TWO ARMS ON A PERSON)

(THE FUNCTION USED IS . .)
PARTRN-SELECT
((GENERIC . PERSON) (2 . ARM))
(THE REPLY . .)
(I UNDERSTAND THE SUPERPART-OF-EACH RELATION BETWEEN PERSON AND ARM)
(I REALIZE THE NUMBER RELATION BETWEEN 2 AND (PLIST NAME PERSON))
(I UNDERSTAND THE SUBPART-OF-EACH RELATION BETWEEN ARM AND PERSON)
(I REALIZE THE NUMBER RELATION BETWEEN 2 AND (PLIST NAME ARM))


(THE NEXT SENTENCE IS . .)
(HOW MANY FINGERS DOES JOHN HAVE Q)

(THE FUNCTION USED IS . .)
HAVE-RESOLVE
(FINGER (UNIQUE . JOHN))
(THE REPLY . .)
(THE ABOVE SENTENCE IS AMBIGUOUS ** BUT I ASSUME (HAS) MEANS (HAS AS PARTS))
(I KNOW THE SUPERPART-OF-EACH RELATION BETWEEN HAND AND FINGER)
((HOW MANY FINGER PER HAND Q))

(THE NEXT SENTENCE IS . .)
(A HAND HAS 5 FINGERS)

(THE FUNCTION USED IS . .)
HASN-RESOLVE


((5 . FINGER) (GENERIC . HAND))
(THE REPLY . .)
(THE ABOVE SENTENCE IS AMBIGUOUS ** BUT I ASSUME (HAS) MEANS (HAS AS PARTS))
(I KNOW THE SUPERPART-OF-EACH RELATION BETWEEN HAND AND FINGER)
(I REALIZE THE NUMBER RELATION BETWEEN 5 AND (PLIST NAME HAND))
(I KNOW THE SUBPART-OF-EACH RELATION BETWEEN FINGER AND HAND)
(I REALIZE THE NUMBER RELATION BETWEEN 5 AND (PLIST NAME FINGER))


(THE NEXT SENTENCE IS . .)
(HOW MANY FINGERS DOES JOHN HAVE Q)

(THE FUNCTION USED IS . .)
HAVE-RESOLVE
(FINGER (UNIQUE . JOHN))
(THE REPLY . .)
(THE ABOVE SENTENCE IS AMBIGUOUS ** BUT I ASSUME (HAS) MEANS (HAS AS PARTS))
(I KNOW THE SUPERPART-OF-EACH RELATION BETWEEN HAND AND FINGER)
(I KNOW THE SUPERPART-OF-EACH RELATION BETWEEN ARM AND HAND)
(I KNOW THE SUPERPART-OF-EACH RELATION BETWEEN PERSON AND ARM)
(THE ANSWER IS 10)
```

A.2.3.9. Left-to-Right Position.

```
(THE NEXT SENTENCE IS . .)
(THE TELEPHONE IS JUST TO THE RIGHT OF THE BOOK)

(THE FUNCTION USED IS . .)
JRIGHT-SELECT
((SPECIFIC . TELEPHONE) (SPECIFIC . BOOK))
(THE REPLY . .)
(THE SUB-FUNCTION USED IS . .)
JRIGHT
(TELEPHONE BOOK)
(ITS REPLY . .)
(G02840 IS A TELEPHONE)
(I UNDERSTAND THE ELEMENTS RELATION BETWEEN G02840 AND TELEPHONE)
(I UNDERSTAND THE MEMBER RELATION BETWEEN TELEPHONE AND G02840)
(G02841 IS A BOOK)
(I UNDERSTAND THE ELEMENTS RELATION BETWEEN G02841 AND BOOK)
(I UNDERSTAND THE MEMBER RELATION BETWEEN BOOK AND G02841)
(I REALIZE THE JRIGHT RELATION BETWEEN TELEPHONE AND BOOK)
(I REALIZE THE JLEFT RELATION BETWEEN BOOK AND TELEPHONE)

(THE NEXT SENTENCE IS . .)
(THE TELEPHONE IS JUST TO THE LEFT OF THE PAD)


(THE FUNCTION USED IS . .)
JRIGHT-SELECT
((SPECIFIC . PAD) (SPECIFIC . TELEPHONE))
(THE REPLY . .)
(THE SUB-FUNCTION USED IS . .)
JRIGHT
(PAD TELEPHONE)
(ITS REPLY . .)
(G02842 IS A PAD)
(I UNDERSTAND THE ELEMENTS RELATION BETWEEN G02842 AND PAD)
(I UNDERSTAND THE MEMBER RELATION BETWEEN PAD AND G02842)
(I REALIZE THE JRIGHT RELATION BETWEEN PAD AND TELEPHONE)
(I REALIZE THE JLEFT RELATION BETWEEN TELEPHONE AND PAD)

(THE NEXT SENTENCE IS . .)
(IS THE PAD JUST TO THE RIGHT OF THE BOOK Q)

(THE FUNCTION USED IS . .)
JRIGHTQ-SELECT
((SPECIFIC . PAD) (SPECIFIC . BOOK))
(THE REPLY . .)
(THE SUB-FUNCTION USED IS . .)
JRIGHTSSQ
(PAD BOOK)
(ITS REPLY . .)
NO

(THE NEXT SENTENCE IS . .)
(IS THE BOOK TO THE LEFT OF THE PAD Q)

(THE FUNCTION USED IS . .)
RIGHTQ-SELECT
((SPECIFIC . PAD) (SPECIFIC . BOOK))
(THE REPLY . .)
(THE SUB-FUNCTION USED IS . .)
RIGHTSSQ
(PAD BOOK)
(ITS REPLY . .)
YES
```

```
(THE NEXT SENTENCE IS . .)
(THE PAD IS TO THE RIGHT OF THE TELEPHONE)

(THE FUNCTION USED IS . .)
RIGHT-SELECT
((SPECIFIC . PAD) (SPECIFIC . TELEPHONE))
(THE REPLY . .)
(THE SUB-FUNCTION USED IS . .)
RIGHT
(PAD TELEPHONE)
(ITS REPLY . .)
(THE ABOVE STATEMENT IS ALREADY KNOWN)

(THE NEXT SENTENCE IS . .)
(THE PAD IS TO THE LEFT OF THE TELEPHONE)

(THE FUNCTION USED IS . .)

RIGHT-SELECT
((SPECIFIC . TELEPHONE) (SPECIFIC . PAD))
(THE REPLY . .)
(THE SUB-FUNCTION USED IS . .)
RIGHT
(TELEPHONE PAD)
(ITS REPLY . .)
(THE ABOVE STATEMENT IS IMPOSSIBLE)

(THE NEXT SENTENCE IS . .)
(THE ASH-TRAY IS TO THE LEFT OF THE BOOK)

(THE FUNCTION USED IS . .)
RIGHT-SELECT
((SPECIFIC . BOOK) (SPECIFIC . ASH-TRAY))
(THE REPLY . .)
(THE SUB-FUNCTION USED IS . .)
RIGHT
(BOOK ASH-TRAY)
(ITS REPLY . .)
(G02843 IS A ASH-TRAY)
(I UNDERSTAND THE ELEMENTS RELATION BETWEEN G02843 AND ASH-TRAY)
(I UNDERSTAND THE MEMBER RELATION BETWEEN ASH-TRAY AND G02843)
(I UNDERSTAND THE RIGHT RELATION BETWEEN BOOK AND ASH-TRAY)
(I UNDERSTAND THE LEFT RELATION BETWEEN ASH-TRAY AND BOOK)

(THE NEXT SENTENCE IS . .)
(THE PENCIL IS TO THE LEFT OF THE PAD)

(THE FUNCTION USED IS . .)
RIGHT-SELECT
((SPECIFIC . PAD) (SPECIFIC . PENCIL))
(THE REPLY . .)
(THE SUB-FUNCTION USED IS . .)
RIGHT
(PAD PENCIL)
(ITS REPLY . .)
(G02844 IS A PENCIL)
(I UNDERSTAND THE ELEMENTS RELATION BETWEEN G02844 AND PENCIL)
(I UNDERSTAND THE MEMBER RELATION BETWEEN PENCIL AND G02844)
(I UNDERSTAND THE RIGHT RELATION BETWEEN PAD AND PENCIL)
(I UNDERSTAND THE LEFT RELATION BETWEEN PENCIL AND PAD)
```

```
(THE NEXT SENTENCE IS . .)
(THE PAPER IS TO THE RIGHT OF THE TELEPHONE)

(THE FUNCTION USED IS . .)
RIGHT-SELECT
((SPECIFIC . PAPER) (SPECIFIC . TELEPHONE))
(THE REPLY . .)
(THE SUB-FUNCTION USED IS . .)
RIGHT
(PAPER TELEPHONE)
(ITS REPLY . .)
(G02845 IS A PAPER)
(I UNDERSTAND THE ELEMENTS RELATION BETWEEN G02845 AND PAPER)
(I UNDERSTAND THE MEMBER RELATION BETWEEN PAPER AND G02845)
(I UNDERSTAND THE RIGHT RELATION BETWEEN PAPER AND TELEPHONE)


(I UNDERSTAND THE LEFT RELATION BETWEEN TELEPHONE AND PAPER)


(THE NEXT SENTENCE IS . .)
(WHERE IS THE PAD Q)

(THE FUNCTION USED IS . .)
WHERE-SELECT
((SPECIFIC . PAD))
(THE REPLY . .)
(THE SUB-FUNCTION USED IS . .)
WHERES
(PAD)
(ITS REPLY . .)
(JUST TO THE RIGHT OF THE TELEPHONE)
(SOMEWHERE TO THE RIGHT OF THE FOLLOWING . . (PENCIL))


(THE NEXT SENTENCE IS . .)
(WHAT IS THE POSITION OF THE PAD Q)

(THE FUNCTION USED IS . .)
LOC-SELECT
((SPECIFIC . PAD))
(THE REPLY . .)
(THE SUB-FUNCTION USED IS . .)
LOCATES
(PAD)
(ITS REPLY . .)
(THE LEFT-TO-RIGHT ORDER IS AS FOLLOWS)
(ASH-TRAY (BOOK TELEPHONE PAD) PAPER)
(TO FURTHER SPECIFY THE POSITIONS YOU MUST INDICATE WHERE THE PENCIL IS WITH RESPECT TO THE ASH-TRAY)


(THE NEXT SENTENCE IS . .)
(THE BOOK IS JUST TO THE RIGHT OF THE ASH-TRAY)

(THE FUNCTION USED IS . .)
JRIGHT-SELECT
((SPECIFIC . BOOK) (SPECIFIC . ASH-TRAY))
(THE REPLY . .)
(THE SUB-FUNCTION USED IS . .)
JRIGHT
(BOOK ASH-TRAY)
(ITS REPLY . .)
(I REALIZE THE JRIGHT RELATION BETWEEN BOOK AND ASH-TRAY)
(I REALIZE THE JLEFT RELATION BETWEEN ASH-TRAY AND BOOK)
```

```
(WHAT IS THE POSITION OF THE PAD Q)

(THE FUNCTION USED IS . .)
LOC-SELECT
((SPECIFIC . PAD))
(THE REPLY . .)
(THE SUB-FUNCTION USED IS . .)
LOCATES
(PAD)
(ITS REPLY . .)


(THE LEFT-TO-RIGHT ORDER IS AS FOLLOWS)
(PENCIL (ASH-TRAY BOOK TELEPHONE PAD) PAPER)


(THE NEXT SENTENCE IS . .)
(A TELEPHONE IS AN AUDIO-TRANSDUCER)

(THE FUNCTION USED IS . .)
SETR-SELECT
((GENERIC . TELEPHONE) (GENERIC . AUDIO-TRANSDUCER))
(THE REPLY . .)
(THE SUB-FUNCTION USED IS . .)
SETR
(TELEPHONE AUDIO-TRANSDUCER)
(ITS REPLY . .)
(I UNDERSTAND THE SUPERSET RELATION BETWEEN AUDIO-TRANSDUCER AND TELEPHONE)
(I UNDERSTAND THE SUBSET RELATION BETWEEN TELEPHONE AND AUDIO-TRANSDUCER)


(THE NEXT SENTENCE IS . .)
(A DIAPHRAGM IS PART OF AN AUDIO-TRANSDUCER)

(THE FUNCTION USED IS . .)
PARTR-SELECT
((GENERIC . DIAPHRAGM) (GENERIC . AUDIO-TRANSDUCER))
(THE REPLY . .)
(THE SUB-FUNCTION USED IS . .)
PARTR
(DIAPHRAGM AUDIO-TRANSDUCER)
(ITS REPLY . .)
(I UNDERSTAND THE SUBPART-OF-EACH RELATION BETWEEN DIAPHRAGM AND AUDIO-TRANSDUCER)
(I UNDERSTAND THE SUPERPART-OF-EACH RELATION BETWEEN AUDIO-TRANSDUCER AND DIAPHRAGM)


(THE NEXT SENTENCE IS . .)
(WHERE IS A DIAPHRAGM Q)

(THE FUNCTION USED IS . .)
WHERE-SELECT
((GENERIC . DIAPHRAGM))
(THE REPLY . .)
(THE SUB-FUNCTION USED IS . .)
WHEREG
(DIAPHRAGM)
(ITS REPLY . .)
(JUST TO THE LEFT OF THE PAD)
(JUST TO THE RIGHT OF THE BOOK)
(SOMEWHERE TO THE LEFT OF THE FOLLOWING . . (PAPER))
```

Bibliography

1. ACF Industries, Avion Div., "Translating From Ordinary Discourse Into Formal Logic – A Preliminary Study," Scientific Report AF CRC-TN-56-770.
2. Bennett, J. L., "A Computer Program for Word Relations," Memo 1961-1, Mechanical Translation Group, RLE, M.I.T., Cambridge, Mass., 1961.
3. Bobrow, D. G., "Syntactic Analysis of English by Computer – A Survey," *Proc. FJCC,* Spartan Press, Baltimore, Md., 1963.
4. Bobrow, D. G., and Raphael, B., "A Comparison of List-Processing Computer Languages," *Comm. ACM,* April 1964.
5. Carnap, R., *Meaning and Necessity,* University of Chicago Press, Chicago, Ill., 1947.
6. Carnap, R., "Foundations of Logic and Mathematics," *International Encyclopedia of Unified Science,* Vol. 1, No. 3, University of Chicago Press, Chicago, Ill., 1939.
7. Carroll, J. D., Abelson, R. P., and Reinfeld, W., "A Computer Program Which Assesses the Credibility of Assertions," draft, Yale University, New Haven, Conn., July 1963.
8. Charney, E., "Word-Meaning and Sentence-Meaning," abstract in *Mechanical Translation,* Vol. 7, No. 2, 1963.
9. Chomsky, N., *Syntactic Structures,* Mouton and Co., The Hague, 1957.
10. Cohen, D., "Picture Processing in a Picture Language Machine," National Bureau of Standards Report 7885, Washington, D.C., April 1963.
11. Corbato, F. J., et al., *The Compatible Time-Sharing System,* M.I.T. Press, Cambridge, Mass., 1963.
12. Darlington, J. L., "Translating Ordinary Language into Symbolic Logic," abstract in *Mechanical Translation,* Vol. 7, No. 2, 1963.
13. Davis, M., and Putnam, H., "A Computational Proof Procedure," AFOSR TR 59-124, Rensselaer Polytechnic Institute, Troy, N.Y., 1959.
14. Feigenbaum, E. A., "The Simulation of Verbal Learning Behavior," in Feigenbaum, E. A., and Feldman, J. (eds.), *Computers and Thought*, McGraw-Hill, New York, 1963.
15. Freudenthal, H., *LINCOS: Design of a Language for Cosmic Intercourse,* North-Holland Press, Amsterdam, 1960.
16. Fries, C. C., *The Structure of English,* Harcourt, Brace, New York, 1952.
17. Green, B. F., Jr., et al., "Baseball: An Automatic Question-Answerer," *Proc. WJCC,* Vol. 19, 1961.
18. Kazemier, B. H., and Vuysje, D. (eds.), *The Concept and the Role of the Model in Mathematics and Natural and Social Sciences,* Gordon and Breach Science Publishers, New York, 1963.
19. Klein, S., "Some Experiments Performed with an Automatic Paraphraser," abstract in *Mechanical Translation,* Vol. 7, No. 2, 1963.
20. Kochen, M., "Experimental Study of 'Hypothesis Formation' by Computer," *Proc. 4th* London Symposium on Information Theory, C. Cherry (ed.), London, 1961.
21. Lindsay, R. K., "A Program for Parsing Sentences and Making Inferences about Kinship Relations," *Proc. Western Management Science Conference on Simulation,* A. Hogatt (ed.).
22. McCarthy, J., "Programs with Common Sense," *Proc. Symposium on Mechanisation of Thought Processes.* Her Majesty's Stationery Office, London, 1959 (Section 7.1 of the present volume).
23. McCarthy, J., et al., *LISP 1.5 Programmer's Manual,* The M.I.T. Press, Cambridge, Mass., 1963.

24. Maron, I., RAND Corp., Santa Monica, Calif., private communication, 1963.
25. Minsky, M., "Steps Toward Artificial Intelligence," *Proc. IRE,* Vol. 49, No. 1, 1961.
26. Newell, A. (ed.), *Information Processing Language V Manual,* Prentice-Hall, Englewood Cliffs, N.J., 1961.
27. Newell, A., et al., "Empirical Explorations of the Logic Theory Machine: A Case Study in Heuristics," *Proc. WJCC, IRE,* 1957.
28. Newell, A., et al., "Report on a General Problem-Solving Program," *Proc. International Conference on Information Processing,* UNESCO House, Paris, 1959.
29. O'Donnell, M., *The New Day In and Day Out,* Row, Peterson and Co., Evanston, Ill., 1948.
30. Ogden, C. K., *Basic English,* Paul, Trench, Trubner and Co., London, 1932.
31. Phillips, A. V., "A Question-Answering Routine," Master's Thesis, M.I.T. Mathematics Department, Cambridge, Mass., 1960.
32. Quillian, R., "A Revised Design for an Understanding Machine," *Mechanical Translation,* Vol. 7, No. 1, 1962.
33. Quine, W. V., *Word and Object,* The M.I.T. Press, Cambridge, Mass., 1960.
34. Reichenbach, H., *Elements of Symbolic Logic,* The Macmillan Co., New York, 1947.
35. Research Laboratory of Electronics and Computation Center, M.I.T. *COMIT Programmer's Reference Manual,* The M.I.T. Press, Cambridge, Mass., 1961.
36. Samuel, A. L., "Some Studies in Machine Learning Using the Game of Checkers," *IBM J. of Research and Development,* Vol. 3, No. 3, 1959.
37. Shaw, C. J., "JOVIAL and Its Documentation," *Comm. ACM,* Vol. 3, No. 6, 1963.
38. Simmons, R. F., et al., "Toward the Synthesis of Human Language Behavior," *Behavioral Science*, Vol. 7, No. 3, 1962.
39. Simon, H. A., "Experiments With a Heuristic Compiler," Paper P-2349, RAND Corp., Santa Monica, Calif., 1961.
40. Slagle, J., "A Computer Program for Solving Problems in Freshman Calculus," *J. ACM.,* 1964; also doctoral dissertation, Mathematics Department, M.I.T., May 1961.
41. Solomonoff, R. J., "An Inductive Inference Machine," *IRE National Convention Record,* pt. 2, 1957.
42. Sommers, F. T., "Semantic Structures and Automatic Clarification of Linguistic Ambiguity," International Electric Corp., Paramus, N.J., 1961.
43. Suppes, P., *Introduction to Logic,* Van Nostrand Co., Princeton, N.J., 1957.
44. Ullman, S., *Words and Their Use,* Philosophical Library, New York, 1951.
45. Walpole, H. R., *Semantics: The Nature of Words and Their Meanings,* W. W. Norton and Co., New York, 1941.
46. Wang, H., "Toward Mechanical Mathematics," *IBM J. of Research and Development,* Vol. 4, No. 1, 1960.
47. Ziff, P., *Semantic Analysis,* Cornell University Press, Ithaca, N.Y., 1960.

3. Natural Language Input for a Computer Problem-Solving System

Daniel G. Bobrow

3.1 Introduction

The aim of the research reported here was to discover how to build a computer program that could communicate with people in a natural language within some restricted problem domain. In the course of this investigation, I wrote a set of computer programs, the STUDENT system, which accepts as input a comfortable but restricted subset of English which can be used to express a wide variety of algebra story problems. The problems shown in Fig. 3-1 illustrate some of the communication and problem-solving capabilities of this system.

In the following discussion, I shall use phrases such as "the computer understands English." In all such cases, the "English" is just the restricted subset of English allowable as input for the computer program under discussion. In addition, for purposes of this report I have adopted the following operational definition of "understanding." A computer *understands* a subset of English if it accepts input sentences which are members of this subset and answers questions based on information contained in the input. The STUDENT system understands English in this sense.

3.1.1 The Problem Context of the STUDENT System

In the construction of a question-answering system many problems are greatly simplified if the problem context is restricted. The simplification resulting from the restrictions embodied in the STUDENT system and the reasons for these simplifications to arise will be discussed in detail in the body of this report.

```
(THE DISTANCE FROM NEW YORK TO LOS ANGELES IS 3000 MILES .
IF THE AVERAGE SPEED OF A JET PLANE IS 600 MILES PER HOUR ,
FIND THE TIME IT TAKES TO TRAVEL FROM NEW YORK TO LOS ANGELES
BY JET .)

(THE EQUATIONS TO BE SOLVED ARE)

(EQUAL G02517 (TIME (IT / PRO) TAKES TO TRAVEL FROM NEW YORK
TO LOS ANGELES BY JET))

(EQUAL (AVERAGE SPEED OF JET PLANE) (QUOTIENT (TIMES 600 (MILES))
(TIMES 1 (HOURS))))

(EQUAL (DISTANCE FROM NEW YORK TO LOS ANGELES) (TIMES 3000
(MILES)))

THE EQUATIONS WERE INSUFFICIENT TO FIND A SOLUTION

(USING THE FOLLOWING KNOWN RELATIONSHIPS)
((EQUAL (DISTANCE) (TIMES (SPEED) (TIME))) (EQUAL (DISTANCE)
(TIMES (GAS CONSUMPTION) (NUMBER OF GALLONS OF GAS USED))))

(ASSUMING THAT)
((SPEED) IS EQUAL TO (AVERAGE SPEED OF JET PLANE))

(ASSUMING THAT)
((TIME) IS EQUAL TO (TIME (IT / PRO) TAKES TO TRAVEL FROM NEW
YORK TO LOS ANGELES BY JET))

(ASSUMING THAT)
((DISTANCE) IS EQUAL TO (DISTANCE FROM NEW YORK TO LOS ANGELES))

(THE TIME IT TAKES TO TRAVEL FROM NEW YORK TO LOS ANGELES BY
JET IS  5 HOURS)
```

```
(THE PROBLEM TO BE SOLVED IS)
(THE PRICE OF A RADIO IS  69.70 DOLLARS . IF THIS PRICE IS
15 PERCENT LESS THAN THE MARKED PRICE , FIND THE MARKED PRICE
.)

(THE EQUATIONS TO BE SOLVED ARE)

(EQUAL G02515 (MARKED PRICE))

(EQUAL (PRICE OF RADIO) (TIMES  .8499 (MARKED PRICE)))

(EQUAL (PRICE OF RADIO) (TIMES  69.70 (DOLLARS)))

(THE MARKED PRICE IS  82 DOLLARS)
```

```
(THE SUM OF TWO NUMBERS IS 111 . ONE OF THE NUMBERS IS CONSECUTIVE
TO THE OTHER NUMBER . FIND THE TWO NUMBERS .)

TRYING POSSIBLE IDIOMS

(THE PROBLEM WITH AN IDIOMATIC SUBSTUTION IS)
(THE SUM OF ONE OF THE NUMBERS AND THE OTHER NUMBER IS 111
. ONE OF THE NUMBERS IS CONSECUTIVE TO THE OTHER NUMBER . FIND
THE ONE OF THE NUMBERS AND THE OTHER NUMBER .)

(THE EQUATIONS TO BE SOLVED ARE)

(EQUAL G02522 (OTHER NUMBER))

(EQUAL G02521 (ONE OF NUMBERS))

(EQUAL (ONE OF NUMBERS) (PLUS 1 (OTHER NUMBER)))

(EQUAL (PLUS (ONE OF NUMBERS) (OTHER NUMBER)) 111)

(THE ONE OF THE NUMBERS IS  56)

(THE OTHER NUMBER IS  55)
```

```
(THE PROBLEM TO BE SOLVED IS)
(BILL S FATHER S UNCLE IS TWICE AS OLD AS BILL S FATHER . 2
YEARS FROM NOW BILL S FATHER WILL BE 3 TIMES AS OLD AS BILL
  THE SUM OF THEIR AGES IS 92 . FIND BILL S AGE .)

(THE EQUATIONS TO BE SOLVED ARE)

(EQUAL G02533 ((BILL / PERSON) S AGE))

(EQUAL (PLUS ((BILL / PERSON) S (FATHER / PERSON) S (UNCLE
/ PERSON) S AGE) (PLUS ((BILL / PERSON) S (FATHER / PERSON)
S AGE) ((BILL / PERSON) S AGE))) 92)

(EQUAL (PLUS ((BILL / PERSON) S (FATHER / PERSON) S AGE) 2)
(TIMES 3 (PLUS ((BILL / PERSON) S AGE) 2)))

(EQUAL ((BILL / PERSON) S (FATHER / PERSON) S (UNCLE / PERSON)
S AGE) (TIMES 2 ((BILL / PERSON) S (FATHER / PERSON) S AGE)))

(BILL S AGE IS  8)
```

Figure 3-1. Some Problems Solved by STUDENT

The STUDENT system is designed to answer questions embedded in English language statements of algebra story problems such as those shown in Fig. 3-1. STUDENT does this by constructing from the English input a corresponding set of algebraic equations, and solving this set of equations for the requested unknowns. If needed, STUDENT has access to a store of "global" information, not specific to any particular problem, and can retrieve relevant facts and equations from this store of information. STUDENT comments on its progress in solving a problem, and can request the help of the questioner if it gets stuck.

There are a number of reasons for choosing the context of algebra story problems in which to develop techniques which would allow a computer problem-solving system to accept natural language input. First, we know a good type of data structure in which to store information needed to answer questions in this context, namely, algebraic equations. There exist well-known algorithms for deducing information implicit in the equations, that is, values for particular variables which satisfy the set of equations. Also, many types of algebra story problems are available in school books, and it was not difficult to transcribe them into STUDENT's subset of English. They thus provide a measure of comparison between the speed of question answering by humans and by the STUDENT program. In fact, on an IBM 7094 this program answers most questions that it can handle as fast or faster than humans. (The 7094 can perform over one hundred thousand additions per second.)

3.1.2 Reasons for Wanting Natural Language Input

Why should one want to talk to a computer in English? There are many tongues the computer already understands – such as FORTRAN, COMIT, LISP, ALGOL, COBOL, to name just a few. These serve adequately for a large class of problems. A more pertinent question is really, when is English input to a computer preferable?

English input is desirable, for example, if it is necessary to use the computer for retrieval of information from a text in English. If a computer could accept English input, much information now recorded only in English would be available for computer use without need for human translation.

A computer that understood English would be more accessible to any speaker of English; especially for occasional use where it would not be worthwhile to train the user in a specialized language. For fact retrieval, rather than document retrieval, English is a good vehicle for stating queries. For a good description of the differences between fact and document retrieval, see Cooper (12).

Programming languages are process oriented. They cannot describe a problem, only a method for finding a solution to the problem. A natural language is a convenient vehicle for providing a description of the problem itself, leaving the choice of processing to the problem solver accepting the input. In an extreme case, one would like to talk to the computer about a problem, with appropriate questions and interjections by the computer on assumptions it finds necessary, until the computer claims that the problem is now well formed, and an attempt at solution can be made.

Finally, man's ability to use symbols and language is a prime factor in his intelligence, and if we can learn how to make a computer understand a natural language, we will have taken a big step toward creating an "artificially intelligent" computer (32).

3.1.3 Criteria for Evaluating Question-Answering Systems

We have defined understanding in terms of an ability to answer questions in English. A number of question-answering systems have been built and will be described in the next part. In this part we shall give a number of criteria for evaluating question-answering systems.

In many systems there is a separation of data input and question input. For all systems under consideration, the input questions are in English. The input data may be either in English or in a prestructured format, e.g., a tree or hierarchy. The English data input may be used as a data base as is, or mapped into a structured information store. Simmons, in his competent survey of English question-answering systems (40), calls those systems using a structured information store "data base question-answerers," as opposed to "text-based question-answerers" which retrieve facts from the original text.

The extent of "understanding" possessed by a question-answering system can be measured along three different dimensions: syntactic, semantic, and deductive. Along the syntactic dimension one can measure the grammatical complexity allowable in input sentences. This may differ for the data input and question input. In the simplest case, one or some small number of fixed format sentences are allowable inputs. Less restricted inputs may allow any sentences which can be parsed by a fixed grammar. The nearer this grammar is to a grammar of all of English, the less restricted is the input. Because text-based question-answerers accept as input any string of words without further processing, they have no syntactic limitation on input. However, the fact-retrieval program may only be able to abstract information from those portions of a text with less than some maximum syntactic complexity.

In data-base question-answering systems, only certain relationships between words or objects may be representable in the information store. Other information may be discarded or ignored. This is a limitation in the semantic dimension of understanding.

To obtain answers to questions not explicitly given in the input, a question-answering system must have the power to perform some deductions. The structure of the information store may facilitate such deductive ability. The range of deductive ability is measured along the deductive dimension of understanding. The structure of the information store may also aid in selecting only relevant material for use in the deductive question-answering process, thus improving the efficiency of the system.

Another criterion closely related to the extent of understanding is the facility with which the syntactic, semantic, or deductive abilities of a question-answering system can be extended. In the optimal case one could improve the system along any dimension by talking to it in English. Alternatively, one might have to add some new programs to the system, or at worst, any change might imply complete reprogramming of the entire system.

An important additional consideration for users of a question-answering system is the amount of knowledge of the internal structure of the system that is necessary to use it. At best one need not be aware of the information storage structure used at all. At worst, a thorough knowledge of the internal structure may be necessary to construct suitable input.

Another measure of the usefulness of a question-answering system is its ability to interact with the user. In the worst case, a question is asked and some time later an answer or a report of failure is given. No indication is given of the cause of failure, nor does the system allow the person to give any help. In the best case, the system will ask the user for specific help and accept suggestions for appropriate courses of action.

In this part we have given the following criteria for evaluating question-answering systems:

a. Extent of understanding (syntactic, semantic, and deductive abilities);
b. Facility for extending abilities (syntactic, semantic, deductive);
c. Need by user for knowledge of internal structure of system;
d. Extent of interaction with user.

3.1.4 English Language Question-Answering Systems

This part provides a critical summary of a number of English language question-answering systems, utilizing the criteria outlined in the previous part. This discussion will provide a context for the part of Section 3.7 that summarizes the capabilities of the STUDENT system. For a description of the different syntactic analysis schemes see the survey by Bobrow (4).

1. *Phillips:* One of the earliest question-answering systems was written in 1960 at M.I.T. by Phillips (36). It is a data-base system which accepts sentences that can be parsed by a very simple context-free phrase structure grammar of the type defined by Chomsky (8). Additional syntactic restrictions require that each word must be in only one grammatical class and that a sentence has exactly one parsing.

A parsed sentence is transformed into a list of five elements: the subject, verb, object, time phrase, and place phrase. All other information is disregarded. Questions are answered by matching the list from the transformed question against the list for each input sentence. When a match is found, the corresponding sentence is given as an answer.

Phillips' system has no deductive ability, and adding new abilities would require reprogramming the system. A questioner must be aware that the system utilizes a matching process which does not recognize synonyms, and therefore the sentence, "The teacher eats lunch at noon" will not be recognized as an answer to the question, "What does the teacher do at twelve o'clock?" When Phillips' system cannot find an answer, it reports only "(THE ORACLE DOES NOT KNOW)." It provides for no further interaction with the user.

2. *Green:* "BASEBALL" is a question-answering system designed and programmed at Lincoln Laboratories by Green, Wolf, Chomsky, and Laughery (19). It is a data-base system in which the data are placed in memory in a prestructured tree format. The data consist of the dates, locations, opposing teams, and scores of some American League baseball games. Only questions to the system can be given in English, not the data.

Questions must be simple sentences, with no relative clauses, logical or coordinate connectives. With these restrictions, the program will accept any question couched in words contained in a vocabulary list quite adequate for asking questions about baseball statistics. In addition, the parsing routine, based on techniques developed by Harris (21), must find a parsing for the question.

The questions must pertain to statistics about baseball games found in the information store. One cannot ask questions about extrema, such as "highest" score or "fewest" number of games won. The parsed question is transformed into a standard "specification list," and the question-answering routine utilizes this canonical form for the meaning of the question. For example, the question "Who beat the Yankees on July 4?" would be transformed into the specification list:

Team (losing) = New York
Team (winning) = ?
Date = July 4

Because BASEBALL does not utilize English for data input, we cannot talk about deductions made from information implicit in several sentences. However, BASEBALL can perform operations such as counting (the number of games played by Boston, for example) and thus in the sense that it is utilizing several separate data units in its store, it is performing deductions.

BASEBALL's abilities can only be extended by extensive reprogramming, though the techniques utilized have some general applicability. Because the parsing program has a very complete grammar and the vocabulary list is quite comprehensive for the problem domain, the user needs no knowledge of the internal structure of the BASEBALL program. No provision for interaction with the user was made.

3. *Simmons:* The "SYNTHEX" system is a text-based question-answering system designed and programmed at SDC by Simmons, Klein, and McConlogue (41). The entire contents of a children's encyclopedia has been transcribed to magnetic tape for use as the information store. An index has been prepared listing the location of all the content words in the text, including words like "worm," "eat," and "birds," but excluding function words like "and," "the," and "of." All the content words of a question are extracted, and information-rich sections of the text are retrieved; these are sections that are locally dense in content words contained in the question. For example, if the question were "What do worms eat?" with content words "worms" and "eat," the two sentences, "Birds eat worms on the grass" and "Most worms usually eat grass" might be retrieved. At this time, the program performs a syntactic analysis of the question and of the sentences that may contain the answer. A comparison of the dependency trees of the question and various sentences may eliminate some irrelevant sentences. In the example, "Birds eat worms on the grass" is eliminated because "worms" is the object of the verb "eats" instead of the subject, as in the question. In the general case, the remaining sentences are given in some ranked order as possibly answering the question.

SYNTHEX is limited syntactically by its grammar to the extent that the syntactic analysis eliminates irrelevant statements. It makes no use of the meaning of any statements or words and cannot deduce answers from information implicit in two or more sentences. Because the grammar is independent of the program, the syntactic ability of SYNTHEX can be extended relatively easily. However, before it can become a good question-answering system, some semantic abilities will have to be added.

SYNTHEX does not explicitly provide for interaction with the user, but because it is implemented in the SDC time-sharing system (9), a user may modify a previous question if the sentences retrieved were not suitable. The mechanism for selection of sentences must be kept in mind to get best results.

4. *Lindsay:* At the Carnegie Institute of Technology, Lindsay (28) programmed the "SAD-SAM" question-answering system. The input to the system is a set of sentences in Basic English, a subset of English devised by Ogden (35), which has a vocabulary of about 1500 words and a simple subset of the full English grammar. The SAD part (Syntactic Appraiser and Diagrammer) of SAD-SAM parses the sentence by using a predictive analysis scheme. The Semantic Analyzing Machine

(SAM) extracts from these parsed sentences information about the family relationships of people mentioned; it stores this information on a computer representation of the family tree and ignores all other information in the sentence. For example, from the parsing of "Tom, Mary's brother, went to the store," Lindsay's program would extract the sibling relationship of Tom and Mary, place them on the family tree as descendants of the same mother and father, and ignore the information about where Tom went.

The information storage structure utilized by SAD-SAM, namely, the family tree, facilitates deductions from information implicit in many sentences. Because a family relationship is defined in terms of the relative position (no pun intended) of two people in their family tree, computation of the relationship is independent of the number of sentences required to place in the tree the path between the individuals.

Extending the abilities of the SAD-SAM system would require reprogramming. No provision is made for interaction with the user. No internal knowledge of the program structure is necessary if the user restricts his queries to questions of family relationships, and his language to Basic English.

5. *Raphael:* The SIR question-answering system, designed by Bertram Raphael, accepts simple sentences in any of about 20 fixed formats useful for expressing certain relationships between objects. The semantic relationships extracted from these sentences are those of set membership, set inclusion, subpart, left-to-right position, and ownership.

The information about the relationships between various objects is stored in a semantic network, where the nodes of the network are objects and the relationships are indicated by directed labeled links between nodes. For example, if the three sentences, "John is a boy," "A boy is a person," and "Two hands are part of any person" were an input to SIR, four nodes labeled *John, boy, person,* and *hand* would be created. Included in the network would be a link indicating set membership between *John* and *boy,* another with a label indicating set inclusion between *boy* and *person,* and a link indicating *hand* is a subpart of *person,* with the number of parts equal to 2.

Separate question-answering routines are used for questions involving different relationships. Each routine takes cognizance of the interaction of various relationships and can deduce answers from the linked structure of the network, independent of the number of sentences necessary to set up these links. For example, by tracing the links from *John* to *hand,* SIR would answer "yes" to the question "Is a hand part of John?"

The SIR system can interact with the user. For example, if told that "A finger is part of a hand" and asked "How many fingers does John have?" it would reply, "How many fingers per hand?" Only if it is told, "Every hand has five fingers," it would answer the question with "The answer is 10."

Any extensions of the SIR system necessitate additional programming effort, though it is far easier to add new syntactic forms than new semantic relationships. Within the input limits of the 20 fixed format statements, the user need not know anything of the internal structure of the information storage structure.

3.1.5 Other Related Work

A number of programs have been written to translate English statements into a logical notation to check the consistency of a set of statements and the validity of logical arguments. Given a set of sentences transformed to some logical notation, and another statement, such a system can answer the question, "Is the statement (or its negation) implied by the set?"

Cooper (12) and Darlington (14) both have programs that translate a subset of English into the propositional calculus. Darlington is also working on programs that can translate English into the first-order and second-order predicate calculi. A difficult problem being considered by Darlington in trying to handle implications of English statements in terms of their logical translation is the determination of the proper level of analysis for a particular problem – that is, whether to translate the input into second-order predicate calculus where proofs are very difficult, or to try to use first-order predicate or propositional calculus to prove the theorem and perhaps find it logically insufficient.

At the National Bureau of Standards, Kirsch (22), Cohen (10), and Sillars (39) have designed a system in which pictures and English language statements are converted to expressions in the first-order predicate calculus. One can then check to see if an English language statement is consistent with a given picture.

McCarthy's "Advice Taker" (30), though not designed to accept English input, would make an excellent base for a question-answering system. Black (2) has programmed a system that can do all of McCarthy's Advice-Taker problems and can be adapted to accept a very limited subset of English. The deductive system in Black's program is equivalent to the propositional calculus.

A number of people have done work bearing directly on the problem of solving algebra word problems stated in English. Garfinkle (18) described the heuristics she would use in programming a computer to solve algebra word problems but never wrote the program. Most of the heuristics were too vague for actual use. Our treatment of "this" was taken from Garfinkle's paper, as were a number of simplified statements of algebra story problems transcribed and transformed from problems in a first-year algebra textbook.

Coleman (11), at M.I.T., wrote a term paper describing a program of his which sets up the equations for some types of algebra story problems (also handled by STUDENT). Some of the special heuristics used by me for "age problems" were inspired by his techniques.

Kuck (24) describes his ideas on how to construct this type of program, but also did not implement these ideas. He suggests methods for transformation of English input to equations which would require much more information about words than is used in the STUDENT program and therefore were not applicable in this work. The STUDENT program considers words as symbols, and makes do with as little knowledge about the meaning of words as is compatible with the goal of finding a solution to the particular problem.

3.2 Semantic Generation and Analysis of Discourse

This section will put the techniques of analysis embedded in the STUDENT program into a wider context and indicate how they can fit into a more general language-processing system. A theory of semantic generation and analysis of discourse will be proposed. STUDENT can then be considered a first approximation to a computer implementation of the analytic portion of the theory, with certain restrictions on the interpretation of a discourse to be analyzed. The theory will show why analysis is so greatly simplified by the imposed restrictions.

3.2.1 Language as Communication

Language is an encoding used for communication between a speaker and a listener (or writer and reader). To transmit an "idea," the speaker must first encode it in a message, as a string in the transmission language. To understand this message, a listener must decode it and extract its meaning. The coding of a particular message is a function of both its global and its local context. The global context of a message is the background knowledge of the speaker and the listener, including some knowledge of possible universes of discourse and codings for some simple ideas.

The local context of a message M is the set of messages temporally adjacent to M, which may refer back to earlier messages; or M may be just a modification of a previous message and only understandable in this context. For example, consider the second sentence of the following discourse: "How many chaplains are in the U.S. Army? How many are in the Navy?"

For communication to take place, the information map of both the listener and the speaker must be approximately the same, at least for the universe of discourse; also the decoding process of the listener must be an approximate inverse of the encoding process of the speaker. Education in language is in large part an attempt to force the language processors of different people into a uniform mold to facilitate successful communication.

We are not proposing that identity in detail is achieved, but, as Quine (37) put it:

> Different persons growing up in the same language are like different bushes trimmed and trained to take the shape of identical elephants. The anatomical details of twigs and branches will fulfill the elephantine form differently from bush to bush, but the overall outward results are alike.

As a speaker transmits successive messages concerning some portion of his information map, the listener who understands the messages constructs a model of a "situation." The relation between the listener's model and the speaker's information map is that from each can be extracted the transmitted information relevant to the universe of discourse, including information deducible from the entire set of messages. The internal structure of the listener's model need bear no resemblance to that of the speaker and may in general contain far less detail.

3.2.2 Theories of Language

According to Morris's theory of signs (33), the encoding and decoding of language can be stratified into three levels: The first is *syntactic* analysis, which deals with the relationships of signs to other signs. A syntactic analysis, treating words as members of classes of words, can yield structurings of messages which indicate common processing features. The second level, *semantic* analysis, is concerned with the relationships of signs to the things they denote. A third level, *pragmatic* analysis, deals with the relationships between signs and their interpretations in terms of actions required. Our theory will deal with all three levels, with primary emphasis on the relation of the semantic aspect of language to the generation of discourse.

Many theories of syntax, developed to describe the structure of English, have served as bases for computer programs which perform syntactic analysis. For a complete survey of such systems see Bobrow (4). Almost all of these theories ignore the concepts of meaning and semantics, resulting in programs that often yield many possible structurings for a single sentence which is unambiguous to a person. With some use of meaning, many of the meaningless, ambiguous interpretations could be eliminated. For a good discussion of why ambiguities arise in syntactic analysis see Kuno and Oettinger (25).

Based on some ideas described by Yngve (46), a number of programs have been written which generate syntactically correct English sentences. The sentences generated are predominantly meaningless nonsense, except for the coherent discourse generator of Klein (23). Klein utilizes an input text from which he extracts certain structural dependencies of the words in the input. He then generates sentences, and before they are released for output a postprocessor checks to see if the words in the generated sentence satisfy structural dependencies consistent with those found in the input text. However, even in Klein's program no attempt is made to use the denotive meaning of any word, except insofar as this meaning is reflected in its co-occurrences with other words in the input text.

Some theories that do consider the problem of semantics are now being developed. Pendegraft (27) states that the programs being designed at the Linguistic Research Center of the University of Texas are an explication of Morris's theory of signs. Though not yet implemented, the semantic analysis program will make use of a preliminary phrase-structure syntactic analysis. A number of syntactic structures, with appropriate vocabulary items, will map onto single semantic constants, essentially indicating that these structures all have the same meaning. This gives a type of canonical form for structures in terms of their meanings but does not utilize any explicit model of the world. No provision is made in the theory for deduction of information implicit in a set of sentences.

Lamb (26) also proposed a stratificational theory of grammar, not yet implemented on a computer, in which successive levels of analysis are performed, with a final mapping of the input into structures in a "sememic" stratum of the language, in which there are bundles of "sememes" or meanings, and indications of the relationships between different bundles. Different sentences that mean the same thing should map into the same structure in this sememic stratum. Sememic structures are thus canonical representations of meaning.

3.2.3 Definition of Coherent Discourse

The theory of language generation and analysis which we shall describe here is designed to handle what we call *coherent discourse.* A discourse is a sequence of sentences such that the meaning of the discourse cannot be determined by interpreting each sentence independently. The interpretation of each sentence may be dependent on the local context, in the sense defined previously. A discourse is coherent if it has a complete and consistent interpretation. Completeness implies that there is no substring within the discourse that does not have some interpretation in the model of the situation being built by the listener.

A listener's ability to build a model of a situation from a discourse is dependent on information available to him from his general store of knowledge. Therefore it is quite possible for a discourse to seem coherent to one listener but not to another. A writer reading his own writing may feel that he has generated a coherent sequence of sentences, but in fact it may be incoherent to all other readers. This is unfortunately not a rare occurrence in the scientific literature. Conversely, a listener who is a psychiatrist, for example, may find coherence in a sequence of remarks which a patient thinks are entirely unrelated.

The STUDENT system utilizes an expandable store of general knowledge to build a model of a situation described in a member of a limited class of discourses. The form of this model of a situation built by STUDENT will be discussed in detail later in this section. As far as I know, STUDENT is the only computer implementation of a theory of discourse analysis now extant that maps a discourse into some representation of its meaning. Once the theories of Lamb and Pendegraft are implemented, they should also be able to analyze this class of discourse (and others). Harris also talks about "discourse analysis" (20), but his use of this term specifically excludes the use of meaning:

> The method [of discourse analysis] is formal, depending only on the occurrence of morphemes as distinguishable elements, and not upon the analyst's knowledge of the particular meaning of each morpheme.

3.2.4 The Use of Kernel Sentences in Our Theory

A basic postulate of our theory of language analysis is that a listener understands a discourse by transforming it into an equivalent (in meaning) sequence of simpler *kernel sentences*. A kernel sentence is one which the listener can understand directly; that is, one for which he knows a transformation into his information store. Conversely, a speaker generates a set of kernel sentences from his information map and utilizes a sequence of transformations on this set to yield his spoken discourse. This set of kernel sentences is not invariant from person to person; it even varies for a single individual as he learns.

The use of kernel sentences in this way is controversial. However, the theory is proposed as a good framework for understanding and implementing language processing on a computer, not necessarily as a model for human behavior. The usefulness of this theory as a psychological model is an empirical question. Skinner (42) has given some psychological justification for assuming the existence of a set of base sentences, and Chomsky (7) has discussed the linguistic merits of the use of the concept of kernel sentences. Despite this common concept of kernel sentences, in practice, our use of kernel sentences differs from that of Skinner or Chomsky. As a basis of a language it is analogous to the use of generators in defining a group.

Although we are not proposing our theory as a basis for a psychological model, it has been useful, to avoid circumlocutions, to describe the theory in terms of the properties and actions of a hypothetical speaker and listener. All statements about speakers and listeners should be interpreted as referring to computer programs which, respectively, generate and analyze coherent discourse.

3.2.5 Generation of Coherent Discourse

1. *The Speaker's Model of the World:* We assume that a speaker has some model of the world in his information store. We shall *not* be concerned here with how this model was built or with its exact form. Different forms for the model will be useful for different language tasks, but they must all have the properties described below.

The basic components of the model are a *set of objects,* $\{O_i\}$, a *set of functions* $\{F_i^n\}$, a *set of relations* $\{R_i^n\}$, a *set of propositions* $\{P_i\}$, and a *set of semantic deductive rules.* A *function* F_i^n is a mapping from ordered sets of *n* objects, called the arguments of F_i^n, into the set of objects. The mapping may be multivalued and is defined only if the arguments satisfy a set of conditions associated with F_i^n. A *condition* is essentially membership in a class of objects, but will be defined more precisely later. A *relation* R_i^n is a special type of object in the model and consists of a label (a unique identifier) and an ordered set of *n* conditions, called the argument conditions for the relation. Functions of relations are again relations.

An *elementary proposition* consists of a label associated with some relation, R_i^n and an ordered set of *n* objects satisfying the argument conditions for this relation. One may think of these propositions as the beliefs of a speaker about what relationships between objects he has noticed are true in the world. *Complex propositions* are logical combinations (in the usual sense) of elementary propositions.

The *semantic deductive rules* give procedures for adding new propositions to the model based on the propositions now in the model. In addition to the ordinary rules of logic, these rules include axioms about the relationships of the relations in the model. The semantic deductive rules also include links to the senses of the speaker. For example, one such deductive rule for adding a proposition to the model might be (loosely speaking), "Look in the real world and see if it is true." These rules essentially determine how the model is to be expanded and are the most complex part of a complete system. However, from our present point of view we need only consider these rules as a black box which can extend the set of propositions in the model.

A *closed question* is a relational label for some R_i^n and an ordered set of *n* objects. The answer to this question is affirmative if the proposition, consisting of this label and the *n* objects, is in the model (or can be added to it). If the negation of this proposition is in the model (or can be added), the answer is negative. Otherwise the answer is undefined.

An *open question* consists of a relational label for an n-argument relation, R_i^n, and a set of objects corresponding to n-k of these arguments, where $n \geqslant k \geqslant 1$. An answer to an open question is an ordered set of k objects such that if these objects are associated with the k unspecified arguments of R_i^n, the resulting proposition is in the model or can be added to it. An open question may either have no answers or may have one or more answers. A *condition* is an open question with k = 1, and an object satisfies a condition if it is an answer to the question.

2. *Generation of Kernel Sentences:* We have described the logical properties of the speaker's model of the world. We shall now consider how strings in a language, words, phrases, and sentences, are associated with the model. Corresponding to the set of objects O_i there is a set N_{ij} of strings (in English in our case), called the *names* of the objects. There is a many-one mapping from $\{N_{ij}\}$ onto $\{O_i\}$. It is many-one because one object may have more than one name; e.g., frankfurter and hot dog both map back into the same object in the model.

Recall that functions map *n*-tuples of objects into objects. Thus a function name and an *n*-tuple can specify an object. We can derive a name for this object from the function name and the names of its *n* arguments. Associated with each function is at least one linguistic form, a string of words with blanks in which names of arguments of the function must be inserted. Examples of linguistic forms associated with a model are "number of _____," "father of _____," and "the child of _____ and _____." There is a many-one mapping from the set of linguistic forms $\{L_{ij}^n\}$ onto the set of functions. Two examples of multiple linguistic forms for the same function are "father of _____" and "_____'s father"; and "_____ plus _____" and "the sum of _____ and _____." Thus, if objects *x* and *y* have names "the first number" and "the second number," and associated with the function "*" is the linguistic form "the product of _____ and _____," then the name of the object produced by applying the function "*" to *x* and *y* is "the product of the first number and the second number." A parsing of a name thus must decompose it into the part which is the linguistic form, and the parts which are names of arguments of the corresponding function. We shall call objects defined in terms of a function and an *n*-tuple of objects a *functionally defined object,* and those which are not functionally defined we shall call *simple objects.* Simple objects have *simple names* and functionally defined objects have *composite names.*

In addition to linguistic forms associated with functions, there are linguistic forms associated with relations. For an *n* argument relation there are *n* blanks in the linguistic form. Examples of relational linguistic forms are "_____ equals _____," "_____ gave _____ to _____," and "_____ speaks."

It is this set of linguistic forms, corresponding to the relations in the model, that serves as frames for the kernel sentences.

In a manner similar to the way composite names are built, a kernel sentence corresponding to an elementary proposition is constructed by inserting names corresponding to each argument in the appropriate blank. Names may be simple or composite. An example of a kernel sentence for a proposition built from such a relational linguistic form is "John's father gave .3 times the salary of Bill to Jack," which contains the simple names "John," ".3," "Bill," and "Jack." It contains the functional linguistic forms "_____'s father," "_____ times _____," and "salary of _____," and the relational linguistic form "_____ gave _____ to _____."

A kernel sentence corresponding to a complex proposition is constructed recursively from the kernel sentences corresponding to its elementary propositional constituents by placing them in the corresponding places in the linguistic forms "_____ and _____," "_____ or _____," "not _____," etc.

The kernel sentence corresponding to a closed question is constructed from the kernel of the corresponding proposition by placing it in the linguistic form, "Is it true that _____?" For an open question, dummy objects are placed in the open argument positions to complete a propositional form. These dummy arguments have names "who," "what," "where," etc.; which dummy objects are used depends on the condition on that argument position. A question mark is placed at the end of the kernel sentence constructed in the usual way from the relational linguistic form and the names of the arguments.

In generating a coherent discourse, a speaker chooses a number of propositions in his model and/or some open or closed questions. He then uses linguistic information associated with the model to construct the set of kernel sentences corresponding to this set of chosen propositions. In the next paragraphs we shall discuss how he generates his discourse from this set of kernels.

3. *Transformations on Kernel Sentences:* The set of kernel sentences is the base of the coherent discourse. The meaning of a kernel sentence is the proposition into which it maps, and, similarly, the meaning of any name is the object which is its image under the mapping. To this set of kernels we apply a sequence of meaning-preserving transformations to get the final discourse. We use the word "transformation" in its broad general sense, not in the narrow technical sense defined by Chomsky (7).

There are two distinct types of transformations: structural and definitional. A structural or syntactic transformation is only dependent on the structure of the kernel string(s) on which it operates. For example, one syntactic transformation takes a kernel in the active voice to one in the passive voice.

Another combines two sentences into a single complex coordinate sentence.

One large class of syntactic transformations is used to substitute pronominal phrases for names. Pronominal phrases may be ordinary pronouns, such as "he," "she," or "it." They may be referential phrases such as "the latter," "the former," or "this quantity." They may also be truncations of a full name, such as "the distance" for "the distance between New York and Los Angeles." In cases where such pronominal reference is made, the coherence of the final discourse is dependent on the order in which the resultant strings appear.

The second type of transformation is definitional. It involves substitutions of linguistic strings and forms for ones appearing in the kernel sentences. For example, for any appearance of "2 times" we may substitute "twice," and for ".5 times" substitute "one half of." In addition to this string substitution, some transformations perform form substitution and rearrangement. For example, for a kernel sentence of the form "x is y more than z," where x, y, and z are any names, one definitional transformation can substitute "x exceeds z by y."

Some transformations are optional, and some may be mandatory if certain forms are present in the kernel set. Certain transformations are used by a speaker for stylistic purposes, for example, to emphasize certain objects; other syntactic transformations such as those which perform pronominal substitutions are used because they decrease the depth of a construction, in the sense defined by Yngve (44).

Let us review the steps in the generation of a coherent discourse. The speaker chooses a set of propositions, the "ideas" he wishes to transmit. He then encodes them as language strings called kernel sentences in the manner described. He then chooses a sequence of structural and definitional transformations which are defined on this set of kernels or on the ordered set of sentences which result from applications of the first transformations. The resulting sequence of sentences will be a coherent discourse to a listener if he knows all the definitional transformations applied. In addition, for every pair of distinct names which the speaker maps back into the same object, the listener must also map into a single object.

In order to clarify this theory, we show in Appendix 3.5 a sample semantic generative grammar which will generate coherent discourse understandable by the STUDENT analysis program. The objects are numbers, and the functions are the arithmetic operations of sum, difference, product, and quotient. The only relation in the model is numerical equality. The transformations are described informally; further linguistic investigation is necessary before a formal notation for transformations can be decided upon. Parallel to the grammar is a sample problem generated by utilizing this grammar. This problem is solvable by the STUDENT system.

3.2.6 Analysis of Coherent Discourse

Generation of coherent discourse consists of two distinguishable steps. From propositions in the speaker's model of the world he generates an ordered set of kernel sentences. He then applies a sequence of transformations to this kernel set. The resulting discourse is a coded message which is to be analyzed and decoded by a listener. The listener's problem can be loosely characterized as an attempt to answer the question, "What would I have meant if I had said that?"

To analyze a discourse, the listener must find the set of kernel sentences from which it was generated; one way to do this is to find a set of inverse transformations which, when applied to the input discourse, yield a sequence of kernel sentences. He must then transform these kernel sentences to an appropriate representation in his information store. The appropriateness of a representation is a function of what later use the listener expects to make of the information contained in the discourse. The listener may simultaneously transform a given kernel sentence into a number of different representations in his information store. On a level of pragmatic analysis, statements require only storage of information. Questions and imperatives require appropriate responses from the listener. The difficulties in analysis dichotomize into those associated with finding the kernel sentences which are the base of the discourse, and those associated with transforming the kernel sentences into representations in the information store.

Matthews (29) has suggested that analysis can be performed by synthesis. A sequence of kernel sentences and a sequence of transformations are chosen, and the transformations are applied to the kernel sentences. The resulting discourse is matched against the input. If they are the same, the kernel sentences and transformations give the required analysis of the input. If not, a change is made so that the resulting discourse becomes more like the input.

If the kernel sentences and transformations were chosen randomly, this method would obviously be too inefficient to work in any practical sense. However, by utilizing clues within the input discourse, the choice of kernels and transformations can be greatly restricted. This technique of sentence analysis is being implemented in a program being written at MITRE by Walker and Bartlett (43). It has the advantage that the identical grammar can be utilized for both analysis and generation of discourse.

A more direct analytical approach would utilize a set of inverse analytic transformations. If T_i is a transformation that may be used in generating a discourse, and $T_i(S) = \overline{S}$, where S and $\overline{S}$ are sets of sentences, then the analytic transformation T_i^{-1} is the inverse of T_i if and only if $T_i^{-1}(\overline{S}) = S$. The choice of which inverse transformations to apply and the order of their application may again be restricted by utilizing heuristics concerned with features of the input.

Once the base set of kernel sentences for a given discourse is determined, there remains the problem of entering representations of these sentences in the listener's information store. The major problem in accomplishing this step involves the separation of those words which are part of linguistic forms for relations, and those which are part of a name. This is difficult, because the same word (lexicographic symbol) may have multiple uses in a language. Having separated the relational form from the names that represent the arguments of this relation, one can then analyze the name in terms of components which are functional linguistic forms and others which are simple names. From this parsing in terms of relational linguistic forms, functional linguistic forms, and simple names, the discourse can be transformed into a canonical representation in the information store of the listener.

3.2.7 Limited Deductive Models

A complete understanding of a discourse by a listener would imply that the representation of the discourse in his information store is essentially isomorphic to the speaker's model of the world, at least for the universe of discourse. The listener's representation must preserve all information implicit in the discourse.

If the listener is only interested in certain aspects of the discourse, he need only preserve information relevant to his interest, and discard the rest. Within his area of interest, the listener's model is isomorphic to the speaker's model in the sense that all relevant deductions which can be made by the speaker on the basis of the discourse can also be made by the listener. Outside this area of interest, the listener will be unable to answer any questions. We call such restricted information stores *limited deductive models.*

The question-answering programs of Lindsay and Raphael as well as the STUDENT system all utilize limited deductive models. For the area of interest in each of these programs there was a "natural" representation for the information in the allowable input. These representations were natural in that they facilitated the deduction of implicit information. For example, Lindsay's family-tree representation made it easy to compute the relationship of any two individuals in the tree, independent of the number of sentences necessary to build the tree.

Because the number of relations and functions expressible in the models in all three systems is very limited, there is a corresponding limitation on the number of linguistic forms that may appear in the input. This greatly simplifies the parsing problem discussed earlier, by restricting alternatives for words in the input text.

3.2.8 The STUDENT Deductive Model

The STUDENT system is an implementation of the analytic portion of our theory. STUDENT performs certain inverse transformations to obtain a set of kernel sentences and then transforms these kernel sentences to expressions in a limited deductive model. Utilizing the power of this deductive model, within its limited domain of understanding, it is able to answer questions based on information implicit in the input information.

The analytic and transformational techniques utilized in STUDENT are described in detail in Section 3.4. We shall discuss here the canonical representation of objects, relations, and functions within the model. STUDENT is restricted to answering questions framed in the context of algebra story problems. Algebraic equations are a natural representation for information in the input.

The objects in the model are numbers, or numbers with an associated dimension. The only relation in the model is equality, and the only functions represented directly in the model are the arithmetic operations of addition, negation, multiplication, division, and exponentiation. Other functions are defined in terms of these basic functions, by composition, and/or substitution of constants for arguments of these functions. For example, the operation of squaring is defined as exponentiation with "2" as the second argument of the exponential function; subtraction is a composition of addition and negation.

Within the computer, a parenthesized prefix notation is used for a standard representation of the equations implicit in the English input. The arithmetic operation to be expressed is made the first element of a list, and the arguments of the function are succeeding list elements. The exact notation is given in Fig. 3-2 in which A, B, and C are any representations of objects in the model, either composite or simple names. The usual infix notation for these functional expressions is given for comparison. Because this is a fully parenthesized notation, no ambiguity of operational order arises, as it does, for example, for the unparenthesized infix notation expression A * B + C or its corresponding natural-language expression "A times B plus C." Note also that in this prefix notation *plus* and *times* are not strictly binary operators. Indeed, in the model they may have any finite number of arguments; e.g. (TIMES A B C D), is a legitimate expression in the STUDENT model.

Representations of objects in the STUDENT deductive model are taken from the input. Any string of words *not* containing a linguistic form associated with the arithmetic function expressible in the model is considered

Operation	Infix Notation	Prefix Notation
Equality	A = B	(EQUAL A B)
Addition	A + B	(PLUS A B)
	A + B + C	(PLUS A B C)
Negation	- A	(MINUS A)
Subtraction	A - B	(PLUS A (MINUS B))
Multiplication	A * B	(TIMES A B)
	A * B * C	(TIMES A B C)
Division	A / B	(QUOTIENT A B)
Exponentiation	A^B	(EXPT A B)

Figure 3-2. Notation Within the STUDENT Deductive Model

to be a simple name for an object. Thus, "the age of the child of John and Jane" is considered a simple name because it contains no functional linguistic forms associated with functions represented in STUDENT's limited deductive model. In a more general model it would be considered a composite name, and the functional forms "age of ____" and "child of ____ and ____" would be mapped into their corresponding functions in the model.

Because such complex strings are considered simple names in the model, and objects are distinguished only by their names, it is important to determine when two distinct names actually refer to the same object. In fact, answers to questions in the STUDENT system are statements of the identity of the object referenced by two names. However, one of the names (the desired one) must satisfy certain lexical conditions. Most often this condition is just that the name be a numeral. For a more general model this restriction could be stated as requiring a simple name corresponding to some functionally defined name, because, for example, "number of ____" would be a functional linguistic form in the general model, and the only simple name for such an object would be the numeral corresponding to this number. An answer consists of a statement of identity, e.g., "The number of customers Tom gets is 162."

The other lexical restriction on answers sometimes used in the STUDENT system is insistence that a certain unit (corresponding to a dimension associated with a number) appear in the desired answer. For example, *spans* is the unit specified by the question "How many spans equal 1 fathom?," and the answer given by STUDENT is "1 fathom is 8 spans."

The deductive model described here is useful in answering questions because we know how to extract implicit information from expressions in this model; that is, we know how to solve sets of algebraic equations to find numerical values which satisfy these equations. The solution process used in STUDENT is described in detail in Section 3.6. The transformation process, based on the theory described earlier, which STUDENT uses to go from an English input to this deductive model, is described in Section 3.4.

3.3 Programming Formalisms, and Language Manipulation

Almost any programming language is universal in the sense that with enough time, space, and work at the implementation, any computable function may be programmed. However, the task of programming can be made much easier by the proper choice of a higher-level problem-oriented programming language. The data to be manipulated by the STUDENT system are symbolic and of indefinite length and complexity. For this reason, a list-processing language was the most appropriate type of programming for this task. There are a number of such languages available, each having its own set of advantages and disadvantages. For a description of the general properties of list-processing languages, with a detailed comparison of four of the better known list-processing languages, see reference 5. LISP (31) was chosen as the basic language for the STUDENT system.

The LISP formalism is very convenient for programming recursive tasks, such as the solving of a set of simultaneous equations. However, LISP does not provide any natural mechanisms for representing manipulation of strings of English words, another very important subtask in the STUDENT system. For this type of manipulation one would like to perform a sequence of steps involving operations such as recognizing a sentence format that fits a particular pattern, finding certain elements in a sentence by their context, rearranging a string of words, deleting, inserting, and duplicating parts of strings, and so on.

The LISP formalism cannot easily express such string manipulations, though each sequence of operations could be individually programmed. However, a formalism for just this sort of manipulation is the basis of the COMIT (45) programming system. Rules in this formalism can easily express very complex string manipulations and are easy to read and write. However, COMIT and LISP cannot be used simultaneously, and the problem context necessitates going back and forth between LISP-oriented and COMIT-oriented tasks. I therefore adapted the COMIT rule notation for use in LISP and constructed a LISP program, called METEOR, which would interpret string transformation rules in this notation.

In developing the METEOR interpreter, I effectively extended the eloquence of the LISP programming language; that is, operations which could be done previously but were awkward to invoke could now be expressed easily. An extended language embodying the best features of COMIT and LISP could have been built from scratch, but it is much more economical to achieve such extensions by embedding. The advantages and disadvantages of language extension by embedding are discussed in detail by Bobrow and Weizenbaum (6).

3.3.1 Specifying a Desired String Format

METEOR has been described in detail elsewhere (3), but we include here a brief summary of its features, because use of the notation makes later explication of the transformation process easier. In addition, if any ambiguity becomes apparent in the explanation of the operation of STUDENT, it may be resolved by consulting the listing of the STUDENT program in Appendix 3.2. In this latter case, it may be necessary to consult the more complete specification of METEOR.

A METEOR program consists of a sequence of rules, each specifying a string transformation and giving some control information. Let us first consider how a string transformation is specified. We shall call the string to be transformed the *workspace*. The workspace will be transformed by a rule only if it matches a pattern or format given in the "left half" of the rule, which is a list of elementary patterns which specifies a sequence of items that must be matched in the workspace. For example, if the left half were (THE BOY) then a match would be found only if the workspace contained a THE immediately followed by BOY. In addition to known constituents, one can match unknown constituents. The element "$1" in a left half will match any one workspace constituent. The left half (A $1 B $2 C) will match a contiguous substring of the workspace which consists of an *A* followed by exactly one constituent (specified by the marker "$1") followed by a *B* followed by exactly 2 constituents (matching the "$2") followed by an occurrence of a *C*. Thus $1 will match an element of the workspace with a specified context. If a left half would match more than one substring in the workspace, the left-most such substring is the one found by the matching process.

We have discussed elementary patterns which match a fixed number of unknown constituents (e.g., "$3" matches *3* unknown constituents). METEOR also has an elementary pattern element "$" which matches an arbitrary number of unknown constituents. For example, the left half (THE $ BOY) will match a substring of the workspace which starts with an occurrence of THE followed by any number of constituents (including zero) followed by an occurrence of BOY. It would, for example, match a substring of the workspace (GIVE THE GOOD BOY) or of the workspace (THE BOY HERE). If the left half ($ GLITCH $3) matches a substring of the workspace, then the elementary pattern "$" matches the substring from the beginning of the workspace up to but not including the first occurrence of GLITCH; the pattern "GLITCH" matches this occurrence of GLITCH in the workspace; and the elementary pattern "$3" matches the 3 elements or constituents of the workspace immediately following GLITCH.

Elements in the workspace may be tagged or subscripted to indicate special properties of this element; for example, one might have (HAVE/VERB) or (BOY/NOUN) as elements of the workspace. Such elements can be matched by name (using HAVE or BOY as pattern elements), or identified just by their subscripts (or by both). The elementary pattern ($1/VERB) will match any single constituent which is a verb; that is, one which has the subscript VERB, even if this constituent has other subscripts. Thus the left half (ALFRED ($1/VERB) BOOKS) will match the substring (ALFRED (READS/VERB) BOOKS) in the workspace (NOW ALFRED (READS/VERB) BOOKS IN THE LIBRARY).

Other elementary pattern elements are provided, and new pattern elements can be defined and easily used within the METEOR system.

3.3.2 Specifying a Transformed Workspace

We have discussed how a desired format can be specified through a prototype pattern, called a left half. If we try to match the workspace to a left half but it is not in the format specified, we say the match has *failed*. If a substring of the workspace *is* in the specified format, the match is *successful*. When there is a successful match, we may wish to transform or manipulate the substring matched, or place in a temporary storage location, called a shelf, copies of segments of the matching substring. We shall now discuss the notation used for specifying such transformations, and storage of material.

A left half is a sequence of elementary patterns, and we associate with each elementary pattern a number indicating its position in this left-half sequence. For example, in the left-half ($2 D $ E), the first elementary pattern, $2, would be associated with the number 1, the second, D, with 2, $ with 3, and E with 4. If a match is successful, each elementary pattern element in the left half matches a part of the substring of the workspace matched by this left half. The part matched by an elementary pattern can then be referenced by the number associated with this elementary pattern. For the left half given and the workspace (A B C D B A E G), the left-half match succeeds, and the substring (B C) may then be referenced with the number 1, the substring (D) by 2, (B A) by 3, and (E) by 4.

The transformed workspace is specified by the "right half" of a METEOR rule. This right half may be just the numeral 0, in which case the matched portion of the workspace is deleted. Otherwise this right half must be a list of elements specifying a replacement for the matched substring. Any numbers in this right-half list reference (specify) the appropriate part of the matched substring. Other items in the list may reference themselves, or strings in temporary storage, or functions of any referenceable substrings. In the example discussed, if the right half were (3 2 M 2 H), then the matched portion of the workspace would be replaced by (B A D M D H), and the workspace would become (A B A D M D H G). Note that 1 and 4 were not mentioned in this right half and were therefore deleted from the workspace. Also 3 and 2 were in reverse order, and thus these referenced parts were inserted in the workspace in an order opposite to that in which they had appeared; 2 is referenced twice in this right half and therefore two copies of this referenced substring, (D) appear in the workspace. The elements M and H in this right half reference only themselves, and are therefore inserted directly into the workspace.

Using the right-half elements described, that is, numbers referencing matched substrings and constants (elements referencing themselves), one can express transformations of the workspace in which elements have been added to, deleted from, duplicated in, and rearranged in the workspace. Elements to be added to the workspace thus far can only be constants. Let us consider some other possible right-half elements. They are all indicated by lists which start with special flags.

The contents of any shelf (temporary storage list) can be referenced by a two-element list with a first element either *A (for *A*ll) or *N (for *N*ext), and a second element, the shelf name. For example (*A EQT), references the entire contents of a shelf named EQT. If this element appeared in a right half, the entire contents of that shelf would be placed in the corresponding places in the workspace. The *first* element of a shelf named "SENTENCES" could be put into the workspace by using the element (*N SENTENCES) in a right half.

The flag FN as the first member of a list serving as a right-half element indicates that the next member of this list is a function name, and the following ones are the arguments of this function. The value of the function for this set of arguments is placed in the workspace. In this way, any LISP function can be used within a METEOR rule.

The flag *K indicates that the rest of the list following is to be evaluated as a right-half rule, and then is to be "compressed" into a list which will be a single element of the workspace. Thus, chunks which are longer and have a more complex structure than a single word can be treated as a single unit within the METEOR workspace string. The inverse operation is the expansion of a chunk, so that all its components appear as individual constituents in the workspace. Expansion is indicated by a *E flag at the beginning of a right-half element list.

We have thus far discussed how the transformation of a string, called the workspace, can be expressed in terms of a left half which is a pattern for a desired input format, and a right half which is a pattern for the desired output format. There is no reason to limit to one the number of outputs from a single left-half match. In fact, a third section of a METEOR rule, called the "routing section" (for historical reasons), allows the programmer to give any number of other right halves, and place these referenced lists at the beginning or end of any shelf (temporary storage list). The storage of such a "right half" is indicated in the routing section by a list starting with a *S or a *Q, followed by the shelf name followed by a right-half pattern. The *S indicates that the referenced material is to be *S*tored on the beginning of the named shelf. *Q indicates that it should be *Q*ueued on the end of the shelf. Used with a *N for retrieval, a shelf built up by a *S is a pushdown list (a last-in-first-out list), and a shelf built up by a *Q is a queue (first-in-first-out list).

The only other significant feature of a METEOR program not yet touched on is the control structure in a set of rules. A METEOR rule has a name, and has a "go-to" section. Ordinarily, if the left-half match fails, control is automatically passed to the next rule in sequence. If the left-half match succeeds, the right half and routing sections are interpreted, and then control is passed to the rule named in the "go-to." However, by insertion of a "*" immediately after the rule name in the rule, the method of transfer of control is switched, and only on left-half failure will control pass to the rule named in the "go-to."

Routing control can also be changed by a list of the form "(*D *name*1 *name*2)" in the routing section of a rule. After this list is interpreted, any occurrence of *name*1 in a "go-to" will be interpreted as a "go-to" containing *name*2. This latter feature allows easy return from subroutines. The use of left-half success or failure as a switch for the transfer of control makes it possible to write significant one-rule loops.

A METEOR program is a sequence (list) of rules. Each rule is a list of up to six elements. The following is an example of a METEOR rule containing all six elements:

(NAME * ($ BOY) (2 1) (/ (*S S1 2 2) (*D P1 P2)) P1)

We shall briefly review the function of each of these six elements. The first element of a METEOR rule is a name and must be present in any rule. If no name is needed, the dummy name "*" can be used. The second element is a "*" and is optional. When it is *present* it reverses the switch on flow of control, and transfer of control to the rule named in the "go-to" is made on left-half *failure*.

The third element is mandatory and is a left-half pattern that is to be matched in the workspace. The fourth element is optional and is a right-half pattern specifying the result in the workspace of the string transformation desired. The fifth (optional) element is called the routing section and is a list flagged with a "/" as a first element. The remainder of the routing section is a sequence of lists which specify operations which place items on shelves or set "go-to" values. The final element is called the "go-to" and specifies where control is to be passed if a match succeeds (in the normal case). A "*" in this position specifies the next rule in sequence.

3.3.3 Summary

In this section, we have briefly summarized the features of a language for string manipulation which has been embedded (by building the METEOR interpreter) in the general list-processing language LISP. The ability to describe easily in METEOR the string transformations needed to process English sentences and also use, where appropriate, the functional notation of the general list-processing language LISP was a great advantage in the programming effort.

As a final illustration of the power of the combined METEOR-LISP language we include a program for Wang's algorithm for proving theorems in the propositional calculus, as described on pages 44-45 of the LISP manual (31); a LISP program for the algorithm appears on pages 48-50. Figure 3-3 contains the complete METEOR program for the algorithm, including definitions of four small auxiliary LISP functions used within the METEOR program. In addition, it supplies a trace of the program as it proves the theorem given after the first line containing "(THEOREM)." The other lines give the theorems that are proven by the algorithm as steps in the proof of this theorem. This METEOR program compares quite favorably in both size and understandability to the one given in the LISP manual, and to the one COMIT program which I have seen which performs the Wang algorithm.

3.4 Transformation of English to the STUDENT Deductive Model

The STUDENT system consists of two main subprograms, called STUDENT and REMEMBER. REMEMBER accepts and processes statements that contain global information; that is, information not specific to any one story problem. We shall discuss the processing and information-storage techniques used in REMEMBER in the next section. A listing of the global information given to the STUDENT system may be found in Appendix 3.3. Here we shall describe the techniques embedded in the STUDENT program which are used to transform an English statement of an algebra story problem to expressions in the STUDENT deductive model.

Definition of WANG in METEOR

```
DEFINE((
(WANG (LAMBDA (X) (METEOR (QUOTE (
 (TØP    ((*P THEØREM))                                   *)
(*       ($ $1 $ ARRØW $ 2 $)    ((*K *T*))             END)
(A2      (ARRØW $ (FN MAINCØN NØT))    ((FN ARGØNE (*K 3)) 1
           2)                                           TØP)
(B2      ((FN MAINCØN NØT) $ ARRØW)    (2 3 (FN ARGØNE (*K 1
           )))                                          TØP)
(A3      ($ ARRØW $ (FN MAINCØN AND) $)    ((FN AN2 (FN WANG
           (*K 1 2 3 (FN ARGØNE (*K 4)) 5)) (FN WANG (*K
           1 2 3 (FN ARGTWØ (*K 4)) 5))))               END)
(B3      ((FN MAINCØN AND) $ ARRØW)    ((FN ARGØNE (*K 1)) (
           FN ARGTWØ (*K 1)) 2 3)                       TØP)
(A4      (ARRØW $ (FN MAINCØN ØR))    (1 2 (FN ARGØNE (*K 3)
           ) (FN ARGTWØ (*K 3)))                        TØP)
(B4      ($ (FN MAINCØN ØR) $ ARRØW $)    ((FN AN2 (FN WANG
           (*K 1 (FN ARGØNE (*K 2)) 3 4 5)) (FN WANG (*K
           1 (FN ARGTWØ (*K 2)) 3 4 5))))               END)
(A5      (ARRØW $ (FN MAINCØN IMPLIES))    ((FN ARGØNE (*K 3
           )) 1 2 (FN ARGTWØ (*K 3)))                   TØP)
(B5      ($ (FN MAINCØN IMPLIES) $ ARRØW $)    ((FN AN2 (FN
           WANG (*K 1 (FN ARGTWØ (*K 2)) 3 4 5)) (FN WANG
           (*K 1 3 4 5 (FN ARGØNE (*K 2))))))           END)
(A6      ($ ARRØW $ (FN MAINCØN EQUIV) $)    ((FN AN2 (FN
           WANG (*K 1 (FN ARGØNE (*K 4)) 2 3 (FN ARGTWØ (
           *K 4)) 5)) (FN WANG (*K 1 (FN ARGTWØ (*K 4)) 2
           3 (FN ARGØNE (*K 4)) 5))))                   END)
(B6      ($ (FN MAINCØN EQUIV) $ ARRØW $)    ((FN AN2 (FN
           WANG (*K (FN ARGØNE (*K 2)) (FN ARGTWØ (*K 2))
           3 4 5)) (FN WANG (*K 1 3 4 5 (FN ARGØNE (*K 2
           )) (FN ARGTWØ (*K 2))))))                    END)
(FAILURE    ($)    ((*K))                               END)
))  X)))
))
```

Auxiliary Functions for WANG

```
DEFINE((
(MAINCON (LAMBDA (WS CON)(COND
        ((EQ CON (CAAR WS))(CONS(LIST(CAR WS))(CDR WS)))
        (T NIL) )))
(AN2 (LAMBDA (X Y) (COND (X Y) (T NIL))))
(ARGONE (LAMBDA (X) (LIST(CADAR X))))
(ARGTWO (LAMBDA (X) (LIST(CADDAR X))))
))
```

Trace of a Proof by WANG

```
(THEOREM)
((OR A (NOT B)) ARROW (IMPLIES (AND P Q) (EQUIV P Q)))
(THEOREM)
(A ARROW (IMPLIES (AND P Q) (EQUIV P Q)))
(THEOREM)
(A (AND P Q) ARROW (EQUIV P Q))
(THEOREM)
(A P Q ARROW (EQUIV P Q))
(THEOREM)
(A P Q P ARROW Q)
(THEOREM)
(A P Q Q ARROW P)
(THEOREM)
((NOT B) ARROW (IMPLIES (AND P Q) (EQUIV P Q)))
(THEOREM)
(ARROW B (IMPLIES (AND P Q) (EQUIV P Q)))
(THEOREM)
((AND P Q) ARROW B (EQUIV P Q))
(THEOREM)
(P Q ARROW B (EQUIV P Q))
(THEOREM)
(P Q P ARROW B Q)
(THEOREM)
(P Q Q ARROW B P)
VALUE
(*T*)
```

Figure 3-3. A METEOR Program for the Wang Algorithm

By implication we are also defining the subset of English which is "understood" by the STUDENT program. A more explicit description of this input language is given at the end of the section.

3.4.1 Outline of the Operation of STUDENT

To provide perspective by which to view the detailed heuristic techniques used in the STUDENT program, we shall first give an outline of the operation of the STUDENT program when given a problem to solve. This outline is a verbal description of the flow chart of the program found in Appendix 3.2.

STUDENT is asked to solve a particular problem. We assume that all necessary global information has been stored previously. STUDENT will now transform the English input statement of this problem into expressions in its limited deductive model, and through appropriate deductive procedures attempt to find a solution. More specifically, STUDENT finds the kernel sentences of the input discourse and transforms this sequence of kernels into a set of simultaneous equations, keeping a list of the answers required, a list of the units involved in the problem (e.g., dollars, pounds), and a list of all the variables (simple names) in the equations. Then STUDENT invokes the SOLVE program to solve this set of equations for the desired unknowns. If a solution is found, STUDENT prints the values of the unknowns requested in a fixed format, substituting in "(*variable* IS *value*)" the appropriate phrases for *variable* and *value*. If a solution cannot be found, various heuristics are used to identify two variables (i.e., find two slightly different phrases that refer to the same object in the model). If two variables, A and B, are identified, the equation A = B is added to the set of equations. In addition, the store of global information is searched to find any equations that may be useful in finding the solution to this problem. STUDENT prints out any assumptions it makes about the identity of two variables, and also any equations that it retrieves because it thinks they may be relevant. If the use of global equations or equations from identifications leads to a solution, the answers are printed out in the format described above.

If a solution was not found, and certain idioms are present in the problem (a result of a definitional transformation used in the generation of the problem), a substitution is made for each of these idioms in turn and the transformation and solution process is repeated. If the substitutions for these idioms do not enable the problem to be solved by STUDENT, then STUDENT requests additional information from the questioner, showing him the variables being used in the problem. If any information is given, STUDENT tries to solve the problem again. If none is given, it reports its inability to solve this problem and terminates. If the problem is ever solved, the solution is printed and the program terminates.

3.4.2 Categories of Words in a Transformation

The words and phrases (strings of words) in the English input can be classified into three distinct categories on the basis of how they are handled in the transformation to the deductive model. The first category consists of strings of words which name objects in the model; I call such strings *variables*. Variables are identified only by the string of words in them, and if two strings differ at all, they define distinct variables. One important problem to be considered is how to determine when two distinct variables refer to the same object.

The second class of words and phrases are what I call *substitutors*. Each substitutor may be replaced by another string. Some substitutions are mandatory; others are optional and are only made if the problem cannot be solved without such substitutions. An example of a mandatory substitution is "2 times" for the word "twice." "Twice" always means "2 times" in the context of the model, and therefore this substitution is mandatory. One optional "idiomatic" substitution is "twice the sum of the length and width of the rectangle" for "the perimeter of the rectangle." The use of these substitutions in the transformation process will be discussed later. These substitutions are inverses of definitional transformations as defined in Section 3.2.

Members of the third class of words indicate the presence of linguistic forms which represent functions in the deductive model. I call members of this third class *operators*. Operators may indicate operations which are complex combinations of the basic functions of the deductive model. One simple operator is the word "plus," which indicates that the objects named by the two variables surrounding it are to be added. An example of a more complex operator is the phrase "percent less than," as in "10 percent less than the marked price," which indicates that the number immediately preceding the "percent" is to be subtracted from 100, this result divided by 100, and then this quotient multiplied by the variable following the "than."

Operators may be classified according to where their arguments are found. A prefix operator, such as "the square of _____" precedes its argument. An operator like "_____ percent" is a suffix operator, and follows its argument. Infix operators, such as "_____ plus _____" or "_____ less than _____" appear between their two arguments. In a split prefix operator, such as "difference between _____ and _____," part of the operator precedes and part appears between the two arguments. "The sum of _____ and _____ and _____" is a split prefix operator with an indefinite number of arguments.

Some words may act as operators conditionally, depending on their context. For example, "of" is equivalent to "times" if there is a fraction immediately preceding it; e.g., ".5 of the profit" is equivalent to

".5 times the profit"; however, "Queen of England" does not imply a multiplicative relationship between the Queen and her country.

3.4.3 Transformational Procedures

Let us now consider in detail the transformation procedure used by STUDENT and see how these different categories of phrases interact. To make the process more concrete, let us consider the following example which has been solved by STUDENT:

(THE PROBLEM TO BE SOLVED IS)
(IF THE NUMBER OF CUSTOMERS TOM GETS IS TWICE THE SQUARE OF 20 PER CENT OF THE NUMBER OF ADVERTISEMENTS HE RUNS, AND THE NUMBER OF ADVERTISEMENTS HE RUNS IS 45, WHAT IS THE NUMBER OF CUSTOMERS TOM GETS Q.)

Shown below are copies of actual printout from the STUDENT program, illustrating stages in the transformation and the solution of the problem. The parentheses are an artifact of the LISP programming language, and "Q." is a replacement for the question mark not available on the key punch.

The first stage in the transformation is to perform all mandatory substitutions. In this problem only the three phrases underlined (by the author, not the program) are substitutors: "twice" becomes "2 times," "per cent" becomes the single word "percent," and "square of" is truncated to "square." Having made these substitutions, STUDENT prints:

(WITH MANDATORY SUBSTITUTIONS THE PROBLEM IS)
(IF THE NUMBER OF CUSTOMERS TOM GETS IS 2 TIMES THE SQUARE 20 PERCENT OF THE NUMBER OF ADVERTISEMENTS HE RUNS, AND THE NUMBER OF ADVERTISEMENTS HE RUNS IS 45, WHAT IS THE NUMBER OF CUSTOMERS TOM GETS Q.)

From dictionary entries for each word, the words in the problem are tagged by their function in terms of the transformation process, and STUDENT prints:

(WITH WORDS TAGGED BY FUNCTION THE PROBLEM IS)
(IF THE NUMBER (OF/OP) CUSTOMERS TOM (GETS/VERB) IS 2 (TIMES/OP 1) THE (SQUARE/OP 1) 20 (PERCENT/OP 2)(OF/OP) THE NUMBER (OF/OP) ADVERTISEMENTS (HE/PRO) RUNS, AND THE NUMBER (OF/OP) ADVERTISEMENTS (HE/PRO) RUNS IS 45, (WHAT/QWORD) IS THE NUMBER (OF/OP) CUSTOMERS TOM (GETS/VERB) (QMARK/DLM))

If a word has a tag, or tags, the word followed by "/" followed by the tags becomes a single unit, and is enclosed in parentheses.* Some typical taggings

*In the METEOR system the tag symbol "/" is separated by spaces, as can be seen in the computer printouts. We have suppressed these spaces in the text. [Editor's note.]

have been shown. "(OF / OP)" indicates that "OF" is an operator and other taggings show that "GETS" is a verb, "TIMES" is an operator of level 1 (operator levels will be explained later), "SQUARE" is an operator of level 1, "PERCENT" is an operator of level 2, "HE" is a pronoun, "WHAT" is a question word, and "QMARK" (replacing Q.) is a delimiter of a sentence. These tagged words will play the principal role in the remaining transformation to the set of equations implicit in this problem statement.

The next stage in the transformation is to break the input sentences into "kernel sentences." As in the example, a problem may be stated using sentences of great grammatical complexity; however, the final stage of the transformation is only defined on a set of kernel sentences. The simplification to kernel sentences as done in STUDENT depends on the recursive use of format matching. If an input sentence is of the form "IF" followed by a substring followed by a comma, a question word, and a second substring [i.e., it matches the METEOR left half (IF $, ($1/QWORD($)], then the first substring (between the IF and the comma is made an independent sentence, and everything following the comma is made into a second sentence. In the example, this means that the input is resolved into the following two sentences (where tags are omitted for the sake of brevity):

"The number of customers Tom gets is 2 times the square 20 percent of the number of advertisements he runs, and the number of advertisements he runs is 45." and "What is the number of customers Tom gets?"

This procedure effectively resolves a problem into declarative assumptions and a question sentence. A second complexity resolved by STUDENT is illustrated in the first sentence of this pair. A coordinate sentence consisting of two sentences joined by a comma immediately followed by an AND [i.e., any sentence matching the METEOR left half ($, AND $)] will be resolved into these two independent sentences. The first sentence quoted is therefore resolved into two simpler sentences.

Using these two inverse syntactic transformations, this problem statement is resolved into "simple" kernel sentences. For the example, STUDENT prints

(THE SIMPLE SENTENCES ARE)
(THE NUMBER (OF/OP) CUSTOMERS TOM (GETS/VERB) IS 2 (TIMES/OP 1) THE (SQUARE/OP 1) 20 (PERCENT/OP 2) (OF/OP) THE NUMBER (OF/OP) ADVERTISEMENTS (HE/PRO) RUNS (PERIOD/DLM))
(THE NUMBER (OF/OP) ADVERTISEMENTS (HE/PRO) RUNS IS 45 (PERIOD/DLM))
((WHAT/QWORD) IS THE NUMBER (OF/OP) CUSTOMERS TOM (GETS/VERB) (QMARK/DLM))

Each simple sentence is a separate list, i.e., is enclosed in parentheses, and each ends with a delimiter (a period or question mark). Each of these sentences can now be transformed directly to its interpretation in the model.

3.4.4 From Kernel Sentences to Equations

The transformation from the simple kernel sentences to equations uses three levels of precedence for operators. These will be represented by "/OP 2," "/OP 1," and "/OP." Operators of higher precedence level are used earlier in the transformation. Before utilizing the operators, STUDENT looks for linguistic forms associated with the equality relation. Such forms include the copula "is" and transitive verbs in certain contexts. In the example we are considering, only the copula "is" is used to indicate equality. The use of transitive verbs as indicators of equality, that is, as relational linguistic forms, will be discussed in connection with another example. When the relational linguistic form is identified, the names which are the arguments of the form are broken down into variables and operators (functional linguistic forms). In the present problem, the two names are those on either side of the "is" in each sentence.

The word "is" may also be used meaningfully within algebra story problems as an auxiliary verb (*not* meaning equality) in such verbal phrases as "is multiplied by" or "is divided by." A special check is made for the occurrence of these phrases before proceeding on to the main transformation procedure. The transformation of sentences containing these special verbal phrases will be discussed later. If "is" does not appear as an auxiliary in such a verbal phrase, a sentence of the form "P1 is P2" is interpreted as indicating the equality of the objects named by phrases P1 and P2. No equality relation will be recognized within these phrases, even if an appropriate transitive verb occurs within either of them. If P1* and P2* represent the arithmetic transformations of P1 and P2, then "P1 is P2" is transformed into the equation

(EQUAL P1* P2*)

The transformation of P1 and P2 to give them an interpretation in the model is performed recursively, using a program equivalent to the table in Fig. 3-4, which shows all the operators and formats currently recognized by the STUDENT program. New operators can easily be added to the program equivalent of this table.

In performing the transformation of a phrase P, a left-to-right search is made for an operator of level 2 (indicated by subscripts of "OP" and 2). If there is none, a left-to-right search is made for a level-1 operator (indicated by subscripts "OP" and 1), and finally another left-to-right search is made for an operator of level 0 (indicated by a subscript "OP" and no numerical subscript). The first operator found in this ordered search determines the first step in the transformation of the phrase. This operator and its context are transformed as indicated in the fourth column in the table. If no operator is present, delimiters and articles (a, an, and the) are deleted, and the phrase is treated as an indivisible entity, a variable.

In the example, the first simple sentence is

(THE NUMBER (OF/OP) CUSTOMERS TOM (GETS/VERB) IS 2

Operator	Precedence Level	Context	Interpretation in the Model		
PLUS	2	P1 PLUS P2	(PLUS P1* P2*)	(a)	
PLUSS	0	P1 PLUSS P2	(PLUS P1* P2*)	(b)	
MINUS	2	P1 MINUS P2	(PLUS P1* (MINUS P2*))	(c)	
		MINUS P2	(MINUS P2*)		
MINUSS	0	P1 MINUSS P2	(PLUS P1* (MINUS P2*))	(b)	
TIMES	1	P1 TIMES P2	(TIMES P1* P2*)		
DIVBY	1	P1 DIVBY P2	(QUOTIENT P1* P2*)		
SQUARE	1	SQUARE P1	(EXPT P1* 2)	(d)	
SQUARED	0	P1 SQUARED	(EXPT P1* 2)		
**	0	P1 ** P2	(EXPT P1* P2*)		
LESSTHAN	2	P1 LESSTHAN P2	(PLUS P2* (MINUS P1*))		
PER	0	P1 PER K P2	(QUOTIENT P1* (K P2)*)	(e)	(f)
		P1 PER P2	(QUOTIENT P1* (1 P2)*)		
PERCENT	2	P1 K PERCENT P2	(P1 (K/100) P2)*	(f)	(g)
PERLESS	2	P1 K PERLESS P2	(P1((100-K)/100) P2)*	(f)	(g)
SUM	0	SUM P1 AND P2 AND P3	(PLUS P1* (SUM P2 AND P3)*)		
		SUM P1 AND P2	(PLUS P1* P2*)		
DIFFERENCE	0	DIFFERENCE BETWEEN P1 AND P2	(PLUS P1* (MINUS P2*))		
OF	0	K OF P2	(TIMES K P2*)		
		P1 OF P2	(P1 OF P2)*		

(a) If P1 is a phrase, P1* indicates its interpretation in the model.

(b) <u>PLUSS</u> and <u>MINUSS</u> are identical to PLUS AND MINUS except for precedence level.

(c) When two possible contexts are indicated, they are checked in the order shown.

(d) SQUARE P1 and SUM P1 are idiomatic shortenings of SQUARE OF P1 and SUM OF P1.

(e) * outside a parenthesized expression indicates that the enclosed phrase is to be transformed.

(f) K is a number.

(g) / and - imply that the indicated arithmetic operations are actually performed.

Figure 3-4. Operators Recognized by STUDENT

(TIMES/OP 1) THE (SQUARE/OP 1) 20 (PERCENT/OP 2) (OF/OP) THE NUMBER (OF/OP) ADVERTISEMENTS (HE/PRO) RUNS (PERIOD/DLM))

This is of the form "P1 is P2" and is transformed to (EQUAL P1*P2*). P1 is (THE NUMBER (OF/OP) CUSTOMERS TOM (GETS/VERB)). The occurrence of the verb "gets" is ignored because of the presence of the "is" in the sentence, meaning "equals." The only operator found is (OF/OP). From the table we see that if OF is immediately preceded by a number (*not* the word "number") it is treated as if it were the infix TIMES. In this case, however, OF is not preceded by a number; the subscript OP, indicating that OF is an operator, is stripped away, and the transformation process is repeated on the phrase, with OF no longer acting as an operator. In this repetition, no operators are found, and P1* is the variable

(NUMBER OF CUSTOMERS TOM (GETS/VERB))

To the right of "IS" in the sentence is P2:

(2 (TIMES/OP 1) THE (SQUARE/OP 1) 20 (PERCENT/OP 2) (OF/OP) THE NUMBER (OF/OP) ADVERTISEMENTS (HE/PRO) RUNS (PERIOD/DLM))

The first operator found in P2 is PERCENT, an operator of level 2. From the table in Fig. 3-4, we see that this operator has the effect of dividing the number immediately preceding it by 100. The PERCENT is removed and the transformation is repeated on the remaining phrase. In the example, the ". . . 20 (PERCENT/OP 2) (OF/OP) . . ." becomes ". . . .2000 (OF/OP) . . . . ."

Continuing the transformation, the operators found are, in order, TIMES, SQUARE, OF, and OF. Each is handled as indicated in the table. The "OF" in the context ". . . .2000 (OF/OP) THE . . . ." is treated as an infix TIMES, while at the other occurrence of "OF" the operator marking is removed. The resulting transformed expression for P2 is

(TIME 2 (EXPT (TIMES .2 (NUMBER OF ADVERTISEMENTS HE/PRO) RUNS)) 2))

The transformation of the second sentence of the example is done in a similar manner, and yields the equation

(EQUAL (NUMBER OF ADVERTISEMENTS (HE/PRO) RUNS) 45)

The third sentence is of the form "What is P1?" It starts with a question word and is therefore treated specially. A unique variable, a single word consisting of an *X* or *G* followed by five integers, is created, and the equation (EQUAL Xnnnnn P1*) is stored. For this example, the variable X00001 was created, and this last simple sentence is transformed to the equation

(EQUAL X00001 (NUMBER OF CUSTOMERS TOM (GETS/VERB))

In addition, the created variable is placed on the list of variables for which STUDENT is to find a value. Also, this variable is stored, paired with P1, the untransformed right side, for use in printing out the answer. If a value is found for this variable, STUDENT prints the sentence (P1 is *value*) with the appropriate substitution for *value*. Below we show the full set of equations, and the printed solution given by STUDENT for the example being considered. For ease in solution, the last equations created are put first in the list of equations.

```
(THE EQUATIONS TO BE SOLVED ARE)
(EQUAL X00001 (NUMBER OF CUSTOMERS TOM (GETS/VERB)))
(EQUAL (NUMBER OF ADVERTISEMENTS (HE/PRO) RUNS) 45)
(EQUAL (NUMBER OF CUSTOMERS TOM (GETS/VERB)) (TIMES 2
(EXPT (TIMES .2000 (NUMBER OF ADVERTISEMENTS (HE/PRO)
RUNS)) 2)))
(THE NUMBER OF CUSTOMERS TOM GETS IS 162)
```

In the example just shown, the equality relation was indicated by the copula "is." In the problem shown below, solved by STUDENT, equality is indicated by the occurrence of a transitive verb in the proper context.

```
(THE PROBLEM TO BE SOLVED IS)
(TOM HAS TWICE AS MANY FISH AS MARY HAS GUPPIES. IF MARY
HAS 3 GUPPIES, WHAT IS THE NUMBER OF FISH TOM HAS Q.)

(THE EQUATIONS TO BE SOLVED ARE)
(EQUAL X00001 (NUMBER OF FISH TOM (HAS/VERB)))
(EQUAL (NUMBER OF GUPPIES (MARY/PERSON) (HAS/VERB)) 3)
(EQUAL (NUMBER OF FISH TOM (HAS/VERB)) (TIMES 2 (NUMBER
OF GUPPIES (MARY/PERSON) (HAS/VERB))))
(THE NUMBER OF FISH TOM HAS IS 6)
```

The verb in this case is "has." The simple sentence "Mary has 3 guppies" is transformed to the "equivalent" sentence, "The number of guppies Mary has is 3," and the processing of this latter sentence is done as previously discussed.

The general format for this type of sentence, and the format of the intermediate sentence to which it is transformed are best expressed by the METEOR rule:

```
(* ($ ($1/VERB) ($1/NUMBER) $) (THE NUMBER OF 4 1 2 IS 3) *)
```

This rule may be read: anything (a subject) followed by a verb followed by a number followed by anything (the unit) is transformed to a sentence starting with "THE NUMBER OF" followed by the unit followed by the subject and the verb followed by "IS" and then the number. In "Mary has 3 guppies" the subject is "Mary," the verb "has," and the units "guppies." Similarly, the sentence "The witches of Firth brew 3 magic potions" would be transformed to "The number of magic potions the witches of Firth brew is 3."

In addition to a declaration of number, a single-object transitive verb may be used in a comparative structure, such as exhibited in the sentence "Tom has twice as many fish as Mary has guppies." The METEOR rule which gives the effective transformation for this type of sentence structure is

(* ($ ($1/VERB) $ AS MANY $ AS $ ($1/VERB) $) (THE NUMBER OF 6 1 2 IS 3 THE NUMBER OF 10 8 9) *)

For the example, the transformed sentence is: "The number of fish Tom has is twice the number of guppies Mary has."

Transformation of new sentence formats to formats previously "understood" by the program can be easily added to the program, thereby extending the subset of English "understood" by STUDENT. In the processing that actually takes place within STUDENT the intermediate sentences shown never exist. It was easier to go directly to the model from the format, utilizing subroutines previously defined in terms of the semantics of the model.

The word "is" indicates equality only if it is not used as an auxiliary. The next example shows how verbal phrases containing "is," such as "is multiplied by" and "is increased by," are handled in the transformation:

(THE PROBLEM TO BE SOLVED IS)
(A NUMBER IS MULTIPLIED BY 6. THIS PRODUCT IS INCREASED BY 44. THIS RESULT IS 68. FIND THE NUMBER.)

(THE EQUATIONS TO BE SOLVED ARE)
(EQUAL X00001 (NUMBER))
(EQUAL (PLUS (TIMES (NUMBER) 6) 44) 68)
(THE NUMBER IS 4)

The sentence "A number is multiplied by 6" only indicates that two objects in the model are related multiplicatively and does not explicitly indicate any equality relation. The interpretation of this sentence in the model is the prefix notation product

(TIMES (NUMBER) 6)

This latter phrase is stored in a temporary location for possible later reference. In this problem it is referenced in the next sentence with the phrase THIS PRODUCT. The important word in this last phrase is "THIS"; STUDENT ignores all other words in a variable containing the key word "THIS." The last temporarily stored phrase is substituted for the phrase containing "THIS." Thus, the first three sentences in the problem shown yield only one equation, after two substitutions for "this" phrases. The last sentence "Find the number" is transformed as if it were, "What is the number Q." and yields the first equation shown.

The word "THIS" may occur in a context where it is not referring to a previously stored phrase. Here is an example of such a context:

(THE PROBLEM TO BE SOLVED IS)
(THE PRICE OF A RADIO IS 69.70 DOLLARS. IF THIS PRICE IS 15 PERCENT LESS THAN THE MARKED PRICE, FIND THE MARKED PRICE.)

(THE EQUATIONS TO BE SOLVED ARE)
(EQUAL X00001 (MARKED PRICE))
(EQUAL (PRICE OF RADIO) (TIMES .8499 (MARKED PRICE)))
(EQUAL (PRICE OF RADIO) (TIMES 69.70 (DOLLARS)))
(THE MARKED PRICE IS 82 DOLLARS)

In such contexts, the phrase containing "THIS" is replaced by the left half of the last equation created. In this example, STUDENT breaks the last sentence into two simple sentences, deleting the "IF." Then the phrase THIS PRICE is replaced by the variable PRICE OF RADIO, which is the left half of the previous equation.

This problem illustrates two other features of the STUDENT program. The first is the action of the complex operator "PERCENT LESS THAN." It causes the number immediately preceding it, i.e., 15, to be subtracted from 100, this result divided by 100, to give .85 (printed as .8499 due to a rounding error in floating-point conversion). Then this operator becomes the infix operator TIMES. This is indicated in the table in Fig. 3-4.

The second feature illustrates how units such as "dollars" are handled by the STUDENT program. Any word that immediately follows a number is labeled as a special type of variable called a *unit*. A number followed by a unit is treated in the equation as a product of the number and the unit; e.g., "69.70 DOLLARS" becomes (TIMES 69.70 (DOLLARS)). Units are treated as special variables in solving the set of equations; a unit may appear in the answer though other variables can not. If the value for a variable found by the solver is the product of a number and a unit, STUDENT concatenates the number and the unit. For example, the solution for (MARKED PRICE) in our problem was (TIMES 82 (DOLLARS)) and STUDENT printed out:

(THE MARKED PRICE IS 82 DOLLARS)

There is an exception to the fact that any unit may appear in the answer, as illustrated in the next problem:

(THE PROBLEM TO BE SOLVED IS)
(IF 1 SPAN EQUALS 9 INCHES, AND 1 FATHOM EQUALS 6 FEET, HOW MANY SPANS EQUALS 1 FATHOM Q.)

(THE EQUATIONS TO BE SOLVED ARE)
(EQUAL X00001 (TIMES 1 (FATHOMS)))
(EQUAL (TIMES 1 (FATHOMS)) (TIMES 6 (FEET)))
(EQUAL (TIMES 1 (SPANS)) (TIMES 9 (INCHES)))
THE EQUATIONS WERE INSUFFICIENT TO FIND A SOLUTION

(USING THE FOLLOWING KNOWN RELATIONSHIPS)
((EQUAL (TIMES 1 (YARDS)) (TIMES 3 (FEET))) (EQUAL (TIMES 1 (FEET)) (TIMES 12 (INCHES))))

(1 FATHOM IS 8 SPANS)

If the unit of the answer is specified (in this problem by the phrase "how many *spans*"), then *only* that unit (in this case "spans") may appear in the answer. Without this restriction, STUDENT would blithely answer this problem with (1 FATHOM IS 1 FATHOM).

In the transformation from the English statement of the problem to the equations, "9 INCHES" became (TIMES 9 (INCHES)). However, "1 FATHOM" became (TIMES 1 (FATHOMS)). The plural form for fathom has been used instead of the singular form. STUDENT always uses the plural form if known, to ensure that all units appear in only one form. Since "fathom" and "fathoms" are different, STUDENT would treat them as distinct, unrelated units if both were used. The plural form is part of the global information that can be made available to STUDENT, and the plural form of a word is substituted for any singular form appearing after "1" in any phrase. The inverse operation is carried out for correct printout of the solution.

Notice that the information given in the problem was not sufficient to allow solution of the set of equations to be solved. Therefore, STUDENT looked in its glossary for information concerning each of the units in this set of equations. It found the relationships "1 foot equals 12 inches" and "1 yard equals 3 feet." Using only the first fact and the equation it implies, STUDENT was then able to solve the problem. Thus, in certain cases where a problem is not *analytic*, in the sense that it does not contain, explicitly stated, all the information needed for its solution, STUDENT is able to draw on a body of facts, picking out relevant ones, and use them to obtain a solution.

In certain problems, the transformation process does not yield a set of solvable equations. However, within this set of equations there may exist a pair (or more than one pair) of variables, such that the two variables are only "slightly different" and really name the same object in the model. When a set of equations is unsolvable, STUDENT searches for relevant global equations. In addition, it uses several heuristic techniques for identifying two "slightly different" variables in the equations.The following problem illustrates the identification of two variables where in one variable a pronoun has been substituted for a noun phrase in the other variable. This identification is made by checking all variables appearing *before* one containing the pronoun, and finding one which is identical with this pronoun phrase, with a substitution of a string of any length for the pronoun.

(THE PROBLEM TO BE SOLVED IS)
(THE NUMBER OF SOLDIERS THE RUSSIANS HAVE IS ONE HALF OF THE NUMBER OF GUNS THEY HAVE. THE NUMBER OF GUNS THEY HAVE IS 7000. WHAT IS THE NUMBER OF SOLDIERS THEY HAVE Q.)

(THE EQUATIONS TO BE SOLVED ARE)
(EQUAL X00001 (NUMBER OF SOLDIERS (THEY/PRO) (HAVE/VERB)))
(EQUAL (NUMBER OF GUNS (THEY/PRO) (HAVE/VERB)) 7000)
(EQUAL (NUMBER OF SOLDIERS RUSSIANS (HAVE/VERB)) (TIMES .5000 (NUMBER OF GUNS (THEY/PRO) (HAVE/VERB))))
THE EQUATIONS WERE INSUFFICIENT TO FIND A SOLUTION

(ASSUMING THAT)
((NUMBER OF SOLDIERS (THEY/PRO) (HAVE/VERB)) IS EQUAL TO (NUMBER OF SOLDIERS RUSSIANS (HAVE/VERB)))
(THE NUMBER OF SOLDIERS THEY HAVE IS 3500)

If two variables match in this fashion, STUDENT assumes that the two variables are equal, prints out a statement of this assumption, as shown, and adds an equation expressing this equality to the set to be solved. The solution procedure is tried again, with this additional equation. In the example, the additional equation was sufficient to allow determination of the solution.

The next example is again a "nonanalytic" problem. The first set of equations developed by STUDENT is unsolvable. Therefore, STUDENT tries to find some relevant equations in its store of global information.

(THE PROBLEM TO BE SOLVED IS)
(THE GAS CONSUMPTION OF MY CAR IS 15 MILES PER GALLON. THE DISTANCE BETWEEN BOSTON AND NEW YORK IS 250 MILES. WHAT IS THE NUMBER OF GALLONS OF GAS USED ON A TRIP BETWEEN NEW YORK AND BOSTON Q.)

(THE EQUATIONS TO BE SOLVED ARE)
(EQUAL X00001 (NUMBER OF GALLONS OF GAS USED ON TRIP BETWEEN NEW YORK AND BOSTON))
(EQUAL (DISTANCE BETWEEN BOSTON AND NEW YORK) (TIMES 250 (MILES)))
(EQUAL (GAS CONSUMPTION OF MY CAR) (QUOTIENT (TIMES 15 (MILES)) (TIMES 1 (GALLONS))))

THE EQUATIONS WERE INSUFFICIENT TO FIND A SOLUTION
(USING THE FOLLOWING KNOWN RELATIONSHIPS)
((EQUAL (DISTANCE) (TIMES (SPEED) (TIME))) (EQUAL (DISTANCE) (TIMES (GAS CONSUMPTION) (NUMBER OF GALLONS OF GAS USED))))
(ASSUMING THAT)
((DISTANCE) IS EQUAL TO (DISTANCE BETWEEN BOSTON AND NEW YORK))
(ASSUMING THAT)
((GAS CONSUMPTION) IS EQUAL TO (GAS CONSUMPTION OF MY CAR))

(ASSUMING THAT)
((NUMBER OF GALLONS OF GAS USED) IS EQUAL TO (NUMBER OF GALLONS OF GAS USED ON TRIP BETWEEN NEW YORK AND BOSTON))

(THE NUMBER OF GALLONS OF GAS USED ON A TRIP BETWEEN NEW YORK AND BOSTON IS 16.66 GALLONS)

STUDENT uses the first word of each variable string as a key to its glossary. The one exception to this rule is that the words "number of" are ignored if they are the first two words of a variable string. Thus, in this problem STUDENT retrieved equations which were stored under the key words DISTANCE, GALLONS, GAS, and MILES. Two facts about DISTANCE had been stored earlier; "distance equals speed times time" and "distance equals gas consumption times number of gallons of gas used." The equations implicit in these sentences were stored and retrieved now as possibly useful for the solution of this problem. In fact, only the second is relevant.

Before any attempt is made to solve this augmented set of equations, the variables in the augmented set are matched, to identify "slightly different" variables which refer to the same object in the model. In this example (DISTANCE), (GAS CONSUMPTION), and (NUMBER OF GALLONS OF GAS USED) are all identified with "similar" variables. The following conditions must be satisfied for this type of identification of variables P1 and P2:

P1 must appear later in the problem than P2.

P1 is completely contained in P2 in the sense that P1 is a contiguous substring within P2.

This identification reflects a syntactic phenomenon where a truncated phrase, with one or more modifying phrases dropped, is often used in place of the original phrase. For example, if the phrase "the length of a rectangle" has occurred, the phrase "the length" may be used to mean the same thing. This type of identification is distinct from that made using pronoun substitution.

In the example above, a stored schema was used by identifying the variables in the schema with the variables that occur in the problem. This problem is solvable because the key phrases "distance," "gas consumption," and "number of gallons of gas used" occur as substrings of the variables in the problem. Since STUDENT identifies each generic key phrase of the schema with a particular variable of the problem, any schema can be used only once in a problem. Because STUDENT handles schema in this *ad hoc* fashion, it cannot solve problems in which a relationship such as "distance equals speed times time" is needed for two different values of distance, speed and time.

3.4.5 Possible Idiomatic Substitutions

Some phrases have a dual character, depending on the context. In the following example, the phrase "perimeter of a rectangle" becomes a variable with no reference to its meaning, or definition, in terms of the length and width of the rectangle. This definition is unneeded for solution.

(THE PROBLEM TO BE SOLVED IS)
(THE SUM OF THE PERIMETER OF A RECTANGLE AND THE PERIMETER OF A TRIANGLE IS 24 INCHES. IF THE PERIMETER OF THE RECTANGLE IS TWICE THE PERIMETER OF THE TRIANGLE, WHAT IS THE PERIMETER OF THE TRIANGLE Q.)

(THE EQUATIONS TO BE SOLVED ARE)
(EQUAL X00001 (PERIMETER OF TRIANGLE))
(EQUAL (PERIMETER OF RECTANGLE) (TIMES 2 (PERIMETER OF TRIANGLE)))
(EQUAL (PLUS (PERIMETER OF RECTANGLE) (PERIMETER OF TRIANGLE)) (TIMES 24 (INCHES)))

(THE PERIMETER OF THE TRIANGLE IS 8 INCHES)

However, the following problem is stated in terms of the perimeter, length, and width of the rectangle. Transforming the English into equations is not sufficient for solution. Neither retrieving and using an equation about "inches," the unit in the problem, nor identifying "length" with a longer phrase serve to make the problem solvable. Therefore, STUDENT looks in its dictionary of possible idioms and finds one that it can try in the problem. STUDENT actually had two possible idiomatic substitutions it could have made for "perimeter of a rectangle"; one was in terms of the length and width of the rectangle and the other in terms of the shortest and longest sides of the rectangle. When there are two possible substitutions for a given phrase, the one STUDENT has been told about most recently is tried first. In this problem, the correct one was fortunately first. If the other had been first, the revised problem would not have been any more solvable than the original, and eventually the second (correct) substitution would have been made. Only one nonmandatory idiomatic substitution is ever made at one time, although the substitution is made for all occurrences of the phrase chosen. Another example is:

(THE PROBLEM TO BE SOLVED IS)
(THE LENGTH OF A RECTANGLE IS 8 INCHES MORE THAN THE WIDTH OF THE RECTANGLE . ONE HALF OF THE PERIMETER OF THE RECTANGLE IS 18 INCHES . FIND THE LENGTH AND THE WIDTH OF THE RECTANGLE.)

(THE EQUATIONS TO BE SOLVED ARE)
(EQUAL G02516 (WIDTH OF RECTANGLE))
(EQUAL G02515 (LENGTH))
(EQUAL (TIMES .5000 (PERIMETER OF RECTANGLE)) (TIMES 18

```
(INCHES)))
(EQUAL (LENGTH OF RECTANGLE) (PLUS (TIMES 8 (INCHES))
(WIDTH OF RECTANGLE)))
THE EQUATIONS WERE INSUFFICIENT TO FIND A SOLUTION
(USING THE FOLLOWING KNOWN RELATIONSHIPS)
((EQUAL (TIMES 1 (FEET)) (TIMES 12 (INCHES))))
(ASSUMING THAT)
((LENGTH) IS EQUAL TO (LENGTH OF RECTANGLE))
THE EQUATIONS WERE INSUFFICIENT TO FIND A SOLUTION

TRYING POSSIBLE IDIOMS
(THE PROBLEM WITH AN IDIOMATIC SUBSTITUTION IS)
(THE LENGTH OF A RECTANGLE IS 8 INCHES MORE THAN THE
WIDTH OF THE RECTANGLE . ONE HALF OF TWICE THE SUM OF
THE LENGTH AND WIDTH OF THE RECTANGLE IS 18 INCHES .
FIND THE LENGTH AND THE WIDTH OF THE RECTANGLE .)

(THE EQUATIONS TO BE SOLVED ARE)
(EQUAL G02518 (WIDTH OF RECTANGLE))
(EQUAL G02517 (LENGTH))
(EQUAL (TIMES (TIMES .5000 2) (PLUS (LENGTH) (WIDTH OF
RECTANGLE))) (TIMES 18 (INCHES)))
(EQUAL (LENGTH OF RECTANGLE) (PLUS TIMES 8 (INCHES))
(WIDTH OF RECTANGLE)))
THE EQUATIONS WERE INSUFFICIENT TO FIND A SOLUTION

(USING THE FOLLOWING KNOWN RELATIONSHIPS)
((EQUAL (TIMES 1 (FEET)) (TIMES 12 (INCHES))))
(ASSUMING THAT)
((LENGTH) IS EQUAL TO (LENGTH OF RECTANGLE))
(THE LENGTH IS 13 INCHES)
(THE WIDTH OF THE RECTANGLE IS 5 INCHES)
```

In this problem the idiomatic substitution made allows the problem to be solved after identification of the variables "length" and "length of rectangle." The retrieved equation about inches was not needed. However, its presence in the set of equations to be solved did not sidetrack the solver in any way.

This use of possible but nonmandatory idiomatic substitutions can also be used to give STUDENT a way to solve problems in which two phrases denoting one particular variable are quite different. For example, the phrase, "students who passed the admissions test" and "successful candidates" might be describing the same set of people. However, since STUDENT knows nothing of the "real world" and its value system for success, it would never identify these two phrases. However, if told that "successful candidates" sometime means "students who passed the admissions test," it would be able to solve a problem using these two phrases to identify the same variable. Thus, possible idiomatic substitutions serve the dual purpose of providing tentative substitutions of definitions and identification of synonymous phrases.

3.4.6 Special Heuristics

The methods thus far discussed have been applicable to the entire range of algebra problems. However, for special classes of problems, additional heuristics may be used which are needed for members of the class but not applicable to other problems. An example is the class of age problems, as typified by this problem:

(THE PROBLEM TO BE SOLVED IS)
(BILL S FATHER S UNCLE IS TWICE AS OLD AS BILL S FATHER. 2 YEARS FROM NOW BILL S FATHER WILL BE 3 TIMES AS OLD AS BILL. THE SUM OF THEIR AGES IS 92 . FIND BILL S AGE .)

(THE EQUATIONS TO BE SOLVED ARE)
(EQUAL X00001 ((BILL/PERSON) S AGE))
(EQUAL (PLUS ((BILL/PERSON) S (FATHER/PERSON) S (UNCLE/PERSON) S AGE) (PLUS ((BILL/PERSON) S (FATHER/PERSON) S AGE) ((BILL/PERSON) S AGE))) 92)
(EQUAL (PLUS ((BILL/PERSON) S (FATHER/PERSON) S AGE) 2) (TIMES 3 (PLUS ((BILL/PERSON) S AGE)))
(BILL S AGE IS 8)

Before the age-problem heuristics are used, a problem must be identified as belonging to that class of problems. STUDENT identifies age problems by any occurrence of one of the following phrases, "as old as," "years old," and "age." This identification is made immediately after all words are looked up in the dictionary and tagged by function. After the special heuristics are used, the modified problem is transformed to equations. The need for special methods for age problems arises because of the conventions used for denoting the variables, all of which are ages. The word age is usually not used explicitly, but is implicit in such phrases as "as old as." People's names are used where their ages are really the implicit variables. In the example, for instance, the phrase "Bill's father's uncle" is used instead of the phrase "Bill's father's uncle's age."

STUDENT uses a special heuristic to make all these ages explicit. To do this, it must know which words are "person words" and may therefore be associated with an age. For this problem, STUDENT has been told that BILL, FATHER, and UNCLE are person words. They can be seen tagged as such in the equations. The space – following a word is the STUDENT representation for possessive, used, for programming convenience, instead of "apostrophe – s." STUDENT inserts a "S AGE" after every person word *not* followed by a "S" (because this "S" indicates that the person word is being used in a possessive sense, not as an independent age variable). Thus, as indicated, the phrase "BILL S FATHER S UNCLE" becomes "BILL S FATHER S UNCLE S AGE."

In addition to changing phrases that name people to ones that name ages, STUDENT makes certain special idiomatic substitutions. For the phrase THEIR AGES, STUDENT substitutes a conjunction of all the age variables encountered in the problem. In our example, for "THEIR AGES" STUDENT substitutes "BILL S FATHER S UNCLE S AGE AND BILL S FATHER S AGE AND BILL S AGE." The phrases "as old as" and "years old" are then deleted as dummy phrases not having any meaning, and "will be" and "was" are changed to "is." There is no need to preserve the tense of the copula, since the sense of the future or past tense is preserved in such prefix phrases as "2 years from now," or "3 years ago."

The remaining special age-problem heuristics are used to process the phrases "in 2 years," "5 years ago," and "now." The phrase "2 years from now" is transformed to "in 2 years" before processing. These three time phrases may occur immediately after the word "age" (e.g., "Bill's age 3 years ago") or at the beginning of the sentence. If a time phrase occurs at the beginning of the sentence, it implicitly modifies all ages mentioned in the sentence, *except* those followed by their own time phrase. For example, "In 2 years Bill's father's age will be 3 times Bill's age" is equivalent to "Bill's father's age in 2 years will be 3 times Bill's age in 2 years." However, "3 years ago Mary's age was 2 times Ann's age now" is equivalent to "Mary's age 3 years ago was 2 times Ann's age now." Thus prefix time phrases are handled by distributing them over all ages not modified by another time phrase.

After these prefix phrases have been distributed, each time phrase is translated appropriately. The phrase "in 5 years" causes 5 to be added to the age it follows, and "7 years ago" causes 7 to be subtracted from the age preceding this phrase. The word "now" is deleted.

Only the special heuristics described thus far were necessary to solve the first age problem. The second age problem, which follows, requires one additional heuristic not previously mentioned, a substitution for the phrase "WAS WHEN" which effectively decouples the two facts combined in the first sentence. For "WAS WHEN," STUDENT substitutes "WAS K YEARS AGO . K YEARS AGO," where K is a new variable created for this purpose.

```
(THE PROBLEM TO BE SOLVED IS)
(MARY IS TWICE AS OLD AS ANN WAS WHEN MARY WAS AS OLD
AS ANN IS NOW . IF MARY IS 24 YEARS OLD, HOW OLD IS ANN Q.)

(THE EQUATIONS TO BE SOLVED ARE)
(EQUAL X00008 ((ANN/PERSON) S AGE))
```

(EQUAL ((MARY/PERSON) S AGE) 24)
(EQUAL (PLUS ((MARY/PERSON) S AGE) MINUS (X00007))) ((ANN/
PERSON) S AGE))
(EQUAL (PLUS ((MARY/PERSON) S AGE) (MINUS (X00007))) ((ANN/
S AGE) (MINUS (X00007)))))
(ANN S AGE IS 18)

In the example, the first sentence becomes the two sentences: "Mary is twice as old as Ann X00007 years ago. X00007 years ago Mary was as old as Ann is now." These two occurrences of time phrases are handled as discussed previously. Similarly, the phrase "WILL BE WHEN" would be transformed to "IN K YEARS. IN K YEARS".

These decoupling heuristics are useful not only for the STUDENT program but for people trying to solve age problems. The classic age problem about Mary and Ann took an MIT graduate student more than 5 minutes to solve, because he did not know this heuristic. With the heuristic he was able to set up the appropriate equations much more rapidly. As a crude measure of STUDENT's relative speed, note that STUDENT took less than one minute to solve this problem.

3.4.7 When All Else Fails

For all the problems discussed thus far, STUDENT was able to find a solution eventually. In some cases, however, necessary global information is missing from its store of information, or variables which name the same object cannot be identified by the heuristics of the program. Whenever STUDENT cannot find a solution for any reason, it turns to the questioner for help. As in the problem following, it prints out "(DO YOU KNOW ANY MORE RELATIONSHIPS BETWEEN THESE VARIABLES)" followed by a list of the variables in the problem. The questioner can answer "yes" or "no." If he says "yes," STUDENT says "TELL ME," and the questioner can append another sentence to the statement of the problem.

(THE PROBLEM TO BE SOLVED IS)
(THE GROSS WEIGHT OF A SHIP IS 20000 TONS . IF ITS NET
WEIGHT IS 15000 TONS , WHAT IS THE WEIGHT OF THE SHIPS
CARGO Q.)
THE EQUATIONS WERE INSUFFICIENT TO FIND A SOLUTION
TRYING POSSIBLE IDIOMS
(DO YOU KNOW ANY MORE RELATIONSHIPS AMONG THESE
VARIABLES)
(GROSS WEIGHT OF SHIP)
(TONS)
(ITS NET WEIGHT)
(WEIGHT OF SHIPS CARGO)

yes

TELL ME

(the weight of a ships cargo is the difference between the gross weight and the net weight)

THE EQUATIONS WERE INSUFFICIENT TO FIND A SOLUTION
(ASSUMING THAT)
((NET WEIGHT) IS EQUAL TO (ITS NET WEIGHT))
(ASSUMING THAT)
((GROSS WEIGHT) IS EQUAL TO (GROSS WEIGHT OF SHIP))
(THE WEIGHT OF THE SHIPS CARGO IS 5000 TONS)

In this problem the additional information typed in (in lower-case letters) was sufficient to solve the problem. If it had not been, the question would be repeated until the questioner said "no," or else provides sufficient information for solving the problem.

In the next problem, the solution to the set of equations involves solving a quadratic equation, which is beyond the mathematical ability of the present STUDENT system. Note that in this case STUDENT reports that the equations were unsolvable, not simply insufficient for solution. STUDENT still requests additional information from the questioner. In this example, the questioner says "no," and STUDENT states that "I CANT SOLVE THIS PROBLEM" and terminates.

(THE PROBLEM TO BE SOLVED IS)
(THE SQUARE OF THE DIFFERENCE BETWEEN THE NUMBER OF APPLES AND THE NUMBER OF ORANGES ON THE TABLE IS EQUAL TO 9 . IF THE NUMBER OF APPLES IS 7 , FIND THE NUMBER OF ORANGES ON THE TABLE .)
(THE EQUATIONS TO BE SOLVED ARE)
(EQUAL G02515 (NUMBER OF ORANGES ON TABLE))
(EQUAL (NUMBER OF APPLES) 7)
(EQUAL (EXPT (PLUS (NUMBER OF APPLES) (MINUS (NUMBER OF ORANGES ON TABLE))) 2) 9)
UNABLE TO SOLVE THIS SET OF EQUATIONS

TRYING POSSIBLE IDIOMS

(DO YOU KNOW ANY MORE RELATIONSHIPS AMONG THESE VARIABLES)
(NUMBER OF APPLES)
(NUMBER OF ORANGES ON TABLE)

no

I CANT SOLVE THIS PROBLEM

3.4.8 Summary of the STUDENT Subset of English

The subset of English understandable by STUDENT is built around a core of sentence and phrase formats that can be transformed into expressions in the STUDENT deductive model. On this basic core is built a larger set of formats. Each of these is first transformed into a string built on formats in this basic set; then this string is transformed into an expression in the deductive model. For example, the format ($ IS EQUAL TO $) is changed to the basic format ($ IS $), and the phrase "IS CONSECUTIVE TO" is changed to "IS 1 PLUS." The constructions discussed earlier involving single-object transitive verbs could have been handled this way, though for programming convenience they were not.

The complete list of the basic formats accepted by the present STUDENT system can be determined by examining (in the program listing of Appendix 3.2) the rules from the one labeled OPFORM to the one labeled QSET. The METEOR rules of the STUDENT program precisely specify the acceptable formats and their translations to the model, but I shall try to summarize the basic and extended formats here. Implicitly assumed in the syntax is that any operator appears only within one of the contexts specified in the table given in Section 3.2, and only the operators given in the table appear. The listing of STUDENT starting at the rule labeled IDIOMS gives translations of operators additional to those in the table.

The basic linguistic form which is transformed into an equation is one containing "is" as a copula. The phrases IS EQUAL TO and EQUALS are both changed to the copula IS. The auxiliary verbal constructions IS MULTIPLIED BY, and IS DIVIDED BY, and IS INCREASED BY are also acceptable as principal verbs in a sentence. As discussed earlier, a sentence with no occurrence of "is" can have as a main verb a transitive verb immediately followed by a number. This number must be an element of the phrase that is the direct object of the verb, as in "Mary has three guppies." This type of transitive verb can also have a comparative structure as direct object, e.g., "Mary has twice as many guppies as Tom has fish."

This completes the repertoire of declarative-sentence formats. Any number of declarative sentences may be conjoined, with ", and" between each pair, to form a new (complex) declarative sentence. A declarative sentence (even a complex declarative) can be made a presupposition for a question by preceding it with "IF" and following it with a comma and the question.

Questions, that is, requests for information from STUDENT, will be understood if they match any of the patterns:

(WHAT ARE $ AND $) (WHAT IS $)
(FIND $ AND $) (FIND $)
(HOW MANY $ DO $ HAVE) (HOW MANY $ DOES $ HAVE)
(HOW MANY $1 IS $)

This completes the summary of the set of input formats presently understood by STUDENT. This set can be enlarged in two distinct ways. One is to enlarge the set of basic formats, using standard subroutines to aid in defining, for each new basic format, its interpretation in the deductive model. The other method is to define transformations from new input formats to previously understood basic or extension formats. In the next section we shall discuss how this latter type of extension can be performed at run time, using the STUDENT global information storage facility. A combination of English and METEOR elementary pattern elements can be used to define the input format and transformation.

Even if a story problem is stated within the subset of English acceptable to STUDENT, this does not guarantee that it can be solved by STUDENT (assuming it to be solvable). Two phrases describing the object must be, at worst, only "slightly different" by the criteria prescribed earlier. Appropriate global information must be available to STUDENT, and the algebra involved must not exceed the abilities of the solver. However, though most algebra story problems found in the standard texts cannot be solved by STUDENT exactly as written, the author has usually been able to find some paraphrase of almost all such problems, which is solvable by STUDENT. Appendix 3.4 contains a fair sample of the range of problems that can be handled by the STUDENT system.

3.4.9 Limitations of the STUDENT Subset of English

The techniques presented in this chapter are general and can be used to enable a computer program to accept and understand a fairly extensive subset of English for a fixed semantic base. However, the current STUDENT system is experimental and has a number of limitations.

STUDENT's interpretation of the input is based on format matching. If each format is used to express the meaning understood by STUDENT, no misinterpretation will occur. However, these formats occur in English discourse even in algebra story problems, in semantic contexts not consistent with STUDENT's interpretation of these formats. For example, a sentence matching the format "($, AND $)" is always interpreted by STUDENT as the conjunction of two declarative statements. Therefore, the sentence "Tom has 2 apples, 3 bananas, and 4 pears." would be incorrectly divided into two "sentences": "Tom has 2 apples, 3 bananas." and "4 pears."

Each of the operator words shown in Fig. 3-4 must be used as an operator in the context as shown, or a misinterpretation will result. For example, the phrase "the number of times I went to the movies," which should be interpreted as a variable string, will be interpreted incorrectly as the product of the two variables "number of" and "I went to the movies," because "times" is always considered to be an operator.

These examples obviously do not constitute a complete list of the misinterpretations and errors STUDENT will make, but it should give the reader an idea of limitations on the STUDENT subset of English. In principle, all of these restrictions could be removed. However, while removing some of them would require only minor changes to the program, others would require techniques not used in the current system. A much more sophisticated grammar and parsing program would be necessary to distinguish different occurrences of the format ($, AND $) and correctly extract simpler sentences from complex coordinate and subordinate sentences.

Because of limitations of the sort described and the fact that the STUDENT system currently occupies almost all of the computer memory, STUDENT serves principally as a demonstration of the power of the techniques utilized in its construction. Still, I believe that on a larger computer one could use these techniques to construct a system of practical value which would communicate well with people in English over the limited range of material understood by the program.

3.5 Storage of Global Information

This algebra problem-solving system contains two programs that process English input. One is the program already discussed, STUDENT, which accepts the statement of an algebra story problem and attempts to find the solution to the particular problem. STUDENT does not store any information nor "remember" anything from problem to problem. The information obtained by STUDENT is the local context of the question.

The other program is called REMEMBER and it processes and stores facts not specific to any one problem. These facts make up STUDENT's store of "global information" as opposed to the "local information" specific to the problem. This information is accepted in a subset of English, which overlaps but is different from the subset of English accepted by STUDENT. REMEMBER accepts statements in certain fixed formats, and for each format the information is stored in a way that makes it convenient for retrieval and use within the STUDENT program. Some information is stored by actually adding METEOR rules to the STUDENT program, while other information is stored on property lists of individual words which are unique atoms in the LISP system.

The following are the formats currently understood by REMEMBER, and the processing and information-storage techniques used for each one:

1. Format: P1 *EQUALS* P2

   Example: DISTANCE EQUALS SPEED TIMES TIME

   Processing: The sentence is transformed into an equation in the same way it is done in STUDENT. This equation is stored on the property lists of the atoms which are the first words in each variable. In the example, the equation

(EQUAL (DISTANCE) (TIMES (SPEED) (TIME)))

is stored on the property lists of DISTANCE, SPEED, and TIME. If any one of these words appears as the initial word of a variable in a problem, and global equations are needed to solve the problem, this equation will be retrieved

2. Format: P1 *IS AN OPERATOR OF LEVEL* K

   Example: TIMES IS AN OPERATOR OF LEVEL 1

   Processing: A dictionary entry for P1 is created, with subscripts of OP and K. For TIMES, the dictionary entry (TIMES/OP 1) is created. The dictionary entry for any word is placed on the property list of that word (atom), and is retrieved and used in place of any occurrence of that word in a problem.

3. Format: P1 *IS AN OPERATOR*

   Example: OF IS AN OPERATOR

   Processing: A dictionary entry is created for P1 with the subscript OP. The entry for OF is (OF/OP).

4. Format: P1 *IS A* P2

   Example: BILL IS A PERSON

   Processing: A dictionary entry is created for P1 with subscript P2. The entry for BILL is (BILL/PERSON).

5. Format: P1 *IS THE PLURAL OF* P2

   Example: FEET IS THE PLURAL OF FOOT

   Processing: P2 is stored on the property list of P1, after the flag SING; the word P1 is stored on the property list of P2 after the flag PLURAL. Thus FEET is stored after PLURAL on the property list of the atom FOOT.

6. Format: P1 *SOMETIMES MEANS* P2

   Example: TWO NUMBERS SOMETIMES MEANS ONE NUMBER AND THE OTHER NUMBER.

   Processing: The STUDENT program is modified so that an idiomatic substitution of P2 for P1 will be made in a problem if it is otherwise unsolvable. All such "possible idiomatic substitutions" are tried when necessary, with the last one entered being the first one tried. The STUDENT program is modified by the addition of four new METEOR rules. Since P1 and P2 are inserted as left and right halves of a METEOR rule, they need not contain only words but can use the METEOR elementary patterns to specify a format change instead of just a phrase change. For the example shown, the rules added to the STUDENT program, as listed in Appendix 3.2, are the rule labeled G 02510, the rule following it, the rule labeled G02511, and the rule following that one.

7. Format: P1 *ALWAYS MEANS* P2

   Example: ONE HALF ALWAYS MEANS 0.5

   Processing: The program STUDENT is modified so that if P1 occurs, a mandatory substitution of P2 for P1 will be made in any problem. The *last* sentence in this format processed by REMEMBER will be the *first* mandatory substitution made. Thus "one always means 1" *followed* by "one half always means 0.5" will cause the desired substitutions to be made; if these sentences were reversed, no occurrence of "one half" would ever be found since it would have been changed to "1 half" by mandatory substitution of 1 for one.

For each sentence in this format processed by REMEMBER, a new METEOR rule is added to the STUDENT program, immediately following the rule named IDIOMS. The format of the METEOR rule added is (* (P1) (P2) IDIOMS) where P1 and P2 are the strings in the sentence processed. Thus, by using a combination of English and METEOR elementary patterns and reference numbers in P1 and P2, one can add a new format of sentence to the STUDENT repertoire. For example, the following statement was processed by REMEMBER to allow STUDENT to "understand" (properly transform) a sentence in which the main verb was "exceeds":

($ EXCEEDS $ BY $ ALWAYS MEANS 1 IS 5 MORE THAN 3)

This permanently extended the STUDENT input subset of English, while avoiding the necessity of actually editing and changing the STUDENT program.

The global information stored for STUDENT ranged from equations to format changes to plural forms. Again, the compatible use of the METEOR prototype notation and the use of the general list processing operations in LISP facilitated programming of processing, storage, and retrieval of this wide range of information. Appendix 3.3 is a listing of the global information currently embodied in the STUDENT system.

3.6 Solution of Simultaneous Equations

This section contains a description of the LISP program used by STUDENT to solve sets of simultaneous equations. The definitions of the three top-level functions SOLVE, SOLVER, and SOLVE1 are shown in Fig. 3-5. This description is essentially independent of a detailed knowledge of LISP, although occasional parenthetical comments will be directed to the more knowledgeable.

The top-level function, SOLVE, is a function of three arguments. One, labeled EQT in the definition of SOLVE, is the set of equations to be solved. The argument labeled WANTED in the definition is a list of variables whose values are wanted. The third argument, labeled TERMS, is another list of variables which is disjoint from WANTED. SOLVE will find the value of any variable which is wanted in terms of any or all of the variables on the list TERMS. In use, the list TERMS is a list of units, such as pounds, or feet, which may appear in the answer.

The output of SOLVE is dependent on whether the set of equations given can be solved for the variables wanted. If no solution can be found because

```
(SOLVE
  (LAMBDA (WANTED EQT TERMS ALIS) (PROG (A B)
          (SETQ A (SOLVER WANTED TERMS ALIS))
    START (COND
             ((NULL A) (RETURN B))
             ((NULL (CDR A)) (RETURN (CONS (CAR A) B)))
             ((ATOM A) (RETURN A)))
          (SETQ B (CONS (CONS (CAAR A) (SUBORD (CDAR A) (
CDR A))) B))
          (SETQ A (CDR A))
          (GO START))))

(SOLVER
  (LAMBDA (WANTED TERMS ALIS) (PROG (A B C D E G H J)
          (SETQ A WANTED)
          (SETQ J (QUOTE INSUFFICIENT))
    START (COND
             ((NULL A) (RETURN J)))
          (SETQ B (CAR A))
          (SETQ C (CDR A))
          (SETQ E (SOLVE1 B (APPEND C (APPEND D TERMS)) ALIS
))
          (COND
             ((ATOM E) (GO ON)))
          (SETQ H (NCONC D C))
          (COND
             ((NULL H) (RETURN E)))
          (SETQ E (SOLVER H TERMS E))
          (COND
             ((NOT (ATOM E)) (RETURN E)))
    ON    (COND
             ((EQ E (QUOTE UNSOLVABLE)) (SETQ J E)))
          (SETQ D (CONS B D))
          (SETQ A C)
          (GO START))))
```

```
(SOLVE1
  (LAMBDA (X TERMS ALIS) (PROG (A B C D E G H J)
          (SETQ A EQT)
          (SETQ J (QUOTE INSUFFICIENT))
   $TART  (COND
             ((NULL A) (RETURN J)))
          (SETQ B (CAR A))
          (SETQ C (SUBORD B ALIS))
          (SETQ D (VARTERMS C))
          (COND
             ((MEMBER X D) (GO ON)))
   B      (SETQ E (CONS B E))
          (SETQ A (CDR A))
          (GO START)
   ON     (SETQ G (CONS X TERMS))
          (SETQ H (LOGMINUS D G))
          (SETQ EQT (EFFACE B EQT))
          (COND
             ((NULL H) (GO SOLVEQ)))
          (SETQ G (SOLVER H G ALIS))
          (COND
             ((ATOM G) (GO D)))
          (SETQ ALIS G)
          (SETQ C (SUBORD B ALIS))
   SOLVEQ (SETQ G (SOLVEQ X C))
          (COND
             ((ATOM G) (GO D)))
          (RETURN (APPEND ALIS (LIST
             G)))
   D      (COND
             ((EQ G (QUOTE UNSOLVABLE)) (SETQ J G)))
          (SETQ EQT (APPEND E A))
          (GO B))))
```

Figure 3-5. The SOLVE Program in STUDENT

the solution involves nonlinear processes, SOLVE returns with the value UNSOLVABLE. If no solution is found because not enough equations are given, SOLVE returns with the value INSUFFICIENT. If however, a solution is found, SOLVE returns with a list of pairs. The first element of each pair is a variable, either on the wanted list, or a variable whose value was found while solving for the desired unknowns. The second element of each pair is an arithmetic expression (in the prefix notation shown in Fig. 3-2), which contains only numbers and variables on the list TERMS. Thus, the answer found by SOLVE is an "association list" of variables and their values in the proper terms.

For example, consider the set of seven simultaneous equations shown below, and suppose SOLVE were asked to solve this set of equations for x and z. These are given in infix notation for ease of reading.

(1) $x + w = 9$

(2) $x^2 - C = D$

(3) $C + 3D = 6$

(4) $2C - D = 5$

(5) $x + 2y = 4$

(6) $y^2 - 3y + 2 = z$

(7) $4x - y = 7$

The list TERMS is empty, and thus the values must all be numbers. In this case SOLVE would return with the list of pairs "$((y, 1)\ (x, 2)\ (z, 0))$," which indicates that the values $x = 2$ and $z = 0$ satisfy this set of equations (or those members of this set which were used to determine the values). The value $y = 1$ was found during the solving process.

Most of the work of SOLVE is done by the function SOLVER. SOLVE transmits to SOLVER the list of WANTED variables, the list of TERMS, and a null association list (called ALIS) that is recursively built up to give the answer. The value of SOLVER is this association list of pairs, with the first element of each pair being a variable whose value has been found. The second element of each is an arithmetic expression which may contain any variable on the list TERMS (as was the case for the ALIS of SOLVE). However, it may also contain variables which are first elements of pairs later on the association list. If values for variables given by later pairs are substituted into this arithmetic expression, one gets the arithmetic expression given by SOLVE containing only variables on the list TERMS. In the example, SOLVER would return with the association list $((y, (4x-7))\ (x,2)\ (z,0))$ which gives y in terms of x. SOLVE makes the substitutions and simplification on the association list returned by SOLVER.

SOLVER is a program that solves for a list of wanted variables. It does this by choosing one of these variables, adding the others to the list of terms and calling SOLVE1 to solve for this one variable in terms of the other wanted variables and the original TERMS. If SOLVE1 succeeds in solving for this variable, SOLVER pairs this one variable with the expression found, puts this pair on the end of the ALIS, and, using this substitution in every equation it tries to solve, attempts to solve for the remaining wanted variables. If there are no more, SOLVER is finished and returns the association list built up.

SOLVE1 solves for a single wanted variable by finding an equation containing this variable, after all substitutions of values for variables listed on the ALIS have been made. It then makes a list of all the other variables in the equation, and checks to see if there are any not on the list TERMS. If so it calls SOLVER to solve for these new variables in terms of the wanted variable and the variables in TERMS. If SOLVER is unsuccessful, SOLVE1 tries to find another equation containing the wanted variable, and repeats the process. If there is none, SOLVE1 has the value INSUFFICIENT. If SOLVER is successful, and values for these new variables are found, or if there are no new variables, SOLVE1 finally calls SOLVEQ which attempts to solve this equation for the wanted variable. If the equation is linear in *this* variable, SOLVEQ will be successful and give a solution. SOLVE1 will add a pair consisting of the wanted variable and this value to the end of ALIS, and return with this augmented ALIS as its value. If SOLVEQ is unsuccessful, SOLVE1 tries another equation; but then, if no solution can be found, SOLVE1 returns the value UNSOLVABLE.

This description has been a rather long-winded attempt to explain the one page of LISP program of Fig. 3-5. To make it more specific, let us consider what happens when SOLVER tries to solve the set of seven equations of p. 188.

SOLVER is asked to solve for x and z. It asks SOLVE1 to solve for x in terms of z. SOLVE1 picks equation 1, finds that a new variable, w, has appeared and asks SOLVER to solve for w in terms of x and z. Since there is no other occurrence of w in this set, SOLVER is unsuccessful and SOLVE1 abandons equation 1 and goes to equation 2. Here it calls SOLVER to solve for the two new variables C and D in terms of x and z. In this case SOLVER is successful, using equations 3 and 4, but when these values are substituted in equation 2, SOLVEQ cannot solve for x because the equation is not linear in x.

SOLVE1 now abandons equation 2 and the results it obtained as subgoals for solving 2. It finds an occurrence of x again in equation 3. Again it calls on SOLVER, to solve for the new variable y in terms of x and z. SOLVER tries to use 6, but SOLVEQ cannot solve this equation for y. Using 7, SOLVER returns with an ALIS of $((y, (4x-7)))$. Using this ALIS, substituting this value for y into equation 5, SOLVE1 calls on SOLVEQ to solve this equation for x, which it does; finally SOLVE1 returns to SOLVER the ALIS $((y, (4x-7)), (x,2))$ which does give the value of x in terms of z. Having found x in terms of z, SOLVER will now call SOLVE1 to find the value of z. SOLVE1 finds an occurrence of z in equation 6, and after substitution of terms on the ALIS, SOLVEQ is able to solve this equation for z, because it is linear in z. Adding the pair $(z,0)$ to the ALIS, SOLVE1 returns it to SOLVER, which passes on this ALIS $((y, (4x-7)), (x,2), (z,0))$ to SOLVE. SOLVE, using the function SUBORD, which substitutes in order pairs on an ALIS into an expression and simplifies, finally returns the ALIS $((y,1)\ (x,2)\ (z,0))$.

This example shows the rather tortuous recursions used by these functions to solve a set of equations. Why should we employ this type of solving program instead of a more straightforward matrix method? The principal reason is that, as shown, nonlinear equations may appear in the set. In this case, if appropriate values can be found from other equations which, when substituted into this nonlinear equation, make it linear in the variable for which we want to solve, then SOLVE will find the value of this variable.

The method of operation of SOLVER requires that if n variables appear in any equation, and that equation is used, then at least $n-1$ other independent equations containing these variables must be in the set of equations, or the actual mechanics of solving will not be started. This eliminates much work if there are extraneous equations in the set which contain one or two of the wanted variables. However, it precludes solving a set of equations which is homogeneous in one unwanted variable and would therefore cancel out in the solution process. This is the principal reason why problems such as "Spigot A fills a tub in 1 hour, and spigot B in 2 hours. How long do they take together?" cannot be solved by STUDENT.

This solving subroutine set is an independent package in the STUDENT program. Improvements can therefore be made to it without disturbing the rest of the processing. The routine described here was designed to handle most of the problems found in first-year algebra texts.

3.7 Conclusion

3.7.1 Results

The purpose of the research reported here was to develop techniques to facilitate natural language communication with a computer. A semantic theory of coherent discourse was proposed as a basis for the design and understanding of such man-machine systems. This theory was only outlined, and much additional work remains to be done. However, in its present rough form the theory serves as a guide for construction of the STUDENT system, which can communicate in a limited subset of English.

The language analysis in STUDENT is an implementation of the analytic portion of this theory. The STUDENT system has a very narrow semantic base. From the theory it is clear that by utilizing this knowledge of the limited range of meaning of the input discourse, the parsing problem becomes greatly simplified, since the number of linguistic forms that must be recognized is very small. If a parsing system were based on any small semantic base, this same simplification would occur. This suggests that in a general language processor some time might be spent putting the input into a semantic context before going ahead with the syntactic analysis.

The semantic base of the STUDENT language analysis is delimited by the characteristics of the problem-solving system embedded in it. STUDENT is a question-answering system which answers questions posed in the context of "algebra story problems." In the introduction, we used four criteria for evaluating several question-answering systems. Let us compare the STUDENT system to these others in the light of these criteria.

1. *Extent of Understanding:* All the other question-answering systems discussed analyze input sentence by sentence. Although a representation of the meaning of all input sentences may be placed in some common store, no syntactic connection is ever made between sentences.

In the STUDENT system, an acceptable input is a sequence of sentences, such that these sentences cannot be understood by just finding the meanings of the individual sentences, ignoring their local context. Intersentence dependencies must be determined, and intersentence syntactic relationships must be used in this case for solution of the problem given. This extension of the syntactic dimension of understanding is important because such inter-sentence dependencies (e.g., the use of pronouns) are very commonly used in natural language communication.

The semantic model in the STUDENT system is based on one relationship (equality) and five basic arithmetic functions. Composition of these functions yields other functions, which are also expressed as individual linguistic forms in the input language. The input language is richer in expressing functions than either Lindsay's or Raphael's system. The logical systems discussed may have more relationships (predicates) allowable in the input but do not allow any composition of these predicates. The logical combinations of predicates used are only those expressed in the input as logical combinations (using AND, OR, etc.).

The deductive system in STUDENT, as in Lindsay's and Raphael's programs, is designed for the type of questions to be asked. It can only deduce answers of a certain type from the input information, that is, arithmetic values satisfying a set of equations. In performing its deductions it is reasonably sophisticated in avoiding irrelevant information, as are the other two mentioned. It lacks the general power of a logical system but is much more efficient in obtaining its particular class of deductions than would be a general deductive system utilizing the axioms of arithmetic.

2. *Facility for Extending Abilities:* Extending the syntactic abilities of any of the other question-answering systems discussed would require reprogramming. In the STUDENT system new definitional transformations can be introduced at run time without any reprogramming. The information

concerning these transformations can be input in English, or in a combination of English and METEOR, if that is more appropriate. New syntactic transformations must be added by extending the program.

The semantic base of the STUDENT system can be extended only by adding a new program, as is true of the other question-answering systems discussed. However, STUDENT is organized to facilitate such extensions by minimizing the interactions of different parts of the program. The necessary information need only be added to the program equivalent of the table of operators in Fig. 3-4.

Similarly, the deductive portion of STUDENT, which solves the derived set of equations, is an independent package. Therefore, a new extended solver can be added to the system by just replacing the package and maintaining the input-output characteristics of this subroutine.

3. *Knowledge of Internal Structure Needed by User:* Very little if any internal knowledge of the workings of the STUDENT system need be known by the user. He must have a firm grasp of the type of problem that STUDENT can solve, and a knowledge of the input grammar. For example, he must be aware that the same phrase must always be used to represent the same variable in a problem, within the limits of similarity defined earlier. He must realize that even within these limits STUDENT will not recognize more than one variation on a phrase. But if the user does forget any of these facts he can still use the system, for the interaction discussed in the next section allows him to make amends for almost any mistake.

4. *Interaction With the User:* The STUDENT system is embedded in a time-sharing environment [the MIT Project MAC time-sharing system (13)] ; this greatly facilitates interaction with the user. STUDENT differentiates between its failure to solve a problem because of its mathematical limitations and failure from lack of sufficient information. In case of failure it asks the user for additional information, and suggests the nature of the needed information (relationships among variables of the problem). It can go back to the user repeatedly until it has enough information to solve the problem or until the user gives up.

STUDENT also reports when it does not recognize the format of an input sentence. Using this information as a guide, the user is in a teaching-machine type situation and can quickly learn to speak STUDENT's brand of input English. By monitoring the assumptions that STUDENT makes about the input and the global information it uses, the user can stop the system and reword a problem to avoid an unwanted ambiguity, or add new general information to the global information store.

The crucial point in this user interaction is that STUDENT is embedded in an on-line, time-sharing system and can thus provide more interaction than any of the other systems mentioned.

3.7.2 Extensions

The present STUDENT system has reached the maximum size allowable in the LISP system on a thirty-two-thousand-word IBM 7094. Therefore very little can be added directly to the present system. All the programming extensions mentioned here are predicated on the existence of a much larger memory machine.

Without inventing any new techniques, I think that the STUDENT system could be made to understand most of the algebra story problems that appear in first-year high-school textbooks. If new operators or new combinations of arithmetic operations occur, they can easily be added to OPFORM, the subroutine that maps the kernel English sentences into equations. The number of formats recognizable in the system can be increased without reprogramming through the machinery available for storing global information (see Section 3.5). The problems it cannot handle are those having excessive verbiage or implied information about the world not expressible in a single sentence.

As mentioned earlier, the system can now make use of any given schema only once in solving a problem. This is because the schema equation is added to the set of equations to be solved, and the variables in the schema only identified with one other set of variables appearing in the problem. For example, if "distance equals speed times time" were the schema, then "distance" as a variable in the schema might be set equal to "distance traveled by train" or "distance traveled by plane," but not both in the same problem. This problem could be resolved by not adding the schema equation directly to the set of equations to be solved, but by looking for consistent sets of variables to identify with the schema variables. Then STUDENT could add an instance of the schema equations, with the appropriate substitutions, for each consistent set of variables found which are "similar" to the schema variables.

At the moment the solving subroutine of STUDENT can only perform linear operations on literal equations and substitutions of numbers in polynomials and exponentials. It would be relatively easy to add the facility for solving quadratic or even higher-order solvable equations. One could even add, quite easily, sufficient mechanisms to allow the solver to perform the differentiation needed to do related rate problems in the differential calculus.

The semantic base of the STUDENT system could be expanded. In order to add the relations recognized by the SIR system of Raphael, for example, one would have to add on the lowest level of the STUDENT program the set of kernel sentences understood in SIR, their mapping to the SIR model, and the question-answering routine to retrieve facts. Then the apparatus of the STUDENT system would process much more complicated input statements for the SIR model. One serious problem that arises when the semantic base is extended is based on the fact that one kernel may have an interpretation in terms of two different semantic bases. For example, "Tom has 3 fish" can be interpreted in both SIR and the present STUDENT system. To resolve this semantic ambiguity, the program can check the context of the ambiguous statement to see if there has been one consistent model into which all the other statements have been processed. If the latter condition does not determine a single preferred interpretation for the statement, then both interpretations can be stored.

In addition to these immediate extensions of the STUDENT system, our semantic theory of discourse can be used as a basis for a much more general language-processing system. As a start, one could implement the generative grammar described in Appendix 3.5 to produce coherent discourse problems solvable by the STUDENT system. Another more exciting possibility is to utilize this type of speaker's model of the world to attack Yngve's "Baseball Announcer" problem. The baseball announcer has certain propositions added to his world model from the events he perceives, i.e., the baseball game he is watching. Mandatory application of certain semantic rules adds other propositions and deletes some that are there. While these changes are going on, the announcer is to generate a running commentary (coherent discourse) describing this ball game he is watching. By making the proper assumptions about where the attention of the announcer is focused, that is, which propositions he is going to use as a base of his discourse at any time, I feel that a reasonable facsimile of an announcer can be programmed.

Another use for this model for generation and analysis of discourse is as a hypothesis about the linguistic behavior of people. Psychologists have built reasonable computer models for human behavior in decision making (17), verbal learning of nonsense syllables (15), and some problem-solving situations (34). STUDENT may be a good predictive model for the behavior of people when confronted with an algebra problem to solve.* This can be tested, and such a study may lead to a better understanding of human behavior and/or a better reformulation of this theory of language processing.

I think we are far from writing a program that can understand all, or even a very large segment, of English. However, within its narrow field of competence, STUDENT has demonstrated that "understanding" machines can be built. Indeed, I believe that using the techniques developed in this research, one could construct a system of practical value which would communicate well with people in English over the range of material understood by the program.

*Paige and Simon have tested this hypothesis and found that a slightly modified STUDENT program is a good model for human behavior for one class of people (Paige, J.J., and Simon, H.A., "Cognitive Processes in Solving Algebra Word Problems," in Kleinmuntz, B. (ed.), *Problem Solving: Research, Method, and Theory,* John Wiley, New York, 1966.)

APPENDIX 3.1. Flowchart of the STUDENT Program

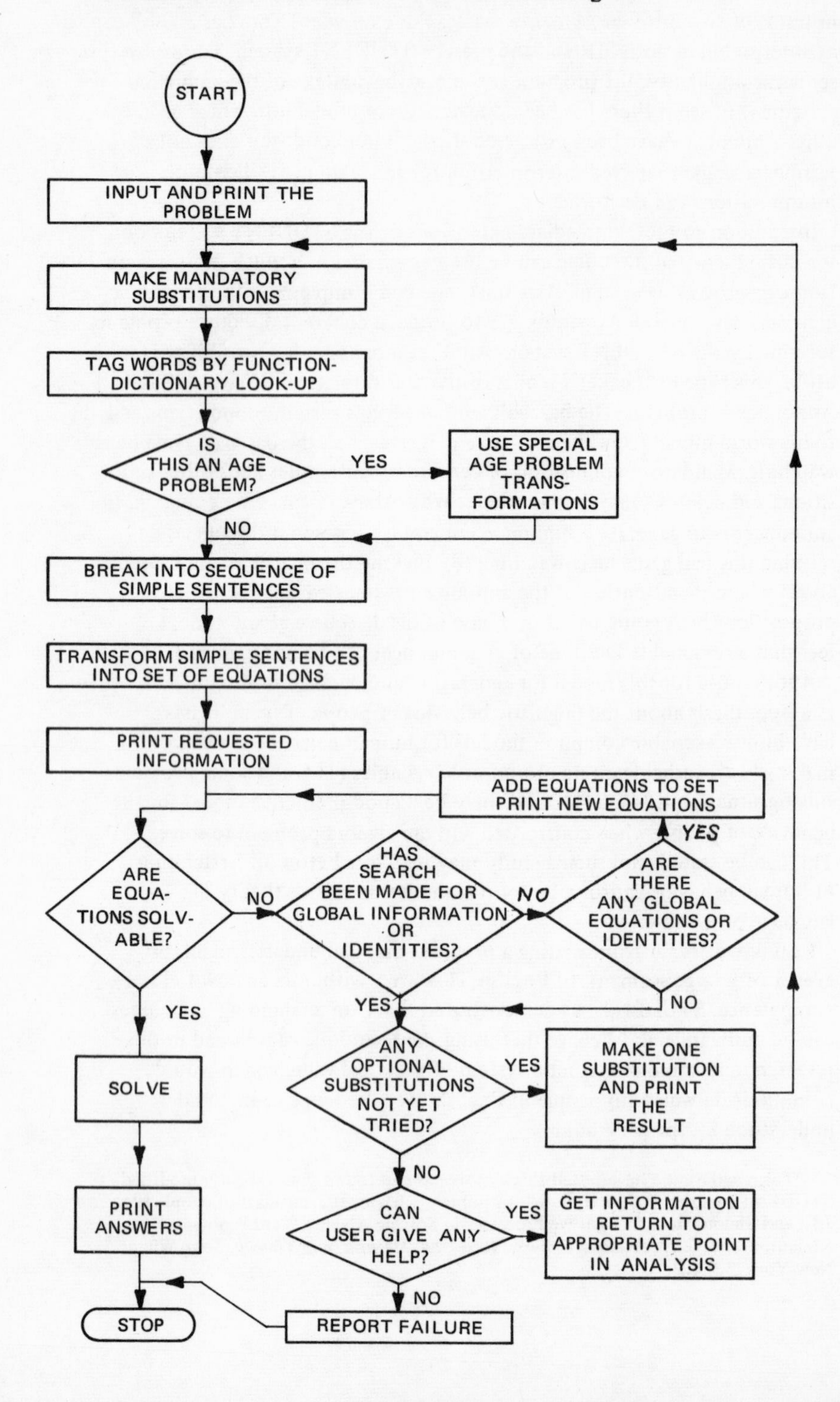

Appendix 3.2 Listing of the STUDENT Program

A3.2.1. Definition of STUDENT

```
((STUDENT    ($)    (/ (*S ORGPRB 1))                         *)
(*       ($)    (1 (FN TERPRI) (FN TERPRI) (FN TERPRI))       *)
(*       ((*P THE PROBLEM TO BE SOLVED IS))                   *)
(IDIOMS ($)                                                   *)
(*       (HOW OLD)    (WHAT)                             IDIOMS)
(*       (IS EQUAL TO)    (IS)                           IDIOMS)
(*       (YEARS YOUNGER THAN)    (LESS THAN)             IDIOMS)
(*       (YEARS OLDER THAN)    (PLUS)                    IDIOMS)
(*       (PERCENT LESS THAN)    (PERLESS)                IDIOMS)
(*       (LESS THAN)    (LESSTHAN)                       IDIOMS)
(*       (THESE)    (THE)                                IDIOMS)
(*       (MORE THAN)    (PLUS)                           IDIOMS)
(*       (FIRST TWO NUMBERS)    (THE FIRST NUMBER AND THE
            SECOND NUMBER)                               IDIOMS)
(*       (THREE NUMBERS)    (THE FIRST NUMBER AND THE SECOND
              NUMBER AND THE THIRD NUMBER)               IDIOMS)
(*       (ONE HALF)    ( .5000)                          IDIOMS)
(*       (TWICE)    (2 TIMES)                            IDIOMS)
(*       (TWO NUMBERS)                                      SIM)
(*       ((* DOLLAR) $1)    (2 DOLLARS)                  IDIOMS)
(*       (CONSECUTIVE TO)    ((QUOTE 1) PLUS)            IDIOMS)
(*       (LARGER THAN)    (PLUS)                         IDIOMS)
(*       (PER CENT)    (PERCENT)                         IDIOMS)
(*       (HOW MANY)    (HOWM)                            IDIOMS)
(*       (SQUARE OF)    (SQUARE)                         IDIOMS)
(*       (($.IS) MULTIPLIED BY)    (TIMES)               IDIOMS)
(*       (($.IS) DIVIDED BY)    (DIVBY)                  IDIOMS)
(*       (THE SUM OF)    (SUM)                           IDIOMS)
(*       ($)    (/ (*S NONID 1))                              *)
(WORDS   ($1)    0    (/ (*Q SHELF (FN GETDCT 1 DICT)))
            WORDS)
(*       ($)    ((*A SHELF))                                  *)
(THE     (THE THE)    (1)                                  THE)
(*       ($)    (/ (*S MARKWD 1))                             *)
(*       (AS OLD AS)                                    AGEPROB)
(*       (AGE)                                          AGEPROB)
(*       (YEARS OLD)                                    AGEPROB)
(*       ($)    (/ (*D RETURN SENTENCE))                BRACKET)
(SENTENCE    ($)    ((*N PROBLEM))                            *)
(*       ($1)    0    (/ (*S FIND (*E 1)) (*D RETURN SENTENCE
            ))                                           OPFORM)
(QUIET   ($)                                                  *)
(SUBSTITUTIONS    ($)    ((FN TERPRI) (*A NONID))             *)
(*       ((*P WITH MANDATORY SUBSTITUTIONS THE PROBLEM IS))
            *)
(TAGGING    ($)    ((FN TERPRI) (*A MARKWD))                  *)
(*       ((*P WITH WORDS TAGGED BY FUNCTION THE PROBLEM IS)
            )                                                 *)
(BRACKETING ($)    ((FN TERPRI) (*A SIMSEN))                  *)
(*          ((FN PRINLIS ((THE SIMPLE SENTENCES ARE))))       *)
(EQUATIONS   ($)    ((FN TERPRI) (*A SHELF))                  *)
(*          ((FN PRINLIS ((THE EQUATIONS TO BE SOLVED ARE))))
                   *)
(*       ($)    (/ (*S SHELF 1))                              *)
(SOLUTION    ($)    ((FN TERPRI))                             *)
(OPRN    ($)    ((FN REMDUP (*K (*A SHELF))))                 *)
(*       ($)    ((*A WANTED))    (/ (*S SHELF 1) (*S EQT 1))
            *)
(*       ($)    ((FN REMDUP (*K (*A UNITS))))    (/ (*S
         WANTED 1) (*S WANT 1))                               *)
(*       ($)    ((FN REMDUP (*K (*A AUNITS))))    (/ (*S
         UNITS 1) (*S UNIT 1))                                *)
(*       ($)    (/ (*S AUNIT 1))                              *)
(*       ($1 $)    ((FN SOLVE (*K (*A WANTED)) (*K (*A SHELF
         )) (*K 1 2) (*K)))                                 OUT)
(*       ($)    ((FN SOLVE (*K (*A WANTED)) (*K (*A SHELF))
         (*K (*A UNITS)) (*K)))                             OUT)
(OUT     ($)                                                  *)
(ANSWER (UNSOLVABLE)    (1 (*W UNABLE TO SOLVE THIS SET OF
           EQUATIONS $EOR$) (FN TERPRI))                 SIMVAR)
(*       (INSUFFICIENT)    ((*W THE EQUATIONS
           WERE INSUFFICIENT TO FIND A  SOLUTION $EOR$)
         (FN TERPRI))                                    SIMVAR)
(*       ($)    ((FN PRLIS (*K (*A ANS)) (*K 1)))             *)
(*       (INCOMPLETE)    (UNSOLVABLE)                    ANSWER)
(*       ($)    (THE PROBLEM IS SOLVED)                     END)
(BRACKET  * ($1)                                            BKT)
(*       ($ ($1 / DLM))    0    (/ (*Q PROBLEM (*K 1 2)))
         BRACKET)
(*       ($)    0    (/ (*Q PROBLEM (*K 1 (PERIOD / DLM))))
            *
         NO END))
(BKT     ($)    (/ (*S SHELF (*A PROBLEM)) (*D BKEND PBKT))
            *)
(BKT1    ($)    ((*N SHELF))                                  *)
(*  *    ($1)    ((*E 1))                                 BKEND)
(*       (IF $ (* COMMA) ($1 / QWORD) $)    0    (/ (*S SHELF
           (*K 2 ((PERIOD / DLM))) (*K 4 5)) (*D BKEND
         BKT))                                             BKT1)
(*       ($ (* COMMA) AND $)    0    (/ (*S SHELF (*K 1 ((
         PERIOD / DLM))) (*K 4)) (*D BKEND BKT))           BKT1)
(*       ($)    (/ (*Q PROBLEM (*K 1)))                    BKT1)
(PBKT    ($)    ((*A PROBLEM))                                *)
(*       ($)    0    (/ (*S PROBLEM 1) (*S SIMSEN 1))    RETURN
         )
```

```
(CRY    ($)   ((FN TERPRI) (*W I CANT SOLVE  THIS PROBLEM
          $EOR$))                                          END)
(GETEXP ($1)   0   (/ (*Q WORDS (FN GETDCT 1 DICT)))
          GETEXP)
(*      ($)   ((FN TERPRI) (*A WORDS))                      *)
(*      ($ IS $)    ((*K EQUAL (FN OPFORM (*K 1)) (FN
          OPFORM (*K 3))))    (/ (*D SIMVAR SIMVAR))
          EQTIN)
(*  *   ((*P I DONT UNDERSTAND THIS))                     CRY)
(IDTABLE ($)                                                *)
(G02514 (THE PERIMETER OF $1 RECTANGLE)   (TWICE THE SUM
          OF THE LENGTH AND WIDTH OF THE RECTANGLE)
          G02514)
(*      ($)                                              PNEW)
(G02512 (TWO NUMBERS)   (ONE OF THE NUMBERS AND THE OTHER
          NUMBER)                                      G02512)
(*      ($)                                              PNEW)
(G02510 (TWO NUMBERS)   (ONE NUMBER AND THE OTHER NUMBER)
          G02510)
(*      ($)                                              PNEW)
(PNEW   ((*P THE PROBLEM WITH AN IDIOMATIC SUBSTUTION IS))
          *)
(*      ($)   ((*K (*A ORGPRB)) 1 (FN NLSHLF) (FN TERPRI))
          *)
(*      ($1 $)   (2)   (/ (*S ORGPRB (*E 1)))          IDIOMS)
(AGEPROB    (AS OLD AS)   0                           AGEPROB)
(YEARSOLD   (YEARS OLD)   0                          YEARSOLD)
(WHENFUT    (WILL BE WHEN)   (WH* IN (FN GENSYM) YEARS (
          PERIOD / DLM))                              WHENBOT)
(*  *   (WAS WHEN)   (WH* (FN GENSYM) YEARS AGO ((PERIOD /
          DLM)))                                       WHENGO)
(WHENBOT    (WH* $ (PERIOD / DLM))   (2 3 2)          WHENFUT)
(WHENGO ((($1 / PERSON) WILL BE IN $1 YEARS)   (1 S AGE 4 5
          6)                                          WHENWAS)
(WAS    (WAS)   (IS)                                      WAS)
(WILLBE (WILL BE)   (IS)                               WILLBE)
(ISNOW  (($1 / PERSON) IS NOW)   (1 S AGE NOW)          ISNOW)
(FROMNOW    ($1 YEARS FROM NOW)   (IN 1 2)            FROMNOW)
(TOP    ($ ($1 / PERSON))   (MM)   (/ (*Q PROBLEM 1 2)) *
          )
(*      (MM S)   0   (/ (*Q PROBLEM 2))                   TOP)
(*      (MM)   0   (/ (*Q PROBLEM S AGE))                 TOP)
(*      ($)   ((*A PROBLEM) 1)                              *)
(*      (($1 / PERSON) $ S AGE)   (/ (*Q SUBJECT 1 2) (*Q
          SUBJECTS 1 2 3))                                  *)
```

```
(SUBPRO  *  ($ ($1 / PRO) $)   ((*A SUBJECT))   (/ (*Q
          PROBLEM 1) (*Q REST 3))                          PPRO)
(*      ($)   ((*A REST))   (/ (*Q PROBLEM 1 S AGE) (*S
          SUBJECT 1))                                    SUBPRO)
(PPRO   ($)   ((*A PROBLEM) 1)                                *)
(POSSPRO  *  ($ ($1 / POSSPRO) $)   ((*A SUBJECTS))   (/ (
          *Q PROBLEM 1) (*Q REST 3))                     ENDPRO)
(*      ($)   ((*A REST))   (/ (*Q PROBLEM 1) (*S SUBJECTS
          1))                                           POSSPRO)
(ENDPRO ($)   ((*A PROBLEM) 1)                                *)
(GETAGE ($ ($1 / PERSON) $ AGE)   0   (/ (*Q PROBLEM 1 2 3
          4) (*Q AGES (*K 2 3 4)))                       GETAGE)
(*      ($)   ((*A PROBLEM) 1)                                *)
(TAGE   ($ THEIR AGES $)   ((FN REMDUP (*K (*A AGES))))
          (/ (*Q LEFT 1) (*Q RIGHT 4))                   THRAGE)
(*      ($)   (/ (*D RETURN AGESEN))                    BRACKET)
(AGESEN ($)   ((*N PROBLEM))                                  *)
(*  *   ($1)   (M* (*E 1))                              AGEDONE)
(*      (M* IN $1 YEARS)   0   (/ (*S AGEOP 2 3 4))   SETOP
          )
(*  *   (M* $1 YEARS AGO)   0   (/ (*S AGEOP 2 3 4))
          GETNEXT)
(SETOP  *   ($ AGE)   (PP*)   (/ (*Q TEMP 1 2))           OPEND)
(*      (PP* IN $1 YEARS)   0   (/ (*Q TEMP 2 3 4))   SETOP
          )
(*      (PP* $1 YEARS AGO)   0   (/ (*Q TEMP 2 3 4))
          SETOP)
(*      (PP* NOW)   0                                     SETOP)
(*      (PP* $)   ((*A AGEOP))   (/ (*Q REST 2))              *)
(*      ($)   ((*A REST))   (/ (*Q TEMP 1) (*S AGEOP 1))
          SETOP)
(GETNEXT    (M*)   0                                      FUTOP)
(OPEND  ($)   ((*A TEMP) 1)   (/ (*S GARBAGE (*A AGEOP)))
          *)
(FUTOP  (IN $1 YEARS)   ((*K PLUSS / OP) 2)               FUTOP)
(PASTOP ($1 YEARS AGO)   ((*K MINUSS / OP) 1)            PASTOP)
(*      (IS ($1 / DLM))   (2)                                 *)
(*      ($)   0   (/ (*Q FIND (*K 1)))                   AGESEN)
(AGEDONE    ($)   0   (/ (*S PROBLEM (*A FIND)))   SENTENCE
          )
(THRAGE ($1)   0   (/ (*Q MIDDLE AND (*E 1)) (*Q AGES 1))
          THRAGE)
(*      ($)   ((*N MIDDLE))                                   *)
(*      ($)   ((*A LEFT) (*A MIDDLE) (*A RIGHT))           TAGE)
)
```

```
(OPFORM ($)    ((*A FIND))                                    *)
(*  *   ($1)                                            RETURN)
(*      (WHAT ARE $ AND $ QMARK)    ((FN GENSYM) 3)     (/ (
            *S FIND 1 2 5 6))                             QSET)
(*      (WHAT ARE $ QMARK)    ((FN GENSYM) 3)             QSET)
(*      (WHAT IS $ QMARK)    ((FN GENSYM) 3)              QSET)
(*      (HOWM $1 IS $)    ((FN GENSYM) 4)    (/ (*S AUNITS (
            *K 2)))                                       QSET)
(*      (HOWM $ DO $ HAVE QMARK)    ((FN GENSYM) THE NUMBER
            OF 2 4 HAS)                                   QSET)
(*      ((HOW / QWORD) $ DOES $ HAVE QMARK)    ((FN GENSYM)
            THE NUMBER OF 2 4 HAVE)                       QSET)
(*      (FIND $ AND $)    ((FN GENSYM) 2)    (/ (*S FIND 1 4
           ))                                             QSET)
(*      (FIND $ ($1 / DLM))    ((FN GENSYM) 2)            QSET)
(*      ($)    ((FN REMART (*K 1)))                          *)
(*      ($ IS MULTIPLIED BY $)    0    (/ (*S REF (*K TIMES
           (FN OPFORM (*K 1)) (FN OPFORM (*K 5)))))
           RETURN)
(*      ($ IS DIVIDED BY $)    0    (/ (*S REF (*K QUOTIENT
           (FN OPFORM (*K 1)) (FN OPFORM (*K 5)))))
           RETURN)
(*      ($ IS INCREASED BY $)    0    (/ (*S REF (*K PLUS (
           FN OPFORM (*K 1)) (FN OPFORM (*K 5)))))
           RETURN)
(*      ($ IS $)    0    (/ (*S SHELF (*K EQUAL (FN OPFORM (
           *K 1)) (FN OPFORM (*K 3)))))                 RETURN)
(*      ($ ($1 / VERB) $ AS MANY $ AS $ ($1 / VERB) $ ($1
           / DLM))    0    (/ (*S SHELF (*K EQUAL (FN
           OPFORM (*K THE NUMBER OF 6 1 2)) (FN OPFORM (
           *K 3 THE NUMBER OF 10 8 9 11)))))            RETURN)
(*      ($ ($1 / VERB) (FN NMTEST) $1 $ ($1 / DLM))    0
           (/ (*S SHELF (*K EQUAL (FN OPFORM (*K THE
           NUMBER OF 4 1 2)) (FN OPFORM (*K 3 5 6)))))
           RETURN)
(*      ((*P THIS SENTENCE FORM IS NOT RECOGNIZED))          *)
(*      ($)    0                                        RETURN)
(QSET   ($1 $)    0    (/ (*S SHELF (*K EQUAL 1 (FN OPFORM (
           *K (FN REMART (*K 2)))))) (*Q WANTED 1) (*Q
           ANS 1 (*K (FN OPREM (*K 2)))))               OPFORM)
(SIMVAR ($)    ((FN GETEQNS (*K (*A VAR))))                 *)
(*      ($1 $)    0    (/ (*S VBL (*E 1)) (*S EQT1 2))      *)
(*      ($)    ((FN REMDUP (*K (*A EQT1))))                 *)
(*  *   ($1 $)    (/ (*S EQT1 1 2))                         SP)
(*      ((*P USING THE FOLLOWING KNOWN RELATIONSHIPS))       *)
(*      ($)    ((FN TERPRI))                                  *)
(SP     ($)    ((*N VBL))    (/ (*D SIMVAR SIM))              *)
(SIMP  *    ($1)    ((*E 1))                             SIMFIN)
(*      ($ ($1 / PRO) $)    (1 (* DOLLAR) 3)    (/ (*S VAR (
           *K 1 2 3)))                                     VTST)
(*      ($)    ((* DOLLAR) 1 (* DOLLAR))    (/ (*S VAR (*K 1
           )))                                               *)
(VTST   ($)    ((*K (*K * (*K 1) (QUOTE 0) END) (QUOTE ((*
           ($) END)))))                                      *)
(VTOP   ($)    ((*N VBL))    (/ (*S TEST 1 1))               *)
(*  *   ($1)    ((FN METRIX2 (*N TEST) 1))    (/ (*S VART 1)
           )                                             TSTEND)
(*      ($1 $)    ((*N TEST))                              VTOP)
(*      ($)    (EQUAL (*N VAR) (*N VART))                    *)
(*      (EQUAL $1 $1)    (2 IS EQUAL TO 3)    (/ (*S VART 3)
           (*S EQT1 (*K 1 2 3)))                             *)
(*      ((*P ASSUMING THAT))                                 *)
(*      ($)    ((FN TERPRI))                                  *)
(TSTEND ($)    ((*N VART))                                    *)
(*      ($1)    0    (/ (*S VBL 1))                      TSTEND)
(*      ($)    ((*A TEST))                                    *)
(*      ($)    ((*N VBL))                                  SIMP)
(SIMFIN ($)    ((*A EQT1))                                    *)
(EQTIN  ($1 $)    0    (/ (*S SHELF 1 2 (*A EQT)) (*S UNITS
           (*A UNIT)) (*S AUNITS (*A AUNIT)) (*S WANTED (
           *A WANT)))                                      OPRN)
(SIM    ($)    ((FN TERPRI) (*A ORGPRB))                      *)
(*      ($)    (1 (*W TRYING POSSIBLE IDIOMS $EOR$) (FN
           TERPRI))    (/ (*S ORGPRB 1) (*D SIMVAR SIMVAR)
           (*D PO PO))                                   IDTEMP)
(IDTEMP ($)                                                   *)
(*      (THE PERIMETER OF $1 RECTANGLE)    (/ (*D IDTEMP
           G02513))                                      G02514)
(G02513 ($)                                                   *)
(*      (TWO NUMBERS)    (/ (*D IDTEMP G02511))          G02512)
(G02511 ($)                                                   *)
(*      (TWO NUMBERS)    (/ (*D IDTEMP G02509))          G02510)
(G02509 ($)                                                   *)
(IDFIN  ($)    ((*A VAR))                                     *)
(*      ((FN PRINLIS ((DO YOU KNOW ANY MORE RELATIONSHIPS
           AMONG THESE VARIABLES))))                          *)
(*      ($)    ((FN RDFLX))    (/ (*S VAR 1))                 *)
(*      (YES)    ((*W TELL ME $EOR$) (FN TERPRI) (FN RDFLX)
           )                                             GETEXP)
```

A3.2.2. Definition of the Function OPFORM

```
((OPFORM    ($)                                              *)
(*     ($ ($1 / OP 2) $)   ((FN CAR (*K 2)))    (/ (*S
        LEFT (*K 1)) (*S RIGHT (*K 3)))                  OPTST)
(*     ($ ($1 / OP 1) $)   ((FN CAR (*K 2)))    (/ (*S
        LEFT (*K 1)) (*S RIGHT (*K 3)))                  OPTST)
(*     ($ ($1 / OP) $)    ((FN CAR (*K 2)))    (/ (*S LEFT
        (*K 1)) (*S RIGHT (*K 3)))                       OPTST)
(*     ($ ($1 / DLM))    (1)                                 *)
(*     ($)    ((FN REMART (*K 1)))                           *)
(*     ($1)                                              NMTST)
(ARGERR  *  ((*P ARGUMENT ERROR))                          END)
(NMTST  (($1) (FN NMTEST))                              ARGERR)
(*     ((QUOTE 1) $1)    (1 (FN GETDCT 2 PLURAL))            *)
(*     ((FN NMTEST) $1 $)    ((*K TIMES 1 (FN OPFORM (*K 2
        3))))   (/ (*S UNITS (*K 2)))                      END)
(*     ((FN NMTEST))                                       END)
(*  *  ($ THIS $)   ((*N REF) MM 1 2 3)                    OUT)
(*     ($1 MM $)    (1)                                    END)
(*     (MM)   ((*N SHELF) 1)                                 *)
(*  *  ($1 MM $)    ((*E 1))    (/ (*S SHELF 1))            MM)
(*     (EQUAL $1 $)    (2)                                 END)
(*     ($)   (ERROR)                                       END)
(MM    (MM THIS $)    ((*K 3))    (/ (*S VAR (*K 3)))      END)
(OUT   ($2 $)    ((*K 1 2))    (/ (*S VAR (*K 1 2)))       END)
(*     (($.ATOM))    ((*K 1))    (/ (*S VAR (*K 1)))       END)
(*     ($1)    ((*E 1))                                      *)
(*     ($0 $1 / $)    ((*K (*K 2 3 4)))    (/ (*S VAR (*K (
        *K 2 3 4))))                                       END)
(GTDCT  ($1)    0    (/ (*Q SDICT (FN GETDCT 1 DICT)))
        GTDCT)
(*     ($)    ((*A SDICT))                              OPFORM)
(OPTST  ($1 $)    (1)                                        $)
(OF    ($)    ((*EN LEFT))                                   *)
(*     (($.NUMBER) $0)                                    OFOK)
(*     ($)    (1 OF (*EN RIGHT))                        OPFORM)
(OFOK  ($)    ((*K TIMES (FN OPFORM (*K 1)) (FN OPFORM (*N
        RIGHT))))                                          END)
(DIVBY  ($)    ((*K QUOTIENT (FN OPFORM (*N LEFT)) (FN
        OPFORM (*N RIGHT))))                               END)
(**    ($)    ((*K EXPT (FN OPFORM (*N LEFT)) (FN OPFORM (
        *N RIGHT))))                                       END)
(PER   ($)    (1 (*EN RIGHT))                                *)
(*     (PER (FN NMTEST))    (2)                         PERNUM)
(*     (PER)    ((QUOTE 1))                                  *)
(PERNUM ($)    ((*K QUOTIENT (FN OPFORM (*N LEFT)) (FN
        OPFORM (*K 1))))                                   END)
(LESSTHAN    ($)    ((*K PLUS (FN OPFORM (*N RIGHT)) (*K
        MINUS (FN OPFORM (*N LEFT)))))                     END)
(MINUSS ($)                                              MINUS)
(MINUS  ($)    ((*EN LEFT))                                  *)
(*     ($1 $)    ((*K PLUS (FN OPFORM (*K 1 2)) (*K MINUS
        (FN OPFORM (*N RIGHT)))))                          END)
(*     ($)    ((*K MINUS (FN OPFORM (*N RIGHT))))          END)
(TIMES  ($)    ((*EN LEFT))                                  *)
(*     ($1)                                               OFOK)
(*  *  ((*P INCORRECT USE OF TIMES))                       END)
(PERLESS    ($)    ((*EN LEFT) 1)                            *)
(*     (($.NUMBER) PERLESS)    ((FN QUOTIENT (FN
        DIFFERENCE 100 1)   100))                   OFOK)
(*     ($)                                              PERERR)
(PERCENT    ($)    ((*EN LEFT) 1)                            *)
(*     (($.NUMBER) PERCENT)    ((FN QUOTIENT 1  100) (
        *EN RIGHT))                                     OPFORM)
(PERERR  *   ((*P INCORRECT USE OF PERCENT))               END)
(SQUARE ($)    ((*EN LEFT))                                  *)
(*     ($)    ((*K EXPT (FN OPFORM (*N RIGHT)) (QUOTE 2)))
        END)
(PLUSS  ($)                                               PLUS)
(PLUS   ($)    ((*K PLUS (FN OPFORM (*N LEFT)) (FN OPFORM (
        *N RIGHT))))                                       END)
(DIFFERENCE ($)    ((*EN RIGHT))                             *)
(*     (BETWEEN $ AND $)    ((*K PLUS (FN OPFORM (*K 2)) (
        *K MINUS (FN OPFORM (*K 4)))))                     END)
(*  *  ((*P INCORRECT USE OF DIFFERENCE))                  END)
(SQUARED    ($)    ((*EN RIGHT))                             *)
(*     ($)    ((*K EXPT (FN OPFORM (*N LEFT)) 2))          END)
(SUM   ($)    ((*N LEFT))                                    *)
(*     ($)    ((*EN RIGHT))                                  *)
(*     ($ AND $ AND $)    ((*K PLUS (FN OPFORM (*K 1)) (FN
        OPFORM (*K (*K SUM / OP) 3 4 5))))                 END)
(*     ($ AND $)    ((*K PLUS (FN OPFORM (*K 1)) (FN
        OPFORM (*K 3))))                                   END)
(*  *  ((*P SUM USED WRONG))                               END)
)
```

Appendix 3.3. Global Information in STUDENT

```
REMEMBER((
(PEOPLE IS THE PLURAL OF PERSON)
(FEET IS THE PLURAL OF FOOT)
(YARDS IS THE PLURAL OF YARD)
(FATHOMS IS THE PLURAL OF FATHOM)
(INCHES IS THE PLURAL OF INCH)
(SPANS IS THE PLURAL OF SPAN)
(ONE HALF ALWAYS MEANS  0.5  )
(THREE NUMBERS ALWAYS MEANS THE FIRST NUMBER AND THE SECOND
NUMBER AND THE THIRD NUMBER)
(FIRST TWO NUMBERS ALWAYS MEANS
THE FIRST NUMBER AND THE SECOND NUMBER)
(MORE THAN ALWAYS MEANS PLUS)
(THESE ALWAYS MEANS THE)
(TWO NUMBERS SOMETIMES MEANS ONE NUMBER AND THE
     OTHER NUMBER)
(TWO NUMBERS SOMETIMES MEANS ONE OF THE
       NUMBERS AND THE OTHER NUMBER)
(HAS IS A VERB)
(GETS IS A VERB)
(HAVE IS A VERB)
(LESS THAN ALWAYS MEANS LESSTHAN)
(LESSTHAN IS AN OPERATOR OF LEVEL 2)
(PERCENT IS AN OPERATOR OF LEVEL 2)
(PERCENT LESS THAN ALWAYS MEANS PERLESS)
(PERLESS IS AN OPERATOR OF LEVEL 2)
(PLUS IS AN OPERATOR OF LEVEL  2)
(SUM IS AN OPERATOR)
(TIMES IS AN OPERATOR OF LEVEL 1)
(SQUARE IS AN OPERATOR OF LEVEL 1)
(DIVBY IS AN OPERATOR OF LEVEL 1)
(OF IS AN OPERATOR)
(DIFFERENCE IS AN OPERATOR)
(SQUARED IS AN OPERATOR)
(MINUS IS AN OPERATOR OF LEVEL 2)
(PER IS AN OPERATOR)
(SQUARED IS AN OPERATOR)
(YEARS OLDER THAN ALWAYS MEANS PLUS)
(YEARS YOUNGER THAN ALWAYS MEANS LESS THAN)
(IS EQUAL TO ALWAYS MEANS IS)
(PLUSS IS AN OPERATOR)
(MINUSS IS AN OPERATOR)
(HOW OLD ALWAYS MEANS WHAT)
(THE PERIMETER OF $1 RECTANGLE SOMETIMES MEANS
TWICE THE SUM OF THE LENGTH AND  WIDTH OF THE RECTANGLE)
(GALLONS IS THE PLURAL OF GALLON)
(HOURS IS THE PLURAL OF HOUR)
(MARY IS A PERSON)
(ANN IS A PERSON)
(BILL IS A PERSON)
(A FATHER IS A PERSON)
(AN UNCLE IS A PERSON)
(POUNDS IS THE PLURAL OF POUND)
(WEIGHS IS A VERB)
))
REMEMBER ((
(DISTANCE EQUALS SPEED TIMES TIME)
(DISTANCE EQUALS GAS CONSUMPTION TIMES
NUMBER OF GALLONS OF GAS USED)
(1 FOOT EQUALS 12 INCHES)
(1 YARD EQUALS 3 FEET)
))
```

Appendix 3.4. Problems Solved by STUDENT

```
(THE PROBLEM TO BE SOLVED IS)
(IF THE NUMBER OF CUSTOMERS TOM GETS IS TWICE THE SQUARE OF
20 PER CENT OF THE NUMBER OF ADVERTISEMENTS HE RUNS , AND THE
NUMBER OF ADVERTISEMENTS HE RUNS IS 45 , WHAT IS THE NUMBER
OF CUSTOMERS TOM GETS Q.)

(WITH MANDATORY SUBSTITUTIONS THE PROBLEM IS)
(IF THE NUMBER OF CUSTOMERS TOM GETS IS 2 TIMES THE SQUARE
20 PERCENT OF THE NUMBER OF ADVERTISEMENTS HE RUNS , AND THE
NUMBER OF ADVERTISEMENTS HE RUNS IS 45 , WHAT IS THE NUMBER
OF CUSTOMERS TOM GETS Q.)

(WITH WORDS TAGGED BY FUNCTION THE PROBLEM IS)
(IF THE NUMBER (OF / OP) CUSTOMERS TOM (GETS / VERB) IS 2 (
TIMES / OP 1) THE (SQUARE / OP 1) 20 (PERCENT / OP 2) (OF /
OP) THE NUMBER (OF / OP) ADVERTISEMENTS (HE / PRO) RUNS , AND
THE NUMBER (OF / OP) ADVERTISEMENTS (HE / PRO) RUNS IS 45 ,
(WHAT / QWORD) IS THE NUMBER (OF / OP) CUSTOMERS TOM (GETS
/ VERB) (QMARK / DLM))


(THE SIMPLE SENTENCES ARE)

(THE NUMBER (OF / OP) CUSTOMERS TOM (GETS / VERB) IS 2 (TIMES
/ OP 1) THE (SQUARE / OP 1) 20 (PERCENT / OP 2) (OF / OP) THE
NUMBER (OF / OP) ADVERTISEMENTS (HE / PRO) RUNS (PERIOD / DLM))

(THE NUMBER (OF / OP) ADVERTISEMENTS (HE / PRO) RUNS IS 45
(PERIOD / DLM))

((WHAT / QWORD) IS THE NUMBER (OF / OP) CUSTOMERS TOM (GETS
/ VERB) (QMARK / DLM))


(THE EQUATIONS TO BE SOLVED ARE)

(EQUAL G02515 (NUMBER OF CUSTOMERS TOM (GETS / VERB)))

(EQUAL (NUMBER OF ADVERTISEMENTS (HE / PRO) RUNS) 45)

(EQUAL (NUMBER OF CUSTOMERS TOM (GETS / VERB)) (TIMES 2 (EXPT
(TIMES  .2000 (NUMBER OF ADVERTISEMENTS (HE / PRO) RUNS)) 2)))


(THE NUMBER OF CUSTOMERS TOM GETS IS  162)
```

```
(THE PROBLEM TO BE SOLVED IS)
(THE SUM OF LOIS SHARE OF SOME MONEY AND BOB S SHARE IS $  4.500
. LOIS SHARE IS TWICE BOB S . FIND BOB S AND LOIS SHARE .)

(WITH MANDATORY SUBSTITUTIONS THE PROBLEM IS)
(SUM LOIS SHARE OF SOME MONEY AND BOB S SHARE IS  4.500 DOLLARS
. LOIS SHARE IS 2 TIMES BOB S . FIND BOB S AND LOIS SHARE .)

(WITH WORDS TAGGED BY FUNCTION THE PROBLEM IS)
((SUM / OP) LOIS SHARE (OF / OP) SOME MONEY AND BOB S SHARE
IS  4.500 DOLLARS (PERIOD / DLM) LOIS SHARE IS 2 (TIMES / OP
1) BOB S (PERIOD / DLM) (FIND / QWORD) BOB S AND LOIS SHARE
(PERIOD / DLM))


(THE SIMPLE SENTENCES ARE)

((SUM / OP) LOIS SHARE (OF / OP) SOME MONEY AND BOB S SHARE
IS  4.500 DOLLARS (PERIOD / DLM))

(LOIS SHARE IS 2 (TIMES / OP 1) BOB S (PERIOD / DLM))

((FIND / QWORD) BOB S AND LOIS SHARE (PERIOD / DLM))


(THE EQUATIONS TO BE SOLVED ARE)

(EQUAL G02519 (LOIS SHARE))

(EQUAL G02518 (BOB S))

(EQUAL (LOIS SHARE) (TIMES 2 (BOB S)))

(EQUAL (PLUS (LOIS SHARE OF SOME MONEY) (BOB S SHARE)) (TIMES
 4.500 (DOLLARS)))


THE EQUATIONS WERE INSUFFICIENT TO FIND A SOLUTION

(ASSUMING THAT)
((BOB S) IS EQUAL TO (BOB S SHARE))

(ASSUMING THAT)
((LOIS SHARE) IS EQUAL TO (LOIS SHARE OF SOME MONEY))


(BOB S IS  1.500 DOLLARS)

(LOIS SHARE IS  3 DOLLARS)
```

```
(THE PROBLEM TO BE SOLVED IS)
(MARY IS TWICE AS OLD AS ANN WAS WHEN MARY WAS AS OLD AS ANN
IS NOW . IF MARY IS 24 YEARS OLD , HOW OLD IS ANN Q.)

(WITH MANDATORY SUBSTITUTIONS THE PROBLEM IS)
(MARY IS 2 TIMES AS OLD AS ANN WAS WHEN MARY WAS AS OLD AS
ANN IS NOW . IF MARY IS 24 YEARS OLD , WHAT IS ANN Q.)

(WITH WORDS TAGGED BY FUNCTION THE PROBLEM IS)
((MARY / PERSON) IS 2 (TIMES / OP 1) AS OLD AS (ANN / PERSON)
WAS WHEN (MARY / PERSON) WAS AS OLD AS (ANN / PERSON) IS NOW
(PERIOD / DLM) IF (MARY / PERSON) IS 24 YEARS OLD , (WHAT /
QWORD) IS (ANN / PERSON) (QMARK / DLM))


(THE SIMPLE SENTENCES ARE)

((MARY / PERSON) S AGE IS 2 (TIMES / OP 1) (ANN / PERSON) S
AGE G02521 YEARS AGO (PERIOD / DLM))

(G02521 YEARS AGO (MARY / PERSON) S AGE IS (ANN / PERSON) S
AGE NOW (PERIOD / DLM))

((MARY / PERSON) S AGE IS 24 (PERIOD / DLM))

((WHAT / QWORD) IS (ANN / PERSON) S AGE (QMARK / DLM))


(THE EQUATIONS TO BE SOLVED ARE)

(EQUAL G02522 ((ANN / PERSON) S AGE))

(EQUAL ((MARY / PERSON) S AGE) 24)

(EQUAL (PLUS ((MARY / PERSON) S AGE) (MINUS (G02521))) ((ANN
/ PERSON) S AGE))

(EQUAL ((MARY / PERSON) S AGE) (TIMES 2 (PLUS ((ANN / PERSON)
S AGE) (MINUS (G02521)))))


(ANN S AGE IS  18)
```

```
(THE PROBLEM TO BE SOLVED IS)
(THE SUM OF THE PERIMETER OF A RECTANGLE AND THE PERIMETER
OF A TRIANGLE IS 24 INCHES . IF THE PERIMETER OF THE RECTANGLE
IS TWICE THE PERIMETER OF THE TRIANGLE , WHAT IS THE PERIMETER
OF THE TRIANGLE Q.)

(WITH MANDATORY SUBSTITUTIONS THE PROBLEM IS)
(SUM THE PERIMETER OF A RECTANGLE AND THE PERIMETER OF A TRIANGLE
IS 24 INCHES . IF THE PERIMETER OF THE RECTANGLE IS 2 TIMES
THE PERIMETER OF THE TRIANGLE , WHAT IS THE PERIMETER OF THE
TRIANGLE Q.)

(WITH WORDS TAGGED BY FUNCTION THE PROBLEM IS)
((SUM / OP) THE PERIMETER (OF / OP) A RECTANGLE AND THE PERIMETER
(OF / OP) A TRIANGLE IS 24 INCHES (PERIOD / DLM) IF THE PERIMETER
(OF / OP) THE RECTANGLE IS 2 (TIMES / OP 1) THE PERIMETER (
OF / OP) THE TRIANGLE , (WHAT / QWORD) IS THE PERIMETER (OF
/ OP) THE TRIANGLE (QMARK / DLM))


(THE SIMPLE SENTENCES ARE)

((SUM / OP) THE PERIMETER (OF / OP) A RECTANGLE AND THE PERIMETER
(OF / OP) A TRIANGLE IS 24 INCHES (PERIOD / DLM))

(THE PERIMETER (OF / OP) THE RECTANGLE IS 2 (TIMES / OP 1)
THE PERIMETER (OF / OP) THE TRIANGLE (PERIOD / DLM))

((WHAT / QWORD) IS THE PERIMETER (OF / OP) THE TRIANGLE (QMARK
/ DLM))


(THE EQUATIONS TO BE SOLVED ARE)

(EQUAL G02517 (PERIMETER OF TRIANGLE))

(EQUAL (PERIMETER OF RECTANGLE) (TIMES 2 (PERIMETER OF TRIANGLE)))

(EQUAL (PLUS (PERIMETER OF RECTANGLE) (PERIMETER OF TRIANGLE))
(TIMES 24 (INCHES)))


(THE PERIMETER OF THE TRIANGLE IS  8 INCHES)
```

```
(THE PROBLEM TO BE SOLVED IS)
(BILL IS ONE HALF OF HIS FATHER S AGE 4 YEARS AGO . IN 20 YEARS
HE WILL BE 2 YEARS OLDER THAN HIS FATHER IS NOW . HOW OLD ARE
BILL AND HIS FATHER Q.)

(THE EQUATIONS TO BE SOLVED ARE)

(EQUAL G02550 ((BILL / PERSON) S (FATHER / PERSON) S AGE))

(EQUAL G02549 ((BILL / PERSON) S AGE))

(EQUAL (PLUS ((BILL / PERSON) S AGE) 20) (PLUS 2 ((BILL / PERSON)
S (FATHER / PERSON) S AGE)))

(EQUAL ((BILL / PERSON) S AGE) (TIMES  .5000 (PLUS ((BILL /
PERSON) S (FATHER / PERSON) S AGE) (MINUS 4))))


(BILL S AGE IS  14)

(BILL S FATHER S AGE IS  32)
```

```
(THE PROBLEM TO BE SOLVED IS)
(BILL S FATHER S UNCLE IS TWICE AS OLD AS BILL S FATHER . 2
YEARS FROM NOW BILL S FATHER WILL BE 3 TIMES AS OLD AS BILL
. THE SUM OF THEIR AGES IS 92 . FIND BILL S AGE .)

(THE EQUATIONS TO BE SOLVED ARE)

(EQUAL G02533 ((BILL / PERSON) S AGE))

(EQUAL (PLUS ((BILL / PERSON) S (FATHER / PERSON) S (UNCLE
/ PERSON) S AGE) (PLUS ((BILL / PERSON) S (FATHER / PERSON)
S AGE) ((BILL / PERSON) S AGE))) 92)

(EQUAL (PLUS ((BILL / PERSON) S (FATHER / PERSON) S AGE) 2)
(TIMES 3 (PLUS ((BILL / PERSON) S AGE) 2)))

(EQUAL ((BILL / PERSON) S (FATHER / PERSON) S (UNCLE / PERSON)
S AGE) (TIMES 2 ((BILL / PERSON) S (FATHER / PERSON) S AGE)))


(BILL S AGE IS  8)
```

```
(THE PROBLEM TO BE SOLVED IS)
(A NUMBER IS MULTIPLIED BY 6 . THIS PRODUCT IS INCREASED BY
44 . THIS RESULT IS 68 . FIND THE NUMBER .)

(THE EQUATIONS TO BE SOLVED ARE)

(EQUAL G02528 (NUMBER))

(EQUAL (PLUS (TIMES (NUMBER) 6) 44) 68)


(THE NUMBER IS  4)
```

```
(THE PROBLEM TO BE SOLVED IS)
(THE PRICE OF A RADIO IS  69.70 DOLLARS . IF THIS PRICE IS
15 PERCENT LESS THAN THE MARKED PRICE , FIND THE MARKED PRICE
.)

(THE EQUATIONS TO BE SOLVED ARE)

(EQUAL G02515 (MARKED PRICE))

(EQUAL (PRICE OF RADIO) (TIMES  .8499 (MARKED PRICE)))

(EQUAL (PRICE OF RADIO) (TIMES  69.70 (DOLLARS)))


(THE MARKED PRICE IS  82 DOLLARS)
```

```
(THE PROBLEM TO BE SOLVED IS)
(TOM HAS TWICE AS MANY FISH AS MARY HAS GUPPIES . IF MARY HAS
3 GUPPIES , WHAT IS THE NUMBER OF FISH TOM HAS Q.)

(THE EQUATIONS TO BE SOLVED ARE)

(EQUAL G02520 (NUMBER OF FISH TOM (HAS / VERB)))

(EQUAL (NUMBER OF GUPPIES (MARY / PERSON) (HAS / VERB)) 3)

(EQUAL (NUMBER OF FISH TOM (HAS / VERB)) (TIMES 2 (NUMBER OF
GUPPIES (MARY / PERSON) (HAS / VERB))))


(THE NUMBER OF FISH TOM HAS IS 6)
```

```
(THE PROBLEM TO BE SOLVED IS)
(IF 1 SPAN EQUALS 9 INCHES , AND 1 FATHOM EQUALS 6 FEET , HOW
MANY SPANS EQUALS 1 FATHOM Q.)

(THE EQUATIONS TO BE SOLVED ARE)

(EQUAL G02529 (TIMES 1 (FATHOMS)))

(EQUAL (TIMES 1 (FATHOMS)) (TIMES 6 (FEET)))

(EQUAL (TIMES 1 (SPANS)) (TIMES 9 (INCHES)))

THE EQUATIONS WERE INSUFFICIENT TO FIND A SOLUTION

(USING THE FOLLOWING KNOWN RELATIONSHIPS)
((EQUAL (TIMES 1 (YARDS)) (TIMES 3 (FEET))) (EQUAL (TIMES 1
(FEET)) (TIMES 12 (INCHES))))

(1 FATHOM IS  8 SPANS)
```

```
(THE PROBLEM TO BE SOLVED IS)
(THE NUMBER OF SOLDIERS THE RUSSIANS HAVE IS ONE HALF OF THE
NUMBER OF GUNS THEY HAVE . THE NUMBER OF GUNS THEY HAVE IS
7000 . WHAT IS THE NUMBER OF SOLDIERS THEY HAVE Q.)

(THE EQUATIONS TO BE SOLVED ARE)

(EQUAL G02519 (NUMBER OF SOLDIERS (THEY / PRO) (HAVE / VERB)))

(EQUAL (NUMBER OF GUNS (THEY / PRO) (HAVE / VERB)) 7000)

(EQUAL (NUMBER OF SOLDIERS RUSSIANS (HAVE / VERB)) (TIMES  .5000
(NUMBER OF GUNS (THEY / PRO) (HAVE / VERB))))

THE EQUATIONS WERE INSUFFICIENT TO FIND A SOLUTION

(ASSUMING THAT)
((NUMBER OF SOLDIERS (THEY / PRO) (HAVE / VERB)) IS EQUAL TO
(NUMBER OF SOLDIERS RUSSIANS (HAVE / VERB)))

(THE NUMBER OF SOLDIERS THEY HAVE IS  3500)
```

```
(THE PROBLEM TO BE SOLVED IS)
(THE RUSSIAN ARMY HAS 6 TIMES AS MANY RESERVES IN A UNIT AS
IT HAS UNIFORMED SOLDIERS . THE PAY FOR RESERVES EACH MONTH
IS 50 DOLLARS TIMES THE NUMBER OF RESERVES IN THE UNIT , AND
THE AMOUNT SPENT ON THE REGULAR ARMY EACH MONTH IS $ 150 TIMES
THE NUMBER OF UNIFORMED SOLDIERS . THE SUM OF THIS LATTER AMOUNT
AND THE PAY FOR RESERVES EACH MONTH EQUALS $ 45000 . FIND THE
NUMBER OF RESERVES IN A UNIT THE RUSSIAN ARMY HAS AND THE NUMBER
OF UNIFORMED SOLDIERS IT HAS .)

(THE EQUATIONS TO BE SOLVED ARE)

(EQUAL G02532 (NUMBER OF UNIFORMED SOLDIERS (IT / PRO) (HAS
/ VERB)))

(EQUAL G02531 (NUMBER OF RESERVES IN UNIT RUSSIAN ARMY (HAS
/ VERB)))

(EQUAL (PLUS (AMOUNT SPENT ON REGULAR ARMY EACH MONTH) (PAY
FOR RESERVES EACH MONTH)) (TIMES 45000 (DOLLARS)))

(EQUAL (AMOUNT SPENT ON REGULAR ARMY EACH MONTH) (TIMES (TIMES
150 (DOLLARS)) (NUMBER OF UNIFORMED SOLDIERS)))

(EQUAL (PAY FOR RESERVES EACH MONTH) (TIMES (TIMES 50 (DOLLARS))
(NUMBER OF RESERVES IN UNIT)))

(EQUAL (NUMBER OF RESERVES IN UNIT RUSSIAN ARMY (HAS / VERB))
(TIMES 6 (NUMBER OF UNIFORMED SOLDIERS (IT / PRO) (HAS / VERB))))

THE EQUATIONS WERE INSUFFICIENT TO FIND A SOLUTION

(ASSUMING THAT)
((NUMBER OF UNIFORMED SOLDIERS) IS EQUAL TO (NUMBER OF UNIFORMED
SOLDIERS (IT / PRO) (HAS / VERB)))

(ASSUMING THAT)
((NUMBER OF RESERVES IN UNIT) IS EQUAL TO (NUMBER OF RESERVES
IN UNIT RUSSIAN ARMY (HAS / VERB)))

(THE NUMBER OF RESERVES IN A UNIT THE RUSSIAN ARMY HAS IS  600)

(THE NUMBER OF UNIFORMED SOLDIERS IT HAS IS  100)
```

```
(THE PROBLEM TO BE SOLVED IS)
(THE NUMBER OF STUDENTS WHO PASSED THE ADMISSIONS TEST IS 10
PERCENT OF THE TOTAL NUMBER OF STUDENTS IN THE HIGH SCHOOL
. IF THE NUMBER OF SUCCESSFUL CANDIDATES IS 72 , WHAT IS THE
NUMBER OF STUDENTS IN THE HIGH SCHOOL Q.)

(THE EQUATIONS TO BE SOLVED ARE)

(EQUAL G02553 (NUMBER OF STUDENTS IN HIGH SCHOOL))

(EQUAL (NUMBER OF SUCCESSFUL CANDIDATES) 72)

(EQUAL (NUMBER OF STUDENTS WHO PASSED ADMISSIONS TEST) (TIMES
 .1000 (TOTAL NUMBER OF STUDENTS IN HIGH SCHOOL)))

THE EQUATIONS WERE INSUFFICIENT TO FIND A SOLUTION

(ASSUMING THAT)
((NUMBER OF STUDENTS IN HIGH SCHOOL) IS EQUAL TO (TOTAL NUMBER
OF STUDENTS IN HIGH SCHOOL))

THE EQUATIONS WERE INSUFFICIENT TO FIND A SOLUTION

TRYING POSSIBLE IDIOMS

(THE PROBLEM WITH AN IDIOMATIC SUBSTUTION IS)
(THE NUMBER OF STUDENTS WHO PASSED THE ADMISSIONS TEST IS 10
PERCENT OF THE TOTAL NUMBER OF STUDENTS IN THE HIGH SCHOOL
. IF THE NUMBER OF STUDENTS WHO PASSED THE ADMISSIONS TEST
IS 72 , WHAT IS THE NUMBER OF STUDENTS IN THE HIGH SCHOOL Q.)

(THE EQUATIONS TO BE SOLVED ARE)

(EQUAL G02554 (NUMBER OF STUDENTS IN HIGH SCHOOL))

(EQUAL (NUMBER OF STUDENTS WHO PASSED ADMISSIONS TEST) 72)

(EQUAL (NUMBER OF STUDENTS WHO PASSED ADMISSIONS TEST) (TIMES
 .1000 (TOTAL NUMBER OF STUDENTS IN HIGH SCHOOL)))

THE EQUATIONS WERE INSUFFICIENT TO FIND A SOLUTION

(ASSUMING THAT)
((NUMBER OF STUDENTS IN HIGH SCHOOL) IS EQUAL TO (TOTAL NUMBER
OF STUDENTS IN HIGH SCHOOL))

(THE NUMBER OF STUDENTS IN THE HIGH SCHOOL IS  720)
```

```
(THE PROBLEM TO BE SOLVED IS)
(THE DISTANCE FROM NEW YORK TO LOS ANGELES IS 3000 MILES .
IF THE AVERAGE SPEED OF A JET PLANE IS 600 MILES PER HOUR ,
FIND THE TIME IT TAKES TO TRAVEL FROM NEW YORK TO LOS ANGELES
BY JET .)

(THE EQUATIONS TO BE SOLVED ARE)

(EQUAL G02517 (TIME (IT / PRO) TAKES TO TRAVEL FROM NEW YORK
TO LOS ANGELES BY JET))

(EQUAL (AVERAGE SPEED OF JET PLANE) (QUOTIENT (TIMES 600 (MILES))
(TIMES 1 (HOURS))))

(EQUAL (DISTANCE FROM NEW YORK TO LOS ANGELES) (TIMES 3000
(MILES)))

THE EQUATIONS WERE INSUFFICIENT TO FIND A SOLUTION

(USING THE FOLLOWING KNOWN RELATIONSHIPS)
((EQUAL (DISTANCE) (TIMES (SPEED) (TIME))) (EQUAL (DISTANCE)
(TIMES (GAS CONSUMPTION) (NUMBER OF GALLONS OF GAS USED))))

(ASSUMING THAT)
((SPEED) IS EQUAL TO (AVERAGE SPEED OF JET PLANE))

(ASSUMING THAT)
((TIME) IS EQUAL TO (TIME (IT / PRO) TAKES TO TRAVEL FROM NEW
YORK TO LOS ANGELES BY JET))

(ASSUMING THAT)
((DISTANCE) IS EQUAL TO (DISTANCE FROM NEW YORK TO LOS ANGELES))

(THE TIME IT TAKES TO TRAVEL FROM NEW YORK TO LOS ANGELES BY
JET IS  5 HOURS)
```

```
(THE PROBLEM TO BE SOLVED IS)
(THE COST OF A BOX OF MIXED NUTS IS THE SUM OF THE COST OF
THE ALMONDS IN THE BOX AND THE COST OF THE PECANS IN THE BOX
. FOR A LARGE BOX THIS COST IS $  3.500 . THE WEIGHT , IN POUNDS
, OF A BOX OF MIXED NUTS IS THE SUM OF THE NUMBER OF POUNDS
OF ALMONDS IN THE BOX AND THE NUMBER OF POUNDS OF PECANS IN
THE BOX . THIS LARGE BOX WEIGHS 3 POUNDS . THE COST OF ALMONDS
PER POUND OF ALMONDS IS $  1 , AND THE COST OF PECANS PER POUND
OF PECANS IS $  1.500 . FIND THE COST OF THE ALMONDS IN THE
BOX AND THE COST OF THE PECANS IN THE BOX .)

(THE EQUATIONS TO BE SOLVED ARE)

(EQUAL G02538 (COST OF PECANS IN BOX))

(EQUAL G02537 (COST OF ALMONDS IN BOX))

(EQUAL (QUOTIENT (COST OF PECANS) (TIMES 1 (POUNDS OF PECANS)))
(TIMES  1.500 (DOLLARS)))

(EQUAL (QUOTIENT (COST OF ALMONDS) (TIMES 1 (POUNDS OF ALMONDS)))
(TIMES  1 (DOLLARS)))

(EQUAL (WEIGHT , IN POUNDS   OF BOX OF MIXED NUTS) 3)

(EQUAL (WEIGHT , IN POUNDS , OF BOX OF MIXED NUTS) (PLUS (NUMBER
OF POUNDS OF ALMONDS IN BOX) (NUMBER OF POUNDS OF PECANS IN
BOX)))

(EQUAL (COST OF BOX OF MIXED NUTS) (TIMES  3.500 (DOLLARS)))

(EQUAL (COST OF BOX OF MIXED NUTS) (PLUS (COST OF ALMONDS IN
BOX) (COST OF PECANS IN BOX)))


THE EQUATIONS WERE INSUFFICIENT TO FIND A SOLUTION

(ASSUMING THAT)
((POUNDS OF PECANS) IS EQUAL TO (NUMBER OF POUNDS OF PECANS
IN BOX))

(ASSUMING THAT)
((COST OF PECANS) IS EQUAL TO (COST OF PECANS IN BOX))

(ASSUMING THAT)
((POUNDS OF ALMONDS) IS EQUAL TO (NUMBER OF POUNDS OF ALMONDS
IN BOX))

(ASSUMING THAT)
((COST OF ALMONDS) IS EQUAL TO (COST OF ALMONDS IN BOX))

(THE COST OF THE ALMONDS IN THE BOX IS  2 DOLLARS)

(THE COST OF THE PECANS IN THE BOX IS  1.500 DOLLARS)
```

```
(THE PROBLEM TO BE SOLVED IS)
(THE GAS CONSUMPTION OF MY CAR IS 15 MILES PER GALLON . THE
DISTANCE BETWEEN BOSTON AND NEW YORK IS 250 MILES . WHAT IS
THE NUMBER OF GALLONS OF GAS USED ON A TRIP BETWEEN NEW YORK
AND BOSTON Q.)

(THE EQUATIONS TO BE SOLVED ARE)

(EQUAL G02556 (NUMBER OF GALLONS OF GAS USED ON TRIP BETWEEN
NEW YORK AND BOSTON))

(EQUAL (DISTANCE BETWEEN BOSTON AND NEW YORK) (TIMES 250 (MILES)))

(EQUAL (GAS CONSUMPTION OF MY CAR) (QUOTIENT (TIMES 15 (MILES))
(TIMES 1 (GALLONS))))


THE EQUATIONS WERE INSUFFICIENT TO FIND A SOLUTION

(USING THE FOLLOWING KNOWN RELATIONSHIPS)
((EQUAL (DISTANCE) (TIMES (SPEED) (TIME))) (EQUAL (DISTANCE)
(TIMES (GAS CONSUMPTION) (NUMBER OF GALLONS OF GAS USED))))

(ASSUMING THAT)
((DISTANCE) IS EQUAL TO (DISTANCE BETWEEN BOSTON AND NEW YORK))

(ASSUMING THAT)
((GAS CONSUMPTION) IS EQUAL TO (GAS CONSUMPTION OF MY CAR))

(ASSUMING THAT)
((NUMBER OF GALLONS OF GAS USED) IS EQUAL TO (NUMBER OF GALLONS
OF GAS USED ON TRIP BETWEEN NEW YORK AND BOSTON))


(THE NUMBER OF GALLONS OF GAS USED ON A TRIP BETWEEN NEW YORK
AND BOSTON IS  16.66 GALLONS)
```

```
(THE PROBLEM TO BE SOLVED IS)
(THE DAILY COST OF LIVING FOR A GROUP IS THE OVERHEAD COST
PLUS THE RUNNING COST FOR EACH PERSON TIMES THE NUMBER OF PEOPLE
IN THE GROUP . THIS COST FOR ONE GROUP EQUALS $ 100 , AND THE
NUMBER OF PEOPLE IN THE GROUP IS 40 . IF THE OVERHEAD COST
IS 10 TIMES THE RUNNING COST , FIND THE OVERHEAD AND THE RUNNING
COST FOR EACH PERSON .)

(THE EQUATIONS TO BE SOLVED ARE)

(EQUAL G02521 (RUNNING COST FOR EACH PERSON))

(EQUAL G02520 (OVERHEAD))

(EQUAL (OVERHEAD COST) (TIMES 10 (RUNNING COST)))

(EQUAL (NUMBER OF PEOPLE IN GROUP) 40)

(EQUAL (DAILY COST OF LIVING FOR GROUP) (TIMES 100 (DOLLARS)))

(EQUAL (DAILY COST OF LIVING FOR GROUP) (PLUS (OVERHEAD COST)
(TIMES (RUNNING COST FOR EACH PERSON) (NUMBER OF PEOPLE IN
GROUP))))

THE EQUATIONS WERE INSUFFICIENT TO FIND A SOLUTION

(ASSUMING THAT)
((OVERHEAD) IS EQUAL TO (OVERHEAD COST))

(ASSUMING THAT)
((RUNNING COST) IS EQUAL TO (RUNNING COST FOR EACH PERSON))

(THE OVERHEAD IS  20 DOLLARS)

(THE RUNNING COST FOR EACH PERSON IS  2 DOLLARS)
```

```
(THE PROBLEM TO BE SOLVED IS)
(THE SUM OF TWO NUMBERS IS 96 , AND ONE NUMBER IS 16 LARGER
THAN THE OTHER NUMBER . FIND THE TWO NUMBERS .)

TRYING POSSIBLE IDIOMS

(THE PROBLEM WITH AN IDIOMATIC SUBSTUTION IS)
(THE SUM OF ONE OF THE NUMBERS AND THE OTHER NUMBER IS 96 ,
AND ONE NUMBER IS 16 LARGER THAN THE OTHER NUMBER . FIND THE
ONE OF THE NUMBERS AND THE OTHER NUMBER .)

(THE EQUATIONS TO BE SOLVED ARE)

(EQUAL G02518 (OTHER NUMBER))

(EQUAL G02517 (ONE OF NUMBERS))

(EQUAL (ONE NUMBER) (PLUS 16 (OTHER NUMBER)))

(EQUAL (PLUS (ONE OF NUMBERS) (OTHER NUMBER)) 96)

THE EQUATIONS WERE INSUFFICIENT TO FIND A SOLUTION

TRYING POSSIBLE IDIOMS

(THE PROBLEM WITH AN IDIOMATIC SUBSTUTION IS)
(THE SUM OF ONE NUMBER AND THE OTHER NUMBER IS 96 , AND ONE
NUMBER IS 16 LARGER THAN THE OTHER NUMBER . FIND THE ONE NUMBER
AND THE OTHER NUMBER .)

(THE EQUATIONS TO BE SOLVED ARE)

(EQUAL G02520 (OTHER NUMBER))

(EQUAL G02519 (ONE NUMBER))

(EQUAL (ONE NUMBER) (PLUS 16 (OTHER NUMBER)))

(EQUAL (PLUS (ONE NUMBER) (OTHER NUMBER)) 96)

(THE ONE NUMBER IS  56)

(THE OTHER NUMBER IS  40)
```

```
(THE PROBLEM TO BE SOLVED IS)
(THE SUM OF TWO NUMBERS IS TWICE THE DIFFERENCE BETWEEN THE
TWO NUMBERS . THE FIRST NUMBER EXCEEDS THE SECOND NUMBER BY
5 . FIND THE TWO NUMBERS .)

TRYING POSSIBLE IDIOMS

(THE PROBLEM WITH AN IDIOMATIC SUBSTUTION IS)
(THE SUM OF FIRST NUMBER AND THE SECOND NUMBER IS TWICE THE
DIFFERENCE BETWEEN THE FIRST NUMBER AND THE SECOND NUMBER .
THE FIRST NUMBER EXCEEDS THE SECOND NUMBER BY 5 . FIND THE
FIRST NUMBER AND THE SECOND NUMBER .)

(THE EQUATIONS TO BE SOLVED ARE)

(EQUAL G02548 (SECOND NUMBER))

(EQUAL G02547 (FIRST NUMBER))

(EQUAL (FIRST NUMBER) (PLUS 5 (SECOND NUMBER)))

(EQUAL (PLUS (FIRST NUMBER) (SECOND NUMBER)) (TIMES 2 (PLUS
(FIRST NUMBER) (MINUS (SECOND NUMBER)))))

(THE FIRST NUMBER IS  7.500)

(THE SECOND NUMBER IS  2.500)
```

```
(THE PROBLEM TO BE SOLVED IS)
(THE SUM OF TWO NUMBERS IS 111 . ONE OF THE NUMBERS IS CONSECUTIVE
TO THE OTHER NUMBER . FIND THE TWO NUMBERS .)

TRYING POSSIBLE IDIOMS

(THE PROBLEM WITH AN IDIOMATIC SUBSTUTION IS)
(THE SUM OF ONE OF THE NUMBERS AND THE OTHER NUMBER IS 111
. ONE OF THE NUMBERS IS CONSECUTIVE TO THE OTHER NUMBER . FIND
THE ONE OF THE NUMBERS AND THE OTHER NUMBER .)

(THE EQUATIONS TO BE SOLVED ARE)

(EQUAL G02516 (OTHER NUMBER))

(EQUAL G02515 (ONE OF NUMBERS))

(EQUAL (ONE OF NUMBERS) (PLUS 1 (OTHER NUMBER)))

(EQUAL (PLUS (ONE OF NUMBERS) (OTHER NUMBER)) 111)

(THE ONE OF THE NUMBERS IS  56)

(THE OTHER NUMBER IS  55)
```

```
(THE PROBLEM TO BE SOLVED IS)
(THE SUM OF THREE NUMBERS IS 9 . THE SECOND NUMBER IS 3 MORE
THAN 2 TIMES THE FIRST NUMBER . THE THIRD NUMBER EQUALS THE
SUM OF THE FIRST TWO NUMBERS . FIND THE THREE NUMBERS .)

(THE EQUATIONS TO BE SOLVED ARE)

(EQUAL G02527 (THIRD NUMBER))

(EQUAL G02526 (SECOND NUMBER))

(EQUAL G02525 (FIRST NUMBER))

(EQUAL (THIRD NUMBER) (PLUS (FIRST NUMBER) (SECOND NUMBER)))

(EQUAL (SECOND NUMBER) (PLUS 3 (TIMES 2 (FIRST NUMBER))))

(EQUAL (PLUS (FIRST NUMBER) (PLUS (SECOND NUMBER) (THIRD NUMBER)))
9)

(THE FIRST NUMBER IS  .5000)

(THE SECOND NUMBER IS  4)

(THE THIRD NUMBER IS  4.500)
```

```
(THE PROBLEM TO BE SOLVED IS)
(THE SUM OF THREE NUMBERS IS 100 . THE THIRD NUMBER EQUALS
THE SUM OF THE FIRST TWO NUMBERS . THE DIFFERENCE BETWEEN THE
FIRST TWO NUMBERS IS 10 PER CENT OF THE THIRD NUMBER . FIND
THE THREE NUMBERS .)

(THE EQUATIONS TO BE SOLVED ARE)

(EQUAL G02536 (THIRD NUMBER))

(EQUAL G02535 (SECOND NUMBER))

(EQUAL G02534 (FIRST NUMBER))

(EQUAL (PLUS (FIRST NUMBER) (MINUS (SECOND NUMBER))) (TIMES
 .1000 (THIRD NUMBER)))

(EQUAL (THIRD NUMBER) (PLUS (FIRST NUMBER) (SECOND NUMBER)))

(EQUAL (PLUS (FIRST NUMBER) (PLUS (SECOND NUMBER) (THIRD NUMBER)))
100)


(THE FIRST NUMBER IS  27.50)

(THE SECOND NUMBER IS  22.50)

(THE THIRD NUMBER IS  50)
```

```
(THE PROBLEM TO BE SOLVED IS)
(IF C EQUALS B TIMES D PLUS 1 , AND B PLUS D EQUALS 3 , AND
B MINUS D EQUALS 1 , FIND C .)


(THE EQUATIONS TO BE SOLVED ARE)

(EQUAL G02539 (C))

(EQUAL (PLUS (B) (MINUS (D))) 1)

(EQUAL (PLUS (B) (D)) 3)

(EQUAL (C) (PLUS (TIMES (B) (D)) 1))


(C IS  3)
```

```
(THE PROBLEM TO BE SOLVED IS)
(3 * X + 4 * Y = 11 .
 5 * X - 2 * Y = 1 .
 FIND X AND Y .)

(THE EQUATIONS TO BE SOLVED ARE)

(EQUAL G02541 (Y))

(EQUAL G02540 (X))

(EQUAL (PLUS (TIMES 5 (X)) (MINUS (TIMES 2 (Y)))) 1)

(EQUAL (PLUS (TIMES 3 (X)) (TIMES 4 (Y))) 11)


(X IS  1)

(Y IS  2)
```

```
(THE PROBLEM TO BE SOLVED IS)
(X / 2 - (Y + 3) / 2 = 0 .
(X - 1) / 3 + 2 * (Y + 1) = 5 .
FIND X AND Y .)


(THE EQUATIONS TO BE SOLVED ARE)

(EQUAL G02543 (Y))

(EQUAL G02542 (X))

(EQUAL (PLUS (QUOTIENT (PLUS (X) (MINUS 1)) 3) (TIMES 2 (PLUS
(Y) 1))) 5)

(EQUAL (PLUS (QUOTIENT (X) 2) (MINUS (QUOTIENT (PLUS (Y) 3)
2))) 0)


(X IS  4)

(Y IS 1)
```

```
(THE PROBLEM TO BE SOLVED IS)
(THE SQUARE OF THE DIFFERENCE BETWEEN THE NUMBER OF APPLES
AND THE NUMBER OF ORANGES ON THE TABLE IS EQUAL TO 9 . IF THE
NUMBER OF APPLES IS 7 , FIND THE NUMBER OF ORANGES ON THE TABLE
.)

(THE EQUATIONS TO BE SOLVED ARE)

(EQUAL G02515 (NUMBER OF ORANGES ON TABLE))

(EQUAL (NUMBER OF APPLES) 7)

(EQUAL (EXPT (PLUS (NUMBER OF APPLES) (MINUS (NUMBER OF ORANGES
ON TABLE))) 2) 9)

UNABLE TO SOLVE THIS SET OF EQUATIONS

TRYING POSSIBLE IDIOMS

(DO YOU KNOW ANY MORE RELATIONSHIPS AMONG THESE VARIABLES)

(NUMBER OF APPLES)

(NUMBER OF ORANGES ON TABLE)
no

I CANT SOLVE THIS PROBLEM
```

```
(THE PROBLEM TO BE SOLVED IS)
(THE GROSS WEIGHT OF A SHIP IS 20000 TONS . IF ITS NET WEIGHT
IS 15000 TONS , WHAT IS THE WEIGHT OF THE SHIPS CARGO Q.)

THE EQUATIONS WERE INSUFFICIENT TO FIND A SOLUTION

TRYING POSSIBLE IDIOMS

(DO YOU KNOW ANY MORE RELATIONSHIPS AMONG THESE VARIABLES)

(GROSS WEIGHT OF SHIP)

(TONS)

(ITS NET WEIGHT)

(WEIGHT OF SHIPS CARGO)

yes
TELL ME

(the weight of a ships cargo is the difference between
the gross weight and the net weight)

THE EQUATIONS WERE INSUFFICIENT TO FIND A SOLUTION

(ASSUMING THAT)
((NET WEIGHT) IS EQUAL TO (ITS NET WEIGHT))

(ASSUMING THAT)
((GROSS WEIGHT) IS EQUAL TO (GROSS WEIGHT OF SHIP))

(THE WEIGHT OF THE SHIPS CARGO IS 5000 TONS)
```

APPENDIX 3.5 A Small Semantic Generative Grammar

The grammar outlined here will generate only word problems solvable by STUDENT, though not the set of all such problems.

RULES	EXAMPLES
Create a set of simultaneous equations which can be solved by strictly linear techniques, except that substitution of numerical values in higher order equations which reduce them to linear equations is allowed. These are the propositions of the speaker's model.	$2x + 3y = 7$ $y = \frac{1}{2}x$ $y + z = x^2$
Choose unknowns for which STUDENT is to solve. This is the question.	$z = ?$
Choose unique names for variables without articles "a," "an," or "the." In the problem any of these articles may be used at any occurrence of a name. In a complete model these names would be associated with the objects in the chosen propositions.	x = first number y = second number Tom chose z = third number
Write one kernel sentence for each equation. Use any appropriate linguistic form given in the table below to represent the arithmetic functions in the equation.	"2 times the first number plus three times the second number Tom chose is 7. The second number Tom chose equals .5 of the first number.
For each unknown whose value is to be found, use a kernel sentence of the form: Find ___ What is ___ or Find ___ and ___ What are ___ and ___ for more than one such unknown.	The sum of the second number Tom chose and a third number is equal to the square of the first number. What is the third number?"
If a name appears more than once in a problem, some (or all) occurrences after the first may be replaced by a "similar" name. Similar names are obtained by	Similar names: "first" for "first number" "second number he chose" for "second number Tom chose"

transformations which:

a) insert a pronoun for a noun phrase in the name.
b) delete initial and/or terminal substrings of the name.

Only one such "similar" string can be used to replace an occurrence of a name, though any number of replacements can be made.

If N_i occurs in S_j and S_{j+1}, and in S_j it is the entire substring to the left of "is", "equals" or "is equal to" (or the entire substring to the right) then in S_{j+1}, N_i may be replaced by any phrase containing the word "this".

Replace "the second number Tom chose" by "this second choice" in the third sentence.

Any phrase P_1 may be replaced by another phrase P_2 which means the same thing. This would mean that STUDENT had been told of this equivalence using REMEMBER and the sentence "P_2 always means P_1" or "P_2 sometimes means P_1"

Replace "2 times" by "twice" and ".5" by "one half".

Two consecutive sentences may be connected by replacing the period after the first by ", and." A sentence can be connected to a question by preceding the sentence by "If" and replacing the period at the end of the sentence by ",".

Connect sentences 1 and 2, and sentence 3 and the final question to give:

"Twice the first number plus three times the second number Tom chose is 7, and the second number he chose is one half of the first. If the sum of this second choice and a third number is equal to the square of the first number, what is the third number?"

Summary of Linguistic Forms to Express Arithmetic Functions and the Equality Relation

$x = y$	x is y; x equals y; x is equal to y
$x + y$	x plus y; the sum of x and y; x more than y
$x - y$	x minus y; the difference between x and y; y less than x
$x * y$	x times y; x multiplied by y; x of y (if x is a number)
x / y	x divided by y; x per y

Bibliography

1. Berkeley, E. C., and Bobrow, D. G. (eds.), *The Programming Language LISP: Its Operation and Applications*, Information International, Inc., Cambridge, Mass., 1964.
2. Black, F., "A Deductive Question-Answering System," Ph.D. Thesis, Division of Engineering and Applied Physics, Harvard University, Cambridge, Mass., 1964 (Chapter 6 of the present volume).
3. Bobrow, D. G., "METEOR: A LIST Interpreter for String Transformations," in reference 1.
4. Bobrow, D. G., "Syntactic Analysis of English by Computer – A Survey," *Proc. FJCC*, Spartan Press, Baltimore, Md., 1963.
5. Bobrow, D. G., and Raphael, B., "A Comparison of List-Processing Computer Languages," *Comm. ACM*, April 1964.
6. Bobrow, D. G., and Weizenbaum, J., "List Processing and the Extension of Language Facility by Embedding," *Trans. IEEE, PGEC,* August 1964.
7. Chomsky, N., "On the Notion 'Rule of Grammar' " *Proc. Symp. in Applied Mathematics*, Vol. 12.
8. Chomsky, N., Syntactic Structures, Mouton and Co., The Hague, 1957.
9. Coffman, E. G., et al., "A General-Purpose Time-Sharing System," *Proc. SJCC,* Spartan Press, Baltimore, Md., April 1964.
10. Cohen, D., "Picture Processing in a Picture Language Machine," National Bureau of Standards Report 7885, Washington, D.C., April 1963.
11. Coleman, M., "A Program to Solve High School Algebra Story Problems," M.I.T. term paper for Course 6.539, Cambridge, Mass., 1964.
12. Cooper, W. S., "Fact Retrieval and Deductive Question Answering," *J. Assn. for Computing Machinery,* Vol. 11, No. 2, 1964.
13. Corbato, F. J., et al., *The Compatible Time-Sharing System,* The M.I.T. Press, Cambridge, Mass., 1963.
14. Darlington, J., "Translating Ordinary Language into Symbolic Logic," Memo MAC-M-149, Project MAC, M.I.T., Cambridge, Mass., March 1964.
15. Feigenbaum, E. A., "The Simulation of Verbal Learning Behavior," in reference 16.
16. Feigenbaum, E. A., and Feldman, J. (eds.), *Computers and Thought*, McGraw-Hill, New York, 1963.
17. Feldman, J., "Simulation of Behavior in the Binary Choice Experiment," in reference 16.
18. Garfinkle, S., "Heuristic Solution of First Year Algebra Problems," Working Paper Number 11, Management Science Group, University of California, Berkeley, Calif., 1962.
19. Green, Jr., B. F., et al., Baseball: An Automatic Question Answerer," *Proc. WJCC*, Vol. 19, 1961.
20. Harris, Z., "Discourse Analysis," *Language*, Vol. 28, No. 1, 1952.
21. Harris, Z., *String Analysis of Sentence Structure*, Mouton and Co., The Hague, 1962.
22. Kirsch, R. A., and Rankin, III, B. K., "Modified Simple Phrase Structure Grammars for Grammatical Induction," National Bureau of Standards Report 7890, Washington, D.C., 1963.
23. Klein, S., and Simmons, R. F., "Syntactic Dependence and the Computer Generation of Coherent Discourse," *Mechanical Translation*, Vol. 7, 1963.
24. Kuck, D., "A Problem Solving System with Natural Language Input," Ph.D. Thesis, Technological Institute, Northwestern University, Evanston, Ill., 1963.
25. Kuno, S., and Oettinger, A., "Syntactic Structure and Ambiguity of English," *Proc. FJCC,* Spartan Press, Baltimore, Md., 1963.

26. Lamb, S. M., *Outline of Stratificational Grammar*, University of California, Berkeley, Calif., 1962.
27. Lehman, W. P., and Pendergraft, E. D., *Machine Language Translation Study No. 16*, Linguistic Research Center, University of Texas, Austin, Texas, June 1963.
28. Lindsay, R. K., "Inferential Memory as the Basis of Machines Which Understand Natural Language," in reference 16.
29. Matthews, G. H., "Analysis by Synthesis of Sentences in a Natural Language," *First International Conference on Machine Translation and Applied Language Analysis*, Her Majesty's Stationery Office, London, 1962.
30. McCarthy, J., "Programs With Common Sense," *Proc. Symposium on Mechanisation of Thought Processes,* Her Majesty's Stationery Office, London, 1959 (Section 7.1 of the present volume).
31. McCarthy, J., et al., *LISP 1.5 Programmer's Manual,* The M.I.T. Press, Cambridge, Mass., 1963.
32. Minsky, M., "Steps Toward Artificial Intelligence," in reference 16.
33. Morris, C. W., "Foundations of the Theory of Signs," *International Encyclopedia of Unified Science,* Vol. 1, No. 2, University of Chicago Press, Chicago, Ill., 1955.
34. Newell, A., et al., "Report on a General Problem Solving Program," *Proc. International Conference on Information Processing,* UNESCO House, Paris, 1959.
35. Ogden, C. K., *A System of Basic English*, Harcourt, Brace, New York, 1934.
36. Phillips, A. V., "A Question-Answering Routine," Master's Thesis, Mathematics Department, M.I.T., Cambridge, Mass., 1960.
37. Quine, W. V., *Word and Object*, The M.I.T. Press, Cambridge, Mass., 1960.
38. Raphael, B., "SIR: A Computer Program for Semantic Information Retrieval," Ph.D. Thesis, Mathematics Dept., M.I.T., Cambridge, Mass., 1964 (Chapter 2 of the present volume).
39. Sillars, W., "An Algorithm for Representing English Sentences in a Formal Language," National Bureau of Standards Report 7884, Washington, D.C., April 1963.
40. Simmons, R. F., "Answering English Questions by Computer – A Survey," SDC Report SP-1556, Santa Monica, Calif., April 1964.
41. Simmons, R. F., Klein, S., and McConlogue, K., "Indexing and Dependency Logic for Answering English Questions," *American Documentation*, Vol. 15, 1964.
42. Skinner, B. F., *Verbal Behavior,* Appleton-Century-Crofts, New York, 1957.
43. Walker, D. E., and Bartlett, J. M., "The Structure of Language for Man and Computers: Problems in Formalization," *Proc. First Congress on the Information Sciences*, Vista Press, 1963.
44. Yngve, V. H., "A Model and an Hypothesis for Language Structure," *Proc. of the American Philosophical Society*, Vol. 104, No. 5, 1960.
45. Yngve, V. H., *COMIT Programmers' Reference Manual*, The M.I.T. Press, Cambridge, Mass., 1961.
46. Yngve, V. H., "Random Generation of English Sentences," *First International Conference on Machine Translation and Applied Language Analysis,* Vol. 1, Her Majesty's Stationery Office, London, 1962.

4. Semantic Memory

M. Ross Quillian

4.1 The Role of Semantic Memory

The central question asked in this research has been: What constitutes a reasonable view of how semantic information is organized within a person's memory? In other words: What sort of representational format can permit the "meanings" of words to be stored, so that humanlike use of these meanings is possible? In the next section an answer to this question is proposed in the form of a complicated but precisely specified model of such a memory structure. The test of this model is its ability to shed light on the various types of behavior dependent on semantic memory, preferably both by accounting for known phenomena and by generating new research data. The model's use in explicating various memory-dependent behaviors will be considered.

The first of these memory-dependent tasks is relatively straightforward: to compare and contrast the meanings of two familiar English words. The first half of this chapter will show that a computer memory, containing information organized as the model dictates, can provide a reasonable simulation of some aspects of human capability at this task. One program, given pairs of English words, locates relevant semantic information within the model memory, draws inferences on the basis of this, and thereby discovers various relationships between the meanings of the two words. Finally, it creates English text to express its conclusions. The design principles embodied in the mem-

***Recent follow-up work to the research reported in this chapter is described in Quillian, R., "The Teachable Language Comprehender: A Program to Understand English," to be published in a forthcoming issue of *Communications of the Association for Computing Machinery*.**

ory model, together with some of the methods used by the program, constitute one theoretical view of how human memory for semantic and perhaps other conceptual material may be represented, organized, and used.

The second behavior investigated in the light of the same theoretical framework is very much more complex: the processing of English text done by a person during careful reading, and which will lead that person to report that he has to some extent "understood" the text. The second part of this chapter is devoted to showing how the representational format and memory model developed and used in the computer program can also serve, first as a methodological innovation to enable collection of new data about the process by which text is understood, and second as part of a theoretical explanation of how that process occurs. This section consists primarily of an analysis of one subject's "thinking aloud" protocol, collected as she performed a complex linguistic task.

4.1.1 Prior Literature: What is to be Stored in Semantic Memory

Literature relevant to the question of what semantic information is and how it may be stored and used in a person's brain includes a sizable portion of philosophy, a good part of psychology, some of linguistics, and much of that computer programming literature which deals with natural-language processing, list processing, or heuristic programs. In this chapter, therefore, prior works will be mentioned only as they help to clarify what our memory model is, or is not, intended to accomplish.

One issue facing the investigator of semantic memory is: exactly what is it about word meanings that is to be considered? First, the memory model here is designed to deal with exactly complementary kinds of meaning to that involved in Osgood's "semantic differential" (57). While the semantic differential is concerned with people's feelings in regard to words, or the words' possible emotive impact on others, this model is explicitly designed to represent the nonemotive, relatively "objective" part of meaning.

The next relevant distinction is between learning and performance. As a theory, this model does not deal directly with the acquisition of semantic information but only with what eventually results after a long period of such acquisition. The problem of how humans acquire long-term semantic concepts is simply finessed by having a trained adult (a "coder") build the memory model primarily by hand.

The model is designed to enable representation and storage of any and all of the nonemotive parts of word meanings, of the sort presumably responsible for the fact that a conditioned response to a word generalizes more readily to words close to it in meaning than to words close in sound (for example, from "style" to "fashion" more readily than from "style" to "stile," 15, 68). More important, the model seeks to represent the memory that a person continuously calls upon in his everyday language behavior.

The memory most generally involved in language is what one might call "recognition memory" as distinguished from "recall memory." For example, if a reader is told that the word "the" can mean "her," he may not immediately *recall* how this can be so. However, if he encounters text that says, "I took my wife by the hand," he will have no hesitation in recognizing what "the" means. It is this sort of recognition capability, not, in general, recall, that a store of semantic information must support, and that is the exclusive concern of this paper. Since one ready source of such semantic information is an ordinary dictionary, a coder building this memory model takes much of his information from the dictionary. No less important, however, the coder will at the same time use common knowledge which he himself possesses and must use to read the dictionary material intelligently: the fund of knowledge that constitutes his own semantic memory.

4.1.2 Semantic Memory in Psychology and Simulation Programs

Another historically important issue for memory is the use it makes of associative links. Early philosophical psychology, most current experimental work on "verbal learning," and behavioristic accounts of performance such as Skinner's (77), all make the assumption, to one degree or another, that cognitive and memory structure consists of nothing more than an aggregate of associated elements. At the same time another tradition and body of work is based on the assumption that attributes and (often) "plans," make up the representational medium in which cognitive processes occur. The notion that attributes (*labeled* associations) are a key part of the thought medium was apparently first recognized and incorporated into a comprehensive theory by Otto Selz (see reference 18). This notion can be found well stated for clinical psychologists by Kelly (33), for psychologists concerned with concept formation by Bruner et al. (9), and in regard to emotive word meanings by Osgood et al. (57). The idea that plans form the key part of memory is classically expressed in the work of Bartlett (2), Piaget (61), Newell et al. (51), and Miller et al. (45). In this tradition, a "schema" is typically a combination of a plan and denotative data related to that plan. (For attempts to extend some of these approaches and to relate them to computer programs, see references 55, 66, and 71.)

It might be felt that the two assumptions cited are contradictory, that the cognitive medium must be either associative links or attributes and plans (cf. reference 13). However, Newell, Shaw, and Simon, attempting to model cognitive processing in a computer, developed a "language" (IPL) in which associative links, attributes, and plans are all homogeneously representable as data. IPL and later list-processing languages provide these, respectively, in the form of lists (items connected by undifferentiated associations), description lists (items connected by labeled associations, thereby forming attributes with values), and routines (equivalent to plans). (For a description of IPL see reference 52.) By constructing a memory model and program in one of these computer languages, it is possible, taking advantage of the substantial foundation of design and development existing in that language, to use associations, attributes, and plans freely as building blocks. Thus, in the programs called BASEBALL (27), SAD-SAM (41), and STUDENT (6) the meanings of certain English words were in part stored as factual information, in part as plans. That this same flexibility prevails in human cognitive structure is also affirmed by sophisticated learning theorists (58).

Therefore, the issue with which a semantic model has to come to grips is not whether to use plans, attributes, *or* simply associations, but rather what particular *sorts* of these are to be used to represent word meanings, and exactly how all of them are to be interlinked.

However, while computer programs *allow* elaborate data structures, very few programs have been much concerned with the structure of long-term memory as such. There are exceptions: part of Simmons' "Synthex" project (74) constituted a thorough exploration of a straightforward approach, namely a memory consisting of verbatim text (bolstered by a complete word index). Simmons demonstrated that such a memory can be used to retrieve possibly relevant statements but not in general to answer questions by inference. Questions formulated within a cognitive orientation different from the one which the input text itself employed are difficult to answer reliably with such a memory. This points up a major goal for a model of semantic memory: the ability to use information input in one frame of reference to answer questions in another, or, what is the same thing, to *infer* from the memory as well as to retrieve parts of it verbatim.

Programs by Green et al. (27) and by Lindsay (41) explored the idea of using a memory organized as a single predefined hierarchy. Green's program showed that such a memory can be interrogated with natural-language questions, and Lindsay's demonstrated that this kind of memory organization can provide certain inference-making properties as long as information is confined to a single subject like a family tree. However, this kind of organization becomes uncomfortably rigid as larger amounts of material are considered and is clearly not a general enough organization for the diverse knowledge people know and utilize.

Actually, most simulation programs (including those of Green and Lindsay) have not been primarily concerned with long-term memory at all but rather with cognitive processing. (For surveys of simulation programs see reference 22 and especially reference 72. See also references 3, 6, 47, 48, 67, 75.) Raphael's SIR program (Chapter 2 of the present volume), creates a small specialized memory from input English sentences, but again is not primarily concerned with memory per se. Thus, the problems of what is to be contained in an over-all, humanlike permanent memory, what format this is to be in, and how this memory is to be organized have not been dealt with in great generality in prior simulation programs. Reitman's investigations of certain features of such memory structures constitute something of an exception (see Chapter 8 of reference 72). For a good survey of data bases used in question-answering programs, see reference 74.

In sum, relatively little work has been done toward simulating really general and large memory structures, especially structures in which newly input symbolic material would typically be put in relation to large quantities of previously stored information about the same kinds of things.

Further advances in simulating problem-solving and game playing (72), as well as language performance, will surely require programs that develop and interact with large memories.

4.1.3 Memory in Linguistic Theory

Current linguistic theories have minimized the role of a permanent memory even more than simulation programs. Transformational and, more generally, all "generation grammar" linguistics analyze language as the application of formal rules. These rules draw minimally on a lexicon (which amounts to a memory for various properties of words). In pp. 120ff. of Chomsky's work (11) as well as in the thesis of Lakoff (38), there are several proposals for expanding the role of such a lexicon; Katz et al. (31, 32) have suggested how a lexicon can be expanded to include semantic information. In addition, Lamb (39, see also reference 69) allocates one "level" in his "stratificational" view of language to semantic units (sememes) and asserts that these should be discovered by the same procedures that linguists have used to isolate phonemes.

However, in none of these cases has any real effort been made actually to set up a quantity of semantic material and see if it can be used. This is partly because linguists feel that what a person actually does with language is outside their jurisdiction. Chomsky, for instance, specifically divorces his theoretical model from considerations of how people actually deal with language, by insisting that he is modeling a completely abstract linguistic "competence," not the concrete performance of *any* one person, even an ideal one. Thus, "a generative grammar is not a model for a speaker or a hearer. It attempts to characterize in the most neutral possible terms the knowledge of the language that provides the basis for actual use of language by a speaker-hearer." However, this disclaimer is generally followed by an assertion to the effect that "no doubt, a reasonable model of language use will incorporate, as a basic component, the generative grammar that expresses the speaker-hearer's knowledge of the language . . ." (both quotes are from reference 11, p. 9. For an explicit attempt to clarify the relation of Chomsky's work to actual language performance, see reference 45).

Since transformational grammar is a powerful and relatively well-developed body of theory, Chomsky's assertion that such a grammar will be a "basic component" of a "reasonable model" is a strong one, and one that is now generating much psycholinguistic research (reference 40).

Given a familiarity with Chomsky's theoretical framework, it will be useful to ask how a model of memory should relate to it. The answer depends on whether a person's memory for semantic information, as conceived by linguists, is separate from his memory for other sorts of things, such as visually perceived facts, or whether, in contrast, it is part of a general memory which includes these.

If one assumes that semantic memory is strictly limited and separate from other memory, then the former may be allocated to the position expressed by Katz and Postal (32), who say:

The syntactic component is *fundamental* in the sense that the other two components both operate on its out-put. That is, *the syntactic component is the generative source* in the linguistic description. This component generates the abstract formal structures underlying actual sentences. . . . In such a tripartite theory of linguistic descriptions, certain *psychological claims* are made about the speaker's capacity to communicate fluently. The fundamental claim is that the fluent speaker's ability to use and understand speech involves a *basic* mechanism that enables him to construct the formal syntactic structures underlying the sentences which these utterances represent, and two *subsidiary* mechanisms: one that associates a set of meanings with each formal syntactic structure and another that maps such structures into phonetic representations, which are, in turn, the input to his speech apparatus (pp. 1-2, italics mine).

Several computer programs have been written that minimize or bypass the role of semantic knowledge in language. These programs generate sentences that are syntactically grammatical but whose meanings are either random (78) or random permutations of the "dependency" constraints imposed by an input text (34, 35).

On the other hand, if one assumes that memory for semantic material is no different from memory for any other kind of conceptual material, then this memory must take on a much more important role in language. Here it will be assumed that humans, in using language, draw upon and interact with the same memory in which their nonlinguistic information is stored. Under this assumption semantic memory is simply general memory and hence must be flexible enough to hold anything that can be stated in language, sensed in perception, or otherwise known and remembered. In particular, this includes facts and assertions as well as just objects and properties.

Further, under this assumption the semantic component becomes the primary factor in language rather than a "secondary" one subordinate to a separate syntactic component. To consider language production in this light is to put the intended message of the language in control of its format and to see the reading of text as a continuous interaction between concepts that the text is currently discussing, the reader's general knowledge of the same concepts (part of which has been acquired through nonlinguistic sources), and what has already been stated about those concepts in the same text (or elsewhere by the same author). Making this kind of three-way interaction natural is therefore a chief aim of the model to be developed here.

This means that the memory model will correspond less to the proposed semantic lexicons of transformational theory than to what is called "deep structure." Thus, when this memory model is used in a program simulating language production, the program will contain something corresponding to transformational rules but nothing corresponding to phrase-structure rules. The reason for this is that the correspondents to phrase structure rules have been incorporated into the conventions specifying the structure of the memory itself (and there broadened almost to triviality). What remains of such rules would be relevant to a learning program, since this would involve building up new parts of the memory, but is not relevant to a program designed simply to use the memory and to express facts it implies in English text.

In other words, it is being proposed that, in people, language is never torn down into the "immediate constituents" that are utilized in rules of the familiar S → NP + VP sort. Instead, language is remembered, dealt with in thought, and united to nonlinguistic concepts in a form that looks like the *result* of phrase structure rules – what Chomsky calls the "base phrase marker" or "basis" of a sentence (reference 11, p. 17). The memory structure will differ from such a basis, or set of bases, in that it will not be divided into small structures, each associated with one sentence, but rather will be one enormous interlinked net. When part of this net is to be expressed in English text, division into sentences will be made by the text producer as convenient, rather than before this text producer begins to work.

While the memory model to be described corresponds most closely to the deep structures in transformational theory, it must at the same time serve the role that transformationalists allocate to a lexicon. The same memory structure to which language adds information during intake and from which it retrieves it during output is also used to interpret language that is read or heard.

The foregoing indicates in general terms the relation of the semantic memory model to linguistic theory, to other simulation programs, and to some common semantic notions. The next section explains the model itself as presently formalized in a computer program. The third section describes this program and its results. The fourth discusses a method for using the memory model to study how people understand sentences and introduces a set of data gathered in this way. The fifth, sixth, and seventh analyze these data, again relying primarily on the memory model, and the final section considers changes of the model that now seem indicated, as well as some implications of the model for a theory of human memory.

4.2 The Memory Model

4.2.1 Overview of the Model

The memory model consists basically of a mass of *nodes* interconnected by different kinds of *associative links.* Each node may for the moment be thought of as named by an English word, but by far the most important feature of the model is that a node may be related to the meaning (concept) of its name word in one of two ways. The first relates directly; i.e., its associative links may lead directly into a configuration of other nodes that represents the meaning of its name word. A node that does this is called a *type* node. In contrast, the second kind of node in the memory refers *indirectly* to a word concept by having one special kind of associative link that points to that concept's type node. Such a node is referred to as a *token node,* or simply *token,* although this usage implies more than is generally meant by a "token," since, within the memory model, a token is a permanent node. For any one word meaning there can be exactly one and only one type node in the memory, but there will in general be *many* token nodes scattered throughout the memory, each with a pointer to the same unique type node for the concept. To see the reason for postulating both type and token nodes within the memory, it will be useful to reflect briefly on the way words are defined in an ordinary dictionary.

To define one word, the dictionary builder always utilizes tokens of other words. However, it is not sufficient for the reader to consider the meaning of the defined word as simply an unordered aggregation of pointers to the other word concepts used in its definition. The configuration of these word concepts is crucial; it modifies the meanings of the individual word concepts that make up its parts and at the same time creates a new gestalt with them, which represents the meaning of the word being defined. In the memory model, ingredients used to build up a concept are represented by the token nodes naming other concepts, while the configurational meaning of the concept is represented by the particular structure of interlinkages connecting those token nodes to each other. It will be useful to think of the configuration of interlinked token nodes that represents a single concept as comprising one *plane* in the memory. Each and every token node in the entire memory lies in some such plane and has both its special associative link pointing "out of the plane" to its type node *and* other associative links pointing *within* the plane to other token nodes comprising the configuration. In short, token nodes make it possible for a word's meaning to be built up from other word meanings as ingredients and at the same time to modify and recombine these ingredients into a new configuration. Although we will not describe the detailed structure of a plane until part 4.2.2, it will be useful for understanding the model's over-all organization to examine Fig. 4-1 at this point.

Figure 4-1a illustrates the planes of three word concepts, corresponding to three meanings of "plant." The three circled words, "plant," "plant2," and

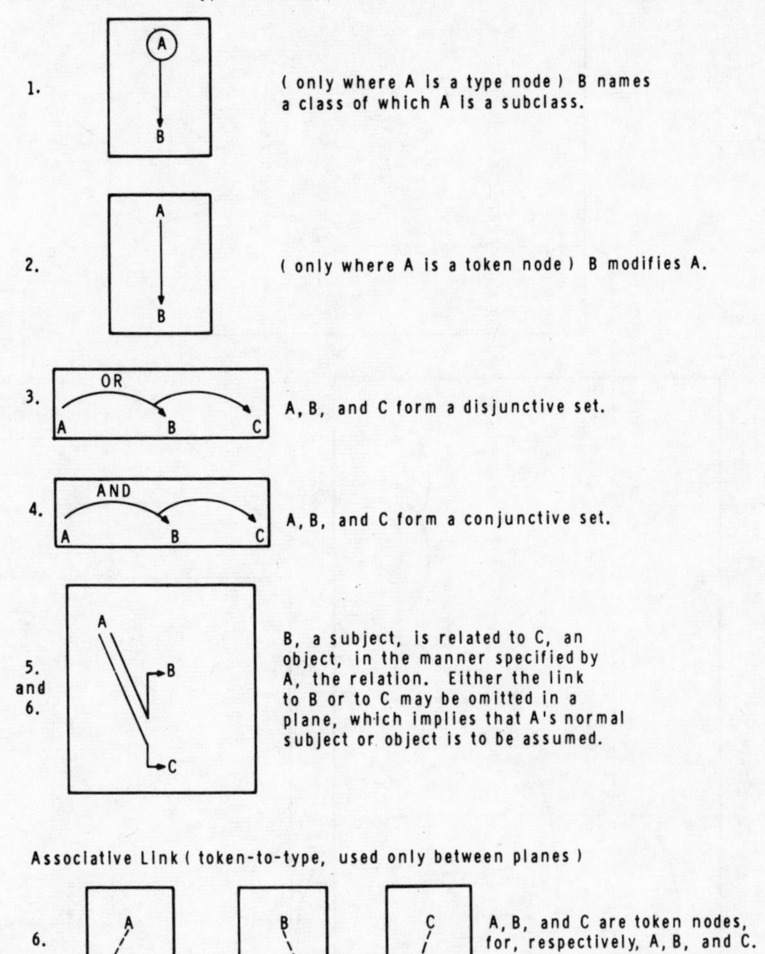

Figure 4-1. Sample Planes from the Memory

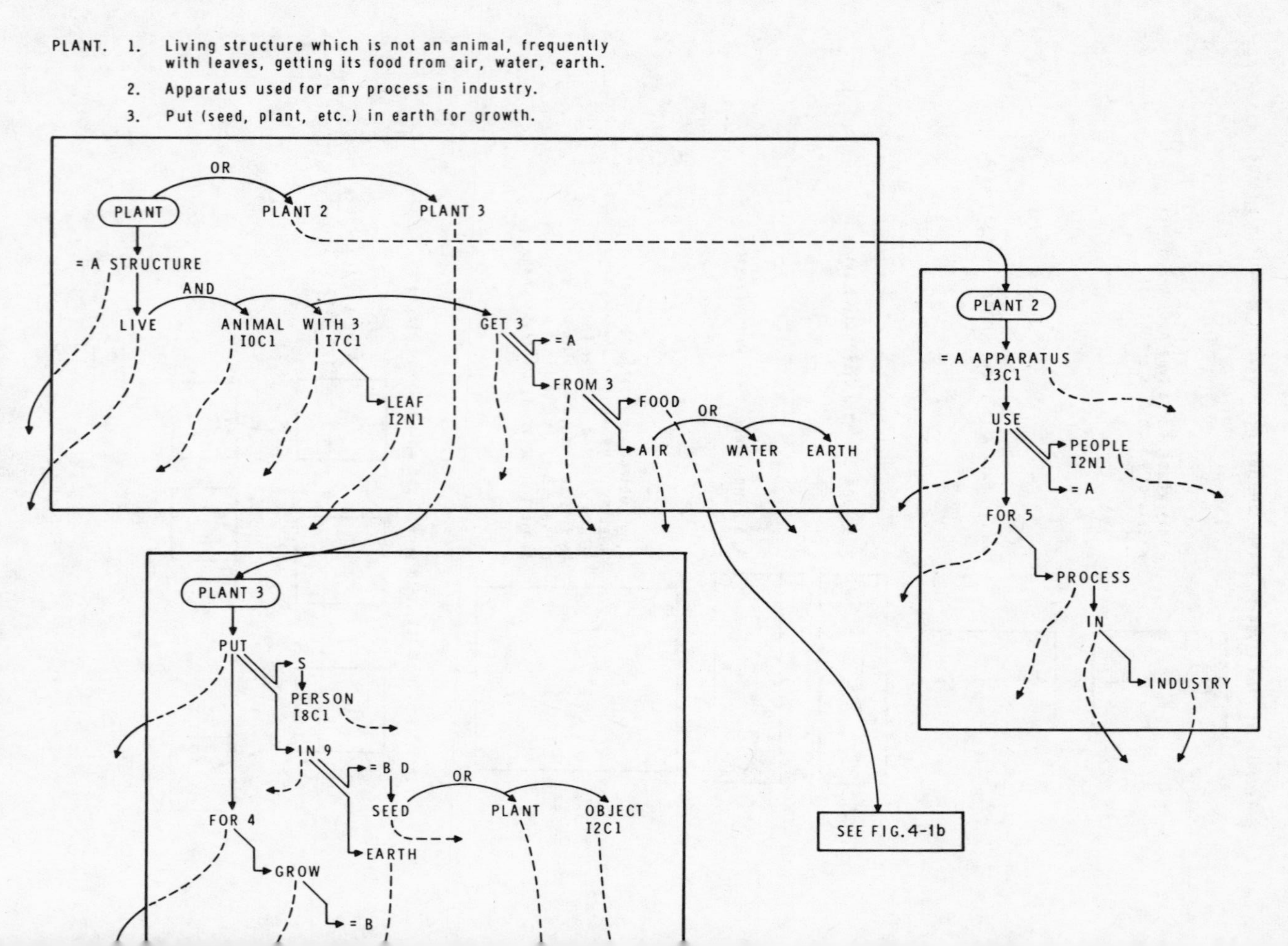

Figure 4-1a. Three Planes Representing Three Meanings of "Plant"

"plant3," placed at the heads (upper left-hand corners) of the three planes, represent type nodes; every other word shown in the Fig. 4-1a planes represents a token node. The nonterminated arrows from tokens indicate that each has its special pointer leading out of its plane to its type definition, i.e., to a type node standing at the head of its own plane somewhere else in the memory. Each of *these* planes, in turn, is itself entirely made up of tokens, except for the type word that heads it. Figure 4-1b illustrates *one* of these planes. Therefore, the over-all structure of the complete memory forms an enormous aggregation of planes, each consisting entirely of token nodes except for its "head" node, which is always a type node.

Now, what is the full content of a word concept in such a memory? Let us define a *full word concept,* as distinguished from its plane or "immediate definition," so as to include *all* the type and token nodes one can get to by starting at the initial type node, or patriarch, and moving first within its immediate definition plane to all the token nodes found there, then on "through" to the type nodes named by *each* of these nodes, then on to all the token nodes in each of *their* immediate definition planes, and so on until every token and type node that can be reached by this process has been traced through at least once.

OD: 1. That which living being has to take in to keep it living and for growth. Things forming meals, especially other than drink

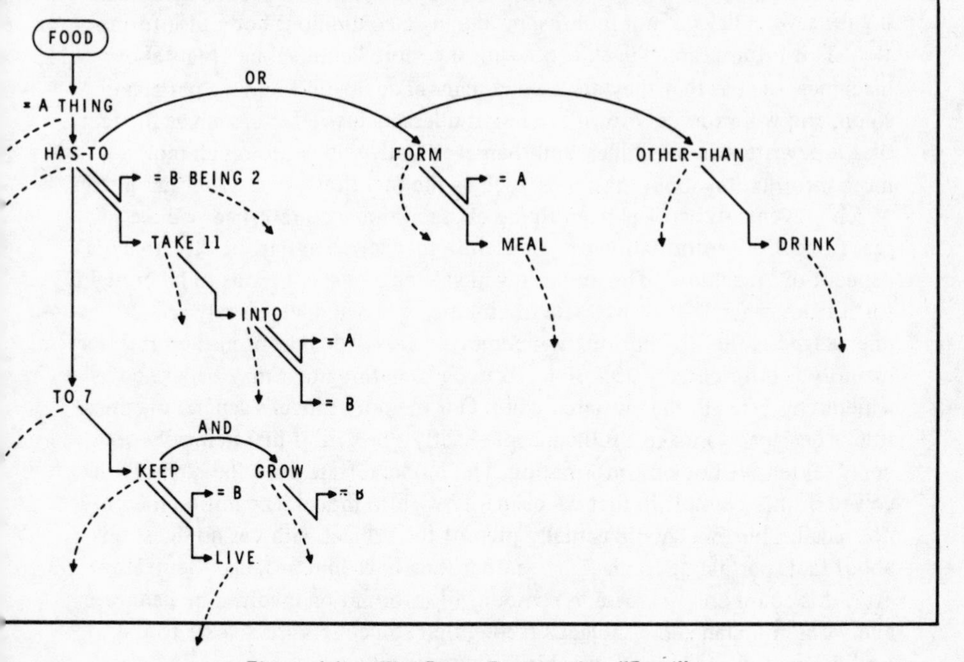

Figure 4-1b. The Plane Representing "Food"

Thus one may think of a full concept analogically as consisting of all the information one would have if he looked up what will be called the "patriarch" word in a dictionary, then looked up every word in each of its definitions, then looked up every word found in each of these, and so on, continually branching outward until every word he could reach by this process had been looked up once. However, since a word meaning includes structure as well as ingredients, one must think of the person doing the looking up as also keeping account of all the relationships in which each word encountered by him had been placed by all earlier definitions.

To summarize, *a word's full concept is defined in the memory model to be all the nodes that can be reached by an exhaustive tracing process, originating at its initial, patriarchical type node, together with the total sum of relationships among these nodes specified by within-plane, token-to-token links.*

Our thesis is that such a memory organization will be useful in performing semantic tasks and also constitute a reasonable description of the general organization of human memory for semantic material.

To illustrate the latter point immediately: Suppose that a subject were asked to state everything he knows about the concept "machine." Each statement he makes in answer is recorded, and when he decides he is finished, he is asked to elaborate further on each thing he has said. As he does so, these statements in turn are recorded, and upon his "completion" he is asked if he cannot elaborate further on each of these. In this way the subject clearly can be kept talking for several days, if not months, producing a voluminous body of information. This information will start off with the more "compelling" facts about machines, such as that they are usually man-made, involve moving parts, and so on, and will proceed "down" to less and less inclusive facts, such as the fact that typewriters are machines, and then eventually will get to much more remote information about machines, such as the fact that a typewriter has a stop which prevents its carriage from flying off each time it is returned. We are suggesting that this information can all usefully be viewed as part of the subject's concept of "machine." The order in which such a concept tends to be brought forth from general, inclusive facts to obscure or less and less closely related ones, suggests that the information comprising a word concept in the subject's memory is differentially accessible, forming something that may be viewed as a hierarchy beneath the patriarch word. Our memory model's general organization is designed to make a full concept exactly this sort of hierarchically ordered, extensive body of information. The model differs from the memory involved in this example in that we primarily wish to model recognition memory, not recall. Thus, we should actually present the subject with yes-no questions about facts pertaining to machines, rather than have him produce them. However, this could only increase the amount of information involved in a concept and wouldn't change the subject's feeling that some facts are "closer to the top" in the full concept of "machine" than are others.

Clearly a subject has hierarchical concepts similar to that for "machine" for innumerable other word-concepts, so that the over-all amount of information in his memory seems almost unlimited. The sheer quantity of information involved in such concepts argues strongly that both the human subject's memory and our model thereof contain as little redundancy as possible and that it contain stored facts only when these cannot otherwise be generated or inferred. In this regard we note that the information a subject has as the meaning of "machine" will include all the information he has as the meaning of "typewriter," among other things, and there is no need to restate the information constituting his concept of "typewriter" each time it occurs as part of the concept named by some other word, such as "machine," "office," and so on. In short, a word concept like "machine" seems to be made up in large part of a particular, ordered arrangement of other word concepts, such as "typewriter," "drill press," and so on.

Again, a large memory structured as outlined capitalizes on this redundancy by running the pointer from each and every token node for a word meaning to the *same* type node. Recall that in such a memory any given type node will have many token nodes, located in various other planes, all pointing to it, and *its* full concept may well contain token nodes pointing *back* to the type node that heads one of these planes. In other words, there is no restriction to prevent reentries or loops within a full concept, so that all routines that search through or process concepts in the memory must take account of these possibilities.

Viewed most abstractly, the memory model forms simply a large, very complex network of nodes and one-way associations between them. Most important, in such a model of semantic memory there is no predetermined hierarchy of superclasses and subclasses; *every* word is the patriarch of its own separate hierarchy *when some search process starts with it.* Similarly, every word lies at various places down within the hierarchies of (i.e., is an ingredient in) a great many other word concepts, when processing starts with them. Moreover, there are no word concepts as such that are "primitive." Everything is simply defined in terms of some ordered configuration of other things in the memory.

A memory organized in this fashion is incomplete, in that other kinds of human information storage and processing – spatio-visual imagery and reasoning, for example – would seem to require other sorts of stored information. It is conceivable that spatio-visual memory is stored in some completely different kind of structure from semantic information. However, it seems at least as reasonable to suppose that a single store of information underlies both "semantic" memory and "spatio-visual" memory; their difference being not in the structure of the information store, but rather in the way that the static information of that store is used. For example, suppose that a person's visual information is stored in the same interlinked network of nodes that we suggest underlies his language processing, but that he also has the ability to generate visual imagery to represent this information directly, in order to reason spatially (reference 26). Conceiving of spatial reasoning in this way, with properties abstracted out of actual visual images for purposes of storage, would seem necessary to provide for the flexibility and freedom with which people are able to visually remember, imagine, etc.

Similarly, the ability to recognize objects perceived through the senses would require at least some additional kinds of linkage within a general network memory such as this one we are discussing. But, a network containing one-way associative links from an object's name to the set of properties of that object (as ours does now) would seem already to contain all the *nodes* needed to recognize a particular object given its sensed properties. What would additionally be required to perform perceptual recognition would be reverse links in the memory, plus a processor able to utilize these links for deciding which object a given stimulus array represented (21). A very close interaction between exposure to words and perceptual functioning in people has been thoroughly established (8, 15). Thus, again, it seems logical to suppose that the same static store of information that underlies semantic reasoning may underlie perception rather than that they rely on separate memory structures, even though such a memory would then have to be richer in interlinkages than that we shall utilize here.

These and other possible additional functions with a network memory are purely speculative at the present time, and will not be discussed further in the present work. (On a possible relation of the present program to the phenomena of perceptual "set," see Quillian et al. (66), pp. 34-36. On the use of spatio-visual imagery in reasoning, see, for example, reference 59.)

4.2.2 Details of the Memory Model

Having established the general structure of the memory model as consisting of "planes," each made up of one type node and a number of token nodes, it is further necessary to determine the format of the nodes themselves and the specific varieties of associative links between nodes to be used within a plane.

The most important constraint determining this arises from our assumption that in order to continue to parallel the properties of human semantic memory the model must be able to link nodes together into configurations that are at least as varied and rich as the ideas expressed in natural language. Hence, simply attempting to represent natural language definitions accurately in the model becomes a very powerful constraint dictating the model's structural properties. Over a lengthy period of attempts to encode English text into such network representations, it has always been found necessary to have available several different kinds of associative links rather than the simple undifferentiated associations assumed in most classical psychological studies of word association. At the same time the model must represent all information in a form sufficiently standardized to allow processing by rules that can be specified explicitly, else it will be no more manageable as a theory of memory than is English itself. (See reference 74 for the most thorough attempt to use English text itself as a computer's store of information on which to base the performance of complex tasks.) The representation now used in the memory model therefore lies at a level somewhere between the freedom of English itself and the standardization of, say, symbolic logic. In the memory model, complex configurations of labeled associations must be built up to represent the meaning inherent in dictionary definitions adequately. These are the structures we have called planes.

The attempt to get the meaning of English definitions accurately represented as planes of nodes within the memory model constitutes one major constraint on its structure. A second is provided by the attempt to write programs that can do something interesting by using this memory. To some degree these two constraints on the model balance one another: The first urges elaboration and complexity to represent the meaning of definitions accurately, while the second urges that the model be as simple and standardized as possible to make processing feasible.

As stated, the relational complexity built up in an English definition is always represented in the memory by a configuration of token nodes linked together to form one "plane." Each token in a plane is linked to its type node (which lies out of the plane) by a kind of association that was shown in Fig. 4-1 as a dashed line, while it is related to other token nodes (in the plane) by one or more of the six distinct kinds of associative link listed in the key to Fig. 4-1. In encoding dictionary definitions, these intraplane links are used, respectively, as follows:

Link

1. Dictionary definitions require the use of the subclass-to-superclass pointer whenever they define a word by stating the name of some larger class of which it is a subclass. For example, in the dictionary definition of "plant" shown in Fig. 4-1a, the word's third meaning is said to be a subclass of the class of "putting."
2. Any word or phrase used adjectively or adverbially dictates use of the modification pointer.
3. The multiple meanings of a word, and any phrase such as "air, earth, or water," require the formation of a disjunctive set.
4. Any phrase like "old, red house" or "old house with a red porch" requires that the modifiers of "house" be formed into a conjunctive set.

5-6. Together these two links form the open-ended category, by means of which all the remaining kinds of relationships are encoded. This is necessary because in natural language text almost *anything* can be considered as a relationship, so that there is no way to specify in advance what relationships are to be needed (67). This means that a memory model must provide a way to take any *two* tokens and relate them by any third token, which by virtue of this use becomes a relationship.

Stated this way, it appears that the semantic model amounts in structure to a kind of parsing system and that encoding dictionary definitions into it is in part, at least, similar to parsing these definitions.

This is true, and what appears on one plane of the memory model has many points of correspondence with what Chomsky calls a "deep structure." In particular, the ternary relations formed by our subject-object links resemble the structure of what were called "kernel" sentences. However, our use of terms like "subject," "object," and "modifier" does not always correspond to that of linguistics, and also a plane encodes the meaning of a number of sentences, whereas a deep structure is explicitly limited to the representation of what can be represented in a single sentence (reference 11, pp. 138f). Also the correspondence, insofar as it exists, is between one of our planes and one of Chomsky's deep structures, not between a plane and a generative grammar. A generative grammar is an attempt to state explicitly *when and how* structural information can be related to sentences, whereas the job of a person encoding dictionary definitions into our memory model is simply to *get* a representation of their structures, i.e., to go ahead and *use* his language-processing abilities rather than to describe these. Hence our coder *does* transformations rather than describe them.

As to the nature of the nodes themselves, it will be assumed that these correspond not in fact to words, to sentences, or to visual pictures, but instead to what we ordinarily call "properties." As indicated earlier, this assumption is now common in work on concepts (30), because properties provide a more elemental and hence more flexible medium than visual pictures or words, and because either a mental picture or a language concept may be thought of as some bundle of properties (attribute values) and associations among them.

Thus, the nodes of the memory model actually correspond more to properties than to words, even though they may be expressed with words. Representing a property requires the name of something that is variable, an attribute, plus some value or range of values of that attribute. This feature is achieved in the memory model by the fact that every token is considered to have appended to it a specification of its appropriate amount or intensity in the particular concept being defined. Omitting this specification from a token (which is generally what is done) means that no restriction is placed on the total range of variation in amount of intensity open to the attribute. On the other hand, whenever such specification does appear overtly with a token node, it consists principally of numerical values, stating how the node's total possible range of amount or intensity *is* restricted. These values allow encoding restrictions to a fineness of nine gradations, i.e., permit nine degrees of "absolute discrimination" to be represented (44). The exact rationale for this kind of specification "tag" has been described elsewhere (64, 65), along with that of the other two tags, representing, respectively, the "number" and the "criteriality" of a token (9), that are available in the model. Here it will only be noted that in encoding dictionary definitions all grammatical inflections, along with all words like "a," "six," "much," "very," "probably," "not," "perhaps," and others of similar meaning, do not become nodes themselves but instead dictate that various range-restricting tags be appended to the token nodes of certain other words. Removing all inflections during encoding permits all nodes in the memory model to represent canonical forms of words; this is of importance in reducing the model's over-all size and in locating conceptual similarities within it (see Section 4.3).

Certain other words are also dropped during the encoding process; e.g., "and," "or," "is," "which," "there," and "that," these being interpreted either directly as relationships that are basic structural aspects of the model or else as *directions* to the coder about how he is to form the plane structure, i.e., as specifications for how the configurations of tokens on a plane are to be structured. Similarly, punctuation shows up only in the associative structure of the model.

All pronouns, as well as *all* words used to refer again to something mentioned previously in the definition, are replaced in the model by explicit references to the earlier nodes. (In Fig. 4-1 such referencing is being done by =A and =B, where some higher token node in the plane has been designated temporarily to be A or B by giving it a *prefix* of =A or =B. A more recent version of the loading program also allows referring to *any* token node in any plane, by a sort of "indirect addressing" feature.) This ability to, in essence, reuse tokens repeatedly in a plane, perhaps modifying them slightly each time, is extremely important in making the model correspond to humanlike memory. In the course of coding many words into the current and earlier network representations, I have come to believe that the greatest difference between dictionary entries and the corresponding semantic concepts that people have in their heads is that, while dictionary makers try hard to specify all the *distinctions* between separate meanings of a word, they make only a very haphazard effort to indicate what these various meanings have in *common* conceptually. Although they may not be aware of it, there is a very good reason for this seeming oversight: The best the dictionary maker has available for showing common elements of meaning is an outlinelike format, in which meanings that have something in common are brought together under the same heading. However, as anyone who has ever reorganized a paper several times will realize, an outline organization is only adequate for *one* hierarchical grouping, when in fact the common elements existing between various meanings of a word call for a complex cross classification. In other words, the common elements within and between various meanings of a word are many, and any one outline designed to get some of these together under common headings must at the same time necessarily separate other common elements, equally valid from some other point of view. Making the present memory network a general graph rather than a tree (the network equivalent of an outline) and setting up tokens as distinct nodes makes it possible to loop as many points as necessary back into any single node and hence in effect to show any and every common element within and between the meanings of a word. The =A notation causes the network-building program to create such a link.

In all this, it is clear that not only dictionary definitions but also much of the everyday knowledge of the person doing the coding are being tapped and represented in the memory model being built up. For instance, the reader will already have noticed that a numeral is suffixed to the end of some words (a "1" is to be assumed whenever no such numeral appears). This is simply because it is convenient to have each sense of a word named distinctly within the memory in order to be able to use these in building other configurations. This means that a person building such configurations for input to the model must always *decide* which possible sense is intended for every token and use the appropriate suffix.

4.2.3 The Parameter Symbols S, D, and M

In an attempt to encode dictionary definitions it was found that the memory must provide a mechanism for stating that certain nodes in the immediate definition plane of a type node are variable parameters. A value for one of these parameters will be provided only when the word in whose concept the parameter symbol appears is used in text. Other words within that surrounding text will then form certain parts of the current word's concept; the parameter symbols tell how. To accomplish this, parameter symbols are of three kinds, corresponding to certain ways in which other words in text may be related to the word to which the parameter symbols belong: *S* is the parameter symbol whose value is to be any word related to the present word as its subject; *D* is the parameter symbol whose value is to be any word related to the present word as its direct object; and *M* is the parameter symbol whose value is to be any word that the present word directly modifies.

To include a parameter symbol in a word's definition plane is therefore to state where within that concept related subjects, objects, and modificands are to be placed, if one or more of these is provided by text in which the present word is used. For example, when the verb "to comb" is defined by the phrase, "to put a comb through (hair), to get in order," this definition is saying that, when used in text, the verb "to comb" is likely to have an object, which is then to be integrated into its meaning in a certain place, viz., as the object of the node "through." In coding the above definition of "to comb," the object parameter symbol D would be used as a sort of "slot" to hold a place for this object until "comb" is actually used in text. It is important not to confuse the sense in which D refers to some object of "comb" and the sense in which there are object links within a plane. D *always refers to an object of the word in whose defining plane it appears,* while its placement in that plane – indicated by the kind of link from some other token node to it – is another matter. For example, in Fig. 4-1a, in the plane for "plant3," the symbol D (which happens also to have been labeled by =B) has been placed as the *subject* of "in9," but *it* is still a D, because it refers to any direct object of the verb "to plant." The symbol D specifies that any such object of "plant" is to be integrated into the meaning of "plant3" at the place where the D is placed.

A dictionary definition, in addition to stating where within a concept particular sorts of parameter-value information is to be "placed," may offer one or more *clue words* about what such information is likely to be. Thus, in our definition of "to comb" we are told that its direct object is likely to be "hair."

Clue words play several roles in the memory model, one of which corresponds approximately to the role transformational linguists ascribe to "selectional restrictions." In other words, the material comprising a full word concept in the memory model can be viewed as consisting of two sorts of information: On the one hand there is information about the content of the concept itself; on the other there is information about what that concept is likely to combine with when the word is used in text. This latter information is represented by the clue words associated with its parameter symbols. It is significant that this same distinction has been identified in verbal association studies, the associations that subjects give to words being divided into paradigmatic (content information), and syntagmatic (parameter clue information) (17). Ervin (19) has shown that the ratio of content associations to syntagmatic associations given by young children steadily increases with age.

In the versions of the memory model used in the programs to be described in this chapter, clue words have been sought and coded only reluctantly; both they and the parameter symbols having initially been included only because the sort of information comprising them was embarrassingly present in some dictionary definitions. However, it turns out that parameter symbols of some kind play a very crucial role in any such memory, because they make it possible to recognize that two different ways of stating the same thing are in fact synonymous.*

As a final point, we note that the model's *range* readings on tags, together with its ability to form disjunctive sets of attributes, provide it with a ready facility for representing information having a great deal of vagueness. This is essential. It is the very vagueness of the meaning of most language terms that makes them useful; indeed, speech as we know it would be completely impossible if, for instance, one had to specify exactly which machines he had reference

***This subject is developed more fully in Quillian's dissertation. [Editor's note.]**

to every time he said "machine," and similarly for any other term whose meaning contains some ambiguity.

To summarize, the memory model, together with the process by which dictionary information is encoded into it, are such that what begins as the English definition of a word seems better viewed after encoding as a complexly structured bundle of attribute values – a full concept, as defined above – whose total content typically extends to an enormous size and complexity throughout the memory. Over all, the memory is a complex network of attribute-value nodes and labeled associations between them. These associations create both within-plane and between-plane ties, with several links emanating out from the typical token node and many links coming into almost every type node.

4.3 Use of the Memory Model in a Simulation Program

4.3.1 The Task of the Program

In selecting a task to perform with a model memory, one thinks first of the ability to understand unfamiliar sentences. It seems reasonable to suppose that people must necessarily understand new sentences by retrieving *stored* information about the meaning of isolated words and phrases and then combining and perhaps altering these retrieved word meanings to build up the meanings of sentences. Accordingly, one should be able to take a model of stored semantic knowledge and formulate rules of combination (cf. the "projection rules," reference 32) that would describe how sentence meanings get built up from stored word meanings.

It further seems likely that if one could manage to get even a few word meanings adequately encoded and stored in a computer memory and a workable set of combination rules formalized as a computer program, he could then bootstrap his store of encoded word meanings by having the computer itself "understand" sentences that he had written to constitute the definitions of *other* single words (64). That is, whenever a new, as yet uncoded, word could be defined by a sentence using only words whose meanings had already been encoded, then the representation of this sentence's meaning, which the machine could build up by using its previous knowledge together with its combination rules, would be the appropriate representation to *add* to its memory as the meaning of the new word. Unfortunately, two years of work on this problem led to the conclusion that the task is much too difficult to execute at our present stage of knowledge. The processing that goes on in a person's head when he "understands" a sentence and incorporates its meaning into his memory is very large indeed, practically all of it being done without his conscious knowledge.

As an example, consider the sentence, "After the strike, the president sent him away." One understands this sentence easily, probably without realizing that he has had to look into his stored knowledge of "president" to resolve a multiple meaning of the word "strike." (Consider, e.g., the same sentence with the word "umpire" substituted for "president." Such a decision in favor of one meaning of a word that has more than one possible meaning will hereafter be referred to as "disambiguation" of that word. See, e.g., reference 73.) Just *what* subconscious processing is involved in unearthing and using the fact that presidents more typically have something to with labor strikes than with strikes of the baseball variety is by no means obvious, and a good part of this chapter is devoted to stating one way by which this can be accomplished, given that it has been decided that "president" is the correct word to attend to. Sentence understanding involves a great number of such, at present, poorly understood processes; the second half of this chapter will be devoted to developing and using a method of studying how people perform that process, preliminary, we hope, to an eventual simulation program to do so. Meanwhile, the two language functions performed by the present program are far humbler than sentence understanding, although, as will become apparent, one of them is a crucial part of sentence understanding.

The first of these functions is to compare and contrast two word concepts: Given any two words whose meanings are encoded in the memory model, the program must find the more compelling conceptual similarities and contrasts between their meanings. Since, in the usual case, each of the two words to be compared will have several possible meanings, the program is also to specify, for each semantic similarity or contrast it finds, just *which* meaning of each word is involved. This is one step toward the disambiguation of semantic ambiguity in the text. The second major task of the program is to express all the similarities and contrasts found between the two compared words in terms of understandable, though not necessarily grammatically perfect, sentences.

The above tasks are only a part of what apparently is involved in sentence understanding; yet their performance in a fashion comparable to human performance still calls for a basic degree of semantic horse sense, in which up to now computers have been conspicuously lacking and which apparently must be based on an extensive and expressively rich store of conceptual knowledge. Thus, being able to get a computer to perform these tasks indicates to some degree the plausibility of the semantic memory model used.

In briefest form, the program we have developed is used as follows:

1. The experimenter selects a group of words whose definitions are to provide the total store of information in the memory model during a given series of tests.
2. He looks up each of these words in some ordinary dictionary.
3. He encodes each of the definitions given for each word into the specified format and loads them into the machine with a program that combines them

into a single network of token and type nodes and associative links – the machine's model of a human memory.

4. He is then free to select arbitrarily any pair of words in the store and to ask the program to compare and contrast the meanings of those two words (requiring that its answers be expressed in sentences).

5. He may then give some fluent speaker the same pair of words, asking him also to compare and contrast them.

6. He compares the sentences the program generates to those the human has produced and, more importantly, considers whether or not the machine's output is one that might reasonably have been produced by a subject.

If this procedure reveals any changes which the experimenter would like to see in the program's performance, he must then revise either some part of the program, some part of the memory structure or content, or all of these, and test further on new examples to see if the program now operates in a manner closer to what he desires. Repetitions of this kind of test-correct-retest cycle constitute the essence of the simulation method; however, it is important to realize that for the purpose of developing a theory of memory, the result of this development process should *not* be thought of as the computer output which the program will now produce but rather as what now may or may not have become clear about the characteristics of workable concept-like memories. Most of the characteristics of which we are aware are incorporated in the model as already described; alterations of this which now seem indicated will be discussed in Section 4.5.

The present program is designed to compare and contrast the meaning of any two word concepts in the memory store and then to generate English text to express each of its findings. This is *not* the same task as merely using the two words in sentences – a vastly simpler job for which one need not even consider the semantic concepts associated with the words (78).

4.3.2 Locating Intersection Nodes

The actual processing system is made up of three separate programs. The first of these transforms input data (definitions that have been encoded as described in the preceding section) into IPL form and interlinks these to form the total memory model. This program will not be considered further here. The second program compares and contrasts the two given word concepts. It outputs anything found, but in a form expressed in the memory model's own internal language of nodes and links. The third program takes these findings, one at a time, and for each generates English text sufficient to express its meaning. Thus, this third program states (in a sort of "me Tarzan, you Jane" style of English) each similarity or contrast of meaning that the second program has found between the two given words.

It is in the operation of the second program, the comparing and contrasting of two concepts, that the interlocking, token-type structure of the over-all memory begins to pay off. For to do this it is no longer necessary in such a memory to line up some representation of each of the two concepts side by side and try to compare them. Instead, the entire investigation is simply a matter of searching for points in the memory at which the two *full* concepts intersect (full concept was defined in Section 4.2). To see how this is accomplished, recall that the entire memory is a network of nodes and connecting links. Beginning with the two nodes that the program is given to compare (the two patriarch words), this program works alternately on one full word concept and then the other, moving out node by node along the various tokens and types within each. While it will be convenient to visualize this as creating two slowly expanding spheres of activated nodes around each patriarch, actually there is no spatial significance to the expansion of a concept; the nodes in one concept may be located anywhere in the memory model.

The program simulates the gradual activation of each concept outward through the vast proliferation of associations originating from each patriarch, by moving out along these links, tagging each node encountered with a special two-part tag, the "activation tag." Part of this tag always names the patriarch from which the search began, i.e., the name of the concept within which the current node has been reached. Now, the program detects any intersection of meaning between the two concepts simply by asking, every time a node is reached, whether or not it already contains an activation tag naming the *other* patriarch, i.e., showing that this node has previously been reached in the tracing out of the other concept. If there is no such tag, the program next checks to see if there is already an activation tag naming the *current* patriarch, i.e., indicating that this node has been reached previously in tracing out this same concept. If so, the program must take account of this, to inhibit retracing out from the node again and hence repeating its effort, perhaps getting into a loop. Only if neither of these tags is found is the node tagged, and further search leading to the nodes to which *it* points is considered legitimate.

The second part of each activation tag is the name of the "immediate parent" of the current node, i.e., the node at which the associative link leading *directly* to it originated. Thus, the "activated" areas of the memory are turned from a one-way into a two-way network, and, whenever a tag from the opposite patriarch is found, these immediate-parent parts of activation tags permit the program to trace back "up" from the intersection node to the two patriarchs. This produces two *paths,* except when the intersection node *is* one of the patriarchs, in which case only a single path is needed, leading from one patriarch directly to the other.

Examples of such paths and pairs of paths occur in Figs. 4-2a and 4-2b, respectively. The paths from a patriarch to an intersection node produced by the

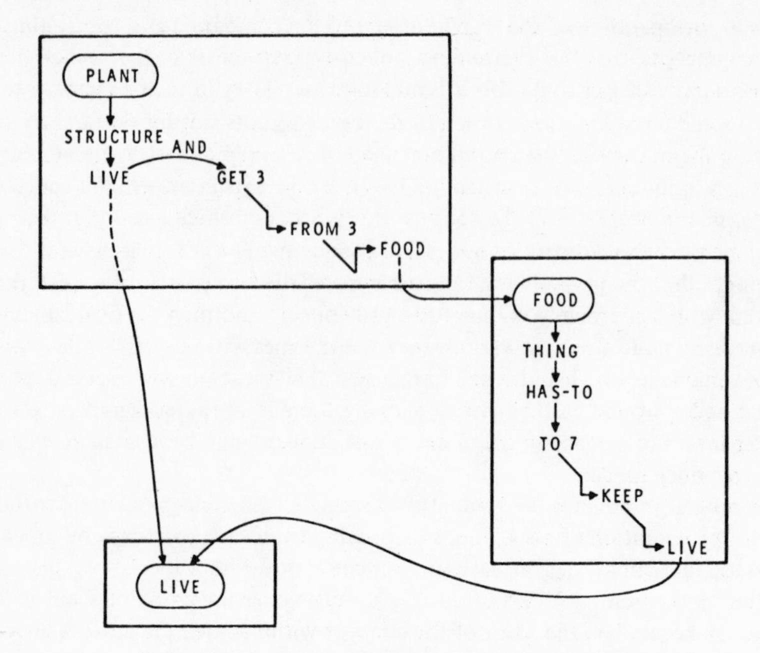

Figure 4-2a. Two Paths Direct from Plant to Live

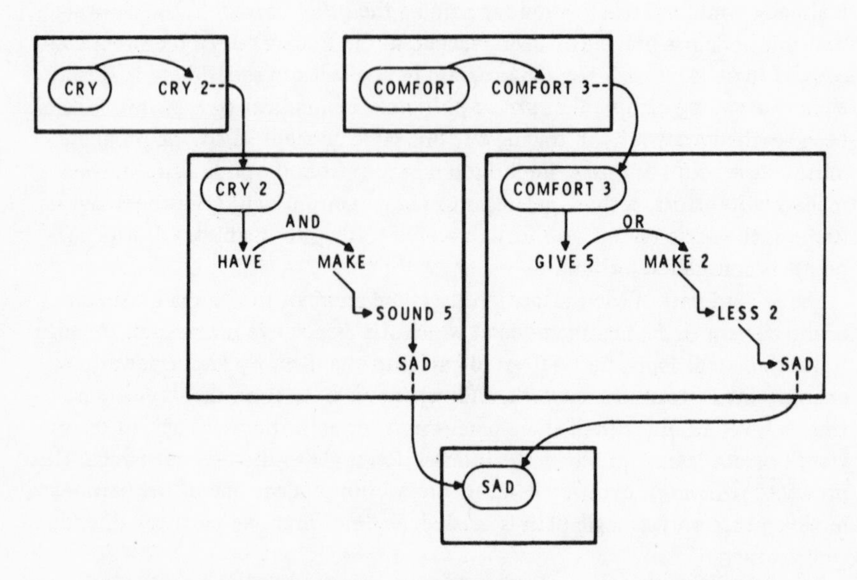

Figure 4-2b. A Path from "Cry" and a Path from "Comfort" which Reach the Same (i.e., an Intersection) Node

second program should not be confused with the "activation" it makes from each patriarch. While this activation is equivalent to an expanding "sphere," a path is only one particular "line" from the center of the sphere to some point within it, one at which it intersects the other full concept's "sphere."

Expanding the two concepts alternately is extremely important; in effect this converts both concepts into searchers for each other and gives both the maximal number of targets to look for at any given stage of the search.

4.3.3 Making Inferences and Expressing Findings in English

The third program, which generates a piece of text to express each path given it by the second program, produces output of the sort illustrated in Table 4-1. (In this table the paths that the third program has been given to work on are omitted, while the paths for Examples 1 and 2 are those of Fig. 4-2.)

The most important point about the sentence producer is that there seems to be excellent justification for considering it, when taken in conjunction with the first two programs, as an inference maker rather than just a retriever of information. From a relatively small amount of input data, the over-all program will derive a very large number of implicit assertions indeed, and make each such assertion explicit in the form of English text. As an example of an interesting type of "inferential" behavior, consider the output shown in Table 4-1 as Example 2-B. The path expressed by this output is the longer of the two shown in Fig. 4-2a. As can be seen from a study of Fig. 4-2b, this kind of performance is made possible by the fact that the memory model interconnects related information that has been input from a great many different definitions, so that in order to answer some particular question the search program can trace out a "plane-hopping" path. While a path lying completely within one plane (except for its terminal points) amounts only to a representation of some piece of the information put into the memory, a "plane-hopping" path represents an idea that was implied by, but by no means directly expressed in, the data that were input.

By analogy, suppose we fed a machine "A is greater than B," and "B is greater than C." If then, in answer to the question "what is A greater than?" the machine responded "B," we would not want to call this an inference, but only a "retrieval." However, if it went on to say, "A is also greater than C," then we would say that it had made a simple inference. The kind of path that we have been calling "plane-hopping" is exactly the representation of such an inference, since it combines information input in one definition with that input in another. But the fact that our planes are not simple propositions but rather sizable configurations, every node of which provides the possibility of branching off to another plane means that the number of "inferential" paths becomes very large as paths of any appreciable length are considered. Moreover, the possibility that a path may contain fragments from *several* planes seems to indicate clearly that the inferences need not be at all simple, although we do not yet have actual computer output with which to demonstrate this very conclusively.

Assuming a "complete" semantic memory – one in which every word used in any definition also has a definition encoded – a concept fans out very rapidly from its patriarch. It appears that in such a full memory model the average node would branch to at least three other nodes, considering both its ties to tokens and to its type, if it is itself a token. This means that the average number of paths of, say, up to ten nodes in length emanating from any type node would be over 88,000, each of which would require at least one unique sentence to express. This is to be compared to 2046 paths emanating from such a type node if no token-to-type links are available.

Another way to look at the potential of a memory store such as the theory specifies is to compute what the present programs could generate if one could get the definitions of say, 850 words encoded and stored in a memory model. There would then be 360,000 word pairs to ask it about. Since at a conservative estimate a memory model of this size would provide ten nontrivial semantic connections, and hence sentences or sentence sets, between the average word pair, the present programs would have the capability to generate well over 3,500,000 short batches of text to express this total conceptual knowledge, ignoring all that information present only in longer paths. The definitions of 850 words comprise far more information than can be modeled in the core of today's computers, even though an efficient packing scheme might greatly increase the storable amount. Nevertheless, calculations such as these seem relevant in evaluating the potential of the model as a general theory of long-term conceptual memory.

While a path represents an idea, it is up to the sentence-producing program to get that idea expressed in English. Thus this program must check a path for restriction tags and other features which make it necessary to insert words such as "not" or "among other things" into the sentence generated to express its meaning.

In attempting to express the meaning of a path, this program also deletes, rearranges, and adds words to those given in the path. It works not only with nodes mentioned in the path itself but sometimes looks *around* these nodes in the memory model to retrieve additional information and to check on things it considers saying. For instance, in Example 2-B the word "air," although not in the path being expressed, was retrieved to produce legitimate English.

In expressing a complex path, such as that of Fig. 4-2a, this text-producing program realizes when the capability of its sentence grammar is being exceeded and starts a new sentence (see e.g., Example 7-C-1 of Table 4-1.) Unfortunately it does this rather often, and a more powerful program clearly would be one which instead of the two sentences shown as Examples 3-A-1 and 3-A-2 would output the single sentence: "A plant is not an animal but a man is." Some of

Table 4-1. Example Output from the Current Program
(Paths have been omitted, but see Fig. 4-2)

Example 1. Compare: CRY, COMFORT
A. Intersect: SAD
(1) CRY2 IS AMONG OTHER THINGS TO MAKE A SAD SOUND.*
(2) TO COMFORT3 CAN BE TO MAKE2 SOMETHING LESS2 SAD.
(Note that the program has selected particular meanings of "cry" and "comfort" as appropriate for this intersection. The path on which this output is based is shown in Fig. 4-2b.

Example 2. Compare: PLANT, LIVE
A. 1st Intersect: LIVE
(1) PLANT IS A LIVE STRUCTURE.
B. 2nd Intersect: LIVE
(1) PLANT IS STRUCTURE WHICH GET3-FOOD FROM AIR. THIS FOOD IS THING WHICH BEING2 HAS-TO TAKE INTO ITSELF TO7 KEEP LIVE.
(The paths which these two replies express are shown in Fig. 4-2a.)

Example 3. Compare: PLANT, MAN
A. 1st Intersect: ANIMAL
(1) PLANT IS NOT A ANIMAL STRUCTURE.
(2) MAN IS ANIMAL.
B. 2nd Intersect: PERSON
(1) TO PLANT3 IS FOR A PERSON SOMEONE TO PUT SOMETHING INTO EARTH.
(2) MAN3 IS PERSON.
(Here the program is treating "person" as an adjective modifier of "someone.")

Example 4. Compare: PLANT, INDUSTRY
A. 1st Intersect: INDUSTRY
(1) PLANT2 IS APPARATUS WHICH PERSON USE FOR 5 PROCESS IN INDUSTRY.

Example 5. Compare: EARTH, LIVE
A. 1st Intersect: ANIMAL
(1) EARTH IS PLANET OF7 ANIMAL.
(2) TO LIVE IS TO HAVE EXISTENCE AS7 ANIMAL.

*"AMONG OTHER THINGS" and "CAN BE" are canned phrases which the program inserts when the next thing it is going to mention is one out of a set of things recorded in its memory. At one point, the program was programmed to insert "AMONG OTHER THINGS" *whenever* it was about to assert one fact out of such a set. We expected this to make its output have a proper, scientifically cautious ring. However, where it had been saying (rather cloddishly, we felt), "TO CRY IS TO MAKE A SAD SOUND," it now said: "TO CRY, AMONG OTHER THINGS, IS, AMONG OTHER THINGS, TO MAKE, AMONG OTHER THINGS, A, AMONG OTHER THINGS, SAD SOUND." In short, it turns out that if the program is really made to hedge whenever it knows more than it is going to say, one sits around the console all day waiting for it to get around to saying anything. This may not be such a bad simulation of certain individuals, but wasn't what we had had in mind. Thus, the program is now severely restricted as to just when it can hedge. Science marches on!

Example 6. Compare: FRIEND, COMFORT
- A. 1st Intersect: PERSON
  - (1) FRIEND IS PERSON.
  - (2) COMFORT CAN BE WORD TO4 PERSON.

Example 7. Compare: FIRE, BURN
- A. 1st Intersect: BURN
  - (1) FIRE IS CONDITION WHICH BURN.
- B. 2nd Intersect: FIRE
  - (1) TO BURN2 CAN BE TO DESTROY2 SOMETHING BY4 FIRE.
- C. 3rd Intersect: BURN
  - (1) FIRE IS A FLAME CONDITION. THIS FLAME CAN BE A GAS TONGUE4. THIS GAS IS GAS WHICH BURN.
    (The sentence producer starts a new sentence whenever it needs to say something more about something it has used adjectively.)

Example 8. Compare: BUSINESS, COMFORT
- A. 1st Intersect: PERSON
  - (1) BUSINESS5 IS ACT3 WHICH PERSON DO.
  - (2) COMFORT2 IS CONDITION3 WHICH PERSON HAVE NEED4.
    (The code contains information indicating that "person" should be plural here, but the sentence producer does not yet make use of this information.)
- B. 2nd Intersect: PERSON
  - (1) BUSINESS5 IS ACT3 WHICH PERSON DO.
  - (2) COMFORT CAN BE WORD TO4 PERSON.

Example 9. Compare: MAN, BUSINESS
- A. 1st Intersect: PERSON
  - (1) MAN3 IS PERSON.
  - (2) BUSINESS CAN BE ACTIVITY WHICH PERSON MUST DO WORK2.
    (Something wrong here. I believe a miscoding in the input data.)
- B. 2nd Intersect: GROUP
  - (1) MAN2 IS MAN AS9 GROUP.
  - (2) BUSINESS2 IS QUESTION3 FOR ATTENTION OF GROUP.

Example 10. Compare: MAN, LIVE
- A. 1st Intersect: ANIMAL
  - (1) MAN IS ANIMAL.
  - (2) TO LIVE IS TO HAVE EXISTENCE AS7 ANIMAL.
- B. 2nd Intersect: LIVE
  - (1) MAN IS A LIVE +BEING2.

the minor improvements of this single sentence over the two which the program now produces would not be difficult to program, but the unification of the two paths into one is a bit more complicated. Clearly, the sentence-generation program involves something very close to what Chomsky calls "transformations."

In summary, the operation of the sentence producer has little in common with other sentence-generation programs, and in fact its whole philosophy is contradictory to a good part of the spirit of modern linguistics, which attempts to treat syntactic facts in isolation from semantic ones. The program is also designed in complete contradiction to the subordinate place for semantic information that the formulation of Katz and Postal (quoted on p. 221) would seem to imply for a performance model. As a theory, the program implies that a person first has something to say, expressed somehow in his own conceptual terms (which is what a "path" is to the program), and that all his decisions about the syntactic form that a generated sentence is to take are then made *in the service of* this intention. The sentence producer works entirely in this fashion, figuring out grammatical properties of sentences only as these are needed to solve the problem of expressing a path given to it by the search program.

The programs were tested only on very small memory models, built from no more than 50 or 60 definitions (about 5,000 IPL cells), and on only a few such memories (see Table 4-2).

Table 4.2. Words with Definitions Encoded for Use in Model Memories

(Note: Computer memory limitations have so far required that definitions of no more than twenty of these words be used to constitute a model memory during a given series of word comparisons. Since this paper was written, almost all of the 850 words of basic English have been encoded, but not yet run in the program.)

instrument	flame	country	leather
insurance	experience	desire	land
invent	fact	sex	kiss
interest	comfort	plant	know
iron	cloth	family	laugh
ice	cause	meal	light
idea	attack	animal	language
friend	argue	food	law
develop	business	man	lead
event	burn	live	jelly
earth	build	level	journey
exist	bread	lift	jump
drink	behave	letter	judge
fire	cry	learn	

A small total memory implies that most branches of the proliferating search of a concept are always getting cut short upon reaching a type node for which no definition has yet been encoded. One of the most surprising findings from running the program has been that even with this relative paucity of over-all information, the program almost invariably succeeds in finding some intersections of meaning. Actually, Table 4-1 lists only a selected sample of the program's output for each compared pair of words; there are usually five or six pairs of sentences generated for each problem pair given to it, although most of these are only trivial variations of a couple of basic sentences, such as those in Table 4-1. The larger the memory model, the greater the number of search branches that remain active, so that the search program becomes able to unearth a great many more semantic connections at a relatively shallow depth beneath any two patriarchs. This ultimately can only improve the program's performance, although it may also require that more concern be given to directing searches than has so far been the case. At present, but for one exception, a search just "progressively proliferates" along all possible branches from the two patriarchs until it has covered a given number of nodes, e.g., 400.

The one exception to this blind, "breadth first," search occurs whenever two concepts are found to intersect on a word used prepositionally, such as "for5" in the concept "plant2." Instead of treating this as a substantive semantic intersection, the search program merely concentrates an immediate burst of search activity out from the two tokens of the preposition. The reasoning here is simply that, while a match on such a word is not in itself sufficient to be treated as a significant conceptual similarity, it is a good bet to examine immediately the subjects, objects, and modifiers of such prepositions rather than continue the usual search schedule, which normally would not get to these nodes for some time. Unfortunately there is not yet enough evidence available to assess the value of this search heuristic, since its effectiveness, if any, will not show up until the memory model is relatively large.

4.4* The Memory Model as Basis for a Theory of How People Comprehend Language

Sections 4.1 to 4.3 demonstrate that the memory model, once built, can support simulation of a relatively simple type of language behavior. However, this memory model had to be laboriously created by a human "coder." A detailed study of the way in which one such coder encodes seven sentences of English text into the data format of the memory model has been omitted here because of space limitations. The aim of this study is to develop some theoretical understanding of how a person may comprehend text.

As stated earlier, encoding of text into the memory model format is not a procedure for which complete algorithmic rules are available but rather one that depends heavily upon the coder developing his own understanding of what the text means. Whenever a coder represents the meaning of some

*Because this book is concerned more with the art of obtaining semantic behavior in computers and less with the development of theories of human semantic behavior, the editor asked Quillian to condense the four chapters of his dissertation that describe experiments in that area. This section summarizes his results of that investigation; further details were given in Chapters IV-VII and several appendixes of the original dissertation. Quillian informed me that since the thesis was completed he has made substantial progress on his theory of encoding and has developed a text-understanding program that achieves some success in encoding. [Editor's note.]

segment of text in the format of the model, relationships and features of this meaning that were not explicit in the text itself must be made explicit. This provides a methodological advantage in studying how a coder-subject comprehends text, since certain parts of the coder's otherwise covert "understanding" of the text become externalized and available for observation during coding.

As our coder-subject encoded the seven sentences, she was also required to describe into a tape recorder a running account of the steps she took and of the reasoning she carried out. This verbal protocol has been analyzed for use in developing the theoretical picture of how the process of text understanding may in fact proceed, at least for this one subject.

What does it mean to say that a reader or coder "understands" a piece of text? It seems clear that understanding text includes recognizing the structure of relations between words of the text (as in parsing it), recognizing the referent words of pronouns and of other words used anaphorically, and recognizing the appropriate sense intended for all words with multiple meanings. I take it that the over-all effect of these processes is to encode the text's meaning into some form more or less parallel to that in which the subject's general knowledge is stored, so that its meaning may be compared to that knowledge and perhaps added to it.

There are great methodological difficulties in attempting to study how people understand sentences. The Fifth Annual Report of the Center for Cognitive Studies of Harvard (reference 23) states:

To "explain" speech perception we must propose a device whose input would be the acoustic speech signal and whose output would be the meaning that native speakers retrieve from that acoustic signal. *Without a satisfactory semantic theory, we cannot even specify the output of such a device* (p. 16, italics mine).

The methodological importance of a semantic memory model for a study of understanding stems from the fact that it *does*, to some extent, provide a way to make a reader's "output" not only specifiable, but also visible. That is, a coder who is encoding is taking English text as "input" and then giving as "output" a plane representing the meaning of the text. In this plane a great many of the direct results of his process of understanding the text are represented overtly. In particular, in such a plane the results of the coder's parsing of the text, of his disambiguation of its words' multiple meanings, and of his identification of its anaphoric references, can all be identified. For the researcher this means that he is able to *observe,* for a subject performing a process very much like "understanding," not only an input – the text – but also an output – the representation the subject builds to represent its meaning. To my knowledge there is no other representation existing that permits this in any such comprehensive, economical manner.

While the encoding process is of course not identical to the covert processing that constitutes the understanding of the same text during normal reading, it is at least very heavily dependent upon such understanding, and is in some ways a slowed-down, overt version of it. And it is precisely such a slowed-down version that is needed to investigate the understanding process. Having a recorded protocol of this slowed-down version, we can study the encoding process in the same way that other cognitive processes, such as playing chess, have been studied, and apply part of what has been learned from those analyses to the problem of text understanding. Of course we do not suppose that the step-by-step verbal protocol generated by the coder-subject is identical or even very close to her actual thought processes. However, the two are certainly related, with the protocol revealing various reasoning procedures, logical steps, and her general sequence of operations. All of these are otherwise obscure.

In building a theoretical picture of the text-understanding process from our analysis of this protocol, we assume that text understanding operates on the basis of selective interaction between the text being read and the coder's general over-all memory. It is further assumed that her memory has essentially the same structure as that of our model, and also that the task the text understander faces is to recode the meaning of the text into some similar form so that she can compare it with and perhaps incorporate it into her general memory.

Specifically, the following four steps were taken in this study of the text-understanding process:

1. The total *possible* moves toward comprehension of one of the seven sentences were enumerated, to show the size of the "problem space" these afford the reader-coder. That is, all the *possible* choices facing the understander of this sentence were enumerated, in the same way that possible moves facing a chess player at any given position may be enumerated. This problem space turns out to be very large indeed, with hundreds of thousands of ways available to the reader for combining the separate words of a sentence. A very substantial part of it is due to lexical ambiguity, so that the elimination of such ambiguity is one key step a reader must take toward understanding the sentence.

2. It was then demonstrated experimentally that a computer program, given an appropriate version of the memory model, could go some distance toward effectively resolving the lexical ambiguities of these sentences. In this experiment 19 ambiguous words were considered; of these the program correctly disambiguated 12, left 4 ambiguous, and incorrectly disambiguated 3. This program operated *solely* on the basis of semantic considerations, with no syntactic analysis at all. However, improving its level of performance until it compares with human capability will not be possible unless and until a program *does* also make some use of syntax.

3. A step-by-step characterization of what the coder-subject does during the protocol was undertaken. The main conclusion from this is that the understanding process seems to divide naturally into episodes, created because the coder-subject "bites off" small *segments* of a sentence for intensive processing as she reads it.

4. The particular segmenting of text done by our subject was then analyzed to suggest a way that syntactic processing of text by a reader may guide, and be guided by, his semantic processing of it. *We argue that the same kind of search for semantic intersections carried out by the program described in Section 4.3 must be a key process in this semantic processing.* Several ways to extend and strengthen such search processes in order to adapt them for use in understanding text can also be proposed. Assuming such a continuous interaction between syntactic analysis and semantic processing, a tentative theoretical view of how text understanding may proceed was constructed.

4.5 Some Final Implications and Relations to Linguistic Theory

A tentative theory of the general structure of long-term memory has now been explored in three ways: First, a model of such memory has been utilized in a computer program to simulate human performance on a semantic task. Second, the memory model has been combined with the techniques of protocol collection to produce a methodology for gathering data relevant to how a subject understands text. Third, this subject's internal semantic memory has been assumed to be structured and used as is the memory model, and the implications of this assumption have been utilized to explain the subject's performance and to develop a tentative theory of how text is understood.

*4.5.1 Improvements of the Model**

In the model as presented so far, modification of a concept has been encoded by attaching a link labeled "modifier" to a token for the concept to be modified. This modifier link leads to some other node which forms the head of the modifying structure. (In IPL terms, the token node is given an attribute whose name is "modifier" and whose value is the top node of the modifying structure.) In a case where the modifying structure is a prepositional phrase modifying a noun or a verb, it now appears that it would be much better simply to label the modifying link with the preposition itself and run this link from the token node to be modified to the object of the preposition. This would eliminate the link labeled "modifier" and hence would reduce the size of the over-all model. More importantly, it would permit a search (activation of a full concept in the memory) to be directed more readily. Such

*Alterations discussed in this section are being incorporated into a new version of the memory model and program now being developed in conjunction with Dr. D. G. Bobrow.

direction is required in connection with the parsing of prepositional phrases.

In general, it appears that labeling links with words themselves, and especially with prepositions, instead of with predefined linkage names, such as "modifier," is a development worth further exploration. The use of prepositions to label links between tokens in the model would seem to go along with another change, the need for which is pointed up in reference 24. This work, although motivated by purely grammatical considerations, indicates convincingly that the parameter symbols S, D, and M, as conceived in the model so far, are not adequate to achieve the "carrying" of information into alternate forms. Briefly, the examples given in this work and those by Fillmore (24) raise issues of the following sort: Suppose the verb "to swarm" were given the definition: "for (bees, ants, etc.) to cluster in some area." As this definition has been encoded, the parenthesized phrase becomes a parameter symbol S, representing whatever the subject of "swarm" is in some sentence or plane where it occurs. Suppose, however, that we now encounter the sentence: "The gardens swarm with bees." If the subject of "swarm" in this sentence is treated as a value for the parameter symbol S, it will mean that "the gardens cluster in some area." This misinterpretation is due to the fact that S is too gross and undifferentiated a notion, and Fillmore's examples indicate that our S's, D's, and perhaps M's must be subdivided into more precise categories. Fillmore proposes syntactic terms such as "ergative," "agentive," and "locative," as more precise categories which should replace the grosser notions of subject (S) and object (D).

We know that the kinds of parameter symbols utilized in the memory must have a clear-cut correspondence to the kinds of intertoken links used in it. It would appear that using prepositions to label intertoken links refines the memory's ability to differentiate these relationships in a way that matches the more differentiated parameter symbols that Fillmore shows a need for. In this regard, it appears that, whenever possible, prepositions should be used as links between verbs and their subjects and objects, thereby replacing (↘↱→) and (↘↳). For example, the definition of "swarm" given above might be rewritten before encoding to say: " 'swarming' is clustering in (some area) by (bees, ants)." During encoding, *both* parenthesized phrases in this definition would then become parameter symbols, perhaps called, respectively, the "ergative" (E) and the "locative" (L). Then the sentence, "the gardens swarm with bees," would be interpreted by taking "gardens" as the value of L, rather than of the grosser S. Once this was done, the kind of misinterpretation described would be avoided.

To refine the memory by using more differentiated intertoken links and parameter symbols is to move it to a level of specificity one step further from natural language than it has been. (And from the usual specificity of transformational structures; as one questioner at Fillmore's presentation put it, his examples concern the "deep, deep structure" of language.) To move the code further from natural language appears to put more burden on whatever processes translate back and forth between the model's representation and natural language, e.g., the sentence producing routines of our Chapter III program, and the coder (or eventual program) that encodes textual material into the model's representation. However, the opposite may in fact be the case; Fillmore suggests what may be *more* general generation rules based on his "deep, deep" structures, and, on the encoding or "understanding" side, more precisely differentiated parameter symbols may be *easier* to select values for than are the grosser categories S, D, and M. For example, for the sentence stated, consider intersecting "garden," taken as one patriarch, with the total set of clue words: "bees," "ants," and "area," taken together as the other patriarch set. It would appear that an intersection program could easily select the matching member of this set, "area," and hence the correct parameter for "garden" to fill. Turning the sentence around ("bees swarm in the garden,") would not effect the "understanding" achieved and would hardly even change the process by which it was achieved, since the essential part of this process is the semantic intersecting, rather than syntactic analysis.

Another change in the model relates to its ability to represent ambiguity easily. A coding convention which the reader may have noticed to be a departure from ordinary grammatical procedure was to make some prepositions which modify a verb the object of that verb. This was done to allow indirect objects and other nouns to be made the subject of the preposition, and hence permit certain fine distinctions of meaning to be encoded. For example, consider a sentence like "I threw the man in the ring." This sentence can mean: (a) "While in the ring I threw the man," (b) "I threw the man who was in the ring," or (c) "I threw the man into the ring." The encodings corresponding to these three meanings are shown in Fig. 4-3, parts A, B, and C, respectively.

Presented in this way the distinctions of meaning between (a), (b), and (c) are clear, and the encodings logical, even though using a prepositional phrase as an object of a verb (in c) is contrary to usual practice. However, when such a sentence is encountered in text it is often impossible to decide which of its meanings is intended. It turns out, moreover, that coders are most unreliable and unhappy about making this distinction, even in cases in which one meaning does seem clearly indicated.

Thus it would appear that our coders at least mentally encode most cases of this kind in some form that leaves it ambiguous as to which exact meaning is intended. In order to be ambiguous on this matter in the code as it stands the coder must set up all the alternate forms, A, B, and C, and then group these into a disjunctive set. In the program now under development all meanings strictly like (c) will be encoded in the form of A, while all meanings strictly

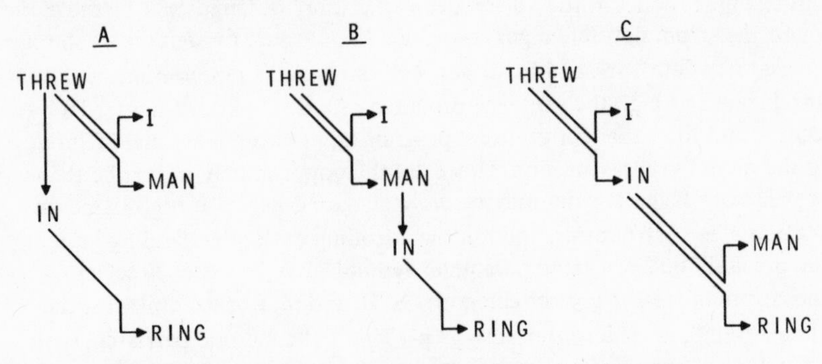

Figure 4-3. Encoding of Three Meanings of a Sentence

like (a) will be encoded as modifiers of the subject ("I" in the above example). This eliminates forms of type C and brings the code more in line with standard terminology. More importantly, however, a new parenthesis notation is being added that will allow a phrase like "in the ring" to modify the entire remainder of the sentence while remaining uncommitted as to just which subelement it modifies and hence which precise interpretation is intended. Thus the ambiguous form will be easily represented, while the finer distinctions will require slightly more structure. This clearly will increase the psychological verisimilitude of the model and provide a more useful representation. Considerations of this kind, incidentally, cast doubt on efforts to recode natural language into symbolic logic and also suggest that programs attempting to process natural language have their greatest hope of success if they are kept as close as possible to human methods and representations.

4.5.2 Implications for the Relationship of Transformational Grammars to Psychological Performance Models

The viewpoint that emerges from this research conflicts at several points with the relationship that has been said to exist between current linguistic theories and performance models, especially insofar as these involve semantics. The rest of this section will be devoted to clarifying this relationship as it appears once a semantic memory is assumed to be part of the mechanism or organism that deals with natural language.

In the first place, we do not believe that performance theories or computer models can ignore or put off semantics, as most language-processing programs so far have done, and yet hope to achieve success. Whether a program is intended to parse sentences, to translate languages, or to answer natural-language questions, if it does not take account of semantic facts both early and often, I do not think it has a chance of approaching the level of human competence.

Correspondingly, any theory of language, such as that prescribed by Katz et al. (31, 32), which asserts that semantic processing is in any sense temporally or logically subordinate to syntactic processing, would seem to be of very dubious value in performance models.

Secondly, it has already been pointed out that the normal mechanism for understanding language, as we see it, need not refuse to process any sentence because the sentence is "semantically anomalous." This is because the memory model provides a natural measure of the relative semantic similarity between one full concept and any others, and hence allows an understanding process to select the best available interpretation for any given word string instead of first insisting that that string meet previously anticipated conditions in order to be semantically interpretable. Viewing the process of language understanding in this way eliminates the embarrassing necessity to say that people must interpret an "anomalous" sentence by some mysterious process based on the sentence's "direct analogy to well-formed sentences" (reference 11, p. 149). Positing such a semantic memory thus makes the judgment as to what constitutes a semantically anomalous sentence arbitrary – as, incidentally, it has always seemed to many people anyhow. For example, Katz and Postal's assertion that the sentence, "the paint is silent," cannot be understood by the normal rules of language interpretation (reference 32, p. 25) is not easy to accept.

It has also been noted that positing a semantic memory seems to abrogate the need in a performance model for the phrase-structure component of a transformational grammar, that a set of rules corresponding to the transformational component is all that our program employs to generate sentences.

Another of the unquestioned tenets of transformational linguistics is that a single grammar should be considered to underlie both the production and the understanding of sentences. This notion, if feasible, would provide a great simplification of abstract linguistic theory and seems to be almost universally accepted among transformational linguists (note, e.g., the constant reference to an undifferentiated "speaker-hearer" in reference 11).

However, it seems clear that while generative grammars are very natural parts of a sentence-production mechanism, these same grammars raise immediate problems when one attempts to base a parsing or understanding program on them. To parse according to such a grammar must involve a series of trial matching operations, and the tree of possible matches, even if pruned by heuristics, as has been suggested, seems inevitably destined to make it more difficult to parse and hence to *understand* sentences with any given grammar than it is to *produce* them with that same grammar. This is blatantly opposite to the facts about people: A child can understand more complex sentences than he can generate, a student in a foreign language finds it easier to understand or read correct sentences than to speak them, and a person can read language faster than he can compose it.

In spite of these contradictory facts, the assumption that a single grammar is the best way to explain the competence both of a speaker and of a hearer is widely held. To explain a grammar's use in understanding, Miller and Chomsky (reference 45, p. 465) have adopted a version of the "analysis-by-synthesis" theory apparently first put forward by Halle and Stevens for phonemics in 1959 (see also reference 42).

The key assumption of the analysis-by-synthesis theory is that in order to understand language one essentially must re-create the generation process by which that language was created. This re-creation is thought to rely upon the grammar and to be guided by cues in the given text. The re-creation is continuously checked and corrected by testing tentative steps of generation against further text. Hence, from this viewpoint, to understand text is to locate all the steps that, given the same grammar, might have generated it.*

This analysis-by-synthesis model follows naturally from assuming that all language competence is to be explained in terms of a single basic set of *rules,* to be called the grammar. On the other hand, if the understanding of text is viewed as the creation of some mental symbolic *representation,* such as that comprising the memory model, then *there is little reason to suppose that a reader or hearer must retrace the steps by which a sentence might have been generated in order to understand it.* The relationship between producing and understanding a given piece of language lies only in the single message content underlying both, not in the processes for moving between English and that message content.

For instance, suppose a bundle of facts $x_1, x_2, \ldots, x_n$ modify object y. Speaker A knows this, and wishes to tell hearer B. To do so he must utilize some way of turning the conceptual connections that represent this information in his head into natural language. For this he has many choices: how many sentences to use; which x's to make into adjectives of y, which ones into predicate nominatives, and which ones into prepositional phrases; whether to use passive sentences, subordinate clauses, rhetorical questions, and so on. However, to obtain an adequate conception of A's meaning, B only needs somehow to arrive at a mental state in which all the x's are represented in his cognitive representation and linked as modifiers to a representation of y. The question of how A happened to *express* each of these facts is of no necessary concern to B; all he must obtain is some mental *representation* corresponding roughly to that which A is trying to communicate.

*From this sort of conception Chomsky has been led to a heavily a priori, anti-environmental theory of language acquisition (11). His reasoning seems to be: A person can understand a very wide range of sentence structures, yet he can only understand what he also could have generated. Therefore, the person must be born with a very high-powered but latent generation grammar and must somehow be able to actualize a latent rule of this grammar whenever it is needed in order to understand some sentence containing an unfamiliar syntactic complication.

Since much of the information that is in A's language can therefore be ignored by B, the tests that he must apply to extract from A's speech what he needs to know clearly can be much simpler than the tests he would have to apply to regenerate B's sentence-generation process fully. In other words, it appears, both from thinking about the problem in terms of a semantic memory model and from the obvious facts about the relative difficulty of understanding language versus producing it, that the process by which a person understands language is most likely "primary" in the sense that it does not rely on any generative grammar or sentence production process. Rather than understanding language by relating it to how a generation grammar would allow the same text to be produced, the understanding process is an autonomous process of its own.

To view a person's understanding of language as a separate problem, independent of any generation grammar, is of course not to say that an understander can ignore the facts of sentence structure – even though people can in fact understand text whose sentence structure is incorrect, wildly distorted, and so on – but merely that a generative grammar need not be in any sense a "component" of the understander's language processor.

Once the domain that a generative grammar has to account for is thus restricted to sentence production, it becomes unnecessary to think of the grammar as a single set of rules that will generate *all* constructions of English. Nine years after the publication of *Syntactic Structures* (Chomsky, 1957) no one has succeeded in building a general generative grammar for all of English. This alone is no condemnation of his proposals, but it does seem much more reasonable to hope for a grammar capable of accounting for how any given idea may be expressed in *some* stretch of acceptable English text. Then, to get this grammar to express the same thought in some other style, i.e., in different sentence structure(s), a higher-level rule could perhaps be written which would alter the grammar itself. This would provide a mechanism similar to that in a person, in that it could express itself in text of some style and perhaps change that style for various occasions but would not simultaneously contain rules capable of producing English of *all* possible styles.

The situation here parallels that for speech accents. Many Americans can approximate a Southern accent, or an Irish or German or French one, but no one can simultaneously speak with all these accents. The task of formulating a single phonological grammar adequate to generate speech in all accents at once clearly is unnecessarily difficult, if even possible. Similarly, it seems unreasonable to seek a grammar that will generate English sentences of all possible styles at once.

The requirement that a generative grammar be universal across all of a natural language's styles of expression *cannot* be escaped as long as the grammar is considered to underlie sentence understanding as well as sentence production, for an intelligent native speaker has the competence to understand almost any grammatically acceptable sentence style. However, this situation changes as soon as the grammar's job is restricted to language production and language understanding is attacked as a separate problem.

In summary, therefore, the implications of assuming a semantic memory for what we might call "generative psycholinguistics" are: that dichotomous judgments of semantic well-formedness versus anomaly are not essential or inherent to language performance; that the transformational component of a grammar is the part most relevant to performance models; that a generative grammar's role should be viewed as restricted to language production, whereas sentence understanding should be treated as a problem of extracting a cognitive representation of a text's message; that until *some* theoretical notion of cognitive representation is incorporated into linguistic conceptions, they are unlikely to provide either powerful language-processing programs or psychologically relevant theories.

Although these implications conflict with the way others have viewed the relationship of transformational grammars to semantics and to human performance, they do not eliminate the importance of such grammars to psychologists, an importance stressed in, and indeed largely created by, the work of Chomsky. It is precisely because of a growing interdependence between such linguistic theory and psychological performance models that their relationship needs to be clarified.

Bibliography

1. Banerji, R. B., *A Language for the Description of Concepts,* unpublished dittoed paper, Systems Research Center, Case Inst. of Technology, Cleveland, 1964.
2. Bartlett, F. C., *Remembering, a Study in Experimental and Social Psychology,* Cambridge University Press, Cambridge, England, 1932.
3. Baylor, G. W., and Simon, H. A., "A Chess Mating Combination Program," *Proc. SJCC,* Spartan Press, Baltimore, Md., 1966.
4. Berkeley, E. C., and Bobrow, D. G., (eds.) *The Programming Language LISP: Its Operation and Applications,* Information International, Inc., Cambridge, Mass., 1964.
5. Bobrow, D. G., "Syntactic Analysis of Language by Computer – a Survey." *Proc. FJCC,* Spartan Press, Baltimore, Md., 1963.
6. Bobrow, D. G., *Natural Language Input for a Computer Problem Solving System.* Unpublished Ph.D. dissertation, M.I.T., 1964, also Project MAC, Report TR-1, 1964, Chapter 3 of the present volume is a slightly revised version.
7. Bobrow, D. G., and Teitelman, W., "Format-Directed List Processing in LISP," Bolt, Beranek and Newman Report 1366, Cambridge, Mass., 1966.
8. Bruner, J. S., "On Perceptual Readiness," *Psych. Rev.,* Vol. 64, 1957.
9. Bruner, J. S., Goodnow, J. J., and Austin, C. A., *A Study of Thinking,* John Wiley, New York, 1956.
10. Bruner, J. S., and Minturn, A. L., "Perceptual Identification and Perceptual Organization," *J. Gen. Psych.,* Vol. 53, 1955.
11. Chomsky, N., *Aspects of the Theory of Syntax,* The M.I.T. Press, Cambridge, Mass., 1965.
12. Chomsky, N., and Miller, G. A., "Introduction to the Formal Analysis of Natural Languages, Luce, D. R., Bush, R. R., and Galanter, E. (eds.), *Handbook of Mathematical Psychology, Vol. II,* John Wiley, New York, 1963.
13. Chomsky, N., Review of Skinner, B. F., "Verbal Behavior," *Language,* Vol. 35, 1959.
14. Cliff, N., "Adverbs as Multipliers." *Psych. Rev.,* Vol. 66, 1959.
15. Creelman, M. B., *The Experimental Investigation of Meaning,* Springer, New York, 1966.
16. Darlington, J., "Translating Ordinary Language into Symbolic Logic." Memo. MAC-M-149, Project MAC, M.I.T., Cambridge, Mass., 1962.
17. Deese, J., "On the Structure of Associative Meaning," *Psych. Rev.,* Vol. 69, 1962.
18. De Groot, A. D., *Thought and Choice in Chess,* Mouton and Co., The Hague, 1965.
19. Ervin, S. M., "Changes with Age in the Verbal Determinants of Word Association," *Am. J. Psych.,* Vol. 74, 1961.
20. Feigenbaum, E. A., and Simon, H. A., "Performance of a Reading Task by an Elementary Perceiving and Memorizing Program," *Behavioral Science,* Vol. 8, 1963.
21. Feigenbaum, E. A., "An Information Processing Theory of Verbal Learning," Report P-1817, RAND Corp., Santa Monica, Calif., 1959.
22. Feigenbaum, E. A., and Feldman, J. (eds.), *Computers and Thought,* McGraw-Hill, New York, 1963.
23. *Fifth Annual Report, the Center for Cognitive Studies, 1964-65.* The Center for Cognitive Studies, Harvard University, Cambridge, Mass., 1965.
24. Fillmore, C. J., "A Proposal Concerning English Prepositions," paper presented at M.I.T., Cambridge, Mass., April 1966.

25. *Funk and Wagnalls' New "Standard" Dictionary of the English Language,* Funk and Wagnalls, New York, 1959.
26. Gelernter, H., Hansen, J. R., and Loveland, D. W., "Empirical Explorations of the Geometry-Theorem Proving Machine," *Proc. WJCC,* Vol. 17, 1960.
27. Green, Jr., B. F., et al., "Baseball: An Automatic Question Answerer," *Proc. WJCC,* Vol. 19, 1961.
28. Halle, M., and Stevens, K. N., "Speech Recognition: A Model and a Program for Research," in Fodor, J. A., and Katz, J. J. (eds.), *The Structure of Language; Readings in the Philosophy of Language,* Prentice-Hall, Englewood Cliffs, N.J., 1964.
29. Hays, D. G. (ed.), *Readings in Automatic Language Processing,* Elsevier, New York, 1966.
30. Hunt, E. B., *Concept Learning: An Information Processing Problem,* John Wiley, New York, 1966.
31. Katz, J. J., and Fodor, J. A., "The Structure of a Semantic Theory," *Language,* Vol. 39, 1963.
32. Katz, J. J., and Postal, P. M., *An Integrated Theory of Linguistic Descriptions,* The M.I.T. Press, Cambridge, Mass., 1964.
33. Kelly, G., *The Psychology of Personal Constructs,* Vol. I, W. W. Norton, New York, 1955.
34. Klein, S., "Automatic Paraphrasing in Essay Format," SP-1602/001/00, System Development, Santa Monica, Calif., 1964.
35. Klein, S., and Simmons, R. F., "Syntactic Dependence and the Computer Generation of Coherent Discourse," *Mechanical Translation,* Vol. 7, 1963.
36. Kuno, S. K., "Multiple-Path Syntactic Analyzer," *Mathematical Linguistics and Automatic Translation,* Report NSF-8, Computation Laboratory, Harvard University, Cambridge, Mass., 1963.
37. Kuno, S. K., "The Predictive Analyzer," Communications of the Association for Computing Machinery, Vol. 8, 1965, reprinted reference 28.
38. Lakoff, G., "On the Nature of Syntactic Irregularity," *Mathematical Linguistics and Automatic Translation.* Report NSF-16, Computation Laboratory, Harvard University, Cambridge, Mass., 1965.
39. Lamb, S., "The Sememic Approach to Structural Semantics," Romney, K. A., and D'Andrede (eds.), Transcultural studies in cognition, *Am. Anthropologist,* Vol. 66, Part 2, 1964.
40. Lane, H., and Schneider, B., "Some Discriminative Properties of Syntactic Structures," *Verbal Learning and Verbal Behavior,* Vol. 2, 1963.
41. Lindsay, R. K., "Inferential Memory as the Basis of Machines which Understand Natural Language," Feigenbaum, E., and Feldman, J. (eds.), *Computers and Thought,* McGraw-Hill, New York, 1963.
42. Matthews, G. H., "Analysis by Synthesis of Sentences in a Natural Language," *First International Conference on Machine Translation and Applied Language Analysis,* Her Majesty's Stationery Office, London, 1962.
43. McCarthy, J., et al., *LISP 1.5 Programmer's Manual,* The M.I.T. Press, Cambridge, Mass., 1963.
44. Miller, G. A., "The Magical Number Seven, Plus or Minus Two: Some Limits on our Capacity for Processing Information," *Psych. Rev.,* Vol. 63, 1956.
45. Miller, G. A., and Chomsky, N., "Finite Models of Language Users," in Luce, R. D., Bush, R. L., and Glanter, E. (eds.), *Handbook of Mathematical Psychology,* Vol. II, John Wiley, New York, 1963.

46. Miller, G. A., Galenter, E., and Pribam, K. H., *Plans and the Structure of Behavior,* Holt, New York, 1960.
47. Minsky, M., "Steps Toward Artificial Intelligence," *Proc. IRE,* Vol. 49, No. 1, 1961, also in reference 22.
48. Minsky, M., "A Selected Descriptor-Indexed Bibliography to the Literature on Artificial Intelligence," in reference 22.
49. Newell, A. (ed.), "IPL-V Programmer's Reference Manual," Memorandum RM-3739-RC, RAND Corp., Santa Monica, Calif., 1963.
50. Newell, A., Shaw, J. C., and Simon, H. A., "The Processes of Creative Thinking," in H. E. Gruber, Terrell, G., and Wertheimer, M. (eds.), *Contemporary Approaches to Creative Thinking,* Atherton Press, New York, 1962.
51. Newell, A., Shaw, J. C., and Simon, H. A., "Chess Playing Programs and the Problem of Complexity," *IBM J. Research and Development,* Vol. 2, 1958.
52. Newell, A., and Simon, H. A., "Computers in Psychology," in Luce, R. D., Bush, R., and Galanter, E. (eds.), *Handbook of Mathematical Psychology,* Vol. 1, John Wiley, New York, 1963.
53. Newell, A., and Simon, H. A., "An Example of Human Chess Play in the Light of Chess Playing Programs," Carnegie Inst. Tech., Pittsburgh, Pa., 1964 (dittoed).
54. Ogden, C. K., *The General Basic English Dictionary,* W. W. Norton, New York, 1942.
55. Olney, J., "Building a Concept Network for Retrieving Information from Large Libraries: Part I." TM-634/001/11, System Development Corp., Santa Monica, Calif., 1962.
56. Olney, J. C., "Some Patterns Observed in the Contextual Specialization of Word Senses," *Information Storage and Retrieval,* Vol. 2, 1964.
57. Osgood, E. C., Suci, G. J., and Tannenbaum, P. H., *The Measurement of Meaning,* University of Illinois Press, Urbana, Ill., 1957.
58. Osgood, C. E., "On Understanding and Creating Sentences," *Am. Psychologist,* Vol. 18, 1965.
59. Paige, J. J., and Simon, H. A., "Cognitive Processes in Solving Algebra Word Problems," in Kleinmuntz, B. (ed.), *Problem Solving: Research, Method and Theory,* John Wiley, New York, 1966.
60. Petrick, S. R., "A Recognition Procedure for Transformational Grammars," unpublished Ph.D. thesis, M.I.T., 1965.
61. Piaget, J., *The Psychology of Intelligence,* translated by M. Cook and D. E. Berlyne, Routledge and Kegan Paul, London, England, 1950.
62. Quillian, R., "A Design for an Understanding Machine," paper presented at a colloquium: *Semantic Problems in Natural Language,* King's College, Cambridge, England, September 1961.
63. Quillian, R., "A Revised Design for an Understanding Machine," *Mechanical Translation,* Vol. 7, 1967.
64. Quillian, R., "A Semantic Coding Technique for Mechanical English Paraphrasing," Internal memorandum of the Mechanical Translation Group, Research Laboratory of Electronics, M.I.T., Cambridge, Mass., August 1962.
65. Quillian, R., "A Notation for Representing Conceptual Information: An Application to Semantics and Mechanical English Paraphrasing," SP-1395, System Development Corp., Santa Monica, Calif., 1963.
66. Quillian, R., Wortman, P., and Baylor, G. W., "The Programmable Piaget: Behavior from the Standpoint of a Radical Computerist." Unpublished dittoed Paper, Carnegie Inst. Tech., Pittsburgh, Pa., 1965.

67. Raphael, B., "A Computer Program Which 'Understands,'" *Proc. AFIPS,* 1964, *FJCC* (see also Chapter 2 of the present volume).
68. Razran, G. H. S., "A Quantitative Study of Meaning by a Conditioned Salivary Technique (Semantic Conditioning)," *Science,* Vol. 90, 1939.
69. Reich, P. A., "A Stratificational Theory of Language Acquisition," Working Paper No. 4 (IP-4), Dept. of Psychology and Mental Health Research Institute, University of Michigan, Ann Arbor, Mich., 1966.
70. Reid, L. S., Henneman, R. H., and Long, E. R., "An Experimental Analysis of Set: The Effect of Categorical Restriction," *Am. J. Psych.,* Vol. 73, 1960.
71. Reiss, R. F., "An Abstract Machine Based on Classical Association Psychology," Technical memorandum, Librascope Division, General Precision, Inc., Glendale, Calif., 1961.
72. Reitman, W. R., *Cognition and Thought: An Information Processing Approach,* John Wiley, New York, 1965.
73. Rubenstein, H., "Problems in Automatic Word Disambiguation," paper presented at a conference on Computer-Aided Semantic Research, Las Vegas, Nev., December 1965.
74. Simmons, R. F., "Synthetic Language Behavior," *Data Processing Management,* Vol. 5, 1963.
75. Simon, H. A., and Feigenbaum, E. A., "An Information-Processing Theory of Some Effects of Similarity, Familiarization, and Meaningfulness in Verbal Learning," *J. Verbal Learning and Verbal Behavior,* Vol. 3, 1964.
76. Simon, H. A., and Kotovsky, J., "Human Acquisition of Concepts for Sequential Patterns," *Psych. Rev.,* Vol. 70, 1963.
77. Skinner, B. F., *Verbal Behavior,* Appleton Century Crofts, New York, 1957.
78. Yngve, V. H., "A Model and an Hypothesis for Language Structure," *Proc. of the American Philosophical Society,* Vol. 104, No. 5, 1960.
79. Yngve, V. H., *COMIT Programmers' Reference Manual,* The M.I.T. Press, Cambridge, Mass., 1961.

5. A Program for the Solution of a Class of Geometric-Analogy Intelligence-Test Questions

Thomas G. Evans

5.1 Introduction

5.1.1 The Problem Area

We shall be considering the solution by machine of so-called "geometric-analogy" intelligence-test questions. Each member of this class of problems consists of a set of labeled line drawings. The task to be performed can be described by the question: "Figure A is to Figure B as Figure C is to which of the following figures?" For example:

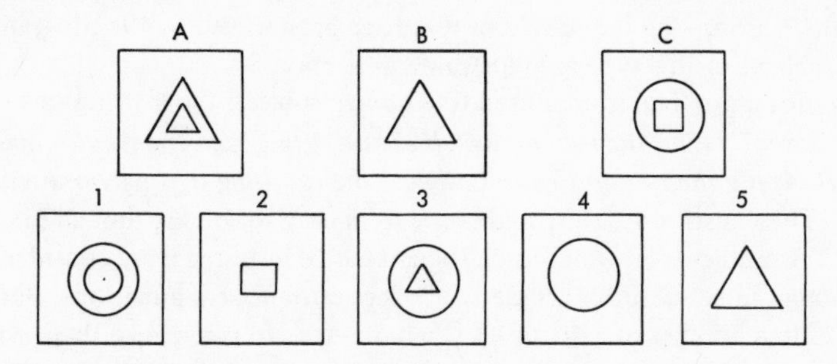

It seems safe to say that most people would agree with the program we are about to describe, in choosing Figure 4 as the desired answer.

The mechanical solution of such questions presents an interesting problem for the worker in Artificial Intelligence. Some of the reasons for the attractiveness of this particular problem domain are given here. The discussion of several of these features is pursued in greater detail in Part 5.1.4.

5.1.2 Problem Requirements

Problems of this kind require elaborate processing of complex line drawings, an interesting problem per se, and one which can reasonably be expected to be of great practical importance in the near future.

The nature of the problem requires us to find a transformation that takes Figure A into Figure B and (when altered as necessary) transforms Figure C into one of the answer figures. Given the availability of a language like LISP, this situation provides a natural opportunity for trying out certain ideas on the use of flexible internal "descriptions" in a problem-solving program.

Problems of this type are widely regarded as requiring a high degree of intelligence for their solution and in fact are used as a touchstone of intelligence in some general intelligence tests used for college admission and other purposes. This suggests a nontrivial aspect of any attempt to mechanize their solution.

For these reasons as well as others this problem area was chosen and the program developed.

5.1.3 Description of Problem Type

To fix ideas, a more precise description of the problem type will be given first. The problems to be considered can be described as follows: Given a set of eight separate line drawings; each drawing need not be connected and may contain dots as well as lines; only one "thickness" or "shading" of line is allowed. The precise specification of what is permitted in these drawings will be given in Section 5.3. For later reference, these eight drawings will be designated by A, B, C, 1, 2, 3, 4, and 5, as in the examples of Figs. 5-1 to 5-4, all of which are among the problems that have been solved by the program. More problems of this type are illustrated in Section 5.5.

When such a problem is presented to a human subject, the instructions might be as follows:* "*Find the rule by which Figure A has been changed to make Figure B. Apply the rule to Figure C. Select the resulting figure from Figures 1 to 5.*" These instructions, by and large, seem easy to follow, though many of the very problems on which the program has been tested were considered hard enough to be usefully included in college-entrance examinations. But they lead to a number of difficulties when one tries to mechanize their execution. Two of these difficulties, together with an indication of the attitudes taken toward them in the design of the program, are:

First, one must develop a suitable way of presenting the figures to the machine. A great deal of work has been done on methods for converting a picture to a representation that can be handled by a computer. Some of this work is referenced in Part 5.1.4. Since our basic concern is with the later

*From examinations of the American Council on Education.

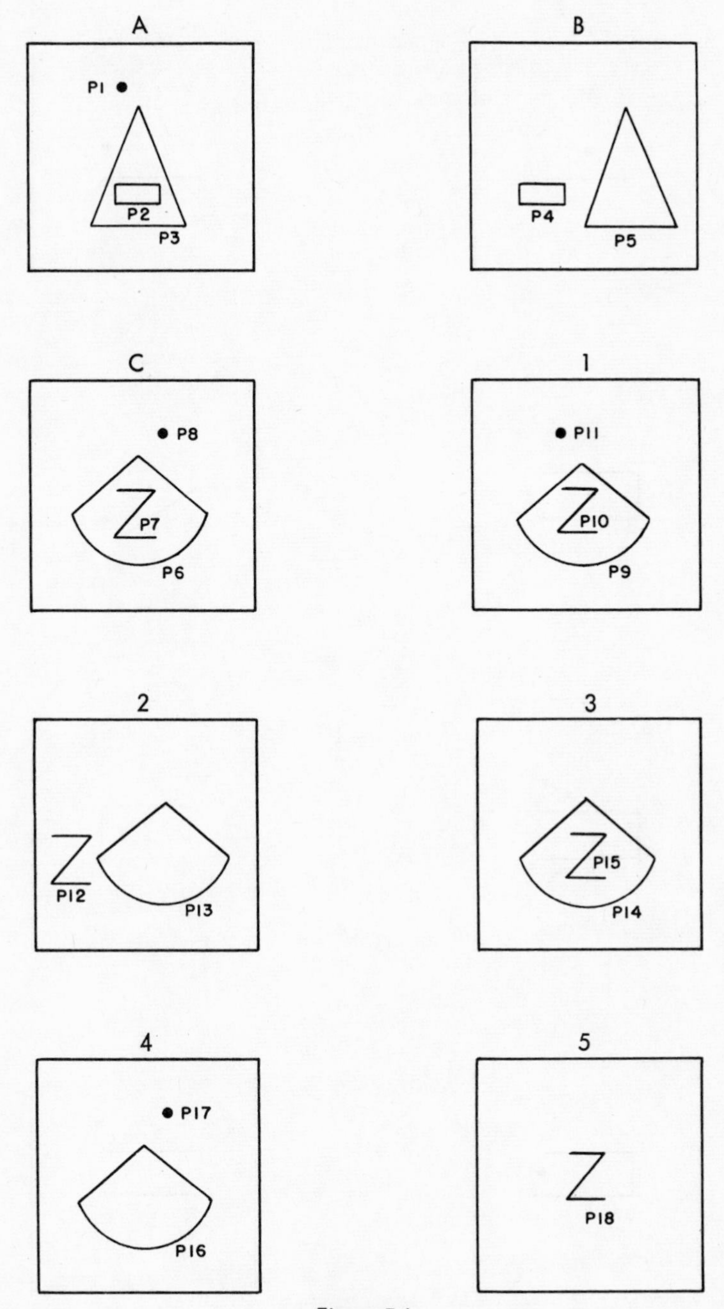
A
P1
P2
P3
B
P4
P5
C
P8
P7
P6
1
P11
P10
P9
2
P12
P13
3
P15
P14
4
P17
P16
5
P18

Figure 5-1.

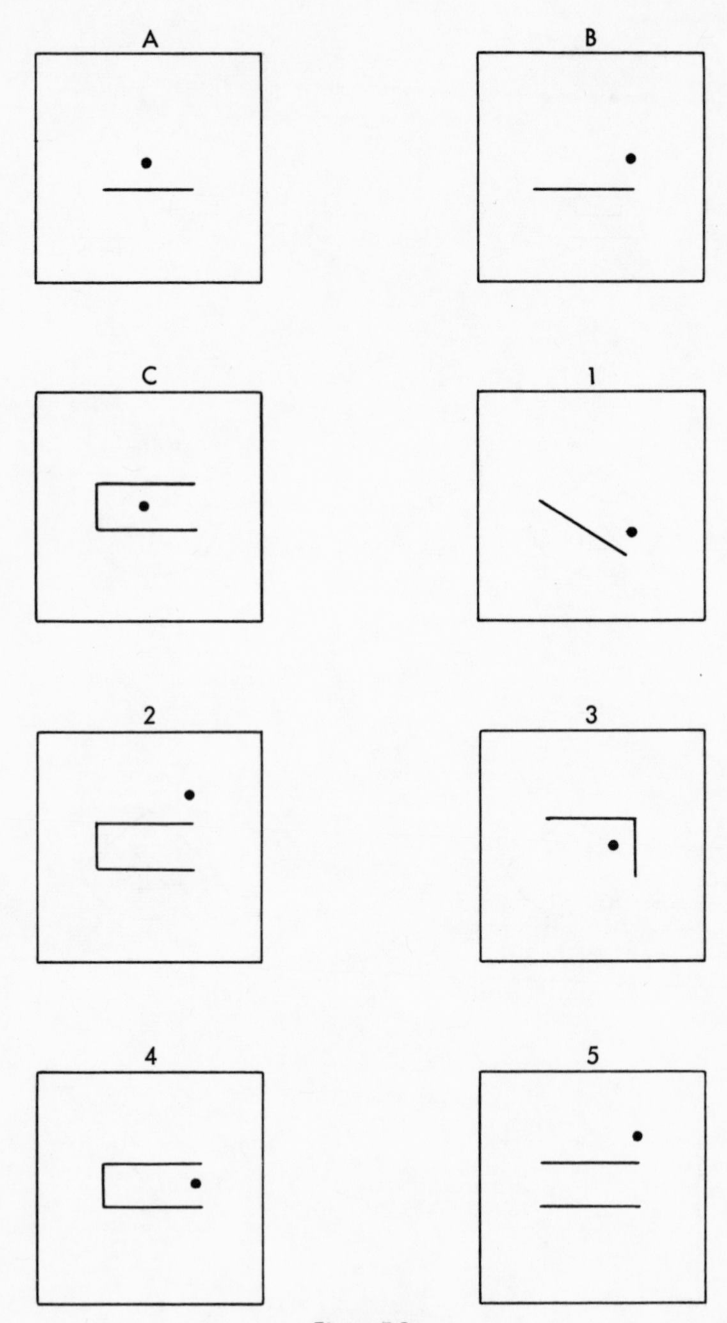

Figure 5-2.

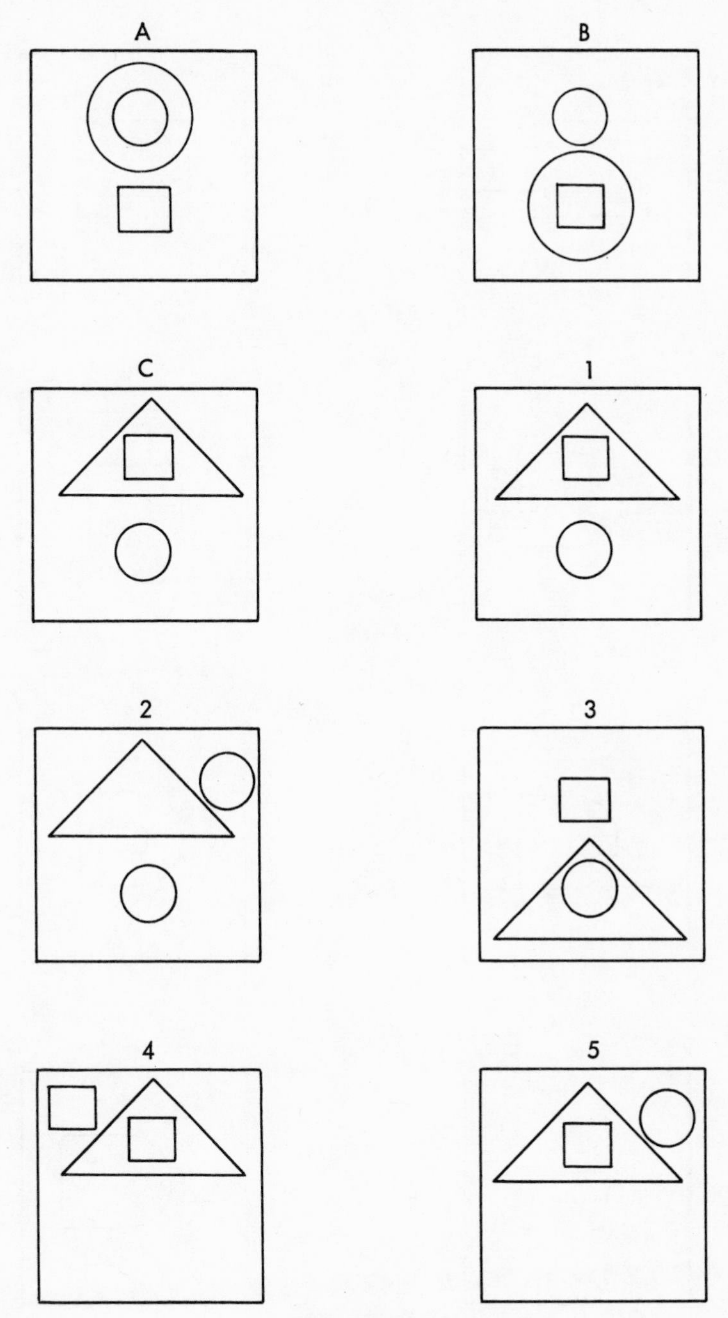

Figure 5-3.

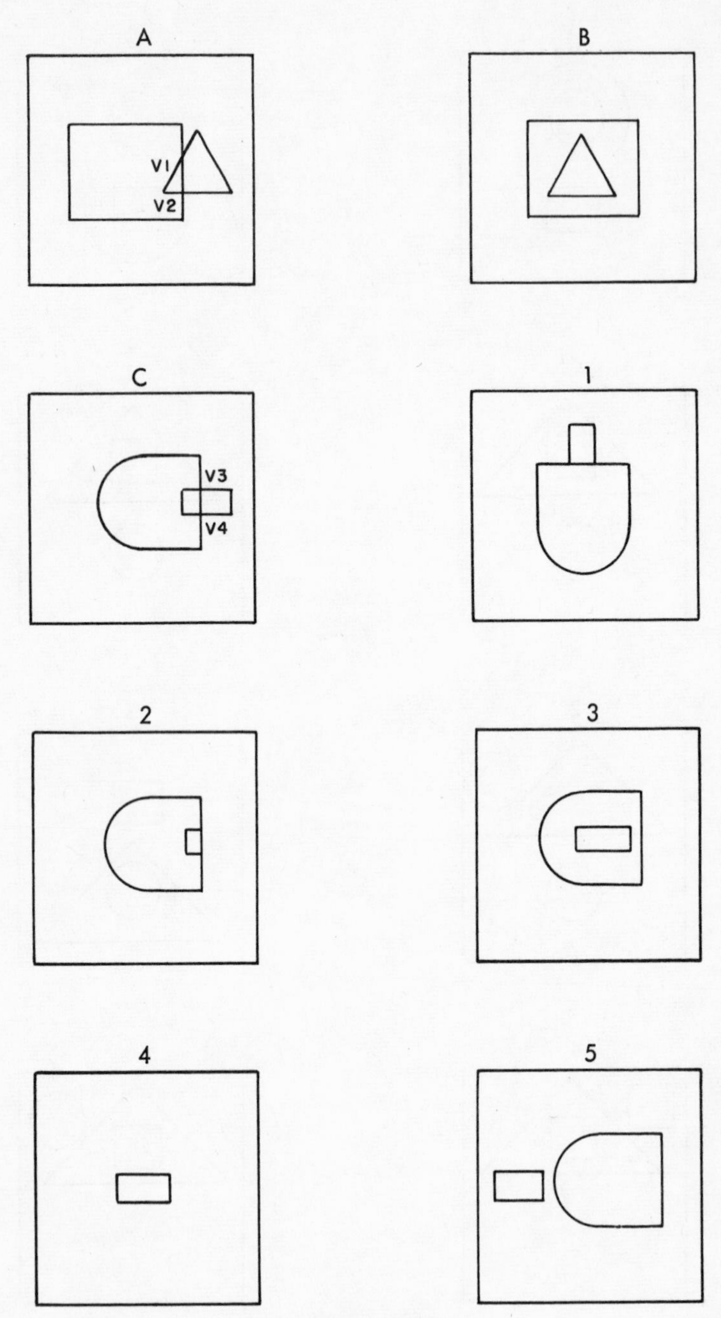

Figure 5-4.

processing, such problems have been bypassed, for the present; we start off with a representation of the figures in list-structure form, read in from punched cards. This representation is a quite primitive form of description that could be obtained *via* any of the input hardware and line tracing techniques already described in the literature. (Some further comments on this problem are contained in Section 5.5.) The representation chosen permits the description of an arbitrary line drawing to any degree of accuracy: A line is represented by a sequence of as many straight-line segments and arcs of circles as desired. The details of this list-structure representation are given in Section 5.3. This representation permits quite economical descriptions of typical problem figures and lends itself well to the necessary programmed manipulations. The nature of these manipulations on the figures is indicated in Part 5.2.1 and will be described in fuller detail in Section 5.3.

Next, one must decide what is meant by "rule"; that is, what class of transformations on the figures is to be admitted. Several considerations might govern this choice:

a. One could admit only a formally-defined class of rules R that, together with some formal representation of the problem figures, would permit him to obtain "theorems" about the resulting system. It might be shown, for example, that for a given problem there is a unique rule T in R such that T(A) = B and T(C) = exactly one of the Figures 1 to 5; or

b. He could attempt to achieve a very high level of performance by gathering a set of essentially *ad hoc* tricks, well adapted for success on a few particular problem types of interest and restricting the inputs to these types.

However, since our object is neither the formal study nor the maximally efficient solution of geometric-analogy problems per se but the use of these problems as a vehicle for the study of the use of descriptive-language methods in problem-solving, our approach is rather different. Though rejecting the alternative of a formal study, we *do* have formally defined rules that can be manipulated formally to obtain new ones; though rejecting that of maximal efficiency, we *do* employ techniques special to geometric problems and, in fact, to restricted classes of them (for example, line drawings in the plane). However, great pains have been taken to avoid *ad hoc* solutions that do not contribute to the main goals of the study.

ANALOGY, a program embodying a set of definite design solutions reflecting the foregoing considerations and influenced by other considerations discussed at length in Part 5.1.4, has been developed and tested on many cases.

The process which ANALOGY carries out on the inputs representing the eight line drawings that constitute a problem is, very briefly, as follows:

In Part 1 of ANALOGY (Section 5.3) the input figures are decomposed into subfigures and various properties of and relations between these subfigures are computed. Then this information (a new description of the input figures at a "higher level") is made available to a program (Part 2, Section 5.4) that uses it to attempt to construct a rule which transforms Figure A into Figure B and Figure C into exactly one of the five answer figures. Furthermore, Part 2 attempts to construct the "best" such rule (in a sense to be defined) among the class of permitted rules.

Section 5.2 contains a longer sketch of the procedure, with several examples; Sections 5.3 and 5.4 describe in further detail the workings of the two main parts of the program; and Section 5.5 discusses the results obtained from the application of the program to a variety of test cases. Section 5.6 has some conclusions and remarks on possible extensions to the work described here.

5.1.4 Background and Goals

These paragraphs discuss some relevant background, connections to previous work, and a more detailed consideration of factors that have shaped the present form of the program. The discussion of other work falls fairly naturally into two parts: one concerned with the problems of handling geometric entities by computer; the other concerned with methods of heuristic problem-solving. These topics will be treated in that order. For a standard survey of both these areas, particularly the latter and the specifically pattern-recognition aspects of the former, and for a comprehensive bibliography in both areas, see references 20 and 21.

Picture Processing by Computer. As computers interact more and more extensively with human activities, it becomes important to have flexible methods for computer processing of geometric material available. For example, techniques for character recognition, for certain restricted forms of input, have become feasible using special-purpose hardware, but the problem of processing unrestricted handwriting is still far from solved. Also, there is a need for facilities for processing graphical or pictorial materials of any kind, such as maps, photographs, or engineering drawings. Recently, emphasis has been put on the desirability of making graphical input and output facilities available to a user in real-time interaction with a large time-shared computer system.

The problems involved in making such facilities available in a general-purpose computer system divide fairly naturally (though with far-from-negligible cross influences) into input-output problems and problems of internal representation and processing. The former are essentially those of engineering, and one can expect such facilities to be available soon. The work reported in this thesis is concerned exclusively with the latter except where (in Section 5.5) we consider briefly the problem of converting a picture outside the computer to exactly the form now accepted as input by the ANALOGY program.

Regardless of what devices are used to put pictorial information into the computer and get it out again, we must meet the questions of what form the internal representation is to take and how it is to be processed. This area is far less developed than the input-output hardware situation, in which a wide variety of techniques are currently available, each appropriate to certain classes of problems. The problems of internal representation and processing of geometrical material have not given rise to such a variety of alternate techniques from which a user can select according to his needs.

Typically, the data on which the processing programs have operated (including virtually all reported work in the area of visual pattern recognition) have been those obtained directly from the input medium, usually either a bit matrix corresponding to input from a photocell matrix or a non-computer-controlled scanner, or a table of coordinates corresponding to the path of a scanning device under control of a line-following program of some sort. For a discussion of an input scheme of this nature with which the present author has been associated, see reference 16. The reader's attention is called to an interesting discussion of schemes for encoding arbitrary continuous plane curves into representations suitable for computers (8). Among pattern-recognition programs perhaps only that of Grimsdale et al. (10, 11) could be viewed as generating from such input something that could reasonably be regarded as a higher-level description of the input figure. A pattern-recognition program of Sherman (34) also involves some elements of description. A good example of a pattern-recognition program based on a so-called "property-list" scheme, rather than on description, is that of Doyle (5).

The general tendency of workers in the visual pattern-recognition area to get along without explicit higher-level descriptions can be attributed, in large part, to two factors: the nature of the specific pattern-recognition problems being treated, and the lack of appropriate languages in which to express such descriptions. To elaborate slightly: At least one great merit of description processing is that it permits convenient treatment of complex pictorial material that can best be treated as comprising one or more levels of interrelated parts (as are the figures occurring in the geometric-analogy questions). Typically in pattern-recognition work to date, the objects of interest have not been such as to force this approach on the investigators. Furthermore, description-making and use require an unpredictable amount of storage for the descriptions and the ability to specify conveniently rather complex processes on these descriptions. Languages of the list type recently developed (for example, LISP, IPL-V) furnish quite convenient answers to both of these problems.

Only recently have there been attempts at processing of pictorial material using description techniques. To the best of our knowledge, no work of this type has yet been reported in the published literature. Noteworthy in particular are programs of Hodes (6), Canaday (3) (which should also be mentioned as a heuristic problem-solving program),* Sutherland (37, 38), Roberts (30), and

*In its use of LISP and of heuristic methods applied to geometric subject matter, this work is closer in approach to that reported here than anything else in the literature.

Kirsch (13). Hodes used LISP to process line drawings expressed in a form rather like the input to the present program. Canaday uses description methods (again in LISP) to separate certain types of overlapping figures into component parts. Sutherland's work is concerned with a scheme for on-line picture drawing using a light-pen. The internal representation of line drawings in his program is similar to what we have been calling a "description." Roberts is concerned with the representation and display of three-dimensional scenes. He employs internal representation techniques similar to those of Sutherland. Kirsch is primarily concerned with complex line drawings as subject matter for programs involving the analysis of English-language descriptions of such figures. In Section 5.3, where the input to our Part 1 is fully described, a further comparison to the forms used by Hodes and Canaday is given.

Apparently the first advocacy of the use of description techniques for picture processing occurs in Minsky (20). These ideas seem to have had a strong influence on all the work cited as well as on the present study. Later we shall discuss in some detail the description concept and its application to geometrical and other subject matter, but we first try to provide some background on the development of problem-solving programs.

Heuristic Problem-Solving Programs. The development of large heuristic problem-solving programs (and concurrently, the development of suitable languages in which to write them) begins with LT, the program of Newell, Simon, and Shaw (24, 25), for proving theorems of the propositional calculus. It is carried further in their GPS (General Problem Solver) (26, 27), where an attempt has been made to separate the organization of the program from the specific subject matter. Other significant heuristic programs are the plane-geometry theorem-proving program of Gelernter and Rochester (9) and the formal integration program of Slagle (35). Further important heuristic programs include various game-playing programs, such as the checker-playing program of Samuel (31). Finally we mention a heuristic program of Knowlton(14) for performing syntactic analyses on English sentences. Newell (28) provides the following capsule survey of such problem-solving programs (including all the preceding examples):

> These programs are all rather similar in nature. For each the task is difficult enough to allow us to assert that the programs problem-solve, rather than simply carry out the steps of a procedure for a solution invented by the programmer. They all operate on formalized tasks, which, although difficult, are not unstructured. All the programs use the same conceptual approach: they interpret the problem as combinatorial, involving the discovery of the right sequence of operations out of a set of possible sequences. All of the programs generate some sort of tree of possibilities to gradually explore the possible sequences. The set of all sequences is much too large to generate and examine *in toto,* so that various devices, called heuristics, are employed to narrow the range of possibilities to a set that can be handled within the available limits of processing effort.

The geometric-analogy program also fits this description. Stated very briefly, given a problem of this type, the program uses various heuristics to select a "correct" rule (in a reasonable time) from a very extensive class of possible rules.

We are about to discuss programs of this type from a somewhat different point of view: that of the internal representation of the problem to be solved and of the various intermediate stages in its solution. The emphasis we place on this aspect of the design of problem-solving processes corresponds to the emphasis given to it in the design of the geometric-analogy program, our feeling that it is in the types of internal representation employed that the geometric-analogy program differs most interestingly from a number of other heuristic programs, and our opinion that advances in this area in the near future are likely to be crucial to the development of problem-solving programs with capabilities far in advance of present-day ones.

Before turning to a discussion of the relatively modest exploitation and exploration of these description ideas in the geometric-analogy program, we shall attempt to characterize the idea and discuss its implications for future programs. The central contention is that powerful problem-solving programs must have "good" internal representations of the problems they deal with and of the methods available for attacking such problems. In particular, this seems to be a requirement for programs having very much more sophisticated learning capabilities than those of present-generation learning programs, in that the automatic alteration of behavior we call machine learning corresponds to the modification of this internal representation. To illustrate this point: The most sophisticated (and most successful) of present-day programs incorporating learning is probably the checker-playing program of Samuel (31). The "experience" of the machine is incorporated in its play through alteration in the weighting coefficients of the terms in the polynomial used to evaluate a given board position (the terms in this polynomial are values of functions of the position designed to reflect such notions as material advantage, advancement, center control, etc.). Thus, in our terms, the part of the internal representation of the machine's strategy of play accessible to the learning mechanism is quite restricted, consisting of a small set of numbers. Thus, there is for example no possibility of the learning program ever discovering for itself brand-new properties of a position analogous to advancement or center control, or even of significantly altering the ones that it has built into it. This is by no means a limitation unique to Samuel's checker program; it was mentioned only as an outstanding example among currently operating learning programs, all of which have intrinsic limitations of this sort. It seems reasonable to argue that the basic difficulty here is that these properties are not expressed in an appropriate "checker language" which could perhaps be manipulated by a learning program to produce, say, generalizations or properties "similar" (in a meaningful sense reflected by syntactic similarities) to ones which have been successful in the past. Such notions are not new. They appear for example in Minsky (22), in Selfridge (33), who discussed these ideas in terms of such a "linguistic" approach to chess, and in McCarthy (17), who proposes a machine (the Advice-Taker) with a corpus of knowledge in an appropriate language and facilities for making various kinds of inferences from statements of the corpus. A further important aspect of such "linguistic" internal representations deserves to be mentioned: They may be even more useful in situations involving close man-machine interaction than in autonomous machine problem-solving, since such representations should be in general more appropriate for human comprehension than are other forms of representation of the internal state of the machine.

A large amount of effort, associated primarily with the names of Hovland and Hunt (7) and Kochen (15), has been devoted to so-called "concept formation" by machine. The subject matter of these investigations has been chiefly the attainment of "concepts" by a program in a series of trials or guesses, where "concept" has meant in essence a Boolean function of moderate complexity. The paucity in structure of the "concepts" considered is somewhat compensated for by their clarity. An extensive treatment of human performance on such tasks is found in Bruner (2).

However, up to now, though the desirability of work in the area of descriptions seems clear, little has been done toward exploiting these ideas in problem-solving programs (particularly outside of areas where a rather "linguistic" representation was imposed by the very problem itself). The work of Solomonoff (36) on inductive inference should also be mentioned here as providing a suggestive theoretical framework for future developments in machine learning based on internal use of descriptive languages.

We shall now examine the uses of these ideas in ANALOGY and sketch how their use here can be viewed as a paradigm of an approach to more general situations. Three distinct kinds of expressions that can reasonably be called descriptions occur in the geometric-analogy program. The first two are descriptions of line drawings at two levels of abstraction. Expressions of the third type constitute descriptions of rules (from a fairly extensive class) by which one line drawing can be transformed into another. These three types of descriptions form the entire subject matter of the geometric-analogy programs. More precisely, descriptions of the first type are the inputs to Part 1 and provide the necessary information for Part 1 to generate its outputs, which are descriptions of the second type. These expressions, which are descriptions of the same figures at a level of abstraction suitable for the computations required later, are then given to Part 2 as input. Using this information, Part 2 generates rule candidates (described by expressions of the third type), tests them, alters them as necessary, and then selects a "simplest" rule (thus choosing an "answer figure"). The scope and structure of these description types are described in full detail in Sections 5.3 and 5.4. We feel that the current program represents a constructive step in the direction of more powerful description methods and in particular a convincing demonstration of the utility of such methods on one nontrivial class of problems.

To place ANALOGY as a paradigm for future developments in machine learning we describe it in general terms, as follows:

The program, given certain complex data (Figures A and B) forms a "theory" or set of rival "theories" (transformation rules taking Figure A into Figure B) with respect to the given data.

It then attempts to "generalize" these "theories" to cover additional data (Figure C and the answer figures). This results, typically, in a number of "admissible theories" (transformation rules taking Figure A into Figure B and Figure C into exactly one answer figure).

Finally, the program chooses the "strongest theory" from these "admissible theories" (the transformation rule that, in a sense to be defined later, "says the most").

One can also describe the rule-finding performed by ANALOGY as a process of "concept-formation," placing it in the line of development of the work of Kochen and of Hovland and Hunt, though the geometric-analogy program is required to deal with far more complex concepts. A third, and perhaps the most fruitful, interpretation of the significance of ANALOGY for further work with problem-solving programs will be considered at length in Section 5.6, where concrete proposals are made for future work based on ideas arising from our work with ANALOGY.

5.1.5 Descriptive References

T. M. Marill (16). This report describes a pattern-recognition system (Cyclops-1) with light-pen input to the display scope of a PDP-1 computer. One can sketch in an arbitrary line drawing (erasing, as desired), upon which the program performs line-tracing operations. These segment the figure into a form (amounting to a partial description) convenient for the recognition program. The most novel feature of Cyclops is the ease with which sections of the recognition program may be written and altered. It uses a set of what are essentially macro-instructions.

H. Freeman (8). Here we find a discussion of some clever schemes for the computer representation of plane curves that are quite different from those we have used in ANALOGY. Freeman's schemes emphasize, as ours does not, efficient coding in an information-theoretic sense and permit a limited class of manipulations on the representations to be performed very efficiently. However, this compactness and efficiency could be obtained only at the cost of many of the advantages gained by performing our manipulations in LISP.

R. L. Grimsdale et al. (10). The work reported represents the closest approach in published pattern-recognition studies to a pure description scheme. After a TV-type scan produces an internal representation of a pattern as a bit matrix, line-tracing techniques produce a segmentation of the pattern into parts. From this is generated what Grimsdale calls a one-dimensional encoding of the pattern. The recognition process consists of matching this encoding versus corresponding "template" encodings of various patterns. Thus, what is essentially a description is produced and a fairly complex matching process between two such descriptions is carried out.

H. Sherman (34). His pattern-recognition program is the first to use topological classification as part of the recognition process. The input mechanism is a 32 times 32 photocell matrix. A line-tracing program generates a connectivity matrix for the line-drawing, after some preliminary line-thinning is carried out. The recognition is made by a decision tree employing a mixture of topological characteristics and metric characteristics in an *ad hoc* but empirically effective fashion. No attempt is made to construct a complete topological equivalence algorithm.

W. Doyle (5). This work is perhaps the most successful example of a pattern-recognition program based on a "property-list" scheme (cf. reference 20, pp. 12 ff.). A large number of rather sophisticated properties of the given pattern are computed. Then the program chooses the possible answer that is "closest," in a simple sense, to the input pattern with respect to the outcomes of the set of property tests. Furthermore, this scheme is amenable to a simple learning procedure: the property test results corresponding to each recognition category are obtained by averaging the results for each test obtained on a set of labeled examples.

L. Hodes (6). This brief report discusses two developments in the machine processing of line drawings: (a) A program (written largely in FORTRAN) to go from a figure in bit matrix form to its description in a LISP format. For comparison with ours, we describe this format in some detail in Section 5.3. This process involves a quite complex line-tracing mechanism. (b) A set of programs (written in LISP) capable of finding all triangles in a line drawing presented in this LISP format.

R. Canaday (3). The work here involved the construction of a heuristic program (in LISP) to solve "overlap" problems. Given a number of polygons (straight sides, no holes), piled up in some fashion, with overlap, we consider the line drawing corresponding to the top view of this pile. The problem is to discover how the pile is formed of overlapping objects. Because the program is given only this top view, not the component pieces, the process must involve removing a level at a time, guessing completions of figures initially partially hidden by overlap from a higher level in the pile. The figure-manipulation techniques used in this process are quite similar to those used in ANALOGY, particularly in our decomposition program.

I. Sutherland (37, 38). Here we have an elaborate system (called *Sketchpad*) for drawing pictures on-line with a light-pen. One can draw a figure and impose certain constraints on it, such as requiring two lines to be parallel. A relaxation procedure is employed to satisfy simultaneously all constraints that have been imposed. To facilitate such manipulation on the figures, *Sketchpad* represents them in a form somewhat similar to the list structures that correspond internally to our description expressions in LISP. In particular, they are stored in a stratified fashion with the connectivity information "on top," as is the case in our descriptions. However, this program is not written in a list-processing language.

L. Roberts (30). This program is capable of analyzing three-dimensional scenes that consist of simple objects. Given a photograph of such a scene, the program reduces it to a line drawing, then finds the separate objects in it. As a result of this analysis it is capable of showing the scene from other perspectives. For convenience in manipulation, the internal representation of the scene is again in a form somewhat similar to our list structures. This program, like *Sketchpad,* is written for the TX-2 computer at MIT Lincoln Laboratory.

R. Kirsch (13). This is a program for matching pictures that are quite similar to the drawings in our geometric-analogy problems with English-language sentences describing them, for example, "The small black triangle which is below a small white triangle is to the right of a large white circle in the picture." The system consists of several parts. The pictures are entered into the computer *via* a scanner and given to a picture-analysis program. The sentences are parsed by a syntactical analysis program. Its output is then converted to a form in which it can be compared with the information about the picture produced by the picture-analysis routine to determine whether a given sentence is a correct description of a given picture. The emphasis has been placed on the syntactic analysis portion of the system; the picture-analysis program is apparently rather simple.

A. Newell, H. A. Simon, and J. C. Shaw (24, 25). The program LT, reported in these papers, was the earliest major contribution to the field of heuristic programming and has strongly affected subsequent work by influencing both the design of problem-solving programs and stimulating the development of suitable languages for the construction of such programs. LT (the Logic Theory Machine) was designed to be capable of proving theorems within the Russell and Whitehead version of the propositional calculus. It used various heuristic methods centered around the notion of finding a proof by working backward.

A. Newell, H. A. Simon, and J. C. Shaw (26, 27). These references discuss GPS (The General Problem Solver), which represents a further development by the designers of LT. Probably the most important feature of GPS is the attempt, in its design, to introduce problem-solving methods independent of any particular subject matter. In the course of attempting to solve a problem, GPS sets up an elaborate hierarchy of goals and subgoals, applying itself recursively, in the course of trying to attain a particular goal, to subgoals of that goal. GPS has been used as a problem solver in a number of different areas.

H. Gelernter and N. Rochester (9). This paper discusses an elaborate program for proving theorems in plane geometry. In addition to machinery common to other theorem-proving programs, the program makes use of the semantic model underlying the formal system of plane geometry. Suppose at some stage the program has generated, as a prospective subgoal, some statement of plane geometry, perhaps because, in the proof context at that point, the addition of this statement would suffice to prove the theorem being worked on. If the new statement happens to be false, it is desirable to avoid setting it up as a subgoal and trying to prove it. What the program does, as a human being might, is to construct one or more typical diagrams appropriate to the statement and test its truth on these. If it succeeds, the machine sets it up as a subgoal; if not, it can be rejected. Thus, the search tree involved in finding a proof can be drastically pruned.

J. Slagle (35). This is a heuristic program, written in LISP, capable of performing very well on formal integration problems at the first-year calculus level. The program like GPS, has, a recursive subgoal structure particularly appropriate to the nested character of the algebraic expressions which it must manipulate.

A. L. Samuel (31). This paper describes what is almost certainly the most successful program, relative to human performance, yet developed for playing a widely known nontrivial game, in this case checkers. Furthermore, it is the most conspicuous example to appear of a program successfully incorporating learning. Samuel has investigated two-types of learning mechanism: (a) A form of "book learning," which "remembers" a large number of checker positions, together with their values. When one of these is encountered in the search through the move tree, it effectively amounts to doubling the depth of the search along that branch at no additional computing cost. (b) A process called "generalization learning," which involves exploiting the machine's experience, by a scheme too elaborate to explain here, to alter the coefficients of the polynomial by which the program calculates the value of a position.

K. Knowlton (14). This is a heuristic program for the syntactic analysis of English sentences. The underlying grammar is of the discontinuous-constituent context-free phase-structure type. The program incorporates a learning scheme based on the alteration of certain parameters, each of which corresponds to the observed probability that an occurrence of a certain configuration is in a correct parsing. These are the parameters in terms of which the parsing strategy of the program is stated and their alteration by experience affects the success of the program.

A. Newell (28). This paper, by one of the developers of LT and GPS, is devoted not to the discussion of a particular program but to an instructive discussion of some of the organizational problems encountered in the development of any complex problem-solving program. Examples of organizational problems and solutions, successful and otherwise, from LT and from several versions of GPS are given.

M. L. Minsky (22). This brief paper presents a variety of arguments in support of the position that the development of powerful problem-solving programs can best be accomplished through the use of descriptive languages. In addition, it considers some of the design problems raised by the introduction of descriptive language techniques.

O. Selfridge (33). This paper presents arguments developed for the use of "rich" descriptive languages in complex problem-solving programs. The discussion is oriented toward the use of description techniques in self-organizing systems. Chess is used as an example.

J. McCarthy (17). This paper describes a proposed program called the Advice-Taker, capable of accepting a large body of declarative statements in a relatively rich language and using it, together with some facilities for making logical deductions, to solve problems. This process requires an elaborate heuristic program to control the selection of appropriate statements and to control the application of deductive routines to them.

C. I. Hovland and E. B. Hunt (7). This work is concerned with the development of a heuristic program for solving problems in "concept formation." The emphasis throughout, in the spirit of much of the work of Newell and Simon, is on computer simulation of observed human behavior on such problems rather than an attempt to devise optimal strategies.

M.Kochen (15). A program to solve "concept-formation" problems is here developed. In contrast to the work of Hovland and Hunt, its object is the establishment of highly efficient hypothesis-revision procedures for the solution of such problems, with no particular concern for modeling human behavior.

J. S. Bruner et al. (2). This reference has nothing whatever to do with heuristic programming per se. However, it is an extensive source book of experimental results and discussion related to human performance on certain so-called "concept-attainment" tasks and as such is of interest in relation to work concerned with programs to perform such tasks.

R. Solomonoff (36). The work is aimed at providing a mechanizable method for inductive inference. The ideas are centered around what has been called "grammatical induction" (cf. reference 20, pp. 26-27), where a brief sketch of this approach is given).

5.2 The Complete Solution Process: Two Examples

5.2.1 Summary of the Solution Process

The intent of this section is to give a brief summary of the entire solution process, followed by several examples. First, a problem of the type already described is chosen. The corresponding primitive descriptions are written down for each of the eight figures and punched on cards. These cards are the input to Part 1 of the program; because of storage considerations the current program is segmented into two large blocks which occupy core at different times (see Sections 5.3 and 5.4).

The first step is to decompose each figure into "objects" (subfigures). The decomposition program originally written, which suffices to handle many of the examples, including example 1, to follow, was quite simple. It merely separates a figure into its connected subparts; for example, Figure A of the example illustrated as Fig. 5-1 consists of the three objects labeled P1, P2, and P3. It became desirable to have a more sophisticated decomposition program with, in particular, the capability of separating overlapped objects on appropriate cues. If Figure A is 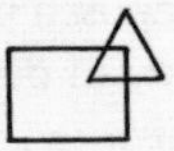 and Figure B  , the decomposition program should be able to separate the single object 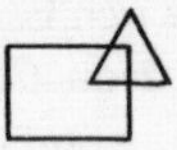 into the two objects 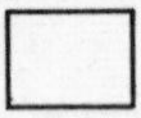 and , from which point the remaining mechanism of Parts 1 and 2 could proceed with the problem. While a decomposition program of the full generality desirable has not been constructed, the most recent version of the program is capable of finding all occurrences of an arbitrary simple closed figure x (see Part 5.3.3) in an arbitrary connected Figure y; for each such occurrence the program can, if required, separate y into two objects: that occurrence of x and the rest of y. The use of this decomposition program will be illustrated in example 2.

Next, the "objects" generated from the decomposition process are given to a routine which calculates a specified set of properties of these objects and relations among them. The program is designed so that this set can be changed easily. Furthermore, lists of these properties and relations are program parameters, specifying which of the ones currently present in the system are to be calculated on a given run. As a sample of a relation-calculating subroutine, we cite one that calculates, in Figure A of Fig. 5-1, that the object labeled P2 lies inside that labeled P3 and generates a corresponding expression (INSIDE P2 P3), to be added to the Part 1 output description of Figure A. The method used involves calculating all intersections with P3 of a line segment drawn from a point on P2 to the edge of the field (all figures are considered as drawn on a unit square). In this case, P2 lies inside P3 since the number of such intersections is odd, namely 1 (and P3 is known to be a simple closed curve). To do this, a substantial repertoire of "analytic geometry" routines is required for Part 1, to determine, for example, intersections of straight-line segments and arcs of circles in all cases and combinations.

The principal business of Part 1, aside from the property and relation calculations, is a set of "similarity" calculations. Here Part 1 determines, for each appropriate pair of objects, from a certain class T of transformations, all members of which carry one object of the pair into the other. The elements of T are compositions of Euclidean similarity transformations (rotation and uniform scale change) with horizontal and vertical reflections. (The exact specification of T is given in Section 5.3.) Given descriptions of virtually any pair of arbitrary line drawings *x* and *y*, the routines of Part 1 will calculate the parameters of all instances of transformations from T that map *x* into *y*. More precisely, an acceptable map is a member of T for which T(*x*) is congruent to *y* up to certain metric tolerances, which are parameters in the corresponding programs.

This routine is in effect a pattern-recognition program with built-in invariance under scale changes, rotations, and certain types of reflections. It consists essentially of a topological matching process, with comparisons being made between pairs of lines selected by the topological process. (Incidentally, if we suppress the metric parts we obtain a completely general topological equivalence test for networks.)

This similarity information is computed for every required pair of objects, both within a problem figure and between figures. This information, together with the property, decomposition, and other relation information, is punched out on cards in a standard format for input to Part 2. (For a typical set of figures, the total output of Part 1, punched at up to 72 columns/card, usually comes to 15 to 20 cards.)

Part 2 receives these cards as input. Its final output is either the number of the solution figure or a statement that it failed to find an answer. The selective trace-printing facility of LISP provides an easy and flexible means of getting more information about the intermediate stages of the problem-solving process. The first step generates a rule (or frequently several alternate rules) transforming Figure A into Figure B. Such a rule specifies how the objects of Figure A are removed, added to, or altered in their properties and relations to other objects to generate Figure B. Once this set of rule possibilities has been generated, the next task is to "generalize" each rule just enough so that the resulting rules still take Figure A into Figure B and now take Figure C into exactly one of the answer figures. Finally, a "best" rule is chosen from these possibilities. This process requires a complex mechanism for manipulating and testing the rules and deciding which of the several rule candidates, the results of different initial rules or of different "generalizations," is to be chosen.

The principal method embodied in Part 2 at present is able to deal quite generally with problems in which the numbers of parts added, removed, and matched in taking Figure A into Figure B are the same as the numbers of parts added, removed, and matched, respectively, in taking Figure C into the answer figure. A substantial majority of the ACE test questions are of this type; under a sufficiently "foresighted" decomposition process virtually all would be. Both examples of this section fall in this class with the use of the present decomposition machinery; this restriction still permits a wide variety of transformation rules. It should be mentioned that all the methods of Part 2 have been kept subject-matter-free; no use is made of any geometric meaning of the properties and relations appearing in the input to Part 2. The more detailed workings of both Parts 1 and 2 are best introduced through examples; the following two parts are devoted to them.

5.2.2 Discussion and Comments

In discussing the two examples to follow and in Sections 3 and 4 as well, we will frequently exhibit LISP expressions and occasionally refer to features of the LISP system. This calls for several comments:

Detailed information about the MIT LISP system is available in an expository article of McCarthy (18) and in a programmer's manual (19).

It is often possible, in LISP, to represent one structure in alternate forms by using either dot or list notation in various combinations. For example, (A.(B)) represents the same internal list-structure as does (A B). In writing the LISP expressions we have taken certain liberties throughout, for greater clarity, with the form that would be produced by the LISP print program (which produces list notation wherever possible). In every case where this has been done, the meaning of the expression in terms of list structure is unchanged by the rewriting.

One special point of possible confusion in the LISP expressions should be mentioned. Many of our expressions contain subexpressions which look like (0.3 . 0.4). The $(x \,.\, y)$ form corresponds to a dotted pair of LISP expressions x and y. In the case in question, both x and y happen to be single floating-point numbers. Hence, the first and third dots in (0.3 . 0.4) are decimal points, while the second (middle) one is a LISP dot. We most frequently use such expressions to represent the two coordinates of a point; for example, the expression above corresponds to $x = 0.3$ and $y = 0.4$. Occasionally, we use this form to contain the scale factor and angle associated with a similarity transformation.

5.2.3 Example 1: A Typical Case

We now discuss the solution of a first sample problem (shown in Fig. 5-1). To convey some feeling for the nature of the input to Part 1, we exhibit part of it, namely the input description of Figure A. It looks like:

```
(
(DOT (0.4 . 0.8))
(SCC ((0.3 . 0.2) 0.0 (0.7 . 0.2) 0.0 (0.5 . 0.7) 0.0 (0.3 . 0.2)))
(SCC ((0.4 . 0.3) 0.0 (0.6 . 0.3) 0.0 (0.6 . 0.4) 0.0 (0.4 . 0.4) 0.0 (0.4 . 0.3)))
)
```

The first line corresponds to the dot (at coordinates $x = 0.4$ and $y = 0.8$ on the unit square). The next two lines correspond to the triangle (SCC stands for simple closed curve). All connected figures are divided into three classes: dots, simple closed curves, and all the rest. This is solely for reasons of programming convenience; no other use is made of this three-way classification. Each non-connected figure is represented simply by a list of descriptions of its connected parts.

A curve (which may consist of an arbitrary sequence of elements chosen from straight-line segments and arcs of circles) is represented by a list in which coordinate pairs alternate with the curvatures of the line elements between (all curvatures are zero here since the lines in question are all straight). Similarly, the final line corresponds to the rectangle; the entire description is a list of the descriptions of these three parts. The format corresponding to the non-SCC figures like the Z of Figure C is similar though somewhat more complex; the top-level list describes the connectivity by stating which vertices are connected to which and how often; sublists describe in detail the curves making these connections. (A vertex is either an endpoint of a curve or a point at which three or more curves come together.) Again, the details are given in Section 5.3.

When this and the corresponding inputs for the other seven figures are processed, the output from Part 1 is, in its entirety, the ten LISP expressions shown below. For brevity, all similarity information concerning non-null reflections has been deleted. Also, we have replaced the meaningless symbols generated internally (by the LISP function *gensym*) for the parts found by the decomposition program by the names (P1, P2, etc.) which appear as labels on Fig. 5-1.

The ten output expressions are:

```
(1) ((P1 P2 P3) . ((INSIDE P2 P3) (ABOVE P1 P3) (ABOVE P1 P2)))
(2) ((P4 P5) . ((LEFT P4 P5)))
(3) ((P6 P7 P8) . ((INSIDE P7 P6) (ABOVE P8 P6) (ABOVE P8 P7)))
(4) ((P2 P4 (((1.0 . 0.0) . (N.N)) ((1.0 . 3.14) . (N.N)))) (P3 P5 (((1.0 . 0.0) .
      (N.N)))))
(5) ((P1 P8 (((1.0 . 0.0) . (N.N)))))
(6) NIL
(7) ( (P9 P10 P11) (P12 P13) (P14 P15) (P16 P17) (P18))
(8) ( ((INSIDE P10 P9) (ABOVE P11 P9) (ABOVE P11 P10))
      ((LEFT P12 P13)) ((INSIDE P15 P14)) ((ABOVE P17 P16)) NIL )
```

```
(9) ( ((P6 P9 (((1.0 . 0.0) . (N.N)))) (P7 P10 (((1.0 . 0.0) . (N.N))
        ((1.0 . -3.14) . (N.N)))) (P8 P11 (((1.0 . 0.0) . (N.N)))))
        ((P6 P13 (((1.0 . 0.0) . (N.N)))) (P7 P12 (((1.0 . 0.0) . (N.N))
        ((1.0 . -3.14) . (N.N)))))
        ((P6 P14 (((1.0 . 0.0) . (N.N)))) (P7 P15 (((1.0 . 0.0) . (N.N))
        ((1.0 . -3.14) . (N.N)))))
        ((P6 P16 (((1.0 . 0.0) . (N.N)))) (P8 P17 (((1.0 . 0.0) . (N.N)))))
        ((P7 P18 (((1.0 . 0.0) . (N.N)) ((1.0 . -3.14) . (N.N))))))
(10) ( ( ((P1 P11 (((1.0 . 0.0) . (N.N))))) NIL NIL
        ((P1 P17 (((1.0 . 0.0) . (N.N))))) NIL )
        . (NIL NIL NIL NIL NIL))
```

To explain some of this: The first expression corresponds to Figure A. It says that Figure A has been decomposed into three parts, which have been given the names P1, P2, and P3. Then we have a list of properties and relations and similarity information internal to Figure A, namely that P2 is inside P3, P1 is above P2, and P1 is above P3. The next two expressions give the corresponding information for Figures B and C. The fourth expression gives information about similarities between Figures A and B. For example, P3 goes into P5 under a "scale factor = 1, rotation angle = 0, and both reflections null" transformation. The next two expressions contain the corresponding information between Figures A and C and between Figures B and C, respectively. The seventh list is a five-element list of lists of the parts of the five answer figures; the eighth, a five-element list of lists, one for each answer figure, giving their property, relation, and similarity information. The ninth is again a five-element list, each a "similarity" list from Figure C to one of the answer figures. The last expression is a dotted pair of expressions, the first again a five-element list, a "similarity" list from Figure A to each of the answer figures, the second the same from Figure B to each of the answer figures. This brief description leaves certain loose ends, but it should provide a reasonably adequate notion of what is done by Part 1.

The ten foregoing expressions are given as arguments to the top-level function of Part 2 (optimistically called *solve*). The basic method employed by *solve,* which suffices to do this problem, begins by matching the parts of Figure A and those of Figure B in all possible ways compatible with the similarity information. From this process it concludes, in the case in question, that P2 ↔ P4, P3 ↔ P5, and P1 is removed in going from A to B. (The machinery can also handle far more complicated cases, in which alternate matchings are possible and parts are both added and removed.) On the basis of this matching, a statement of a rule taking A into B is generated. It looks like:

```
(
(REMOVE A1 ((ABOVE A1 A3) (ABOVE A1 A2) (SIM OB3 A1
    (((1.0 . 0.0) . (N.N))))))
```

```
(MATCH A2 (((INSIDE A2 A3) (ABOVE A1 A2) (SIM OB2 A2
    (((1.0 . 0.0) . (N.N))))) . ((LEFT A2 A3) (SIM OB2 A2
    (((1.0 . 0.0) . (N.N)) ((1.0 . 3.14) . (N.N))))
    (SIMTRAN (((1.0 . 0.0) . (N.N)) ((1.0 . 3.14) . (N.N)))))))
(MATCH A3 (((INSIDE A2 A3) (ABOVE A1 A3) (SIM OB1 A3
    (((1.0 . 0.0) . (N.N))))) . (LEFT A2 A3) (SIM OB1 A3
    (((1.0 . 0.0) . (N.N)))) (SIMTRAN (((1.0 . 0.0) . (N.N)))))))
)
```

The A's are used as "variables" representing objects. The format is rather simple. For each object added, removed, or matched, there is a list of the properties, relations and similarity information pertaining to it. (In the case of a matched object, there are two such lists, one pertaining to Figure A and the other to Figure B.) There are two special devices; the (SIM OB1 . . .)-form expressions give a means of comparing types of objects between, say, Figure A and Figure C; the other device is the use of the SIMTRAN expressions in the Figure B list for each matched object. This enables us to handle conveniently some additional situations which will be described in Section 5.4.

This rule expresses everything about Figures A and B and their relationship that is used in the rest of the process. (The reader may verify that the rule does, in some sense, describe the transformation of Figure A into Figure B in the example.)

Next a similarity matching is carried out between Figure C and each of the five answer figures. Matchings that do not correspond to the ones between Figure A and Figure B in numbers of parts added, removed, and matched are discarded. If all are rejected, this method has failed and *solve* goes on to try a further method. In the present case, Figures 1 and 5 are rejected on this basis. However Figures 2, 3, and 4 pass this test and are examined further, as follows: Choose an answer figure. For a given matching of Figure C to the answer figure in question (and *solve* goes through all possible matchings compatible with similarity) we take each "Figure A → Figure B" rule and attempt to fit it to the new case, making all matchings of objects between the A's of the rule statement and the objects of Figure C and the answer figures which are compatible with preserving add, remove, and match categories; then testing to see which information is preserved, thus getting a new, "reduced" rule which fits Figure A → B as well as Figure C → the answer figure in question. In our case, for each of the three possible answer figures we get two reduced rules in this way (since there are two possible pairings between A and C, namely, P1 ↔ P8, P2 ↔ P7, and P3 ↔ P6, or P1 ↔ P8, P2 ↔ P6, and P3 ↔ P7).

In some sense, each of these rules provides an answer. However, we want a "best" or "strongest" rule, that is one that says the most or is the least alteration in the original "Figure A → Figure B" rule that still maps C onto exactly one answer figure. A simple device seems to approximate human opinion on this question rather well; we define a rather crude "strength" function on the rules and sort them by this. If a rule is a clear winner in this test, the corresponding answer figure is chosen; if the test results in a tie, the entire method has failed and *solve* goes on to try something else. In our case, when the values for the six rules are computed, the winner is one of the rules corresponding to Fig. 2; thus, the program, like all humans so far consulted, chooses it as the answer. The rule chosen looks like this:

```
(
(REMOVE A1 ((ABOVE A1 A3) (ABOVE A1 A2) (SIM OB3 A1
    (((1.0 . 0.0) . (N.N))))))
(MATCH A2 (((INSIDE A2 A3) (ABOVE A1 A2)) . ((LEFT
    A2 A3) (SIMTRAN (((1.0 . 0.0) . (N.N)) ((1.0 . 3.14) . (N.N)))))))
(MATCH A3 (((INSIDE A2 A3) (ABOVE A1 A3)) . ((LEFT A2 A3)
    (SIMTRAN (((1.0 . 0.0) . (N.N)))))))
)
```

Again, it is easy to check that this rule both takes Figure A into Figure B and Figure C into Figure 2, but not into any of the other answer figures.

5.2.4 Example 2. A Case Requiring Decomposition

The sample problem we are about to discuss is shown as Fig. 5-4. It is included here to illustrate the use of the decomposition process available to Part 1 of ANALOGY. The capabilities and limitations of this decomposition program in its present state are treated at some length in Part 5.3.3. As is stated there, space limitations required a change in the original plan. At first it was intended simply to replace the primitive decomposition program originally built into Part 1 with more elaborate versions as they became available. However, it proved impossible to fit such a program into core with the rest of Part 1, without severe difficulties at best. For this reason an alternative approach was taken. The decomposition programs occupy core separately, along with certain requisite Part 1 programs, to perform preprocessing on inputs before Part 1 "sees" them. That is, it acts as a "Part 0." What it does is to read in a set of inputs given in exactly the Part 1 input form, perform certain processing on these, and punch out the results, again in the same format, ready for input to Part 1.

First we shall exhibit the input expressions to "Part 0" corresponding to Figures A and C of Fig. 5-4, and then, with explanation, the altered versions of these two expressions as they occur in the output of "Part 0." The other six expressions pass unaltered through the decomposition program. Finally we summarize the Part 1 and Part 2 processing which starts from the "Part 0" output and results in the choice of an answer figure. The discussion of this phase of the solution process will be very brief, since it closely parallels that of example 1.

The description of Figure A of our example is:

```
(
(REG ((V1 (V2 (0.0 (0.7 . 0.7) 0.0 (0.2 . 0.7) 0.0
              (0.2 . 0.3) 0.0 (0.7 . 0.3) 0.0))
          (V2 (0.0 (0.6 . 0.4) 0.0))
          (V2 (0.0))
          (V2 (0.0 (0.75 . 0.7) 0.0 (0.9 . 0.4) 0.0)))
      (V2 (V1 (0.0 (0.9 . 0.4) 0.0 (0.75 . 0.7) 0.0))
          (V1 (0.0))
          (V1 (0.0 (0.6 . 0.4) 0.0))
          (V1 (0.0 (0.7 . 0.3) 0.0 (0.2 . 0.3) 0.0
              (0.2 . 0.7) 0.0 (0.7 . 0.7) 0.0)))) )
)
```

where V1 is a vertex with $x = 0.7$ and $y = 0.6$ and V2 one with $x = 0.7$ and and $y = 0.4$.

Figure C is represented by:

```
(
(REG ((V3 (V4 (0.0 (0.7 . 0.7) 0.0 (0.5 . 0.7) 5.0
              (0.5 . 0.2) 0.0 (0.7 . 0.3) 0.0))
          (V4 (0.0 (0.65 . 0.55) 0.0 (0.65 . 0.45) 0.0))
          (V4 (0.0))
          (V4 (0.0 (0.85 . 0.55) 0.0 (0.85 . 0.45) 0.0)))
      (V4 (V3 (0.0 (0.85 . 0.45) 0.0 (0.85 . 0.55) 0.0))
          (V3 (0.0))
          (V3 (0.0 (0.65 . 0.45) 0.0 (0.65 . 0.55) 0.0))
          (V3 (0.0 (0.7 . 0.3) 0.0 (0.5 . 0.2) 5.0
              (0.5 . 0.7) 0.0 (0.7 . 0.7) 0.0)))) )
)
```

where V3 is a vertex with $x = 0.7$ and $y = 0.55$ and V4 one with $x = 0.7$ and $y = 0.45$.

These descriptions are written in an indented form to exhibit more clearly the connectivity of the figure. The description of Figure A, for example, consists in saying that it has two vertices connected to each other by four separate paths, which are then described (note that the vertices are correspondingly labeled on Fig. 5-4).

Essentially what "Part 0" does in the case in question is to decompose Figure A, a □△, into a □ and a △ on the basis that these figures are present in Figure B and, similarly, to decompose Figure C, which is a , into a and a , on the basis that these figures are present in several of the answer figures.

The output expressions that replace the expressions here given, reflecting the carrying out of the decomposition process, look as follows (note that each REG-type figure has been broken down into two SCC-type figures):

For Figure A the output is:

```
(
(SCC ((0.2 . 0.3) 0.0 (0.7 . 0.3) 0.0 (0.7 . 0.7)
      0.0 (0.2 . 0.7) 0.0 (0.2 . 0.3)))
(SCC ((0.6 . 0.4) 0.0 (0.9 . 0.4) 0.0 (0.75 . 0.7)
      0.0 (0.6 . 0.4)))
)
```

and for Figure C we have:

```
(
(SCC ((0.5 . 0.3) 0.0 (0.7 . 0.3) 0.0 (0.7 . 0.7)
      0.0 (0.5 . 0.7) 5.0 (0.5 . 0.3)))
(SCC ((0.65 . 0.45) 0.0 (0.85 . 0.45) 0.0 (0.85 . 0.55)
      0.0 (0.65 . 0.55) 0.0 (0.65 . 0.45)))
)
```

The eight output expressions from "Part 0" are given to Part 1, which generates its description of them. The critical items it produces are:

In Figure A, the △ is to the right of the □

In Figure B, the △ is inside the □

In Figure C, the □ is to the right of the

In Figure 3, the □ is inside the

In Figure 5, the □ is to the left of the

When Part 2 is presented with the Part 1 output, it is able to discard answer Figures 1, 2, and 4 on the basis of nonmatching in the sense we discussed under example 1. It then calculates its "Figure A → Figure B" rule and attempts to extend it to the remaining answer figures. Because of the five critical statements made, the rule corresponding to the choice of Figure 3 as the answer is "stronger," and that answer, again in agreement with human judgment of what was intended, is selected.

5.3 Analogy: Part 1

5.3.1 Introduction

The function of Part 1 of ANALOGY, as described in Part 5.2.3, is to process rather primitive input descriptions of line drawings to obtain new descriptions in a form suited to the needs of Part 2. In Part 1, the input figures are decomposed into subfigures, various geometric properties of these subfigures and relations between them are calculated, and the results encoded into the format required by the remainder of the program. Therefore this section must treat the form of the input descriptions, the manner in which these are processed to obtain the desired information, and the output format.

5.3.2 The Input Description Format

Basically, the input descriptions permit one to describe any line drawing that can be composed from dots, straight line segments, and arcs of circles. In principle, this permits descriptions to arbitrary accuracy of any line drawing whatever (even without the arcs of circles), though possibly at the cost of prohibitively lengthy descriptions. For problems of the type considered here, all the essential features of the input figures can usually be represented by quite economical descriptions of this form. We have chosen a representation of line drawings that permits the encoding of any line drawing and moreover permits particularly efficient encodings for the class of line drawings under consideration. The format is most easily understood from a set of examples, given with appropriate explanation. After these we shall give a precise formulation of the syntax of the descriptions. Finally, we shall compare them with those used in references 3 and 6, the only works employing descriptions similar enough to permit meaningful comparison.

Simple Closed Curves. In a description of simple closed curves, consider a rectangle (Fig. 5-5*a*). As with all these figures, we consider the rectangle as lying in the positive unit square, $0 \leq x \leq 1$, $0 \leq y \leq 1$, for the purpose of giving coordinates where required. The description of this curve reads as follows: start from any "link-point," that is, intersection of two line elements, and proceed *counterclockwise* making a list of, alternately, *x-y* coordinate pairs and curvatures of intervening line elements (straight-line segments or arcs of circles). The choice of starting point is completely arbitrary; the processing programs are independent of it. In this example, all curvatures are zero, since we have only straight line segments. The description ends with the same coordinate pair with which we started (a useful small redundancy). Thus, starting from the lower left corner we would have (where (p . q) represents an *x-y* coordinate pair, x = p, y = q):

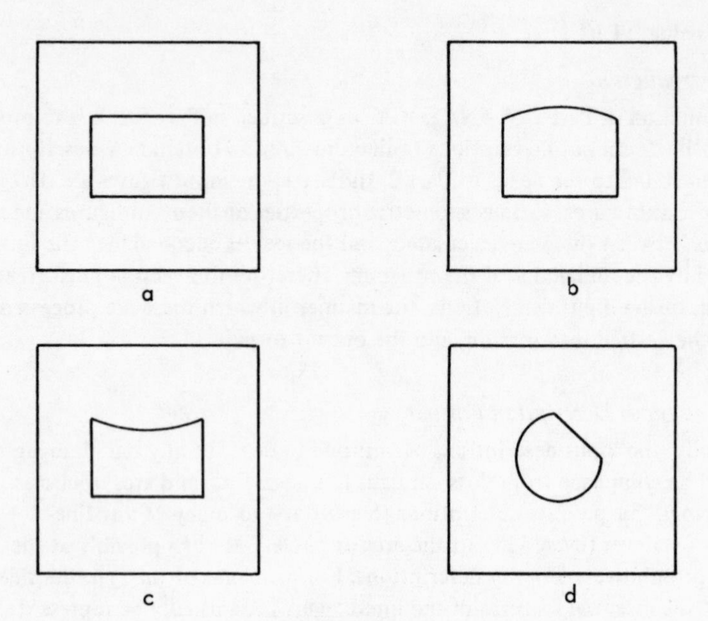

Figure 5-5.

(SCC ((0.2 . 0.3) 0.0 (0.8 . 0.3) 0.0 (0.8 . 0.7)
0.0 (0.2 . 0.7) 0.0 (0.2 . 0.3)))

For internal processing, all connected figures are divided into three classes: simple closed curves, dots, and the rest. These are labeled by SCC, DOT, and REG, respectively, at the beginning of the description. (The counterclockwise restriction stated on the SCC-descriptions could be avoided by making the program test for it and reverse the list [changing sign on all the curvatures] if necessary, but this frill was omitted to save some computation.)

Now suppose we have instead Fig. 5-5*b*, with an arc of a circle replacing a straight-line segment. The description is just as above except for one curvature being nonzero, say +1.0:

(SCC ((0.2 . 0.3) 0.0 (0.8 . 0.3) 0.0 (0.8 . 0.7)
1.0 (0.2 . 0.7) 0.0 (0.2 . 0.3)))

The sign of the curvature is determined by the following convention: The sign is + if, as we go from point A to point B along a path (which corresponds to reading left-to-right in the description of the curve) the curve is concave to the left; otherwise the sign is -. Thus, to describe Fig. 5-5*c*, we change only the sign of the appropriate curvature and get:

(SCC ((0.2 . 0.3) 0.0 (0.8 . 0.3) 0.0 (0.8 . 0.7)
−1] .0 (0.2 . 0.7) 0.0 (0.2 . 0.3)))

To remove any possibility of ambiguity, the largest permitted single arc of a circle is a semicircle. Larger portions of circles or whole circles must be composed from arcs $\leq$ a semicircle. For example, a ¾ – circle + straight line (Fig. 5-5*d*) could be described as:

(SCC ((0.5 . 0.7) 5.0 (0.5 . 0.3) 5.0 (0.7 . 0.5)
0.0 (0.5 . 0.7)))

Dots. The special case of a dot is easily handled. The form for a dot at, for example, $x = 0.5$, $y = 0.3$, is

(DOT ((0.5 . 0.3)))

Other Connected Figures. Next, all connected figures other than simple closed curves or dots are treated as follows: All the vertices of the figure are given arbitrary names (LISP atomic symbols). By "vertices" we mean either endpoints of curves or points where three or more line elements (straight line segments or arcs) meet. Note that, in this sense, simple closed curves have no vertices at all. Then the description consists of a list, with one element for each "vertex." This element is itself a list: its first element is a vertex name; each subsequent element consists of the name of a vertex (possibly the same one), followed by the description of a curve in the same form as was used for the simple closed curves (that is, alternating coordinate pairs and curvatures). Thus details about the shape of the component curves "hang," so to speak, from the connectivity information. Every curve connecting two vertices will thus be described twice; this redundancy pays in programming convenience for the additional storage space occupied.

One restriction is placed on the ordering of these curve descriptions. Suppose any two vertices, A and B, are connected directly by more than one such curve. The expressions of form (B "description of A→B curve") in the list of connections belonging to vertex A must occur contiguously on that list and in left-to-right order corresponding to counterclockwise ordering, as seen from A looking toward B. (Figure 5-6*b* is of this type; its description, given below, illustrates the required ordering.) This restriction could be removed at the cost of some additional program.

An example of a figure of the non-simple-closed-curve class is shown as Fig. 5-6*a*. With its vertices named A, B, C, and D, as labeled, it can be described as follows:

(REG ((A (D (0.0))) (B (D (0.0))) (C (D (0.0))) (D
(A (0.0)) (B (0.0)) (C (0.0)))))

with auxiliary coordinate list:

((A. (0.3 . 0.7)) (B. (0.5 . 0.2)) (C. (0.7 . 0.7))
(D. (0.5 . 0.7)))

The description requires at input time an auxiliary list (in the form shown) of coordinate pairs corresponding to the vertices. These coordinates are not carried along with the description throughout the processing–rather, the coordinate pairs are attached as values (*via* the LISP APVAL feature, reference 19, p. 26) to the coordinate names, permitting their easy retrieval when required. Furthermore, in view of this easy retrieval, the descriptions are abbreviated by omitting the beginning and end coordinate pairs (that is, those corresponding to the named vertices) from the curve descriptions. Since the curves in the above example are all single straight-line segments, all that this leaves are the (0, 0)'s, which correspond to the curvatures.

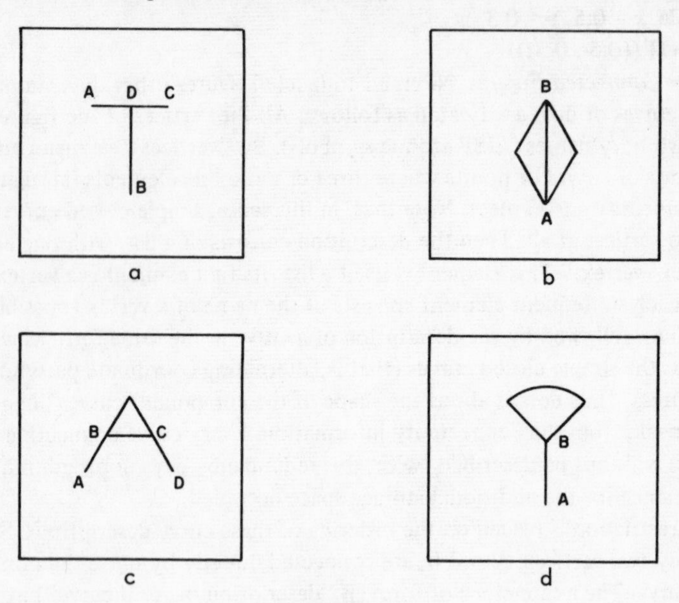

Figure 5-6.

Another example is that of Fig. 5-6*b*, which can be described by:

(REG ((A (B (0.0) (0.7 . 0.5) 0.0)) (B (0.0))
(B (0.0 (0.3 . 0.5) 0.0)))
(B (A (0.0 (0.3 . 0.5) 0.0)) (A (0.0))
(A (0.0 (0.7 . 0.5) 0.0)))))

with coordinate list:

((A. (0.5 . 0.2)) (B. (0.5 . 0.8)))

(We remark again that this description illustrates the ordering restriction mentioned above.)

A third example of this type is the "A" of Fig. 5-6*c*, with description:

(REG ((A (B (0.0))) (B (A (0.0)) (C (0.0)) (C (0.0
(0.5 . 0.7) 0.0))) (C (B (0.0 (0.5 . 0.7)
0.0)) (B (0.0)) (D (0.0))) (D (C (0.0)))))

and coordinate list:

((A. (0.3 . 0.3)) (B. (0.4 . 0.5)) (C. (0.6 . 0.5))
(D. (0.3 . 0.7)))

A last example (Fig. 5-6*d*) illustrates the possibility of a vertex connecting to itself. This can be described by:

(REG ((A (B (0.0))) (B (A (0.0)) (B (0.0 (0.7 . 0.7)
2.5 (0.3 . 0.7) 0.0)))))

with coordinate list:

((A. (0.5 . 0.2)) (B. (0.5 . 0.5)))

A vertex may have more than one connection to itself; an example is a figure eight (8). Here the corresponding descriptions must occur together but are not ordered in any way.

This concludes the treatment of connected figures. The extension to arbitrary figures is now trivial: The description of any figure consists of a list of descriptions of its connected parts (with, at input, a list associating every vertex of the figure with its coordinates).

For completeness, we now supplement this informal treatment with a formal description of the syntax of the descriptions. Most readers will prefer to skip this section. This syntax is expressed in the notation introduced in references 1 and 23 (so-called "Backus normal form," one scheme for writing the productions of a context-free phrase-structure grammar). It defines a class of expressions wider than that allowed as inputs: Certain supplementary conditions (all of which are mentioned above) must still be applied. However, up to these conditions, the following set of productions do characterize the syntax of a figure description (figrep) rather concisely (in these productions Δ is used to indicate explicitly the presence of a blank as a terminal character):

```
<figrep> ::=(<cfigrep1>
<cfigrep1> ::=<cfigrep>)|<cfigrep> Δ <cfigrep1>
<cfigrep> ::=<dotrep>|<sccrep>|<regrep>
<dotrep> ::=(DOTΔ<copair>)
<sccrep> ::=(SCCΔ<cllined> )
<regrep> ::=(REGΔ<connl> )
<connl> ::=<connelem >)|<connelem >Δ<connl>
<connelem> ::(<atom> Δ <nbl>
<nbl> ::~<nbelem>)|<nbelem>Δ<nbl>
<nbelem> ::(<atom>Δ<oplined>)
<oplined> ::(<linedl>)
<linedl> ::<curvno>|<curvno>Δ<copair>Δ< linedl>
<cllined> ::(<copair>Δ< linedl>Δ<copair> )
<copair> ::=(<cono>Δ.Δ<cono>)
<cono> ::= any LISP floating-point number x, 0 ≤ x ≤ 1
<curvno> ::= any LISP floating-point number
```

<atom> ::= any LISP atomic symbol not already having a value attached to it by an APVAL (cf. reference 19)

For simplicity, this syntax has been written to apply to expressions that have been preprocessed as follows (all these are essentially done by the LISP read program): Replace any comma, or string of adjacent commas, by a single blank; where several blanks occur in succession, remove all but one; finally, remove any blank immediately after a left parenthesis and before a right parenthesis.

Now we turn to a comparison with the figure descriptions employed in references 3 and 6. The line drawings which Canaday must describe are a rather special class suited to his "overlapping polygon" problem. Since the input line drawings involved are of the special type implied by this interpretation, no description form capable of handling arbitrary line drawings is introduced. Furthermore, the lines in question are all straight; thus there is no necessity of a provision for curvature information. Within these limitations, the form used is similar to that employed here.

Hodes (6) does introduce a description format capable of handling general line drawings. Like ours, it gives a list of vertices, each with a list of the other vertices to which it connects and descriptions of the corresponding curves between. However, Hodes includes in "vertices" what we called "link-points"; for example, 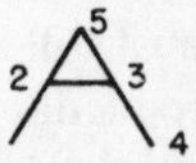 has four vertices (1, 2, 3, 4) in our scheme and five (1, 2, 3, 4, 5) in his. Then a line between two vertices (in his sense) is described by a list of six numbers (end vertex, beginning angle, end angle, length, absolute curvature, curvature), angle and curvature given as an integral number of five-degree increments. There is little reason to prefer one such representation over another. Our representation, in which link-points of line elements along a curve do not appear on the top-level vertex list, sharply separates the connectivity information from the details of curve descriptions. This is a great convenience in our similarity-calculation program, which uses a topological matching process to control the application of detailed metric comparisons.

All of the expressions given in this section were LISP S-expressions, hence can be read directly from punched cards and set up in memory as list structures. The internal representation of S-expressions is described in Chapter 7 of reference 19.

5.3.3 Decomposition

The top-level control program of Part 1, called *punchdescr*, reads in a list of arguments consisting of the description in the above format of the eight input figures. Its first step is to attach the coordinates as values to the vertex names and discard the coordinate lists themselves. Then it calls a routine named *decomp* to decompose the eight input figures into subfigures. The resulting subfigures are again represented in the same format as the input figures–in particular, they need not be connected; each may consist of as many connected parts as required. The simple decomposition which was used in most of our work with the Part 1 program simply separates each input figure into its connected subfigures. However, a more elaborate decomposition program has now been developed, representing a long step toward the full generality one would like to have. This program will be described later.

There appear to be two distinct approaches to the decomposition process: one can attempt to break up a figure on *Gestalt* criteria, such as some formalization of "good continuation," to separate, say,  into  and  . Alternatively one can perform the decomposition on the basis of information external to the figure itself, as, in our case, from the other problem figures. To repeat our example from Part 5.2.1, if Figure A consists of 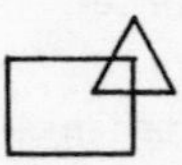 and Figure B of  , it would be natural, having found, trivially, that Figure B consists of the two distinct pieces,  and , to attempt to find one or both of these subfigures, up to similarity transformations, in Figure A. Some combination of these "intrinsic" and "context" heuristics should be suitable as the basis for a quite useful decomposition program–for example, one that can find all occurrences of one figure in another.

A start has been made on this general problem of line-drawing decomposition through the construction of a program with the following capability: Given an arbitrary simple closed curve x and an arbitrary line drawing y, the program returns with the descriptions of all simple-closed-curve subfigures of y that are similar to x (in the sense of "generalized Euclidean similarity" as defined below) and with the parameters of the similarity transformations involved.

For example, given x = and y =  , it would find the in y; given x = and y = 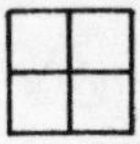 it would find the five subfigures of y which are similar to x; or, given x = and again y =  , it would find the four subfigures of y similar to x. The next step would be the more difficult but still feasible problem of generalizing the above to permit x to be an arbitrary connected line drawing. Most generally, one would like to be able to find a cluster of several specified connected objects in a figure consisting of one or more arbitrary connected line drawings. Once again this extension seems feasible, by a fairly straightforward extension of techniques already in use in Part 1.

We now must elaborate slightly on a point mentioned in Section 5.2. Our original plan was to replace the simple decomposition program with which we began the development of Part 1 by successively more sophisticated versions, until an appreciable degree of decomposition power had been attained. However, limitations of storage space led us to follow a different scheme once the decomposition process routines had grown to their present size. The decomposition process is treated as a matter of preprocessing; the decomposition routines and the routines they require among those already in Part 1 form a third separate package, occupying core alone. This package is given, as arguments, a set of eight expressions in precisely the format for input to Part 1 and, after carrying out its processing on them, punches out a modified set of seven arguments, again in the same format (or several sets of such expressions, if alternate decompositions of comparable *a priori* value are found). The resulting cards are then given as input to Part 1, and the entire two-part ANALOGY process is carried out.

Just as the separation of Parts 1 and 2 into separate blocks imposed certain limitations on the design possibilities, the separation of the decomposition facilities from the rest of Part 1 prevents the use of any information developed in Part 1 to guide the decomposition search. Hence, the decomposition process is a fairly "blind" one. The present top-level decomposition control program is a somewhat primitive one, intended more to test the underlying mechanism than to apply it well to a wide range of situations. However, improving the top-level control is a much easier task than developing the already-built apparatus that it applies.

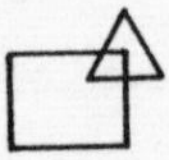

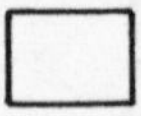

With the similarity-testing program already in existence when the simple-closed-curve extraction program described was written, the basic method used is to find (by a quite compact and efficient recursive procedure) all simple closed paths in y and compare each with x, using the similarity-testing machinery. When a desired subfigure is found, further programs are called to remove that subfigure from y and reformat the remainder, as required. This can require complex manipulation: For example, if △ is removed from [square with overlapping triangle], the remaining □ is now an SCC figure, not a REG as was y, and the description must be appropriately rewritten. Since the similarity program was designed so that it can often terminate a comparison doomed to failure with very little computation, this is reasonably efficient. However, if one were to redesign the entire process, the best course might be to embed the similarity testing in a decomposition procedure. Then testing for ordinary figure-versus-figure similarity would be a special case of testing for figure-versus-subfigure relations. This would also probably be the easiest way to make the extension permitting x to be an arbitrary connected figure and would probably, even with the current memory capacity of the LISP system, permit us to include the decomposition program in Part 1.

A few further remarks about decomposition might be added here:

A figure may of course be susceptible to various decompositions. Which, if any, of these is appropriate depends on the other figures of the problem. In the terms we have used, "intrinsic" decomposition is inadequate and "context" decomposition methods, on which we have based our decomposition program, must be used. For example, Figure A =  and Figure B = requires a decomposition of A into and (thus the rule generated will involve the removal of the), whereas with the same Figure A, Figure B = 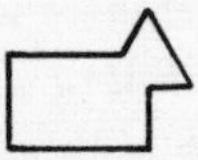 will require decomposition of A into 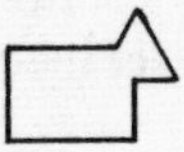 and . The program described is capable of performing either of these decompositions, depending on the "context," that is, on which objects are present in the appropriate answer figures.

Even when one has found a given subfigure in another figure, one is faced with the difficulty of deciding what is left. For example, suppose Figure A is 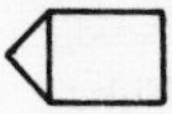 and Figure B is  The desired decomposition might be  + 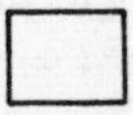 or  +  Thus, questions arise as to whether common parts belong only to the removed object or to both it and the remainder of the figure. This means that a really exhaustive decomposition process must produce all these alternatives. Since this would often result in a vast proliferation of decompositions, what ought to be produced are only the "best" ones, with the generation process controlled by heuristics based, perhaps, partly on some Gestalt-like criterion of "good figure" and partly on "context." The limited decomposition process now available completely removes all of the simple closed curves from the figure in which it is found; for example, we get ⟨ + □ if □ is the figure to be found, and ◁ + □ if 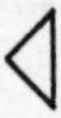 ◁ is to be found.

On the other hand we may have a situation in which "context" decomposition fails and "intrinsic" decomposition is required. This is illustrated by the following example: If Figure A is [figure] and Figure B is [figure], then viewing these figures as each consisting of the parts [figure] and O will fail if the desired rule involves, say, removing the O from inside the △ but leaving it inside the □. Here we have no context cues to guide the decomposition. If the "intrinsic" criterion used (which happens to work in this case) were "look at all decompositions into simple-closed-curve subfigures," a modification of our control program would be able to use the machinery we already possess to effect the decomposition of Figure A and Figure B into △, □, and O, after which Part 1 could calculate the relations (for example, INSIDE, ABOVE) between these objects, enabling Part 2 to find the rule hypothesized above. Such an extension of the control program would not be difficult, but has not been carried out.

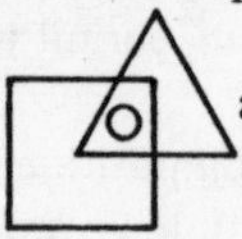

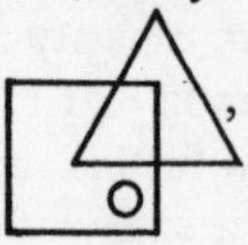

5.3.4 Property and Relation Calculations

At any rate, once the decomposition has been performed in one way or another, *punchdescr* calls routines which perform, for each of the eight problem figures, certain property and relation calculations on its component subfigures as well as similarity calculations between subfigures of different figures. The lists showing which properties and relations (of those currently included in the system) are to be calculated are program parameters, specified at run time.

Typical of these relations between subfigures are three called INSIDE, LEFT, and ABOVE. The following is a brief discussion of how they are defined and how they are currently implemented in Part 1:

Given any two disjoint figures, X and Y, a "center-of-mass" calculation is made on the vertices of each. The resulting two points, one for each figure, are compared as follows: take the point P_X corresponding to "center of mass" of

X and draw the two 45-degree lines through it, for example [diagram: quadrants II, III, I, IV around P_X]. If P_Y is in the quadrant marked I, the expression (LEFT X Y) is generated; if in quadrant III, the expression (LEFT Y X); if in quadrant II, the expression (ABOVE Y X): finally, if in quadrant IV, the expression (ABOVE X Y). (Note that the method is symmetric in X and Y.) Thus for any two disjoint figures, exactly one of these alternatives results (with two exceptions; the highly unlikely case $P_X = P_Y$, currently ignored, and the case in which X lies inside Y or Y inside X, treated as a special case). This is of course a very crude criterion; one can easily produce cases on which it makes an unsatisfactory conclusion. However, though it would be easy to establish and implement more sophisticated criteria, the current one has been quite adequate for most of the cases attempted, and the effort seemed therefore better spent on other aspects of the program.

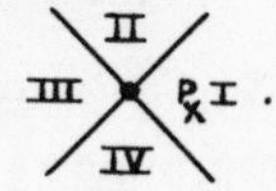

Given any figure X and any simple closed curve figure Y, disjoint from X, the following procedure will determine whether X lies inside Y: Choose any point P on X. Draw a line L from P to any point on the boundary of the unit square on which the figures lie, for example, the (0, 0) corner. Calculate how many times L intersects Y. Because the elements from which Y is built are straight-line segments and arcs of circles, this requires only routines to find the intersection (if any) of two line segments and the intersection(s), if any, of a line segment and a specified arc of a circle. If the number is odd, X lies inside Y, and the expression (INSIDE X Y) is generated; if even, X does not lie inside Y, and nothing is generated. It was necessary in Part 1 to add to this process some machinery to assure that an intersection of L and Y at a link-point of Y is counted only once; one should also add machinery to handle rare cases such as [diagram: P_X, Y, (0,0)], that is, the "P_X to (0, 0)" line is tangent to Y at a vertex, where the program will conclude X lies inside Y; this, like a number of other possible improvements in various parts of the program, seemed of low priority.

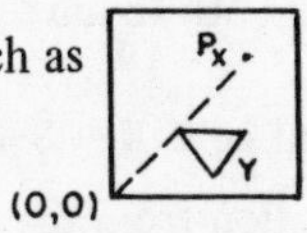

More serious is the restriction that limits Y to being a simple closed curve. This restriction could have been removed (with very little new programming required), by using the procedure constructed for the decomposition process for finding all simple closed curves in a given figure. One would simply use it to find the simple closed loops of Y and use the present procedure to determine whether X lies inside any one of them. If so, we would generate (INSIDE X Y). Unfortunately the decomposition program had to be used as a separate package, because of space limitations.

5.3.5 The Similarity Calculations

We now turn to a discussion of the similarity calculations. First, we must define just what is being calculated: given two figures X and Y, one wishes to determine for what choices of quadruples $(\rho_1, \rho_2, \mu, \theta)$, if any, can Y be taken into X by a reflection ρ_1, followed by a Euclidean similarity transformation $E(\mu, \theta)$ (that is, a uniform scale change μ and rotation θ), followed by a reflection ρ_2 (where $0 < \mu < \infty$, $-\pi < \theta \leq \pi$, and the only permitted reflections are no reflection at all, reflection in a horizontal axis, and reflection in a vertical axis). It is this rather general relation that is determined by the similarity programs.

Originally the program was written without provision for reflections, that is, given an X and Y, it produced all (μ, θ) pairs under which Y was (Euclidean) similar to X. At a later stage, it seemed desirable to handle problems involving at least a reasonably wide class of reflections as well. Some of these are illustrated in Section 5.5.

The form chosen for the transformations may seem unnecessarily complex. After all (forgetting uniform scale change for a moment), if we think of connected line drawings as wire figures, if we can superimpose two such figures it is either purely by rotation (in all this, we ignore translations entirely) or by "flipping" and rotation. That is, any reflection through an axis outside the figure will do. Thus for any such transformation, we will have a number of equivalent $(\rho_1, \rho_2, \mu, \theta)$ quadruples to carry along. We reduce this number appreciably by generating only those where at least one of ρ_1, ρ_2 is the null reflection. This, in view of what we have just said, entails no loss of generality and preserves the two desirable properties for which we originally introduce the $(\rho_1, \rho_2, \mu, \theta)$ representation. These are:

We wished to permit pure horizontal and vertical reflections both to have simple forms.

We wished the form to be symmetric for easy inversion. That is, if $X \rightarrow Y$ by $(\rho_1, \rho_2, \mu, \theta)$, $Y \rightarrow X$ by $(\rho'\text{C}_1, \rho'_2, \mu', \theta')$, again a transformation from the same class, where $\rho'_1 = \rho_2, \rho'_2 = \rho_1, \mu' = 1/\mu$, and $\theta' = -\theta$ (appropriately reduced so $-\pi < \theta' \leq \pi$).

The Topological-Metric Matching Program. The figure-matching program which generates these $(\rho_1, \rho_2, \mu, \theta)$ quadruples has several interesting features. Perhaps the principal one is the over-all organization alluded to in previous sections. Essentially, the top level is a program for topological matching of networks. Suppose this program "conjectures" at some point that (say) vertex A of one figure X corresponds to vertex P of another figure Y, and vertex B to vertex Q. It then compares the curve(s), if any, between A and B with those between P and Q to see if they are similar under one of the (μ, θ)-pair possibilities still alive at that point of the program. Before discussion of other properties of the program and the relative merits of this sort of description-based pattern recognition, it may be useful to sketch the working of the program on one example, that of Fig. 5-7.

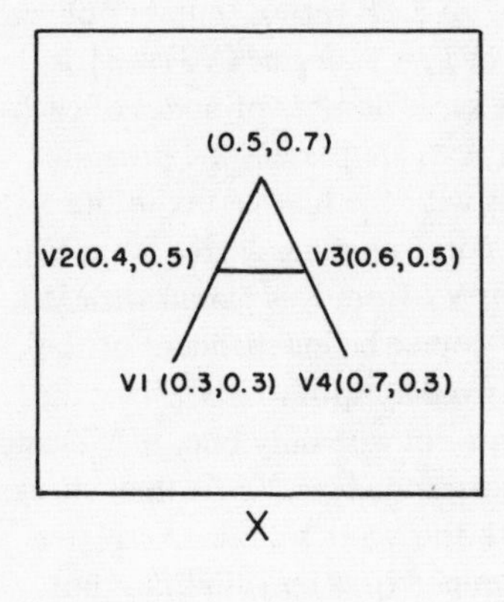

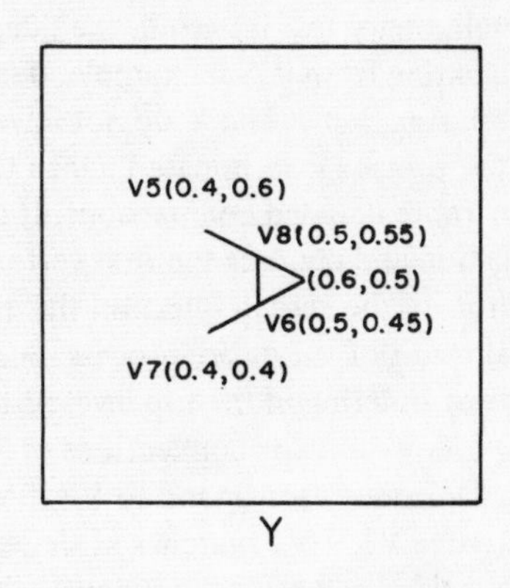

X: ((V1 (V2 (0.0)))

(V2 (V1 (0.0)) (V3 (0.0))(V3 (0.0 (0.5 . 0.7) 0.0)))

(V3 (V2 (0.0 (0.5 . 0.7) 0.0)) (V2 (0.0)) (V4 (0.0)))

(V4 (V3 (0.0))))

Y: ((V5 (V8 (0.0)))

(V6 (V7 (0.0)) (V8 (0.0 (0.6 . 0.5) 0.0)) (V8 (0.0)))

(V7 (V6 (0.0)))

(V8 (V5 (0.0)) (V6 (0.0)) (V6 (0.0 (0.6 . 0.5) 0.0))))

Figure 5-7.

To describe the behavior of the matching program on this illustrative case, we must make a few preliminary remarks. First, given two figures X and Y, the program makes sure they are both either simple closed curves or not simple closed curves. If they are the same type, we proceed; if not, the comparison has failed. The simple-closed-curve case is simpler than the other, which is to be illustrated. It essentially involves trying to compare the shapes of the two figures, starting from each possible matching of a given link-point of X to any from Y. The more interesting case is the one of which Fig. 5-7 is illustrative. We shall follow the program through this case in moderate detail.

The first steps taken by the program are designed to produce a quick exit in many cases of nonmatching. First, the number of vertices of X and Y are counted; if the number is not the same in each figure, the matching has failed. If this preliminary test is passed, the "degree" of each vertex [number of lines emanating from it, for example, degree (V1) = 1, degree (V3) = 3] is calculated. Again, if X and Y do not have the same number of nodes of each degree, the process is terminated. Once these tests are passed, the program begins its more detailed comparisons. It starts with the first vertex in the X-description and chooses the first vertex of corresponding degree from Y to pair with it. In the case in question this means V1 from X is paired with V5 (the final result of the entire process must of course be independent of the accidents of ordering in the top level of the two description lists). Now the program follows out the connections of V1 (in this case only one, to V2) and finds that V2 must correspond to V8 if V1 corresponds to V5. It then checks that the curve V1 $\rightarrow$ V2 matches in shape with the V5 $\rightarrow$ V8 one. At a later stage it would check against previously determined (μ, θ) possibilities, but since this is the first such metric comparison in this attempt to match all vertices, it calculates that the shapes match if $\mu = 2.0$ and $\theta = 1.57$ (recall that the μ and θ are quoted corresponding to the transformation of Y into X, not vice versa). The next step is to follow out the (not previously examined) connections of V2, namely the two to V3. First, it determines that V3 must be matched with V6. The shape tests on the connecting lines are carried out using the (μ, θ) pair obtained above and the tests succeed. Then the "new" connection(s) of V3 are followed out, namely the one to V4. Matching V4 with V7 is the only choice, and again the metric test succeeds. We have thus determined that (under the matchings V1 $\leftrightarrow$ V5, V2 $\leftrightarrow$ V8, V3 $\leftrightarrow$ V6, and V4 $\leftrightarrow$ V7) Y can be transformed into X (up to the built-in tolerances of the metric matching machinery) by a Euclidean similarity transformation with parameters $\mu = 2.0$ and $\theta = 1.57$. However, the program is not yet done with this case, for it attempts to find *all* such transformations; in this case there are no others but it must discover this by attempting other matchings. The only other way to start is by matching V1 and V7. The extension to matching V2 and V6 is successful, with a $\mu = 2.0$, $\theta = 0.64$, but any further extension fails the metric matching test and the process terminates, the program returning with the one (μ, θ) pair it found.

This case is a notably simple one in that there is little choice at each point of the procedure as to what to do next. Frequently things are much more complex and rather elaborate bookkeeping must be provided to permit the process to return to a previous vertex and strike off in a new direction when some stopping point is met. To reduce the dependence of the metric comparisons on the accident of which comparison is done first [and thus provides the

(u, θ) criterion] after each successful metric comparison, the (u, θ) criterion for future comparisons is altered by averaging in the (μ, θ) pair from the test, so that at any point the (μ, θ) "hypothesis" being tested is an average of the (μ, θ)'s from all previous successful comparisons during the current attempt at a complete vertex-matching between the figures. The new average S_{N+1} $[= (a_1 + \ldots + a_{N+1})/N+1]$ is calculated from $S_{N+1} = (NS_N + a_{N+1})/N+1$.

Discussion. Our program is a pattern-recognition scheme organized quite differently from any other with which we are familiar. Sherman (34) introduced some topological classification into a sequential decision-tree program (discussed briefly in Section 5.2) for the recognition of hand-printed letters, but the notion of systematically using the topological information to determine which metric comparisons are made seems to be new. (The entire internal mechanism of the comparing "black box" can be changed with no effect on the over-all structure.) This type of organization is quite different from the so-called "property-list" schemes mentioned earlier, which have been the basis of a number of the most sophisticated pattern-recognition programs developed to date.

The current scheme has its own characteristic advantages and disadvantages. As a factor in its favor we can cite its flexibility. For example, it was easy to construct the metric comparisons so as to make the pattern recognition invariant under size, rotation, and translation. It would be nearly as easy to build the metric part to consider certain types of reflections or to recognize figures under other transformations (for example, any affine transformation in the plane). Unquestionably there are applications in which this sort of generality is required. As mentioned in Section 5.2, suppressing the metric testing entirely would give us a topological equivalence algorithm for networks.

Relative to some class of potential inputs every pattern-recognition scheme has to some degree certain characteristic sensitivities, e.g., "small" (in the sense of the intended application) changes in input figures produce a "large" change, that is, an incorrect recognition. The current scheme, as it stands, is quite sensitive in that arbitrarily small changes in one of the two input figures can change matching to nonmatching and vice versa, namely, any change which changes the connectivity of the figure: for example,  is completely different from  , as far as the program is concerned. Such sensitivity could presumably be largely removed by a preprocessing routine which, given a description of a figure, would generate a new description with almost-joined points joined, small curlicues removed, etc., as desired. In the present work, where the input descriptions are generated by hand rather than by a line-tracing program, such preprocessing is in effect done by hand before any program ever sees the descriptions. Another problem of the same type, which has been largely neglected in the present work for the same reason, has to do not with the connectivity but with the descriptions of the curves. Clearly these are non-unique, as we have described them in Part 5.3.2; for example, a straight line between $x = 0.3, y = 0.3$ and $x = 0.7, y = 0.7$ can be described by ((0.3 . 0.3) 0.0 (0.7 . 0.7)) or by ((0.3 . 0.3) 0.0 (0.5 . 0.5) 0.0 (0.7 . 0.7)). This non-uniqueness would present no problem if the shape-comparing mechanism of the matching program were more general; however, at present it can only succeed in matching two curves with the same number of parts. It *is* able, however, to match corresponding curve parts quite generally; for example, it can accept an arc of low enough curvature as matching a straight segment if the angle and length values determined by their respective endpoint pairs fit with the current (μ, θ) criterion. This difficulty can also be treated without changing the current figure-matching program, by preprocessing, essentially a reduction to a "canonical form," in which each line element of a curve is as large as possible; for example, two successive straight-line segments differing sufficiently little in slope would be replaced by one corresponding segment. Such a minimal form would also result in more efficient processing. Again, this has not been an issue in most of the current work, since the hand-constructed descriptions tend to be already in this form. However, in the preprocessing decomposition program such a reduction program (for simple closed curves) was required. It is capable of removing the (0.5 . 0.5) from the example just cited. The need arises as follows: After the SCC's are extracted from an object from, say, Figure A, they often need such processing before being compared with some SCC object from Figure B.

5.3.6 The Output Description Format

To conclude the discussion of Part 1, we shall describe its output. As mentioned earlier, memory-size limitations decreed that the entire geometric-analogy program be broken into two sections occupying core at separate times. The means of communication adopted between the two parts is punched cards. The expressions generated by Part 1 are written on the LISP punched output tape and punched offline. They are then given as input to Part 2 on a subsequent run. The form of the expressions involved has already been illustrated in Section 5.2 and briefly described. We describe it in more detail, in the light of the description in Parts 5.3.3 to 5.3.5 of what is done in Part 1.

The output consists of ten S-expressions. The first three are all of the same form, but the first refers to Figure A, the second to Figure B, and the third to Figure C. The form of each is that of a dotted pair of S-expressions. The first is a list of the names of the parts into which the figure has been decomposed; the second is a list of expressions which constitute a description of the figure. From the property and relation calculations come expressions for this list such as (INSIDE X Y). The results of similarity calculations between parts of the same problem figure are also included on this list in the form (SIM, name of X-figure, name of Y-figure, a list of elements of the form $((\mu, \theta) . (\rho_1 . \rho_2))$, one for each $(\rho_1, \rho_2, \mu, \theta)$-correspondence between the two figures involved). The μ and θ are floating-point numbers; each ρ is chosen from the atomic symbols H, V, and N, corresponding to reflections about a horizontal axis, reflection about a vertical axis, and null reflection, respectively.

The fourth expression is a list of expressions recording similarity information between the parts of Figure A and those of Figure B; the elements of these expressions are in the same form as the similarity information above except that the SIM is omitted as the first element of each.

The fifth and sixth expressions are in the same format as the fourth except that now the similarity information is the result of matching between the parts of Figure A and Figure C, in expression five, and of Figure B and Figure C, in expression six. The seventh expression is a list of five lists, one for each of the five answer figures. The ith of these lists the names given to the parts of the ith subfigure.

The eighth is a list of five lists, one for each answer figure, the ith describing the ith answer figure in the same format as the 2nd list of the dotted pair in the first, second, or third expressions. The ninth expression is again a list of five lists, the ith of these giving similarity information on matchings between Figure C and the ith answer figure. The tenth and last expression is a dotted pair of two expressions, each in the same format as the ninth expression but providing, respectively, similarity information between the parts of Figure A and the parts of the answer figures and the parts of Figure B and the parts of the answer figures.

Note on Orientation. A useful expression for the (signed) area enclosed by an N-sided simple closed polygon is:

$$\frac{1}{2}\sum_{i=1}^{N}(x_i y_{i+1} - x_{i+1} y_i)$$

where the sum is over all sides of the polygon, the first endpoint of the ith side being (x_i, y_i) and the second (x_{i+1}, y_{i+1}). Remark: The common textbook example, representing the area of a triangle with vertices (x_1, y_1), (x_2, y_2), and (x_3, y_3) by the determinant $\begin{vmatrix} 1 & 1 & 1 \\ x_1 & x_2 & x_3 \\ y_1 & y_2 & y_3 \end{vmatrix}$ is the special case of this expression for N = 3.

The expression can easily be obtained, as follows: first, Stokes's theorem,

$$\int_A \nabla \times \vec{v} \cdot \vec{n}\, d\sigma = \int_C \vec{v} \cdot \vec{t}\, d\sigma$$

when applied to a simple closed plane curve C with $v = -y\vec{i} + x\vec{j}$, gives the familiar expression for the area of a simple closed plane curve:

$$\text{Area} = \int_A d\sigma = \int_C x\,dy - y\,dx$$

Now if the curve C is a polygon and on each side we put $\begin{matrix} x = x_{i+1}\,t - x_i\,(1-t) \\ y = y_{i+1}\,t - y_i\,(1-t) \end{matrix}$

$0 \leq t \leq 1$ and integrate, we get the above formula.

The chief use made of this expression in Part 1 is not for obtaining areas but as a computationally convenient test for orientation of a simple closed curve. As it stands, the formula will give + area for a counterclockwise traversal of the polygon;–area for a clockwise traversal.

Generalized Euclidean Similarity Transformations. We add here some further comments on the "generalized Euclidean similarity" transformations introduced in Part 5.3.5. Recall that the output of the similarity matching program, given two figures x and y, is NIL if the figures are not related by any transformation of that class and otherwise is a list of quadruples $(\rho_1, \rho_2, \mu, \theta)$, each quadruple specifying the parameters of a generalized Euclidean similarity transformation mapping y onto x. This list contains all such quadruples, with the single restriction that at least one of ρ_1, ρ_2 must be N, the null reflection (and the previously stated restriction $-\pi < \theta \leq \pi$).

As we noted earlier, this list of quadruples is a redundant representation, though a useful one for our purposes, since each of the quadruples is equivalent to either a pure rotation and scale change or a rotation and scale change following a reflection in some specified axis external to the figure. That is, several quadruples among the list may correspond to the same transformation expressed in this latter form.

To make the relationship explicit, we first exhibit a table giving, for each quadruple $(\rho_1, \rho_2, \mu, \theta)$ a corresponding transformation of form either rotation and scale change or reflection in an external horizontal axis, followed by rotation and scale change. In other words, we replace the transformation $(\rho_2(\mathrm{T}_{\mu,\theta}(\rho_1 \mathrm{x})))$ by a transformation $(\overline{\mathrm{T}}_{\mu,\theta}(\rho\, \mathrm{x}))$ with the same effect. We now list the corresponding parameters (we omit scale change since it remains the same; what we wish to make explicit are the relationships between the reflections and rotations). As before, H means horizontal reflection, V vertical, and N none at all; when an angle is specified, we imply the reduction of that angle to the appropriate $-\pi < \overline{\theta} \leq \pi$ range.

ρ_2	θ	ρ_1	$\bar{\theta}$	$\bar{\rho}$
N	θ	N	θ	N
N	θ	H	θ	H
H	θ	N	$-\theta$	H
N	θ	V	$\pi+\theta$	H
V	θ	N	$\pi-\theta$	H

Alternatively, this says that, given the $(\bar{\rho}, \bar{\theta}, \mu)$ form of a transformation, we get the quadruple form as follows: if $\bar{\rho}$ = N, we have just (N, N, μ, $\bar{\theta}$) and if ρ = H, we have the four quadruples (H, N, μ, $\bar{\theta}$), (N, H, μ, $-\theta$), (V, N, μ, $\bar{\theta}-\pi$), and (N, V, μ, $\pi-\bar{\theta}$).

This means that internally, in Part 1, we need only calculate the new description corresponding to a horizontal reflection (a relatively easy task) and run the similarity-testing program on this as well to have all we need to generate the similarity information in the form that Part 2 expects. Furthermore, the composition of two transformations given in quadruple form can be easily reduced to the $(\bar{\rho}, \bar{\theta}, \mu)$ form and the quadruples for the composition generated from them by use of the table just given. We now exhibit a table of the results of this reduction; given a $(\rho_{11}, \rho_{12}, \theta_1, \mu_1)$ followed by a $(\rho_{21}, \rho_{22}, \theta_2, \mu_2)$, we calculate a $(\bar{\rho}, \bar{\theta}, \mu)$ corresponding to that composition (in all cases $\mu = \mu_1\mu_2$ so we omit μ, μ_1, μ_2 from the table). That is, we give the parameters $\bar{\rho}$ and $\bar{\theta}$ of a transformation consisting of a reflection $\bar{\rho}$ followed by a rotation $\bar{\theta}$ which is equivalent in effect to a composed transformation consisting, in order of their application, of

a reflection ρ_{11}
a rotation θ_1
a reflection ρ_{12}
a reflection ρ_{21}
a rotation θ_2
a reflection ρ_{22}.

ρ_{22}	ρ_{21}	ρ_{12}	ρ_{11}	$\bar{\theta}$	$\bar{\rho}$
N	N	N	N	$\theta_2+\theta_1$	N
H	N	N	N	$-(\theta_2+\theta_1)$	H
V	N	N	N	$\pi-(\theta_2+\theta_1)$	H

ρ_{22}	ρ_{21}	ρ_{12}	ρ_{11}	$\bar{\theta}$	$\bar{\rho}$
N	H	N	N	$\theta_2-\theta_1$	H
N	V	N	N	$\pi+\theta_2-\theta_1$	H
N	N	H	N	$\theta_2-\theta_1$	H
H	N	H	N	$\theta_1-\theta_2$	N
V	N	H	N	$\pi-\theta_2+\theta_1$	N
N	H	H	N	$\theta_2+\theta_1$	N
N	V	H	N	$\pi+\theta_2+\theta_1$	N
N	N	V	N	$\pi+\theta_2-\theta_1$	H
H	N	V	N	$-(\pi+\theta_2-\theta_1)$	N
V	N	V	N	$\theta_1-\theta_2$	N
N	H	V	N	$-\pi+\theta_2+\theta_1$	N
N	V	V	N	$\theta_2+\theta_1$	N
N	N	N	H	$\theta_2+\theta_1$	H
H	N	N	H	$-(\theta_2+\theta_1)$	N
V	N	N	H	$\pi-(\theta_2+\theta_1)$	N
N	H	N	H	$\theta_2-\theta_1$	N
N	V	N	H	$\pi+\theta_2-\theta_1$	N
N	N	N	V	$\pi+\theta_2+\theta_1$	H
H	N	N	V	$-(\pi+\theta_2+\theta_1)$	N
V	N	N	V	$-(\theta_2+\theta_1)$	N
N	H	N	V	$-(\pi+\theta_1-\theta_2)$	N
N	V	N	V	$\theta_2-\theta_1$	N

Thus, the compositions are easily computed, as are the inverses. This fact can be used to effect a considerable saving in the amount of similarity computation required. If we need information relating x to y and have already computed the information relating x to z and z to y, each in either direction, we can easily calculate what we need. The present form of Part 1 is quite inefficient in that it does not use this method. When similarity information is needed about any pair of figures, it is computed directly. The further complication of programming to remove this inefficiency did not seem of high priority, since Part 1 runs rapidly enough for test purposes. However, a large proportion of Part 1 time is occupied with similarity calculations; in some cases the over-all running time of Part 1 might be reduced by half or better by this change. The reprogramming required is fairly complex, but it would require no change in the similarity-matching programs themselves, only in the much less complex program that controls their application.

5.4 Analogy: Part 2

5.4.1 Introduction

We now turn to a discussion of the second, final, phase of the solution process, corresponding to Part 2 of ANALOGY. In this stage the program, given the output of Part 1, attempts to arrive at a choice of answer figure. The Part 2 program uses the Part 1 output, which constitutes a relatively abstract description of the eight problem figures, to generate transformation rules taking Figure A into Figure B and Figure C into one of the answer figures. A choice between alternate rules satisfying this condition must frequently be made. This selection is based on a simple criterion of "rule strength," which will be described The principal aim of this section is to describe the working of this rule-generating and rule-choosing process as it currently exists. First, however, a few remarks should be made concerning the scope, or generality, of the Part 2 mechanism.

It is important to observe that in the current version of ANALOGY, Part 2 is far more general than Part 1. For example, it can accept information about arbitrary *n*-place relations among subfigures, while Part 1 can only generate information about a relatively small set of relations, such as, LEFT, ABOVE, INSIDE, which have been suitably programmed into it; at present it is restricted to dealing with two-place relations. Furthermore, Part 1 contains all the essentially geometrical processing; Part 2 does not "understand" geometrical concepts, except insofar as similarity information is treated differently from other relational information. Essentially, Part 2 is a complex combinatorial process which could well be applied to nongeometrical subject matter. This sharp decomposition of ANALOGY into two parts with quite separate functions and very restricted communication between them is largely fortuitous, arising from the storage limitations imposed through the use of the 7090 LISP system. It has effectively prevented any scheme of program organization in which the rule-finding part controls the application of the facilities of the geometrical-manipulation part according to its needs of the moment. Such a scheme of organization would have considerable advantages in power and efficiency and would parallel in an interesting way the human capability of returning to the figures for further detail, as required.

However, there are compensating advantages in the scheme adopted. It is relatively easy to simulate Part 1 output corresponding to certain well-defined geometrical manipulations precluded from implementation in the present

Part 1 by considerations of excessive 7090 running time, storage requirements, or programming time. In this way we are able to study the performance of Part 2 on a wider class of problems than can presently be handled by the entire ANALOGY system. Thus, in Section 5.5, where the results of various test runs of ANALOGY are collected and discussed, a number of examples of this type are included in addition to those examples run through the entire system starting in the input format appropriate to Part 1. In all cases where the Part 1 output was simulated, the assumptions made about additional facilities assumed present in Part 1 are stated. Furthermore, since Part 1 running times are typically somewhat longer than Part 2 times, it has been possible to run more cases in the same amount of 7090 time by simulating the Part 1 output for a number of cases which could have been handled by the current Part 1. Once Part 1 had already been extensively checked out on test cases, those cases which had no feature that could be expected to test new aspects of Part 1 were treated in this way. Again in the discussion of test cases run, the cases with this approach are so identified.

From a point of view that considers the combinatorial rule-finding process as the significant part of ANALOGY, the Part 1 program appears as little more than an "existence proof" of the feasibility of mechanically performing sufficiently elaborate manipulations on the primitive inputs to produce descriptions in the form required for Part 2 to solve at least an appreciable variety of problems. From another point of view, concerned not with studies of heuristic problem-solving *per se* but chiefly with the machine manipulation of complex line drawings as a tool in other problem areas, the significance of the Part 1 program is quite different. It then lies rather in the methods of figure representation and manipulation using a list-processing language already embodied in it, as well as the extensions of these methods suggested in our discussions of the current limitations of Part 1. After this prelude we proceed to discuss the detailed working of Part 2.

5.4.2 Matching and Rule Generation

The first step in the Part 2 solution process is to match the objects of Figure A with those of Figure B. The basis for this matching is the similarity information given as input to Part 2. If part x of Figure A corresponds to part y of Figure B under any generalized Euclidean similarity transformation of the type defined in Section 5.3, then x can be matched with y. In this way, we match the objects of Figure A with those of Figure B as far as possible. The result of a matching is an expression stating which objects must be removed from Figure A, which objects must be added to Figure A, and which objects of Figure A must be paired to which in Figure B to transform the set of objects in Figure A to those in Figure B. It is frequently possible to match objects between Figure A and Figure B in a variety of ways. In such cases all possible matchings compatible with our permitted class of similarity transformations are generated. Consider, for example, Figures A and B of Case 5 (see Section 5.5) labeled as shown. (The complete case is also shown as Fig. 5-3.)

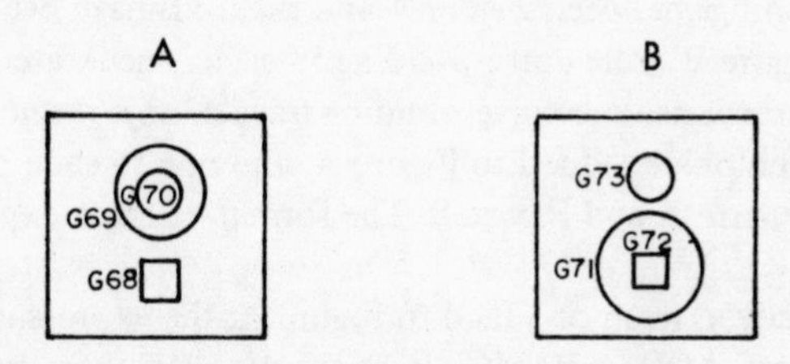

The matching routine *matchab* generates the two possible matchings:

((REMOVE NIL) (ADD NIL) ((G69 . G71) (G68 . G72) (G70 . G73)))

and

((REMOVE NIL) (ADD NIL) ((G70 . G71) (G68 . G72) (G69 . G73)))

The matching expression is a three-element list; the first naming the objects added, the second those removed, and the last the pairings of objects matched.

For an example with addition and removal of parts, consider Figures A and B from Case 8 of Section 5.5, also labeled as follows:

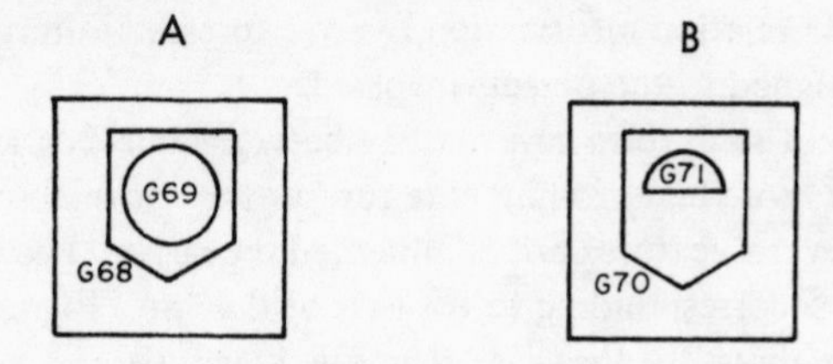

Here only one matching is generated; it looks like:

((REMOVE (G69)) (ADD (G71)) ((G68 . G70)))

The routine *matchab* which we have been discussing is also used at a later stage to match Figure C with each of the answer figures (cf. Part 5.4.3). Our final example of the process comes again from Case 5, this time the matching between Figures C and 2.

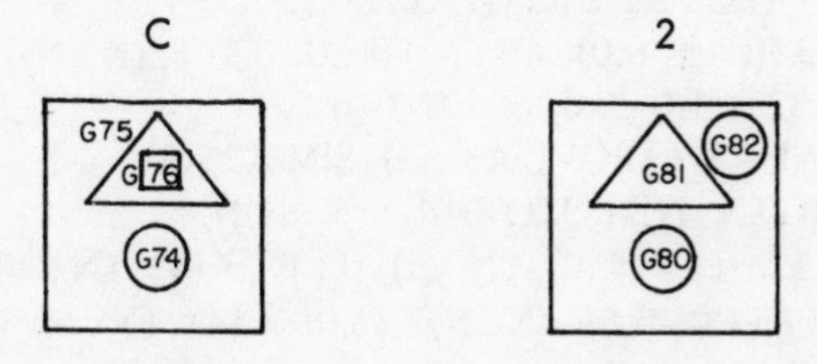

The resulting matchings are:

((REMOVE (G76)) (ADD (G82)) ((G74 . G80) (G75 . G81)))

and

((REMOVE (G76)) (ADD (G80)) ((G74 . G82) (G75 . G81)))

Once all the matchings between Figure A and Figure B have been generated, the "Figure A → Figure B" rule corresponding to each is generated. A rule consists of a list of expressions, one corresponding to each object removed from Figure A, one to each object added to Figure A, and one to each pair of objects matched between Figure A and Figure B. The format of these expressions is as follows:

For an object removed from or added to Figure A, the expression is a list consisting of the word ADD or REMOVE, as appropriate, then the arbitrary name assigned to the object by the rule-formation program, then a list of the property and relation information involving that object in the figure in which it occurs (Figure A if a REMOVE, Figure B if an ADD).

For a matched pair of objects the expression consists again of a list, the first element being the word MATCH, the second being the arbitrary name assigned to the object in its occurrence in both Figure A and Figure B, and the last being a dotted pair of expressions, the first a list of the property and relation information involving this object in its occurrence in Figure A and the second expression the corresponding information for its occurrence in Figure B. The property and relation information is also expressed in terms of the arbitrary names assigned to the objects involved.

Several examples of such rules have already been given in Section 5.2. We shall introduce one more here, to illustrate further the above-described format and to introduce several features not commented on earlier. The example is the rule from Case 5 corresponding to the first of the two "Figure A → Figure B" matchings given above for that case. The rule is as follows:

```
(
(MATCH A1 (((ABOVE A2 A1) (SIM OB1 A1
    (((1.0 . 0.0) . (N . N))))) . ((INSIDE A1 A2) (ABOVE
    A3 A1) (SIM OB1 A1 (((1.0 . 0.0) . (N . N)) ((1.0 . 1.57) . (N . N))
    ((1.0 . 3.14) . (N . N)) ((1.0 . 1.57) . (N . N))))
    (SIMTRAN (((1.0 . 0.0) . (N . N)) ((1.0 . 1.57) . (N . N))
    ((1.0 . –3.14) . (N . N)) ((1.0 . –1.57) . (N . N)))))))
(MATCH A2 (((ABOVE A2 A1) (INSIDE A3 A2)
    (SIM A2 A3 (((2.0 . 0.0) . (N . N)) ((2.0 . 3.14) . (N . N))))
    (SIM OB2 A2 (((1.0 . 0.0) . (N . N)))))
    ((INSIDE A1 A2) (ABOVE A3 A2) (SIM A2 A3
    (((2.0 . 0.0) . (N . N)) ((2.0 . 3.14) . (N . N))))
    (SIM OB2 A2 (((1.0 . 0.0) . (N . N)) ((1.0 . 3.14) . (N . N))))
    (SIMTRAN (((1.0 . 0.0) . (N . N)) ((1.0 . 3.14) . (N . N)))))))
```

```
(MATCH A3 (((ABOVE A3 A1) (INSIDE A3 A2)
    (SIM A2 A3 (((2.0 . 0.0) . (N . N)) ((2.0 . 3.14) . (N . N))))
    (SIM OB2 A3 (((2.0 . 0.0) . (N . N)) ((2.0 . 3.14) . (N . N)))))
    ((ABOVE A3 A1) (ABOVE A3 A2) (SIM A2 A3 (((2.0 . 0.0) . ( N . N))
    ((2.0 . 3.14) . (N . N)))) . (SIM OB2 A3 (((2.0 . 0.0)
    (N . N)) ((2.0 . 3.14) . (N . N)))) (SIMTRAN
    (((1.0 . 0.0) . (N . N)) ((1.0 . 3.14) . (N . N)))))))
)
```

In this rule statement A1 corresponds to the square, A2 to the large circle, and A3 to the small circle in the sketches of both Figure A and Figure B for Case 5 given previously. Most of the detail of the rule is covered by the format description above, but two items must still be explained.

The first of these is the presence of expressions giving similarity information relating each object to an "external" object with a name OB1 or OB2, etc. The presence of such expressions in the rules makes it possible, at the next stage of the process, to utilize the information that an object in Figure A is the same kind, in the sense of being related to it by one of our generalized Euclidean similarity transformations, as an object in Figure C, say. Such information, which in some problems is essential to the choice of an answer figure, would otherwise be lost from the rule and thus not be taken into account in the final choice of a rule, which we wish to depend solely on the content of the explicitly stated rules. Case 15 (cf. Section 5.5) is an example that could not be handled without this device.

Of course it would have been possible instead to leave the rule form unaltered and introduce a highly special submethod to handle this case, but such an approach would have violated the spirit of our "descriptive-language" approach to the design of Part 2, in which the rule expressions themselves carry all the information on which the eventual choice of one of them, and hence of an answer figure, is based. Furthermore this "explicit" approach has the advantage of communicating rather well with the programmer, as well as being rather easy to extend or modify by, for example, the introduction of alternate processes for proceeding from the set of rule expressions to the choice of an answer, without altering any of the current rule-generating mechanism. Below, we describe such a change, in the rule-evaluation procedure, which was easily made with no change in the underlying rule-manipulating apparatus.

The second item is the presence of expressions of the form SIMTRAN, followed by similarity transformation data. This expression, which occurs for each matched object among the property and relation information pertaining to Figure B, simply gives the data corresponding to the possible generalized Euclidean similarity transformations taking the object, as it appears in Figure A into the corresponding object of B. This, strictly speaking, is redundant, since this information can be calculated from the statement relating the object, say x, in Figure A to an OB-object and that relating the corresponding object, say y, in Figure B to the same OB-object. However, it seemed useful to include this information explicitly in the rule, since its presence therein simplifies the rule-"generalization" and rule-comparison processes and contributes to making the rule content more comprehensible to a human observer.

5.4.3 Rule-Generalization and Comparison

At this point we have constructed a rule or, more typically, a set of rules, describing the transformation of Figure A into Figure B. Now we must extend each of these rules to cover as well the transformation of Figure C into each admissible answer figure and then choose among all the rules so generated. This process corresponds to a rather complex program but is fairly easy to describe. First, the matching function *matchab* is called five times to get the possible matchings of Figure C with each of the five answer figures. If a given answer figure does not correspond to the "Figure A → Figure B" matchings in number of objects added, removed, and matched, respectively, that answer figure is discarded. This leaves us with a set of "admissible" answer figures to be considered further. Now for *each* of the original "Figure A → Figure B" rules and for *each* matching of Figure C with *each* of these "admissible" answer figures a set of rules is generated, as follows. We first find all correspondences of objects in the "Figure A → Figure B" situation with those in the "Figure C → answer Figure i" situation. By this we mean that we pair in all possible ways the objects added to Figure B with those added to Figure i; similarly, we pair the objects removed from Figure A with those removed from Figure C; finally, we pair those matched between Figures A and B with those matched between Figures C and i. We then choose from these three categories in all possible ways. This gives us a set of identifications of the objects in each "Figure A → Figure B" rule with the objects of Figures C and i. In general, if n_1 objects are added, n_2 removed, and n_3 matched, the number of such correspondences in $n_1! \times n_2! \times n_3!$ For example, in Case 5 there is no object removed, none added, and three matched in going from Figure A to Figure B and also in going from Figure C to any admissible answer figure. Hence there are only $0! \times 0! \times 3! = 6$ such correspondences in this case.

Now we are in a position to extend our transformation rules. For each original "Figure A → Figure B" rule and each such identification of parts we generate a new rule by removing from the rule those statements and exactly those statements that are not true of the Figure C and Figure i in question under the given part identification. What we have generated is a rule (again in the same rule format) that still takes Figure A into Figure B (though it is "weaker," in general, than the original rule) and also Figure C into Figure i. Under the single constraint that Figure i be "admissible," this can always be done. Of course we may be left with a rule from which all the distinguishing features of the situation have disappeared.

Once this process has been carried out over the whole range of possibilities described, we are left with a list of rule expressions, perhaps rather long, each associated with a particular answer figure. All these rules are, in a literal sense, solutions to the stated problem, as quoted from the ACE test instructions in Section 5.1. Each rule expression represents a rule taking Figure A into Figure B and Figure C into some answer figure, thus, justifying, in some sense, the choice of Figure i as an answer. Clearly, this is not what is wanted; one is expected to choose the answer figure corresponding to that rule which is "best," in some unspecified sense. One might at first think of straightforwardly invoking "rule simplicity" as a criterion; of choosing, say, the "shortest" rule that does the job. However, quite to the contrary, it appears that what is required is something like a "rule complexity" criterion. We are dealing with a class of rules of widely varying discriminatory power, and we wish to pick the "strongest," that is, the one that gives the most information about the common transformation mapping Figure A into Figure B and Figure C into the corresponding answer figure. Incidentally, these considerations suggest what seems an appropriate notion of "simplicity" or "economy" for this problem, namely, some measure of how little alteration in our "theory" of the "Figure A → Figure B" situation is required when we extend the "theory" to a new situation.

Our advocacy of the use of a criterion of "rule strength" in choosing a rule (and thus an answer figure) amounts, in some sense, to a conjecture about human problem-solving behavior, at least in the domain of geometric-analogy problems. Such a criterion of rule strength has been incorporated in Part 2 for choosing from the list of candidate rules. The technique used is a very simple one; a function *rval* is introduced that assigns to each rule a numerical value intended to correspond to its strength. Then the rules are sorted by value and the rule with the largest value chosen, except in case of a tie for largest value between two or more rules corresponding to different answer figures. Roughly, the function *rval* measures the length of the rule. The value of the original version of *rval,* which was used in running most of the test cases, is obtained by the following process: The value associated with a given rule is the sum of the values associated with the elements of the list which constitutes the rule. These values are obtained as follows:

If the rule element is an ADD or REMOVE, count the number of elements in the top level of the description list of that element; for example, if the rule element is (ADD A1 ((ABOVE A1 A3) (INSIDE A1 A2))), its value is 2, that is, the length of the list ((ABOVE A1 A3) (INSIDE A1 A2)).

If the rule element is a MATCH, count the number of elements in both description lists of that element and add the results; for example, the value of

(MATCH A1 (((INSIDE A1 A2) (ABOVE A1 A3)). ((INSIDE A1 A3)))) is 3, that is, *length* [((INSIDE A1 A2) (ABOVE A1 A3))] + *length* [((INSIDE A1 A3))].

After obtaining a value by either of these procedures, supplement it by adding 0.1 for each $((\mu.\theta) . (\rho_1.\rho_2))$ element in a SIM-list and 0.3 for each one in a SIMTRAN-list. (These values were rather arbitrarily chosen; they seem to work adequately on most cases.) The result of these three steps is the value of the given rule element.

More recently, this version of *rval* was slightly altered to incorporate in the evaluation of the SIMTRAN expressions a preference for certain $((\mu.\theta) . (\rho_1.\rho_2))$-elements over others. We still credit each one with a small value, but these values are now determined by the following rule: (We write it as a LISP-type conditional expression; see references 18 or 19.)

$$
\begin{aligned}
(&\mu = 1 \wedge \theta = 0 \wedge \rho_1 = N \wedge \rho_2 = N \rightarrow 0.45;\\
&\theta = 0 \wedge \rho_1 = N \wedge \rho_2 = N \rightarrow 0.40;\\
&\mu = 1 \wedge \rho_1 = N \wedge \rho_2 = N \rightarrow 0.35;\\
&\rho_1 = N \wedge \rho_2 = N \rightarrow 0.30;\\
&\mu = 1 \wedge \theta = 0 \rightarrow 0.07;\\
&\theta = 0 \rightarrow 0.06;\\
&\mu = 1 \rightarrow 0.05;\\
&T \rightarrow 0.03)
\end{aligned}
$$

The SIM-element values are still obtained as above.

One purpose of this alteration was to incorporate a form of simplicity criterion that had not originally been included. To consider one such case, suppose Figure B could be obtained from Figure A either by a rotation or by a rotation and reflection. Furthermore suppose Figure C could be transformed into answer Fig. 5-1, say, by the same rotation only and into Fig. 5-2 by the same rotation and reflection only. In this case the rules could be of exactly the same strength, and a tie in value might result. The new *rval* would settle such a tie by rating the pure rotation higher than the composed rotation and reflection. Case 19 of Section 5.5 illustrates the use of this revised procedure.

Further refinements can easily be incorporated in the evaluation procedure. It would for example be easy to examine the effects of rule comparison based only on the Euclidean similarity information or, alternatively, based on suppressing the Euclidean similarity information completely, merely by simple changes in *rval*, with no alteration in the complex rule-making machinery.

We conclude this section with one further remark on the organization of the Part 2 process. The approach chosen has the elegant property that the problem of uniqueness of the answer figure chosen is handled "automatically," with no special effort. That is, the rule used in selecting an answer figure is to take C into exactly one of the answer figures. If we had proceeded by taking a "Figure A → Figure B" rule and progressively weakening it till it could be applied to Figure C, then, using it to predict an answer, we should have to be careful about getting a rule just "general" enough to choose one of the answer figures given and still specific enough to choose only one (and there would be no certainty of having obtained the "strongest" rule with a unique answer). This would seem to be a difficult process to implement. However, by separately generating a "Figure C → Figure i" rule or set of rules from the "Figure A → Figure B" rule or rules for each admissible Figure i, then ranking them all in one list, we avoid all these problems. For each answer figure there is a "best" rule and the only problematic case, a tie in rule value between the "best" rules of two different figures is highly unlikely, unless in fact the information available to Part 2 is not sufficient to discriminate between two of the answer figures. Thus the scheme of "parallel" rule generation adopted seems to have great advantages, in conceptual simplicity at least, over any sort of "sequential" scheme, except where the number of rules to be generated is prohibitively large. In problems of the ACE test type, this never seems to be the case. Among our test cases, the largest number of rules presented to *rval* was 36 in Case 5. Typically, the number of rules is much smaller.

5.4.4 An Extension to the Basic Procedure

The basic rule-making and choosing mechanism described furnishes a suitable foundation for a variety of extensions capable of substantially increasing its problem-solving power. This section will be devoted to consideration of one particular extension that has been implemented and to the "administrative" problems raised by its introduction.

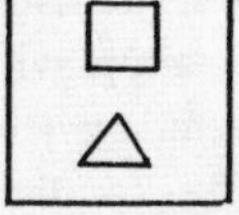

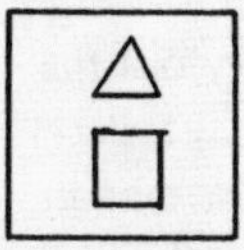

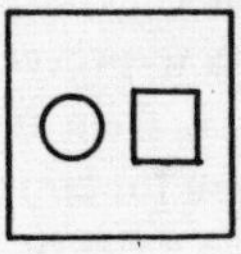

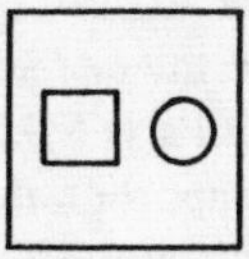

The considerations motivating the extension in question are best seen from a very simple example. Suppose Figure A is [square above triangle], Figure B is [triangle above square], and Figure C is [circle left of square]. If [square left of circle] is among the answer figures, we would like Part 2 to choose it. However, the basic machinery we have been describing is incapable of "seeing" this analogy, since, in our basic scheme, the rule common to 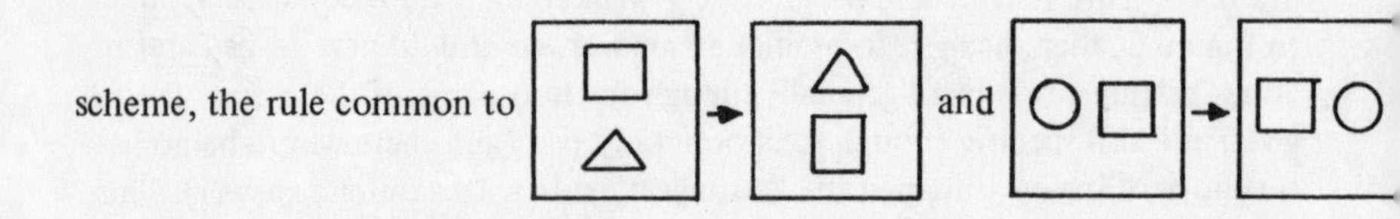

is weak beyond all capacity to distinguish this answer figure from other "admissible" ones, except perhaps quite fortuitously. Various techniques might be adopted to handle such problems, but we wished to adopt one compatible with the basic mechanism already described. What must be conveyed to this basic mechanism is the information that under certain circumstances some properties or relations can be systematically replaced by others in going from the "Figure A → Figure B" situation to the "Figure C → answer figure" situation. This is a rather simple representative of a class of extensions based on the idea of enabling Part 2 to utilize information about "second-order" properties and relations, that is, properties of and relations between the description properties and relations themselves.

The treatment of this simple extension is quite easy. If, say, we want the ABOVE relations to be systematically replaced by LEFT relations, all we need do is substitute the atom LEFT for the atom ABOVE in the "Figure A → Figure B" rules and carry out the remainder of the process using the resulting rules instead of the originals. Such a substitution, or a substitution with the arguments of the relation reversed, corresponding to replacing ABOVE with RIGHT, is a near-trivial operation in LISP. It should be noted that the rule finally resulting from this process no longer explicitly fits the "Figure A → Figure B" case, but the result of the reverse substitution will do so because of the way in which it was constructed.

Once this technique has been selected, what remains is a characteristic "administrative" problem of heuristic programming: Now that we have a method capable of handling certain previously untouched cases, we must give the program the capacity to decide when to use it. That is, since this technique is unnecessary in most cases, we do not wish to generate a large number of variant "Figure A → Figure B" rules and append them to the original ones every time, before we proceed to the rule-generalization and testing. A plausible alternative, and the one adopted, is to proceed as follows: First carry out the basic process of Parts 5.4.1 to 5.4.3. Then at the value-comparing stage, Part 2 calculates an appropriately chosen function of the highest value, its margin over the next highest value, and the value of the original "Figure A → Figure B" rule (calculated by *rval*). On the basis of this calculation, the program determines whether to accept the answer corresponding to that "best" value or to return to the "Figure A → Figure B" rule stage, generate some variant rules, and repeat the rule-generalization process on them. Thus the variant-rule method never gets used until the basic method has failed. Case 20 illustrates the use of this method.

For certain examples of geometric-analogy problems, the interchange of Figures B and C renders the problem more amenable to solution by the process described in Sections 5.3 and 5.4. In two of the cases illustrated in Section 5.5 (Cases 2 and 14) we have made this interchange before running the problem. The justification for doing this is quite simple; with, at worst, twice the running time, a trivial extension of the top-level control program could run the problem both ways (choosing the higher-scoring answer, if one were obtained each way). Furthermore, the addition of a few simple heuristics should make it possible for ANALOGY to decide, quite reliably and in a very short time, whether the interchange should be made.

5.5 Results and Discussion

5.5.1 Introduction

The problems on which ANALOGY has been tested will be discussed and the results provided. After this has been done, we turn to some remarks on topics related to ANALOGY. These include some discussion of possible picture input schemes, a brief comparison of ANALOGY's capabilities with human performance on the same class of problems, and a consideration of the appropriateness of LISP for a program of this type.

5.5.2 Test Cases and Results

This section includes all cases on which ANALOGY has been tested. Where any problem depends on a later improvement not present for the earlier test runs, this fact is explicitly stated.

For each problem we exhibit the eight problem figures, state the answer reached by the program, if any, and, under "Comments," add any further information necessary to understand the conditions and assumptions under which the test case was run. As we remarked in Section 5.4, certain cases were run through Part 2 only, either because they exploit the greater generality of Part 2 (in the sense that it can accept information that the current Part 1 is incapable of providing) or because, by the time they were considered, Part 1 had been sufficiently tested on entirely comparable cases to justify the omission. Note that the earlier cases listed were all run through both parts of ANALOGY. Again, in any case where Part 1 was omitted and any additional feature would be required of it, this fact is noted.

For several reasons to which we return in Part 5.5.3, the actual running times of ANALOGY on these test cases did not seem sufficiently meaningful to justify separate presentation with each test case. Data on typical running times, with some comments on their validity, will be given in Part 5.3.3.

Case 1

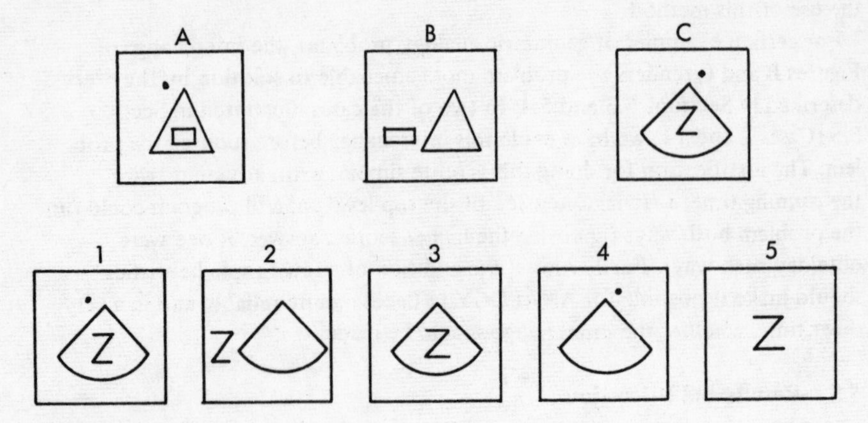

Answer selected: Figure 2

Comments: This case was run through both Part 1 and Part 2. The rule involves both removal of a part and a change in part relationships. This problem is discussed as example 1 in Section 5.2.

Case 2

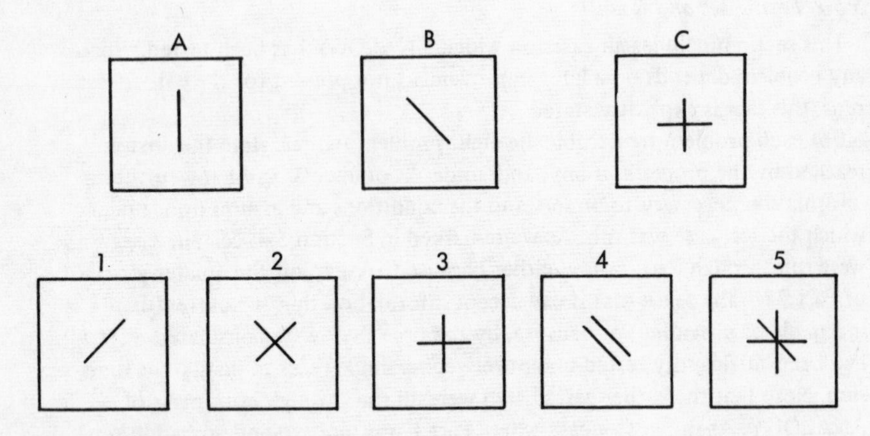

Answer selected: Figure 2

Comments: This case was run through both Part 1 and Part 2. The rule used here to select an answer involves a rotation. The SIMTRAN feature discussed in Section 4 plays an important role in this process. This problem is No. 1 of the 1942 ACE test, with Figures B and C interchanged.

Case 3

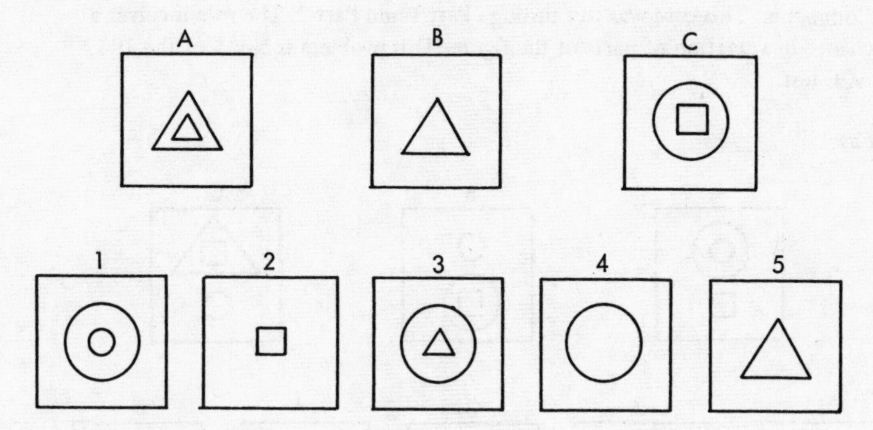

Answer selected: Figure 4

Comments: This case was run through both Part 1 and Part 2. The rule here exemplifies a typical situation. We remove a part satisfying a given relation, namely, the inside figure. If had not been among the answer figures and had, ANALOGY would find a rule of essentially the form "remove the outside figure and enlarge the inside one," resulting in the choice of the as answer (see Case 17). This problem is No. 3 of the 1942 ACE test, slightly modified to avoid use of shaded figures, which Part 1 is not equipped to handle.

Case 4

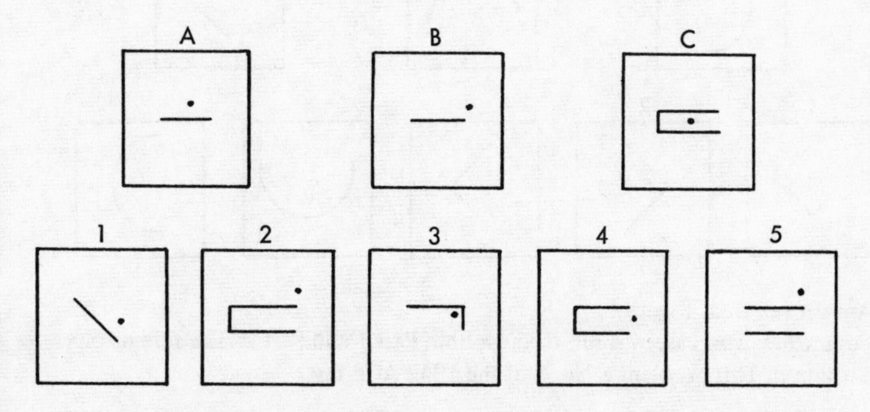

Answer selected: Figure 4
Comments: This case was run through Part 1 and Part 2. The rule involves a change in a relation of parts of the figure. This problem is No. 5 of the 1942 ACE test.

Case 5

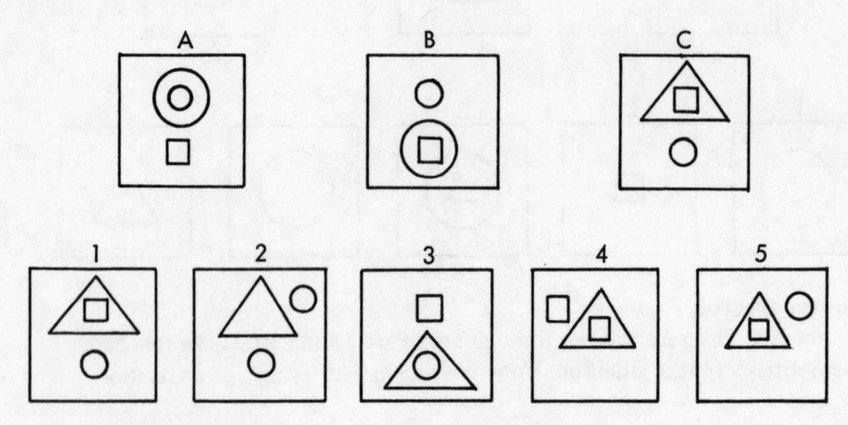

Answer selected: Figure 3
Comments: This case was run through both Part 1 and Part 2. This problem was in some sense the most elaborate for Part 2, since it required the greatest number of rules to be generated and compared of any problem run. This problem is No. 10 of the 1943 ACE test.

Case 6

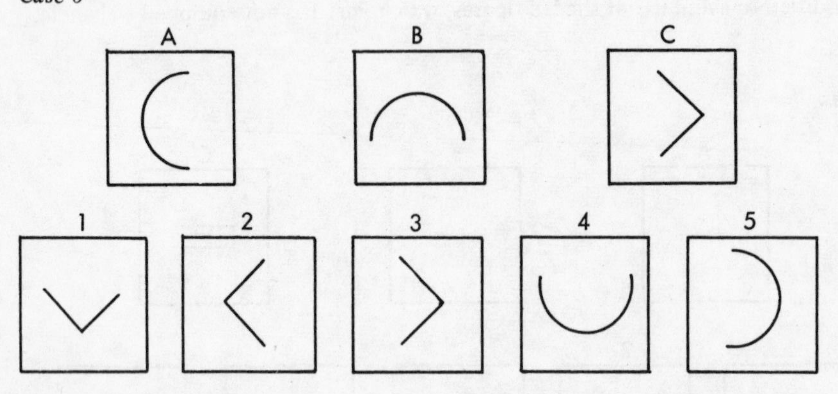

Answer selected: Figure 1
Comments: This case was run through both Part 1 and Part 2. The rule involves a rotation. This problem is No. 8 of the 1942 ACE test.

Case 7

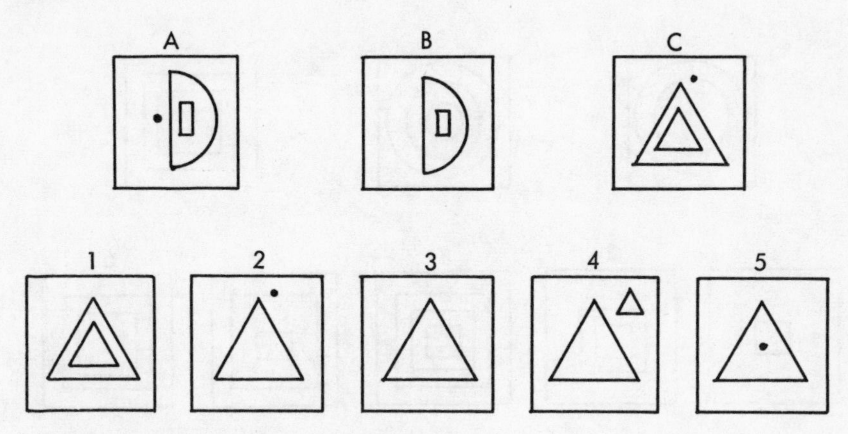

Answer selected: Figure 1
Comments: This case was run through both Part 1 and Part 2. The fact that the removed object is a dot in both cases is not essential to the rule-finding in this case. Part 2 is capable of formulating a rule that effectively says: "remove that part which is not involved in the 'inside' relationship." This problem is No. 2 of the 1942 ACE test.

Case 8

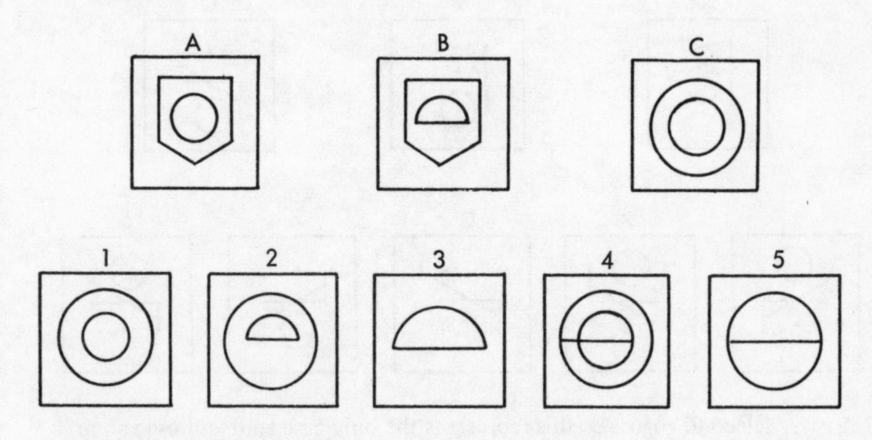

Answer selected: Figure 2
Comments: This problem was run through both Part 1 and Part 2. The rule involves both removal and addition of parts. This problem is No. 6 of the 1944 ACE test.

Case 9

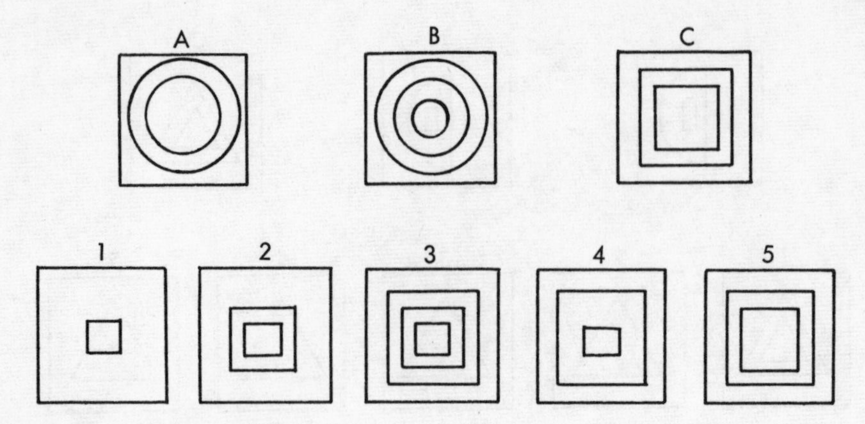

Answer selected: Figure 3
Comments: This problem was run through both Part 1 and Part 2. The Part 2 process is trivial since Figure 3 is the only "admissible" answer figure. This problem is No. 1 of the 1946 ACE test.

Case 10

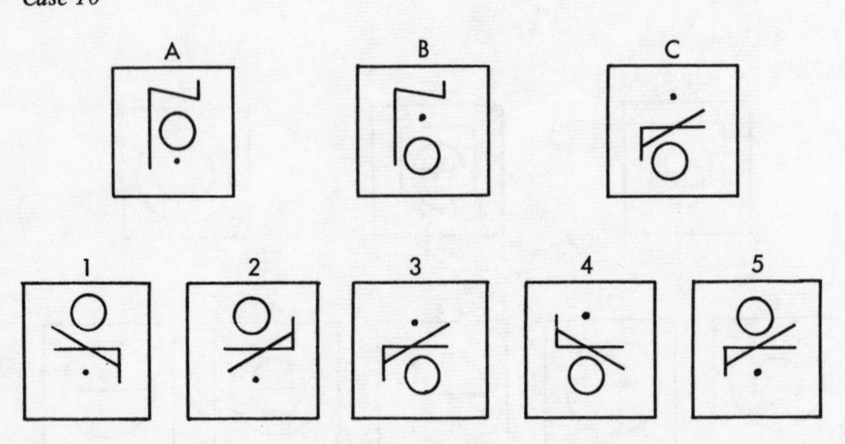

Answer selected: Figure 3 (this represents the only case among those run in which Part 2 arrived at an answer different from that of human opinion).
Comments: This problem was run through Part 1 and Part 2. The failure of Part 2's basic method on this problem indicates the necessity of some extensions to it. This problem is No. 20 of the 1942 ACE test.

Case 11

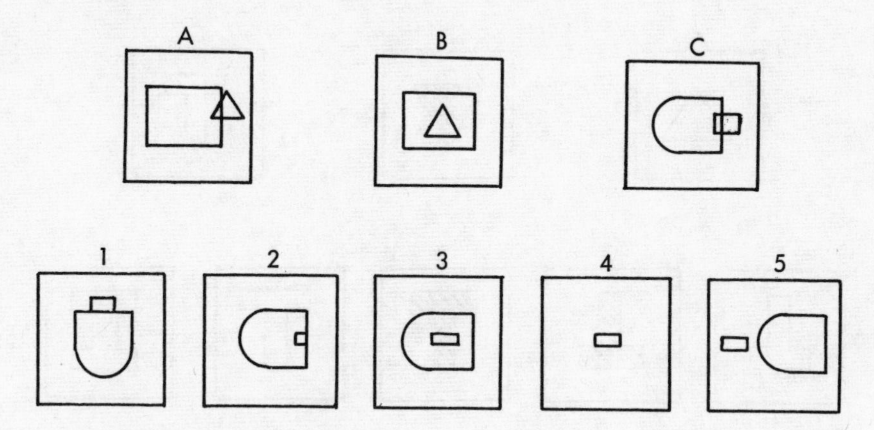

Answer selected: Figure 3
Comments: This case was run through both Part 1 and Part 2, as well as the preprocessing decomposition program. This problem is discussed as example 2 in Section 5.2.

Case 12

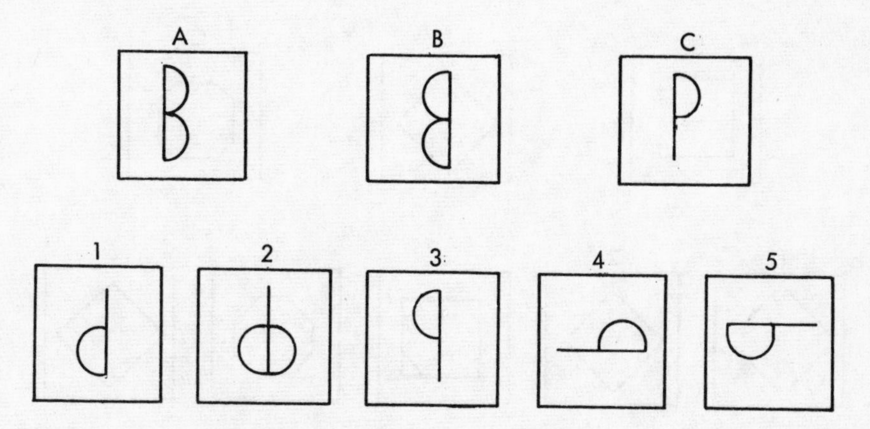

Answer selected: Figure 3
Comments: This case was run through Part 2 only. The rule by which the answer was selected is, essentially, "reflect in a vertical axis." This problem is No. 4 of the 1942 ACE test.

Case 13

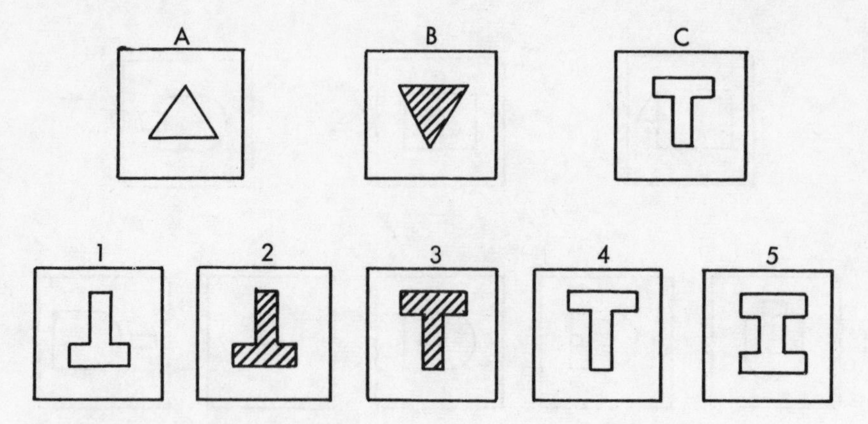

Answer selected: Figure 2
Comments: This case was run through Part 2 only. The only additional facility assumed in Part 1 is a property SHADED; if a simple closed figure X has its interior shaded, the property information (SHADED X) is included in the Part 1 output. This problem is No. 7 of the 1942 ACE test.

Case 14

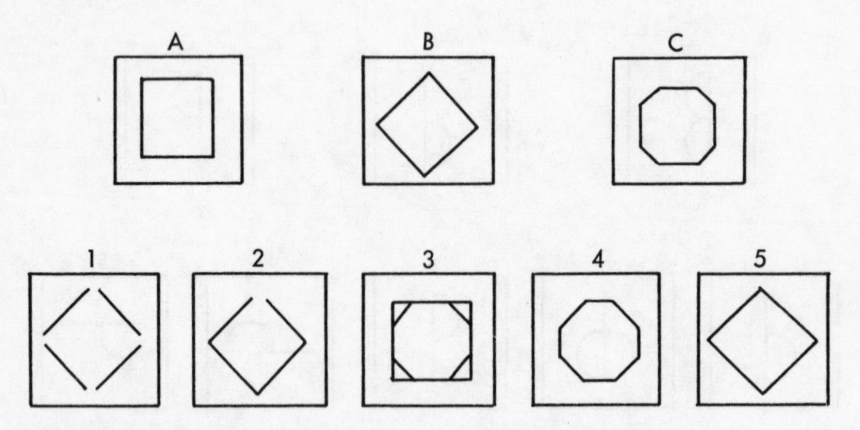

Answer selected: Figure 4
Comments: This case was run through Part 2 only. The rule involved in choosing an answer figure amounts simply to a rotation. This problem is No. 12 of the 1942 ACE test, with Figures B and C interchanged (see note to Section 5.4).

Case 15

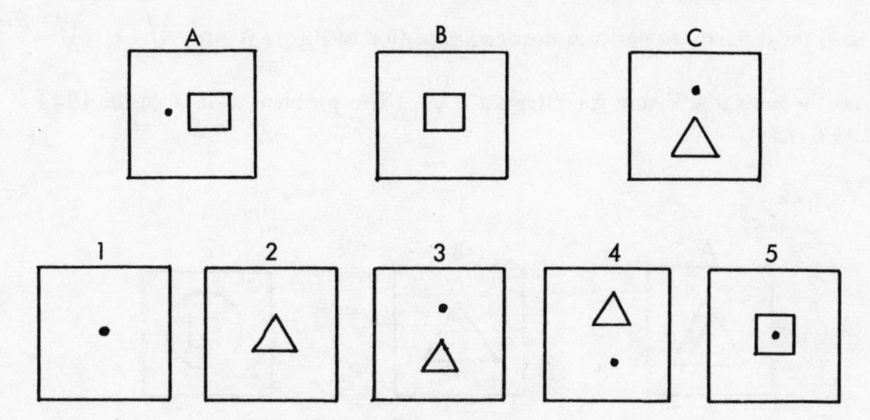

Answer selected: Figure 2
Comments: This case was run through Part 2 only. This example was devised to exhibit the use of the OB-type similarity information in the rules of Part 2. In the absence of anything else to go on, Part 2 selects Figure 2 instead of Figure 1 on the grounds that the same type of object is removed from Figure A to get Figure B and from Figure C to get Figure 2.

Case 16

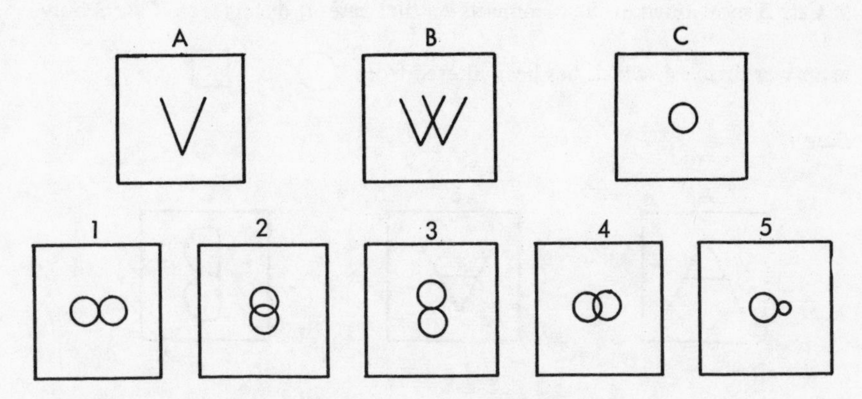

Answer selected: Figure 4
Comments: This case was run through Part 2 only. The additional facility required in Part 1 consists of two new relations (OVERLAP X Y) and (TOUCH X Y) defined in the obvious way (for example, in answer Figure 1, the

and ○ TOUCH; in answer Figure 4, the ○ and ○ OVERLAP), and

also the capacity to perform the decomposition of Figure B into V + V

on the basis that Figure A contains a V . This problem is No. 4 of the 1943 ACE test.

Case 17

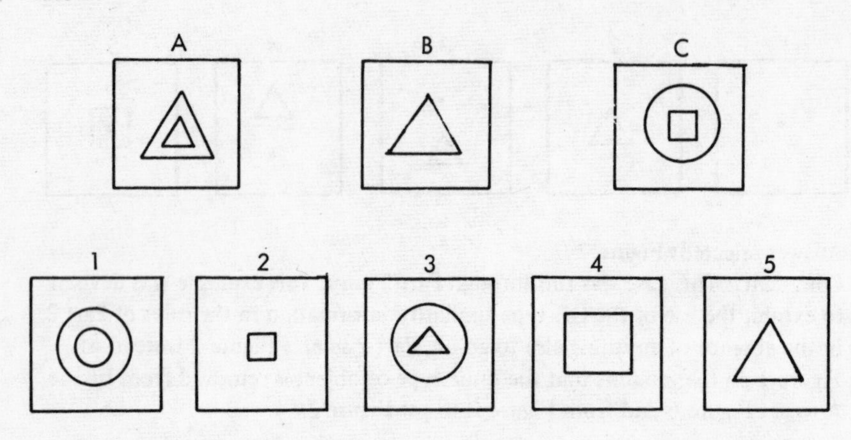

Answer selected: Figure 4
Comments: This case was run through Part 2 only. This example is the variant of Case 3 mentioned in the comments on that case. It differs from Case 3 only

in answer Figure 4, which has been altered from ○ to □

Case 18

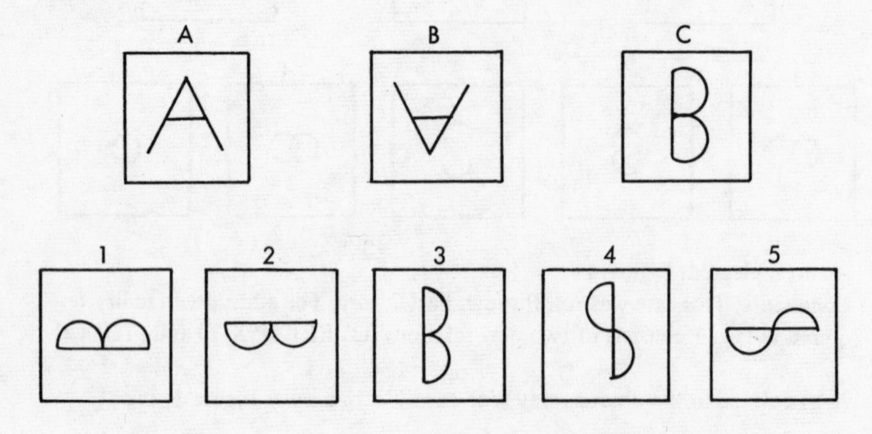

Answer selected: Figure 3
Comments: This case was run through Part 2 only. The rule that results in the selection of an answer here involves a reflection in a horizontal axis. Note that if answer Figure 4, say, were replaced by ꓭ, it would be chosen since A → ∀ and B → ꓭ by pure rotation, and the new *rval* prefers rotations to reflections (see Case 19 for a similar example).

Case 19

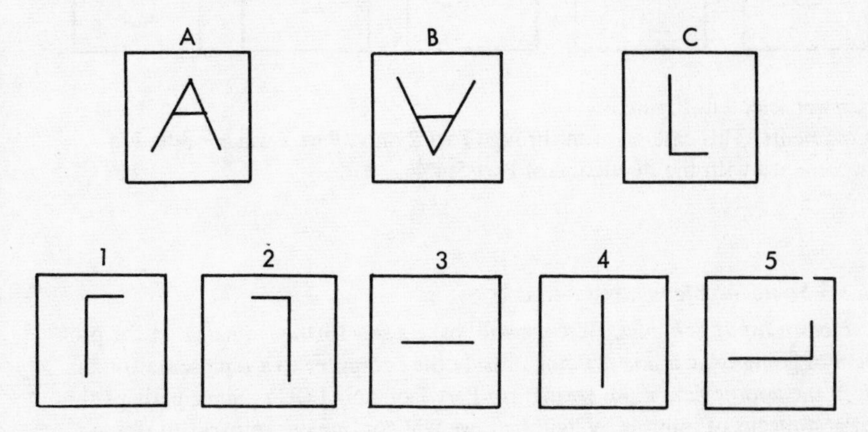

Answer selected: Figure 2
Comments: This case was run through Part 2 only. A rule of form "rotate through π" results in the choice of Figure 2; one of form "reflect in a horizontal axis" results in the choice of Figure 1. The program is built to prefer the pure rotation to the pure reflection, and hence chooses Figure 2.

Case 20

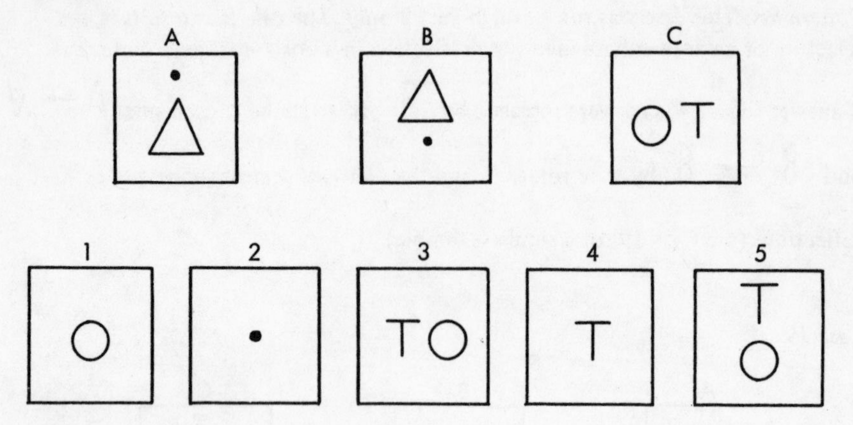

Answer selected: Figure 3
Comments: This case was run through Part 2 only. Part 2 was modified in accordance with the discussion of Part 5.4.4.

5.5.3 Some Supplementary Remarks

Picture Input Schemes. Here we will make a few further remarks on the problem of going from a line drawing outside the computer to a representation of it in the appropriate input format for Part 1 of ANALOGY. Since perhaps the easiest means of input is by light-pen, we will confine our remarks to this technique. There exist two light-pen input programs, at least, for which the task of translating from the internal representation available to our format does not seem too formidable. These, already mentioned in Section 1, are the *Sketchpad* system of Sutherland (37, 38) and the *Cyclops* system of Marill (16). *Sketchpad,* in particular, has some very convenient properties for this purpose: the elements from which its drawings are built up are straight-line segments and arcs of circles, exactly what we need, and the facilities of the system permit easy correction of the drawing until it is sufficiently accurate. Furthermore, the internal representation is essentially in terms of the connectivity of the drawing, as is ours. The *Cyclops* system would be somewhat more difficult to use, but it has the principal elements required for description generation, including line-tracing and segmentation machinery, as well as a curvature-calculating program. In our opinion it would be only a moderately difficult task to get ANALOGY input from light-pen drawings using either system. However, the time seemed better spent on the ANALOGY program itself.

Comparison with Human Performance. In conclusion, it seems appropriate to try to appraise, at least roughly, the current performance level of ANALOGY, especially in comparison to the information we have on human performance on the same class of problems. First, as to time consumed, the estimates in the following paragraphs on the use of LISP indicate that, by completely straightforward means (which did not at present seem a worthwhile expenditure of programming time) the present program could be made to operate under time limitations at least as stringent, and probably substantially more so, than those typically imposed on human subjects in the administration of such tests. (This estimate assumes that the problem figures have already been reduced to the appropriate input form for ANALOGY, either by hand, a very slow process, or by some picture-input scheme, for which we lack a reliable time estimate.)

With respect to problem-solving power the situation is less clear. Viewing Part 2 as fixed, we consider three types of Part 1 features:

(*a*) those already present in Part 1;

(*b*) those which correspond to well-understood extensions of current Part 1 processing;

(*c*) desirable features for which we do not have a well-understood implementation in mind.

Allowing ourselves only type (*a*) facilities, our estimate would be that of the 30 geometric-analogy problems on a typical edition of the ACE tests, ANALOGY can successfully solve at least 15 and possibly as many as 20 problems. Given, in addition, the type (*b*) facilities we have in mind, ANALOGY should be capable of perhaps 25 successful solutions. Extensions of the present Part 2 scheme along the lines suggested in Part 5.4.4 should lead to still better performance.

Distributions of scores on these tests, made available to us by the Educational Records Bureau and accumulated over eight years on a large college-preparatory private-school population (over 10,000 subjects each year), may serve to make a rough comparison of human performance with the estimates above. The median scores, which, incidentally, remain remarkably consistent from year to year as the test form used is changed, are given separately for grades 9 through 12. Averaged over the eight years and given to the nearest integer, they are:

Grade 9: 17 correct answers
Grade 10: 18 correct answers
Grade 11: 19 correct answers
Grade 12: 20 correct answers

The Use of LISP. The ANALOGY program is, so far as we know, the largest program yet written in LISP. Thus, it seems particularly appropriate to devote some space to a consideration of some of the advantages and limitations of LISP for programming of this kind.

First, we wish to praise LISP highly as an extremely convenient and elegant language in which to write and debug complex programs. In particular, in the ANALOGY program, the capability of a list-processing language to handle intermediate expressions of unpredictable size and "shape" (such as our figure descriptions and transformation rules) was of great value. Further, the ease of interconnection of routines, the highly mnemonic nature of the language, and the good tracing facilities all contribute greatly to effective programming.

The principal disadvantages in the use of LISP for ANALOGY were:

LISP programs to perform numerical calculations run quite slowly in comparison to machine-language counterparts. This is due to the fact that, for compatibility, the arguments and results of each elementary numerical process must be put in the LISP number format. It is possible to insert machine-code routines through LAP, a simple assembly language available within the LISP system, but an extremely desirable development would be the introduction of some of the features of an algebraic language into the LISP system. Our Part 1 is a good example of a program that benefits greatly from the facilities of a list-processing language, yet requires a substantial amount of numerical computation. Part 2, on the other hand, is a fairly pure example of the kind of symbol-manipulation program for which the list languages were originally developed.

LISP programs are relatively space-consuming, and the LISP system itself occupies an appreciable part of core. What is needed is some satisfactory scheme for the use of bulk external storage (for example, disk file) as an effective extension of core memory in a list-processing system. With such a scheme it would have been unnecessary to segment ANALOGY.

While we are discussing LISP, some remarks must be made concerning running times. This is an elusive subject, since in LISP, a list-processing system with automatic free-storage reclamation, the running time of a given program depends sharply on what else is in core with it, that is, on how much free storage is available. There also exists the possibility of running a given program either interpretively or compiled, with typically a sharp decrease in running time in the latter mode. The ratio of decrease, which has been estimated as high as 1/100 in certain favorable cases, varies also with the type of program and with the "environment," i.e., the degree to which the program is free-storage-reclamation-limited. Furthermore, a set of programs may be of mixed type, part interpreted and part compiled, in any combination. Also one must know the breakdown in the particular LISP system being used of available space into free storage, binary program space, pushdown list, and full word space (see reference 19).

In view of all these considerations, statements about running times in LISP must be carefully qualified to be meaningful. With this warning, we now give typical running times for Parts 1 and 2 of ANALOGY. The average time, with the LISP system we have been using, for Part 1 is on the order of 1 to 3 minutes, including on-line card-reading time. This is with a number of the most frequently used numerical routines LISP-compiled (but not hand-coded in an assembly language), the rest interpreted, and perhaps 2000 to 3000 words of free storage available. For Part 2, with no compiled routines at all, the typical running time is about 0.5 to 1.5 minutes, again including card-reading time, with 3000 to 4000 words of free storage available. The computer was an IBM 7090.

With Part 2 entirely compiled and the space now devoted to program S-expressions converted to free storage, one can be sure its running time, exclusive of card reading, would be on the order of several seconds. Part 1 (with full compilation, a small number of the most heavily used numerical routines rewritten in LAP, and the internal changes discussed under generalized Euclidean similarity transformations in Part 5.3.6 introduced to reduce the amount of computation required) could be expected to run not much longer. Thus, with no externally visible change at all and no appreciable change in the organization of the present program (but with some quite time-consuming reprogramming) we could confidently expect combined running times (exclusive of input-output time) under, say, ten seconds for a typical problem.

5.6 Conclusions

5.6.1 Introduction

This final section will be devoted to a consideration of the contributions of ANALOGY and its significance for future work. We shall consider it in the context both of earlier research into the design of problem-solving programs and of future developments in this area. To place the contributions from our work with ANALOGY in sharper perspective we shall proceed as follows:

First we introduce, for definiteness, a certain broad class of problem-solving machines. We put forward a widely accepted viewpoint, which we share, on some prerequisites for the design of machines capable of dealing effectively with problems of this class. We next attempt to clarify some of the ideas and terminology associated with this point of view.

We then contrast the requirements inherent in this viewpoint with the capabilities of schemes that have been used in recent investigations of machine problem-solving.

We demonstrate in some detail that the ANALOGY program, under suitable interpretation, exhibits precisely the process advocated. In view of the fact that ANALOGY is the first program to do so, we feel that its development represents a substantial advance in artificial intelligence and a potentially large contribution to the design of future programs.

To begin to realize some of this potential utility of the ideas inherent in the methods used by ANALOGY in dealing with its specialized environment, we make a proposal for future work. It involves implementing, as part of an elaborate problem-solving program, methods based on and suggested by those now used in ANALOGY. For definiteness we shall describe this scheme in a form that could be used as an adjunct to the General Problem Solver of Newell, Simon, and Shaw (26). We feel that the apparatus proposed could well add greatly to the problem-solving power of GPS. At any rate, its implementation, in the form to be described or a similar one, would be a fruitful undertaking.

5.6.2 Some Aspects of the Design of Problem-Solving Machines

To aid our discussion we shall loosely specify at this point a subclass of problem-solving machines and carry out our remarks in terms of these though the ideas involved are by no means limited in applicability to this class. The machines we have in mind are typified by GPS (26) in that the problem posed is to transform one specified "object" or "situation" into another by applying an appropriate sequence of transformations chosen from a class available to the machine. A wide variety of problems may be cast in this form. Subgoals may be generated and attacked as in GPS by such a machine, and elaborate problems of resource allocation may arise. However, these do not concern us here. Our interest lies in the basic task of the machine; given a pair of "objects," it must choose an "appropriate" transformation contributing to transforming one given "object" into the other.

It is a widely held view, with which we agree completely, that a machine capable of highly intelligent behavior on a task of this kind, in a rich environment of objects and transformations (and, in particular, capable of learning at a level more advanced than that of present machines), must have a good internal representation of both its environment ("objects") and its methods ("transformations"), as well as an elaborate set of "pattern-recognition" techniques for matching transformations to object pairs. Furthermore, these matching techniques must be represented in a form in which they themselves are susceptible to improved performance through experience. The central role which "pattern-recognition" techniques must play in sophisticated problem-solving programs and the corresponding importance for effective learning of autonomous improvement in the performance of these techniques are indicated in reference 20. We find:

> In order not to try all possibilities a resourceful program must classify problem situations into categories associated with the domains of effectiveness of the machine's different methods. These pattern-recognition methods must extract the heuristically significant features of the objects in question. . . . In order to solve a new problem one uses what might be called the basic learning heuristic—first try using methods similar to those which have worked, in the past, on similar problems.

Here, the problem is, of course, to have pattern-recognition techniques possessing, or able themselves to learn, criteria of "similarity" appropriate to the subject matter in question. It is easier to observe the need for such techniques than to develop them; however, in the final part of this section we outline a scheme, based on ideas present in ANALOGY, that avoids many of the limitations of schemes currently used. The successful implementation of this scheme would represent a major advance toward the realization of machines with greatly expanded problem-solving capabilities.

In the remainder of this section we shall elaborate somewhat on the notion of "similarity" as it occurs in the foregoing quotation. First to clarify our terminology: When we speak of two situations being "analogous" in some respect, we might also equivalently speak of "similarities" between the situations. And, in our view, "pattern-recognition" is that process which "perceives analogies" or "detects" "similarities." In slightly different terms, Polya (29) characterizes analogy loosely by stating: "Two systems are analogous if they agree in clearly definable relations of their respective parts."

Recognition of the fundamental role played in human thinking by analogy is a commonplace observation (and one source of the viewpoint on problem-solving machines illustrated in our quotations from reference 20).

Again we quote Polya, who has perhaps studied the role of such reasoning in mathematical discovery more extensively than anyone else:

> Now . . . we can learn the use of such fundamental mental operations as generalization, specialization, and the perception of analogies. There is perhaps no discovery, either in elementary or in advanced mathematics, or, for that matter, in any other subject, that could do without these operations, especially without analogy.

One important result, in human thinking, of perceiving an analogy between two *a priori* unrelated situations may be a new "common generalization" based on the common features of both. The capacity to make generalizations, for example, the concept of abstract group as an abstraction of certain common features from a wide variety of superficially quite distinct problem areas, is perhaps the most impressive aspect of human intelligence and the one which to date has been least successfully implemented in a machine. To produce capabilities comparable to those of intelligent humans in this area can be expected to be a formidable but enormously worthwhile undertaking. The difficulty of the associated problems is attested by the paucity of concrete proposals for attacking them, in contrast to the interest that has been shown in the problem and the ease with which it can be identified as a critical area for artificial intelligence. Some of this difficulty arises from the very broadness of the concept. The pervasiveness of what we can call "analogy processes" suggests their appearance in a wide variety of guises; in human thinking we may have analogies between situations and between methods (or even between analogies); we may have analogies so clear-cut as to be, technically, isomorphisms or homomorphisms, or so vague as to be virtually incommunicable from one individual to another, yet of great heuristic value to the individual in question.

A critical aspect of the development of problem-solving machines capable of intelligent behavior is the invention of good pattern-recognition techniques, enabling these machines to match methods to situations well. An important related aspect is the development of techniques whereby the machines can use their experience to improve the effectiveness of this matching process. We have outlined some plausible criteria for the design of procedures with such properties.

The techniques developed to date to perform this task in problem-solving programs do not fully meet these needs. By first considering these methods and then re-examining ANALOGY from a new point of view, we attempt to show how methods suggested by the design of ANALOGY could contribute to overcoming these limitations.

6.3 Pattern-Recognition by Property-List Schemes

In this section we wish to consider the pattern-recognition technique which has been most widely employed in the problem-solving programs now in existence to perform the function of classifying or evaluating situations (in the terminology of our model, matching "transformations" to "objects"). This technique is the "fixed-length property-list," already alluded to in Section 5.1. It has proved a useful technique but one with two serious limitations to which we shall return. It works as follows: Typically, one has routines for computing a number of properties of any of the situations ("objects") with which the program must deal. The results of these tests are combined, in sequential or parallel fashion, and appropriate action taken according to the result. For example, in Samuel's checker program (31), the "situations" are checker positions and the properties are measures of advancement, center control, etc. The results of the property calculations are combined into a single value by a linear polynomial with constant coefficients. The resulting value is used to compare the position in question with others to aid in selecting a move. In Slagle's integration program (35), the "situations" are expressions to be integrated; a typical property is "the expression is a rational function" and the *n*tuple of results is used both to estimate the difficulty of integrating the expression in question and to select a transformation to apply to it. In Doyle's program (5), the "situations" are hand-printed letters (or, more precisely, bit patterns derived from such letters by a photocell matrix technique); the properties are typified by the question, "how many intersections does the pattern have with a horizontal line across the middle of the field?" The results of these tests are combined by a simple scheme which matches the *n*tuple of property test results against the results expected for each of the possible categories and assigns the pattern in question to the "best-fit" category.

A property-list scheme of pattern recognition, as incorporated in the three programs cited, is a useful technique in several ways:
It is easy to implement and the form of the top-level "decision-making" program is independent of which properties are used and how they are computed.
It lends itself well to "parallel" decision-making, that is, computation of all the properties before the decision is made. This is the form used in all three of the above examples. It trades additional computation for an insensitivity to "noise" that cannot be obtained from a sequential organization. (Frequently, in fact, "property-list scheme" is taken as implying parallel organization, which seems misleading; what *we* mean, at any rate, by this term is a pattern-recognition with perhaps quite complex property tests but in which only quite simple results of these tests, each of which is a function of the entire "situation," are available to the top-level decision-making mechanism, whether it be sequential or parallel.)
At least in the parallel form of the scheme it is possible to incorporate rather easily a certain amount of learning in the top-level decision mechanism. In Samuel, the coefficients of the evaluation polynomial are altered; in Doyle, the probabilities corresponding to expected test results for each of the categories are determined from labeled samples.

However, the "property-list" scheme has the following two critical limitations:
While in principle, "given" enough sufficiently elaborate properties, one can make arbitrarily fine discriminations, in practice a given set of properties will begin to fail rapidly as situations become more complex. In particular, for "situations" that must be treated as consisting of interrelated parts, the "global" nature of the scheme in question leaves it helpless.
Such a scheme is very limited in its learning capabilities since it has access to very little information about its component properties; in particular, it is incapable of "knowledgeably" modifying its tests or adding new ones. It has been suggested (32) that useful new properties may be defined by expressing their outputs as, say, Boolean combinations of the outputs of properties already at hand. Such a scheme, combined with a "weeding-out" process based on the observed utility of each property in contributing to "successes," could result in an appreciable improvement in the property set before we encounter the intrinsic limitations of the method.

5.6.4 A Reinterpretation of ANALOGY

We shall now show how ANALOGY serves as a model for a "pattern-recognition" approach which gives promise of overcoming both of these limitations. In view of the limitations of the "property-list" pattern-recognition scheme just discussed, we can formulate some requirements for a pattern-recognition scheme suitable to replace it as a "transformation-selecting" mechanism. First, the scheme must have access to a representation of each "object" in terms of a "descriptive framework" for the subject matter in question, such that useful analogies between "objects" can be extracted relatively simply from the corresponding representations. In the current state of knowledge, this seems to mean that the representation should be devised so that "similarity-finding" and generalization have a natural connection to and can be simply stated in terms of the syntactic structure of the representation. Furthermore, the transformation-selecting rules of the pattern-recognition apparatus should themselves be expressed in a representation suitable for a "learning mechanism" to revise the rule set by adding new rules as experience associates certain "object" pairs with certain transformations and by replacing a set of particular rules by a "common generalization" rule, again represented in the same form. Such facilities could go far toward removing the limitations of which we have spoken and toward providing both a powerful rule language (since the rules can be stated in terms of the "descriptive framework" we have postulated for the "objects") and a learning mode more sophisticated than any yet incorporated in such a general problem-solving program.

So far we have been enumerating desirable features in a "pattern-recognition" mechanism to be used as a transformation-selection device in a larger problem-solver. What has all this to do with ANALOGY, which is not even a problem-solving program of the class we have been considering? A simple reinterpretation will reveal that ANALOGY can be identified with a pattern-recognition program having, to the degree necessary for its particular environment, all the features we have listed. First, the "objects" are the problem figures of ANALOGY and the suitable "sub-object and relation" representation appropriate to these "objects" is the input form for Part 2 of ANALOGY. (Thus Part 1 of ANALOGY corresponds to the apparatus that generates this representation for each object.) A transformation rule found by ANALOGY taking one answer figure into another corresponds to the first kind of learning we listed above, namely, the adding of rules as, with experience, the machine associates certain "object" pairs with certain simple or composite transformations. Finally, the common generalization of two rules in ANALOGY corresponds to the second kind of learning we mentioned, the generation of a common generalization of several rules associating "objects" and "transformations." Furthermore, ANALOGY's process of choosing between "common generalizations" of different rule pairs mirrors a process of choosing to make only those generalizations with the greatest discriminatory power. Thus, under this interpretation ANALOGY appears as a model for a pattern-recognition process with all the characteristics we desired and in this, we feel, lies its greatest importance. In the final pages of this chapter we describe a "pattern-recognition" process of which the main outlines are based on the conception of ANALOGY described. It is more ambitious chiefly in that a more powerful and more general-purpose descriptive framework for the "objects" is introduced.

5.6.5 A Phrase-Structured Description Language for GPS

What seems clear to us, from the considerations of the previous sections, is that the introduction of pattern-recognition techniques based on structured descriptions of situations and methods is of great importance in the development of powerful problem-solving programs, especially if they are to be capable of sophisticated learning. In this section we describe a proposed scheme, suggested by ANALOGY, for implementing such machinery. The scheme represents a considerable advance in power (and difficulty of implementation) over the "property-list" schemes we have discussed; it overcomes to some degree all the limitations we have spoken of earlier. However, it is at this stage a rather primitive exploitation of its basic ideas; it should be possible to refine it and increase its flexibility greatly with no serious change in the underlying structure. However, we have no doubt that it too has serious limitations and, when we understand it more adequately, can be replaced by a more "expressive" descriptive language.

Suppose we are working in the problem-solving environment of GPS. This means we have objects, transformations taking one or more objects into another, differences between objects, a table stating which differences are related to which transformation (in the sense that applying the transformation reduces the difference in question), and a criterion of progress (this amounts essentially to a priority ranking of differences). GPS operates by setting up goals, such as transforming expression E_1 into expression E_2. To do this it sets up, say, the subgoal of reducing some difference between E_1 and E_2. This is done by applying an appropriate transformation to E_1, resulting in, say, E_3. Now the appropriate subgoal of the original goal is to transform E_3 into E_2, a goal of the same form, to which the entire apparatus of GPS can be applied recursively. The two most characteristic features of GPS are this recursive goal-subgoal form of organization and the fact that the goal-setting and achieving mechanism is independent of the particular subject matter (that is, objects, transformations, and differences) involved. GPS has been studied in a number of subject-matter environments; in reference 27 we have examples of its application to the propositional calculus and to trigonometric identities. The scheme to be discussed has no essential connection with GPS; our choice of the GPS environment stems from the fact that it is to some extent general-purpose, as is our scheme, in the same sense, and that it is quite clearly described in reference 26.

Our proposal, in essence, is as follows: GPS remains unchanged, except at the point where decisions on application of transformations are made (now by use of the "difference versus transformation" table mentioned earlier). We propose to give this routine access to a pattern-recognition mechanism to be described below. If our device has no suggestion at a given point or if its suggestion has already been tried and rejected, GPS proceeds exactly as described in reference 26; otherwise, it takes the suggestion. Our basic apparatus consists of four parts:

(*a*) A phrase-structure grammar for the objects with which GPS is dealing. These might be algebraic or logical expressions (the two "environments" illustrated in reference 26), in which case such a phrase-structure grammar is natural, or some set of objects for which an initial encoding into a suitable phrase-structure language might require considerable ingenuity. At any rate, we assume some such class of expressions, with an associated grammar, is available. We place no stress on having an unambiguous grammar; in fact, the existence of alternate parsings, corresponding to the isolation of different aspects of the structure of the expressions in question may be very useful.
(*b*) A corresponding syntactic-analysis routine capable of parsing expressions on the basis of the grammar postulated above. This routine is "hidden" in that it is called only implicitly through statements of the type described under (*c*). Such syntactic analysis, including alternate possible parsings under a given grammar, is theoretically well understood, and considerable body of experience exists in constructing efficient parsing algorithms with sophisticated look-ahead features, etc. This is one major motivation for using phrase-structure as the description syntax.
(*c*) A variable set of rules (in this sketch we assume they are sequentially ordered; possibly something more complex would be desirable); the rules look like "if E (the GPS object being considered) is of form <a> <b> <c>, say, (where <a>, <b>, <c> are syntactic types of the underlying grammar perhaps satisfying further properties as well) then transform E into <c> <b> <a>." That is, if E meets a condition expressed in terms of its structure relative to the grammar, then E is transformed in a manner expressed in terms of the same grammatical components of the grammar (this process is easy to carry out using the tree resulting from the parsing to get the new expression E′). The rule may also quite usefully be a function of, say, the object into which E must be transformed to achieve the current subgoal, as well as the initial object E_i and the desired final object E_f of the top-level task of the run.

(*d*) Some rather simple mechanism to apply these rules to E and carry out the specified transformation, if the condition stated in the rule is met.

The way this basic machinery would be used is this: GPS has a current expression E and is casting about for an appropriate transformation to apply to it. It calls our device. First, E is parsed and the resulting tree made available to the rule-testing routine, which runs through the rules in order until a condition is met, at which point it applies the transformation and exits to GPS with the result. If no condition is satisfied, it returns to GPS with a report of failure.

Why introduce such a mechanism at all? What can it contribute to GPS? GPS treats subobjects of a given object through its goal-subgoal organization. That is, GPS avoids looking at complex structures on a given level by decomposing them into smaller structures tied to subgoals. So GPS never sees a single complex structure as such; when a substructure is handled at some deeper subgoal level, it is "out of context" in that the necessary information as to how the achievement of this subgoal contributes to the achievement of larger goals is lacking. Newell (28) discusses a form of this "lack of context" problem and several rather unsatisfactory attempts at solving it. The mechanism we have sketched provides a pattern-recognition device capable of taking a look at the problem which is "global" yet has access to the full structure. Such "global" guidance could be expected to save GPS a large amount of the time now spent in setting up and pursuing subgoals that do not contribute to achieving goals at or near the top level. This alone would be a worthwhile contribution.

Furthermore, such a device provides easy communication of heuristics to a program. Such rules are rather easy for humans to write, as experience with related uses of phrase-structure-based transformation rules shows. The idea of transformation rules stated in terms of a phrase-structure analysis occurs in the so-called syntax compilers of Irons (12) and others and its use for the purpose of writing programs to perform mathematical manipulations has been considered by Christensen (4).

These reasons would furnish adequate justification for an attempt to implement a version of our scheme, but perhaps the most interesting aspect of the scheme is the possibilities it opens up for introducing learning. The mechanism described consists essentially of two processing programs and two tables. The processing programs will remain fixed, but the two tables, one containing the phrase-structure grammar and one the conditional transformation rules, may be changed by additional processing programs. The details of this processing are hard to foresee, but a number of the possibilities are clear. First, the rule set could be expanded by "packaging" any transformation applied by GPS on its own initiative once such an application had proved empirically successful. The "packaging" should present no difficulties to implement and would provide a source of new conditional transformation rules with a good probability of usefulness, in addition to those which might be added "by hand" from time to time. Now suppose there exist several rules specifying some action. It might be possible to replace these rules by a single rule stated in terms of one of the existing syntactic types that is effectively a "least common generalization" of the syntactic configurations occurring in these rules. That is, the tree structure of the underlying syntax provides a natural framework in which to perform "rule generalizations" which retain as much as possible of the discriminatory power of the original rules (this, and not the details of just how the generalization-testing is carried out, is the important point). The new rule may very well be exactly the appropriate generalization. Furthermore it may be feasible, in the same way, mechanically to add new syntactic types to the grammar to effect such "common generalizations." That alternate parsings may be introduced by including new syntactic types is no problem (unless they proliferate beyond reasonable computational limits), since we permitted alternate parsings from the beginning. Thus, for example, one might envision a program working with algebraic expressions inventing for itself the type "trigonometric expression" from finding empirically that examples of the class should be treated in the same way with respect to certain algebraic manipulations.

What we have said about our fixed scheme (that is, no learning) involves no technique that is not already well established. The remarks on learning and "common generalization" are more speculative, but there seems good reason to believe that processing on the transformation rules and phrase-structure grammar can be successfully implemented. Certainly the study of these problems in the relatively well-understood domain of phrase-structure languages is a natural next step toward the development of genuine "generalization learning" by machines and a prerequisite to consideration of learning in still more complex descriptive language environments. One interesting possibility, since the transformation rules themselves can be described in phrase-structure terms, would be to apply the entire "phrase-structure + GPS" apparatus to improving its own set of transformation rules. This may, of course, turn out to be very difficult.

We conclude with a few more remarks on our scheme:

GPS seemed a natural process to which to adjoin our apparatus, but we could as well consider attaching it, say, to SAINT, Slagle's integration program (35), which has a rather GPS-like structure.

One interesting area of application for heuristic programs like GPS is to the problem of writing or transforming programs, in various source languages, to satisfy certain specifications. All current higher-level programming languages have a phrase-structure description and one could envision program simplification being carried out by GPS guided by the mechanism we have proposed.

As a small example of the merits of the basic scheme, we note that in reference 27 the authors remark that GPS needs new goal types to, among other things, recognize that $\sin^4 x - \cos^4 x$ is of form $y^2 - z^2$, so it can be factored (by operator A1 of the trigonometry set). We note that a conditional rule like "if $E = u \cdot u - v \cdot v$ where u and v are of syntactic type 'algebraic expression'), then $E' = (u + v) \cdot (u - v)$" handles the general situation (we assume low powers written out as products in the object expressions; this is simpler but could be avoided). This case exhibits some of the additional power that can be gained through using phrase-structure syntactic analysis as a description technique.

Bibliography

1. Backus, J. W., "The Syntax and Semantics of the Proposed International Algebraic Language," *Proc. ICIP,* Paris, France, June 1959.
2. Bruner, J. S., et al., *A Study of Thinking,* Wiley, New York, 1956.
3. Canaday, R., M.I.T. Electrical Engineering Dept. Master's Thesis, Cambridge, Mass., Feb. 1962.
4. Christensen, C., private communication.
5. Doyle, W., "Recognition of Sloppy Hand-Printed Characters," *Proc. WJCC,* San Francisco, Calif., 133-142, May 1960.
6. Hodes, L., "Machine Processing of Line Drawings," Lincoln Laboratory Technical Memorandum, Lexington, Mass., March 1961.
7. Hovland, C. I., and Hunt, E. B., "Programming a Model of Human Concept Formation," *Proc. WJCC*, Los Angeles, Calif., May 1961.
8. Freeman, "On the Encoding of Arbitrary Geometric Configurations," *IRE Trans., EC,* Vol. 10, No. 2, 1961.
9. Gelernter, H., and Rochester, N., "Intelligent Behavior in Problem-Solving Machines," *IBM J. Research Develop.,* Vol. 2, No. 4, 1958.
10. Grimsdale, R. L., et al., "A System for the Automatic Recognition of Patterns," *Proc. IEE 106B,* March 1959.
11. Grimsdale, R. L., and Bullingham, J. M., "Computer Recognition by Digital Computer Using a Special Flying-Spot Scanner," *Computer J. 4,* July 1961.
12. Irons, E., "A Syntax-Directed Compiler for ALGOL-60," *Commun. ACM 4,* Jan. 1961.
13. Kirsch, R., private communication.
14. Knowlton, K., Ph.D. Thesis, Department of Electrical Engineering, M.I.T., Sept. 1962.
15. Kochen, M., "An Experimental Program for the Selection of Disjunctive 'Hypotheses,' " *Proc. WJCC*, Los Angeles, Calif., 1961.
16. Marill, T. M., "General Recognition Processes," *Northeast Electronics Research and Engineering Meeting Record,* Boston, Mass., Nov. 1962.
17. McCarthy, J., "Programs with Common Sense," *Proc. Symposium on Mechanisation of Thought Processes,* Her Majesty's Stationery Office, London, 1959 (Section 7.1 of the present volume).
18. McCarthy, J., "Recursive Functions of Symbolic Expressions," *Commun. ACM 3,* April 1960.
19. McCarthy, J., et al., *LISP 1.5 Programmer's Manual,* The M.I.T. Press, Cambridge, Mass., 1963.
20. Minsky, M. L., "Steps Toward Artificial Intelligence," *Proc. IRE 49,* No. 1, 1961.
21. Minsky, M. L., "A Selected Descriptor-Indexed Bibliography to the Literature on Artificial Intelligence," in Feigenbaum, E. A., and Feldman, J. (eds.), *Computers and Thought,* McGraw-Hill, New York, 1963.
22. Minsky, M. L., "Descriptive Languages and Problem-Solving Programs," *Proc. WJCC,* Los Angeles, Calif., May 1961.
23. Naur, P. (ed.), "Report on the Algorithmic Language ALGOL 60," reprinted in *Commun. ACM,* May 1960.
24. Newell, A., and Simon, H. A., "The Logic Theory Machine," *IRE Trans., IT 2,* No. 3, Sept. 1956.
25. Newell, A., Shaw, J. C., and Simon, H. A., "Empirical Explorations of the Logic Theory Machine, *Proc. WJCC,* Los Angeles, Calif., Feb. 1957.
26. Newell, A., Shaw, J. C., and Simon, H. A., "Report on a General Problem-Solving Program," *Proc. ICIP,* Paris, France, June 1959.

27. Newell, A., Shaw, J. C., and Simon, H. A., "A Variety of Intelligent Learning in a General Problem Solver," in Yovits, M., and Cameron, S. (eds), *Self-Organizing Systems,* Pergamon, New York, 1960.
28. Newell, A., "Some Problems of Basic Organization in Problem-Solving Programs," Yovits, M., Jacobi, G., and Goldstein, G. (eds), in *Self-Organizing Systems*, 1962, Spartan Press, Baltimore, Md., 1962.
29. Polya, G., *Induction and Analogy in Mathematics,* Princeton University Press, Princeton, N.J., 1954.
30. Roberts, L., Ph.D. Thesis, Department of Electrical Engineering, M.I.T., May 1963.
31. Samuel, A. L., "Some Studies in Machine Learning Using the Game of Checkers," *IBM J. of Research and Develop.* Vol. 3, No. 3, 1959.
32. Selfridge, O., "Pandemonium: A Paradigm for Learning," *Proc. Symp. on Mechanisation of Thought Processes,* Teddington, England, 1959.
33. Selfridge, O., "The Organization of Organization," in *Self-Organizing Systems,* 1962, Yovits, M., Jacobi, G., and Goldstein, G. (eds.), Spartan Books, 1962.
34. Sherman, H., "A Quasi-Topological Method for the Recognition of Line Patterns," *Proc. ICIP,* Paris, France, June 1959.
35. Slagle, J., Ph.D. Thesis, Department of Mathematics, M.I.T., June 1961.
36. Solomonoff, R., "A Preliminary Report on a General Theory of Inductive Inference," *Zator Tech. Bull.,* V-151, Feb. 1960.
37. Sutherland, I., Ph.D. Thesis, Department of Electrical Engineering, M.I.T., Feb. 1963.
38. Sutherland, I., "Sketchpad: A Man-Machine Graphical Communication System," presented at SJCC, Detroit, Mich., May 1963.

6. A Deductive Question-Answering System

Fischer Black

6.1 Introduction

In September 1962, T. Marill proposed the following problem: Given the statements:

> The guard searched all who entered the premises except those who were accompanied by members of the firm.
> Some of Fiorecchio's men entered the premises unaccompanied by anyone else.
> The guard searched none of Fiorecchio's men.

find the answers to such questions as

> Did any of Fiorecchio's men enter the premises unaccompanied by anyone else?
> Were any of Fiorecchio's men members of the firm?

Marill suggested translating the statements and questions into quantificational schemata, and writing a digital computer program that would deduce answers to the questions from the given statements. He suggested basing the program on the deductive system given by Quine (9). I saw three major difficulties: First, a number of deductive systems have been written for quantificational schemata, but none has been effectively programmed for a computer. There seemed no reason to believe that Quine's deductive system would be easier to program effectively than any of the others. Second, translating statements and questions like the ones given above into quantificational schemata is extremely complex, as shown by Reichenbach (11). Third, all deductive systems for quantificational schemata are oriented toward proving theorems, not answering questions. For answering questions, it seemed better to organize the system more like Baseball (4), but without the restrictions to a specific subject matter that Baseball has.

I decided to try to develop a deductive system with the following properties:

1. It can be programmed effectively for a digital computer.
2. It is relatively easy to translate from mathematical or everyday language to the language used by the deductive system.
3. It is oriented toward answering questions rather than proving theorems.
4. It is not restricted to a specific subject matter.

One way to get property 2 would be to make more or less unrestricted English the language of the system. That would make the deductive system very complex, however, as shown, for example, by the work of Simmons et al. (14). So I decided not to use English, and experimented with various moderately formal languages.

After several versions of the system had been written and were working correctly, I discovered that the system was close to being the Advice Taker proposed by McCarthy (5). At this time I adopted the formal language suggested by McCarthy for the advice taker. The system was able to handle the Airport Problem (5) and two other problems, the Monkey Problem (4), and the Mikado Problem (13), developed by McCarthy and his group at Stanford as typical problems for the advice taker.

Comparing the system with the Logic Theorist (8), which finds proofs for theorems in the propositional calculus, I found a basic similarity of structure. By putting in a single statement plus the necessary theorems, I enabled the system to "prove" theorems by a method very much like the method used by the Logic Theorist. In particular, the system can prove at least one of the theorems the Logic Theorist could not prove. Since the system does not prove theorems explicitly, the "proof" is implicit in the deductive process that results when the theorem is taken as a question and answered.

Finally, I have begun to study some ways of improving the efficiency of the system by rewriting statements and by setting up a hierarchical classification of statements. Improving efficiency seems to be the most promising area for future research.

Some of the major problems that had to be solved in designing the system were the following:

1. What should be allowed as a statement or question?
   What should be given as an answer?
2. In deducing answers to a question, how should statements be chosen,

and how should successive steps in deducing answers be chosen, so that the answers are found fairly directly?

3. How can endless deductions, which may occur in any sufficiently general deductive system, be stopped without causing some questions never to be answered correctly?
4. How can certain deductions, that would normally have to be cut off without our knowing whether we had all the answers, be allowed to continue until all answers are found?
5. What are some techniques for writing statements and questions for the system, so that answers that require complicated deductions can be obtained from a small number of statements?
6. How can statements in the system, or the deductive system itself, be rewritten to reduce the average time it takes to answer a question?

The main results given in this chapter are some solutions to these six problems. Each section is devoted to one of the problems. Here are some results from each section:

1. The basic unit making up a statement, question, or answer is the *phrase;* for example, the phrase

   at(I,airport)

   is a translation of

   I am at the airport.
2. To deduce answers to questions without a large amount of searching, work backwards by setting up subquestions and dealing with them in the same way that questions are dealt with. The question

   Am I in trouble?

   might have as one of its subquestions

   Have I broken a law?
3. A deduction is endless when subquestions are set up more often than answers to subquestions are found. To stop an endless deduction, keep track of all questions that have been asked but have not yet been answered. There are several ways of stopping the use of this list of questions; the simplest is to stop when the list exceeds a given length.
4. When a deduction is endless because a question is reached that has a subquestion identical with it, there are two ways to avoid the endless deduction: We can rewrite the statements used in the deduction, or we can make the system keep track of the answers to questions that have identical subquestions.

   When we *stop* an endless deduction, we may not get all the answers to the question. When we *avoid* an endless deduction, we will get all the answers.
5. A "yes-or-no" question can have the answers

yes
no answer

but not the answer

no.

To find out if the answer is "no," we must ask the denial of the question. Further, we must have written the statements for the system in a way that makes either the question or its denial have an answer of "yes."

6. There are two ways to increase the efficiency of the system, as measured by the average time it takes to answer a question: We can remove certain statements and add new statements that are equivalent but more efficient, or we can set up a hierarchical classification of statements, or both. It seems possible that the system can be made to do both automatically.

Only the results given in Section 6.7 have not been tested as part of the system.

To give an idea of where this work fits in with other work on information retrieval and deductive systems, I will give an outline of the field.

- Information Retrieval
  - Document retrieval (11)
  - Fact retrieval (14)
  - Fact Deduction
    - English (2, 4, 10)
    - Non-English Fact Deduction
      - Propositional calculus (8)
      - Quantification theory (12)
      - Formal Systems
        - Hard-to-find deductions (15)
        - Easy-to-find deductions (5)
          - This work

6.2 Statement, Question, and Answer

6.2.1 Word

What vocabulary of basic symbols shall we use for statements and questions? Since we want to be able to translate easily from informal language of the language of the system, we shall allow as a basic symbol any string of letters and numerals. Such a string will be called a "word." A small list of words will be chosen as "variables," and all other words will be called "constants."

Variables: x,y,z,u,v,w
Constants: car, bus, taxi, have, own, possess

6.2.2 Phrase

How will we combine words into statements, questions, and answers? In the Baseball system (4) a wide variety of English sentences were allowed as questions, and English words and phrases were used in answers. For example, the question: "What parks did the Red Sox play in in July?" had as its answer the expression

Month = July
Team = Red Sox
Place = Boston, New York, etc.

Since the data for the Baseball system were fixed, statements were not allowed. The user could only ask questions; he could not add statements to the system.

In a deductive process, phrases within a statement or question are likely to be taken out and used in forming new statements or questions. Thus, there must be some way to find the phrases in a statement or question. In Baseball, because of the limited subject matter, it was possible to design a syntactic analyzer that would mark the phrases in fairly arbitrary English questions. But a syntactic analyzer for an arbitrary English sentence would be much more complex, judging from the partial analyzers that now exist, and would be many times larger than the entire deductive system described in this paper.

It would also be hard for us to match phrases from English questions with phrases from English statements. The Proto-synthex system (14) contains parts that try to match question phrases with statement phrases; its dictionary alone, with parts of speech of various words, is large. Since it is easy to separate the marking of phrases from the deductive process, we shall insist that phrases be marked in both statements and questions. Phrases within phrases must also be marked.

To make matching of phrases easy, identical words must be used in phrases that are to match. The system should not be asked to recognize that "peach" and "peaches" are forms of the same word. In other words, nouns, verbs, and adjectives should be used everywhere with the same endings, and superfluous words such as articles should be dropped. Finally, every phrase must contain a "key word" not included in any subphrase; this key word is to be written as the first word of the phrase. Phrases within phrases should be marked only when an inner phrase is likely to be used as a separate unit in making deductions.

Formally, we can define a *word* as a constant or variable; a *phrase* as a word or complex phrase; a *complx phrase* as a constant followed by a string of one or more *phrases* separated by commas and enclosed in parentheses. The *components* of a complex phrase are the constant that heads the phrase together with the phrases enclosed in parentheses.

The phrase "very expensive taxis" might be written in any of these ways:
very (expensive (taxis))

very (expensive,taxis)
taxis (expensive (very))
vexpensive (taxis)

depending on what the translator likes and on the other phrases that are expected in statements and questions. The first way of writing it is likely to be both the most convenient and the easiest to read. The components of the first translation are

very
expensive (taxis)

and those of the second translation are

very
expensive
taxis

6.2.3 Direct Statement

How should we combine phrases into statements? Since we want to restrict the writer of statements and questions as little as possible, we will allow any phrase as a direct statement. Usually the phrase used as a direct statement is a translation of a sentence. The translations of the sentences, "I am at the airport" and "I want to be at the airport" might be the direct statements:

at (I,airport)
want (at (I,airport))

A direct statement may also contain variables. Intuitively, that means that any other direct statement obtained by putting phrases for the variables is implied by the given statement. The direct statement "identical (x,x)," which is a translation of "everything is identical with itself," implies the statements:

identical (car,car)
identical (truck,truck)
identical (expensive (house),expensive (house))

6.2.4 Conditional Statement

How should we combine phrases into conditional statements? Given a direct statement with variables, we can deduce new statements by putting phrases for the variables. But we need more powerful deductive rules that will let us combine several statements into a new statement. Therefore we allow statements of the form "$x,y,z \rightarrow w$," which might be read "if x and y and z then w," where x, y, and z are "antecedents" of the statement and w is the "consequent" of the statement.

Formally, a *conditional statement* consists of one or more phrases (its *antecedents*) separated by commas, followed by an arrow, followed by another phrase (its *consequent*). A simple new deductive rule that goes with the conditional statement specifies that if a direct statement is identical with one of the antecedents of a conditional statement we may detach that antecedent from the conditional statement to get a new statement. By applying this rule three times to the statements

never
impossible
unthinkable
never, impossible, unthinkable → no

we can deduce the new statement.

First, from the two statements

never
never, impossible, unthinkable → no

we deduce the new conditional statement

impossible, unthinkable → no

Then, from the 2 statements

impossible
impossible, unthinkable → no

we deduce another new conditional statement

unthinkable → no

Finally, from the 2 statements

unthinkable
unthinkable → no

we deduce the statement "no." Conditional statements, just as direct statements, may contain variables. We may deduce new conditional statements by putting phrases for some or all of the variables in a conditional statement. From the conditional statement "smaller (x,y), smaller (y,z) → smaller (x,z)" where "smaller (x,y)" is a translation of "x is smaller than y," we may deduce any of the statements:

smaller (pluto,y), smaller (y,z) → smaller (pluto,z)
smaller (x,mars), smaller (mars,z) → smaller (x,z)
smaller (x,y), smaller (y,saturn) → smaller (x,saturn)
smaller (pluto,mars), smaller (mars,saturn) → smaller (pluto,saturn)

Combining these two ways of deducing new statements, if we are given the statements

smaller(pluto,mars)
smaller(mars, saturn)
smaller(x,y), smaller(y,z) → smaller(x,z)

we can deduce first the statement

smaller (pluto,mars), smaller (mars,saturn) → smaller (pluto,saturn)

and finally the statement

smaller(pluto,saturn)

One word of caution: The phrases that are put for variables in a statement may themselves contain variables (or they may be variables). There are no restrictions on these variables (they may be the same as other variables in the statement), but if they do interact, the resulting statement may not be the one you want. If in the conditional statement

not(x), not(y) → not(or(x,y))

we were to put "not (x)" for "y," we would get the statement "not (x), not (not (x)) → not (or (x,not (x))),” which is not at all the same as the statement "not (x), not (not (y)) → not (or (x,not (y))),” that we get by putting "not (y)" for "y."

There is a more general deductive rule for conditional statements than detaching antecedents that are identical with direct statements. If the consequent of one conditional statement is identical with an antecedent of a second one, then the latter may be replaced by the antecedents of the first statement. In other words, the antecedents of a conditional statement may replace a copy of its consequent, when the latter occurs as an antecedent of another statement. This rule will be referred to as "putting antecedents for consequents."

From the statement "smaller (x,y), smaller (y,z) → smaller (x,z)" we can deduce the statement "smaller (x,z), smaller (z,w) → smaller (x,w)" by putting "z" for "y" and "w" for "z." Then, since the consequent of the first statement is identical with the first antecedent of the second statement, we can replace "smaller (x,z)" by "smaller (x,y), smaller (y,z)" in the second statement, giving a new statement "smaller (x,y), smaller (y,z), smaller (z,w) → smaller (x,w)."

If we think of a direct statement as a conditional statement with a consequent but no antecedents, then the deductive rule we gave earlier becomes a special case of this deductive rule. If the first statement, a direct statement, is identical with an antecedent of the second statement, then the antecedent of the second statement may be replaced by the antecedents of the first statement. But since the first statement has no antecedents, that amounts to detaching the antecedent of the second statement.

The deductive rule of putting phrases for variables applies equally to direct and to conditional statements, so that, from the point of view of the deductive rules, a direct statement is completely equivalent to a conditional statement with no antecedents.

6.2.5 Corpus

In most versions of the system, a *corpus* is simply a list of statements. A question is matched against all the statements in the corpus. This is not the most efficient way to organize the statements in the corpus, however (see Section 6.7). For efficiency, i.e., speed in answering questions, statements should be organized into groups and the groups into subgroups. Each group or subgroup should be headed by a phrase that "matches" the consequent of every conditional in the group. A sample group of statements might be

smaller (x,y)
smaller (pluto,mars)
smaller (mars,saturn)
smaller (saturn,jupiter)
smaller (x,y), smaller $(y,z) \rightarrow$ smaller (x,z)

where the heading is the phrase "smaller(x,y)," which matches each of the consequents

smaller (pluto,mars)
smaller (mars,saturn)
smaller (saturn,jupiter)
smaller (x,z)

6.2.6 Question

What shall we allow as a question? In theorem-proving systems, if the theorems are thought of as questions then they are "yes-or-no" questions. In Baseball (4), on the other hand, questions can either be "yes-or-no" or they can ask for a larger amount of information.

We will take the Baseball approach and allow questions that ask for a larger amount of information. We will allow any phrase to be a question. If the phrase contains variables, it is a "fill-in-the-blanks" question. If it does not, then it is a "yes-or-no" question. When the phrase "smaller (pluto,mars)" is a statement, it means, "Pluto is smaller than Mars," but when it is a question, it means, "Is Pluto smaller than Mars?"

The questions

smaller $(x$,mars)
smaller(pluto,y)
smaller (x,y)

mean, respectively,

What planets are smaller than Mars?
Pluto is smaller than what planets?
What pairs of planets are there such that the first planet in each pair is smaller than the second planet?

6.2.7 Answer

What will we allow as answers to questions? If a phrase with no variables is a question, then there is only one possible answer: the phrase itself, considered as a statement. The only possible answer to the question "smaller (pluto, mars)" is the phrase "smaller(pluto,mars)."

If a phrase containing variables is a question, then any phrase obtained by putting phrases for some or all of the variables may be an answer. Some possible answers to the question "smaller (x,y)" are the phrases

smaller (pluto,mars)

smaller (mars,pluto)
smaller (pluto,pluto)

Given a corpus of statements and a question, an actual answer to the question is any direct statement that can be deduced from the corpus and that is also a possible answer to the question. Answers to questions will be preceded by *'s to distinguish them from questions. Given the corpus

smaller(pluto,mars)
smaller(mars,saturn)

and the question

smaller(pluto,x)

the answers are

*smaller(pluto,mars)
*smaller(pluto,saturn)

The first answer is already present as a direct statement in the corpus. The second is obtained by putting constants for the variables in the conditional statement and then using the direct statements to detach the antecedents of the resulting statement.

6.3 Deduction

6.3.1 Working Backward

In Section 6.2 we learned to deduce new statements from old ones by putting phrases for variables, by removing any antecedent of a statement that occurs also as a direct statement, or more generally by replacing any antecedent that occurs as the consequent of another statement by the antecedents of that statement. That is how we work forward, from statements we have to new statements.

When a question is asked, we might try to deduce answers by starting with statements in the corpus and working forward, but it would be hard to know what phrases to put for variables and what antecedents to put for consequents. If the question has no variables in it, then we know we want to deduce a statement identical with the question, but we don't know where to start. If the question does have variables in it, then we cannot even know what statements we want to deduce. All we know is that each must be obtainable from the question by putting phrases for variables. If the deductive process is to be programmed effectively for a computer, we cannot have any exhaustive searches for statements that can be deduced and are also answers to the question.

From the Logic Theorist (8) we borrow the basic idea of working backward. Starting with the question, we find a possible last deductive step, and so on, until we come to a statement in the corpus. Then we turn around and fill in the gaps in the deduction. But this idea alone does not tell us very much, because we don't know which steps to try working backward, any more than we know which steps to try working forward.

The next basic idea comes from noticing that every answer to any question must have been obtained by putting phrases for the variables in the consequent of some statement. Both kinds of deductive step (putting phrases for variables and antecedents for consequents) leave the consequents of statements unchanged except perhaps by putting phrases for variables. And if we get a new consequent from an old one by putting phrases for variables twice, we could also have gotten it by putting different phrases for variables just once.

Therefore by "matching" the question with the consequent of every statement in the corpus, we can choose those statements whose consequents might yield answers to the question. Since every answer must be obtainable by putting phrases for variables in the question, and since every direct statement that can be deduced from the statements in the corpus is obtained by putting phrases for variables in some consequent, we would like to define two phrases as "matching" if they can be made identical by putting new phrases for the variables in each. This, however, would lead to a complex matching test. For example, the test would have to be able to tell that the following phrases do not match:

assortment (book, x,x,y,y)
assortment (x,x,y,y,toy)

Since we cannot define the matching of phrases as we want to, we choose the following fundamental definition: Two phrases *match* if (*a*) they are identical, (*b*) one is a variable, or (*c*) they have the same numbers of components and each component of one *matches* the corresponding component of the other. The phrase "in (pencil, y)" matches each of the phrases

x
in (x,y)
in (pencil,z)
in (x,desk)
in (pencil,desk).

The last phrase, incidentally, might be a translation of any of the following:

The pencil is in the desk.
A pencil is in the desk.
Your pencil is in my desk.

When a question matches the consequent of a statement, that statement might be useful in deducing an answer to the question, but first we must get rid of its antecedents. This can be done only if the antecedent in turn matches a direct statement or the consequent of a conditional statement whose antecedents we can get rid of. So the matching process proceeds backward: When the question or an antecedent matches the consequent of a statement, we look at each of its antecedents to see what consequents it, in turn, matches. If we are given the corpus

in(pencil,desk)
in(desk,home)
in(home,county)
in $(x,y) \rightarrow$ at (x,y)
in (x,y), at $(y,z) \rightarrow$ at (x,z)

and we want to answer the question "at (pencil,county)," then we find that the question matches the consequents of

in $(x,y) \rightarrow$ at (x,y)
in (x,y), at $(y,z) \rightarrow$ at (x,z).

The antecedent of the statement "in $(x,y) \rightarrow$ at(x,y)" matches the direct statements

in (pencil,desk)
in (desk,home)
in (home,county)

and so does the first antecedent of the statement "in (x,y), at $(y,z) \rightarrow$ at (x,z)." Its second antecedent matches the statements

in $(x,y) \rightarrow$ at (x,y)
in (x,y), at $(y,z) \rightarrow$ at (x,z).

However, we still do not have a way to deduce answers to questions. Working backward by matching is more concrete than working backward alone, but it is not concrete enough.

6.3.2 Backward Transform

As we work backward, we can use information about the question to guide our search at each step of the way. For example, when the question "at (pencil, home)" matches the consequent of "in (x,y), at $(y,z) \rightarrow$ at (x,z)," we can take the antecedents, not of the original statement, but of the statement "in (pencil, y), at (y, home) $\rightarrow$ at (pencil,home)" that results when "pencil" is put for "x", and "home" is put for "z." Whereas the antecedent "in (x,y)" would match any of the statements

in (pencil,desk)
in (desk,home)
in (home,county)

the new antecedent "in (pencil, y)" matches only the statement "in (pencil,desk)." This shows how using information from the question cuts down the number of paths we must follow when working backward.

When a question matches the consequent of a statement, the *backward transform* of the question and statement is obtained by the following steps:

1. If a variable occurs more than once in the consequent, check that it does not match two different constants or complex phrases in the question. If it does, go on to the next statement.

2. If a variable in the consequent matches a complex phrase containing a variable in the question, make sure this latter variable does not occur in the statement. If it does, pick an entirely new variable and put it for the old variable throughout the entire statement.
3. For every variable in the consequent that matches a constant or complex phrase in the question, put the constant or complex phrase for the variable throughout the entire statement.

Step 1 is necessary because we are using a simplified matching process that does not take care of multiple variables. Changing variables in a statement, as step 2 sometimes requires, does not change the statements that can be deduced from it, so long as the new variables are different from all of its other variables.

The backward transform of the question "at (pencil,home)" and the statement "in $(x,y) \rightarrow$ at (x,y)" is the statement "in (pencil,home) $\rightarrow$ at (pencil,home)," and the backward transform of the same question with the statement "in(x,y), at $(y,z) \rightarrow$ at (x,z)" is the statement "in (pencil, y), at (y, home) $\rightarrow$ at (pencil, home)."

Now that we have the notion of a backward transform, we can make the process of working backward still more concrete. When a question matches the consequent of a statement, we form the backward transform of the question and statement and take the first antecedent of the backward transform as a new question. This new question will not simply be matched against the consequents of statements; it will be answered, and the answers will be used in getting answers to the original question. The new question is a subquestion of the original one and will be answered in exactly the same way as the original question. The first step is to match the subquestion against the consequents of the statements in the corpus, and form backward transforms for those that match. When the question "at (pencil,home)" matches the consequent of "in $(x,y) \rightarrow$ at (x,y)," the new subquestion is "in (pencil,home)." Intuitively, if the answer to the subquestion is "*in (pencil,home)," then the answer to the original question will be "*at (pencil,home)."

When the question matches a direct statement, the backward transform of the question and the direct statement yields an answer to the question, and we can go on to the next statement looking for more answers. For example, the backward transform of question "identical (car, x)" and statement "identical (x,x)" yields the statement "identical (car,car)," which then becomes an answer to the question.

6.3.3 Forward Transform

The backward transform is a way of putting information about a question into a statement that might be used in answering it. Phrases from the question are put for variables in the statement. If the statement has no antecedents, the backward transform gives an answer to the question directly. If the statement does have antecedents, then the first antecedent of the backward transform is taken as a subquestion.

After the subquestion has been answered, each answer is used to put further information into the statement. Each answer gives a different modified statement that may lead to answers for the original question. The same process is used to put information into the statement from the answer as was used to put information into the statement from the question. The only difference is that in the latter the question was matched against the consequent and phrases were carried backward in the statement, whereas now the answer is matched against the first antecedent and phrases are carried forward in the statement. There is one additional step in the forward transform: The first antecedent is detached from the statement, leaving a new statement that is treated just like the original statement. This new statement is a substatement of the original statement, just as the first antecedent of that statement was a subquestion of the original question.

For every answer to a subquestion which is the first antecedent of a statement, the *forward transform* of the answer and statement is obtained by the following steps:

1. If a variable occurs more than once in the antecedent, check that it does not match two different constants or complex phrases in the answer. If it does, go on to the next answer.
2. If a variable in the antecedent matches a phrase containing a variable in the answer, make sure the variable in the answer does not occur in the statement. If it does, pick an entirely new variable and put it for the old variable throughout the entire statement.
3. For every variable in the antecedent that matches a constant or complex phrase in the answer, put the constant or complex phrase for the variable throughout the entire statement.
4. Detach the antecedent from the statement.

Note that, except for step 4, the steps in the forward transform can be obtained from the steps for the backward transform by putting "answer" for "question" and "antecedent" for "consequent." Just as in the backward transform, step 1 is necessary because we are again using a simplified matching process that does not take care of multiple variables. And changing variables in a statement, as step 2 sometimes requires, does not change the statements that can be deduced from it so long as the new variables are different from all of its other variables.

If the statement with which we have been working is "in (pencil,home) → at (pencil,home)" and if the answer we are looking at is "*in (pencil,home)," then the forward transform of the answer and the statement is "at (pencil, home)."

If the statement with which we have been working is "in (pencil,y), at(y,home) → at (pencil,home)" and if the answer we are looking at is "*in(pencil,desk)," then the forward transform of the answer and statement is "at (desk,home) → at (pencil,home)."

If the forward transform of the answer and statement is a direct statement, then that direct statement becomes an answer to the original question. However, if it is not a direct statement, then it is a substatement of the statement and is treated just as the statement was treated. Its first antecedent is taken as a question and answered, and each answer is used to make a forward transform of the substatement.

Now we can get a more complete picture of how to deduce answers to questions. Unlike the original nondirected deductive rules given in Section 6.2, these rules are directed. They tell what to do at every step. Given a question, match it against the consequent of every statement in the corpus. More than one statement may provide answers, so don't stop after getting a few answers. If the question matches the consequent of a statement, form the backward transform of the question and the statement, and take the first antecedent of the transform as a subquestion. For every answer to the subquestion, form the forward transform of the answer and the statement, and take the transform as a substatement. Every answer from any substatement is an answer to the original question. When the statement is a direct statement, the backward transform of the question and statement is an answer to the question, and we don't need to look any further. When the substatement is a direct statement, it is an answer to the question, and we don't need to look any further. A detailed example will be given in Part 6.3.5.

6.3.4 Keeping Track

How do we keep track of where we are in answering a question? We might go through all the statements in the corpus, picking out every one whose consequent matches the question. Then we might form the backward transform of the question with every one of these statements and put all of their first antecedents on a subquestion list. Then we might apply the same process to each of the subquestions, getting a second-generation subquestion list. With each subquestion we would have to store the statement from which it came, so that when we got answers we could make forward transforms to complete the deduction.

Keeping track in this way would have two advantages: First, we could compare subquestions and answer two identical subquestions at the same time. We would not have to answer the same subquestion more than once. Second, we would not have any endless deductions. When we decide we have enough answers, we can simply stop working on subproblems. This is the method adopted by Newell et al. (8).

However, there would also be two disadvantages: First, a great deal of space is needed to store the subquestions and substatements. We might run out of space. Second, much time is used up in bookkeeping; the time needed to compare a subquestion with every question on the subquestion list might be greater than the time it takes to answer the subquestion directly.

The other way of keeping track is to find all the answers to the question provided by the first statement whose consequent is matched by the question, before moving on to the next statement. From the first statement we get a subquestion. We look for a statement whose consequent matches the subquestion. From that statement we get a subquestion of the subquestion. When we get an answer to a subquestion, we do not make a forward transform at once; we wait until we have all the answers and then start by making a forward transform from the first answer. At each point our location is shown by a list of statements, each of which is a substatement of the statement above it on the list. With each statement are listed the answers to its first antecedent that have been found so far. We call this list a *location list.* If we are answering the question "at (pencil,home)" and form the backward transform of the question and the statement "in (x,y), at $(y,z) \rightarrow$ at (x,z)," then the first location list is "in (pencil, y), at (y,home) $\rightarrow$ at (pencil,home)." After we find the answer "*in (pencil,desk)," the location list becomes "in (pencil,y), at (y,home $\rightarrow$ at (pencil,home)," "*in (pencil,desk)."

After getting all the answers to the subquestion, we count how many answers there are. If there are no answers, we remove the substatement from the location list. If there is one answer, we replace the substatement and the answer by their forward transform. If there is more than one answer, we take the forward transform of the highest answer and the substatement and put it at the bottom of the location list. Any answers to the forward transform will be put wherever it is that answers to the substatement from which it came are to be put. Since the substatement in the above location list has just one answer under it, the next location list is simply "at(desk,home)$\rightarrow$ at(pencil,home)."

The principle embodied in the location list is that the only information saved while answering a question is that needed to keep track of where we are and what we do next. This leaves plenty of space to work with in answering the question.

6.3.5 Example

Suppose we are given the corpus

in (pencil,desk)
in (desk,home)
in (home,county)
in $(x,y) \rightarrow$ at (x,y)

in (x,y), at $(y,z) \rightarrow$ at (x,z)

and the question "at (pencil,county)," which might be a translation of "Is my pencil at the county?" The steps through which the system goes in deducing the answers to the question (there happens to be only one answer) will be shown by the location lists created along the way. Each statement on any location list is followed by the answers that have been found so far for its first antecedent:

in (pencil,county) → at (pencil,county)

in (pencil,y), at (y,county) → at (pencil,county)

in (pencil,y), at (y county) → at (pencil,county)
*in (pencil,desk)

at (desk,county) → at (pencil,county)

at (desk,county) → at (pencil, county)
in (desk,county) → at (desk,county)

at (desk,county) → at (pencil,county)
in (desk,y), at (y,county) → at (desk,county)

at (desk,county) → at (pencil,county)
in (desk,y), at (y,county) → at (desk,county)
*in (desk,home)

at (desk,county) → at (pencil,county)
at (home,county) → at (desk,county)

at (desk,county) → at (pencil,county)
at (home,county) → at (desk,county)
in (home,county) → at (home,county)

at (desk,county) → at (pencil,county)
at (home,county) → at (desk,county)
in (home,county) → at (home,county)
*in (home,county)

at (desk,county) → at (pencil,county)
at (home,county) → at (desk,county)
*at (home,county)

at (desk,county) → at (pencil,county)
at (home,county) → at (desk,county)
*at (home,county)
in (home,y), at (y,county) → at (home,county)

at (desk,county) → at (pencil,county)
at (home,county) → at (desk,county)
*at (home,county)

in (home,y), at (y,county) → at (home,county)
*in(home,county)

at (desk,county) → at (pencil,county)
at (home,county) → at (desk,county)
*at (home,county)
at (county,county) → at (home,county)

at (desk,county) → at (pencil,county)
at (home,county) → at (desk,county)
*at (home,county)
at (county,county) → at (home,county)
in (county,county) → at (county,county)

at (desk,county) → at (pencil,county)
at (home,county) → at (desk,county)
*at (home,county)
at (county,county) → at (home,county)
in (county,y), at (y,county) → at (county,county)

at (desk,county) → at (pencil,county)
at (home,county) → at (desk,county)
*at (home,county)
at (county,county) → at (home,county)

at (desk,county) → at (pencil,county)
at (home,county) → at (desk,county)
*at (home,county)

at (desk,county) → at (pencil,county)
*at (desk,county)

*at (pencil,county)

Note that even after the answer "*at (home,county)" was first found, the system continued to look for answers to the question "at (home,county)" and had to follow up a number of blind alleys. The reason is that although a question with no variables can have only a single answer, a question with variables can have many answers, and we must keep looking to see if there are any more. We could stop after getting a single answer to a question with no variables, but the example shows what happens when the question does have variables.

6.4 Stopping Endless Deduction

6.4.1 Repeating Subquestion

Suppose that, instead of the corpus we were given in Part 6.3.5, we are given the corpus

at (pencil,desk)
at (desk,home)
at (home,county)
at (x,y), at (y,z) → at (x,z)

Using the deductive methods given in Section 6.1, we can deduce, from either corpus, the statements

at (pencil,home)
at (pencil,county)
at (desk,county)

However, with use of the methods given in Section 6.3, the system will go into an endless deduction if any of these phrases is taken as a question and answered using the corpus above. What happens is that a subquestion is found which is identical with a question above it on the location list. Since answering the higher instance of the subquestion led to the lower instance of the subquestion, answering the lower instance will lead to a still lower instance, which will lead to yet another instance, and so on. The location list will get longer and longer, and the subquestion will keep repeating. Suppose, for example, that just as in Part 6.3.5 we ask the question "at(pencil,county)"; only this time we are using the corpus at the beginning of this section. The location lists created in trying to answer the question are as follows:

at (pencil, y), at (y, county) → at (pencil,county)

at (pencil, y), at (y,county) → at (pencil,county)
*at (pencil,desk)

at (pencil, y), at (y, county) → at (pencil,county)
*at (pencil,desk)
at (pencil,y), at (y,z) → at (pencil, z)

at (pencil, y), at (y, county) → at (pencil,county)
*at (pencil,desk)
at (pencil, y), at (y,z) → at (pencil,z)
*at (pencil,desk)

at (pencil,y), at (y,county) → at (pencil,county)
*at (pencil,desk)
at (pencil,y), at (y,z) → at (pencil, z)
*at (pencil,desk)
at (pencil,y), at(y,z) → at (pencil, z)

at (pencil,y), at (y,county) → at (pencil,county)
*at (pencil,desk)
at (pencil,y), at (y,z) → at (pencil, z)

at (pencil, y), at (y,z) → at (pencil, z)
*at (pencil,desk)

at (pencil,y), at (y,county) → at (pencil,county)
*at (pencil,desk)
at (pencil,y), at (y,z) → at (pencil,z)
*at (pencil,desk)
at (pencil,y), at (y,z) → at (pencil,z)
*at (pencil,desk)
at (pencil,y), at (y,z) → at (pencil,z)

Note that the substatement "at (pencil,y), at (y,z) → at (pencil,z)" keeps repeating, and that therefore the subquestion "at (pencil,y)" also keeps repeating. Each time the latter is asked, an answer "*at (pencil,desk)" is found, but the deduction continues, looking for further answers. The question matches the statement "at (x,y), at (y,z) → at (x,z)" and the backward transform of this question and statement is the substatement that keeps repeating.

6.4.2 Stopping on Repeated Subquestion

Gelernter (3) had similar difficulty in trying to prove geometry theorems by machine. In trying to prove a theorem, his program would generate a subtheorem that was essentially the same as the theorem, and so would look endlessly for a proof, because it would apply all the techniques to the subtheorem that it applied to the theorem. He solved his problem by cutting off the search for subtheorems whenever a subtheorem was repeated. But his solution will not work for our system.

The corresponding idea for our system is to refuse to add to the location list a substatement whose first antecedent is the same (except perhaps for changed variables) as the original question or the first antecedent of a substatement higher on the list. In other words, we do not follow a path that leads past a repeated subquestion. Stopping on a repeated subquestion will eliminate endless deductions, but it will cause some questions not to be answered correctly.

For example, suppose we are given the corpus

at (pencil,desk)
at (desk,home)
at (home,county)
at (x,y), at (y,z) → at (x,z)

and the question "at(pencil,x)." Using the deductive methods of Section 6.2, we can deduce the answers

*at (pencil,desk)
*at (pencil,home)
*at (pencil,county)

However, with the deductive methods given of Section 6.3, and stopping on a repeated subquestion, we can deduce only one of these answers. The other two answers can be deduced only if a repeated subquestion is allowed; in fact, the subquestion must be allowed to repeat twice to get the third answer. If we decide to stop on a repeated subquestion, only three location lists are created, because the first antecedent of the first substatement is the same as the original question:

*at (pencil,desk)

*at (pencil,desk)
at (pencil,y), at (y,z) → at (pencil, z)

*at (pencil,desk)

We must therefore find some other way of stopping endless deduction.

6.4.3 Growing Subquestion

Even if stopping on a repeated subquestion were successful in stopping endless deductions caused by a repeating subquestion, there is another kind of endless deduction that would not be stopped. In this kind, the location list acquires longer and longer subquestions as it gets longer and longer. For example, suppose we are given the corpus

not (not (at (pencil,desk)))
not (not (x)) → x

and want to deduce answers to the question "at (x,y)." The system will generate a subquestion and find an answer to the subquestion but will get into an endless deduction trying to find more answers. The first few location lists created in trying to answer the question are as follows:

not (not (at (x,y))) → at (x,y))

not (not (at (x,y))) → at (x,y))
*not (not (at (pencil,desk)))

not (not (at (x,y))) → at (x,y)
*not(not(at(pencil,desk)))
not (not (not (not (at (x,y))))) → not (not (at (x,y)))

not (not (at (x,y))) → at (x,y)
*not (not (at (pencil,desk)))
not (not (not (not (at (x,y))))) → not (not (at (x,y)))
not(not(not(not(not(not(at(x,y))))))) →
not(not(not(not(at(x,y)))))

We need a way of stopping endless deductions caused by both repeating subquestions and growing subquestions.

6.4.4 Stopping Points

One basic way to accomplish this is to set a limit on the length of the location list and refuse to accept any subquestion that would go beyond the limit. By choosing different definitions of the length of the location list we get different stopping points and we may get more efficient deductions for one definition than for another. The length of the location list can be defined differently for different corpuses. Since a frequent sign of trouble is a repeating subquestion, we may want to define the length of the location list in terms of the number of repeated subquestions rather than in terms of the total number of subquestions. But subquestions may not repeat at all, and we must have a length that increases from time to time, else we will not stop the endless deduction.

We shall make use of the fact that every subquestion must come from some antecedent of some statement. One subquestion will be counted as a repeat of another if both come from the same antecedent of the same statement.

Each of the straightforward ways given below for measuring the length of a location list begins with the same preliminary operations. First, we number all the antecedents of all the statements in the corpus. Second, we remove all answers from the location list, leaving only substatements. Third, we replace each substatement by the number of its first antecedent. That leaves us with a list of numbers.

To find the length of the location list, we count some of the numbers on this list of numbers. Which ones we count determines which measure of length we are using. The possibilities are:

1. Count all the numbers on the list.
2. Find a number that occurs most often on the list. Count occurrences of that number only.
3. Do not count the first occurrence of any number, but count every occurrence after the first of every number on the list.

For the deduction given in Part 6.4.1, the corpus contains only two antecedents, which can be numbered

1. at (x,y)
2. at (y,z)

Antecedent 2 does not begin any substatement of any location list in that endless deduction; therefore the lists of numbers corresponding to the location lists contain only 1's. For that deduction the first two measures of the length of the location list are thus the same, and the third is always one less than either of the first two. But if we set a limit to the length of the location list and refuse to add any substatement to the location list which would make its length exceed the limit, the deductions that result from choosing different measures of the length are different. If we choose the first measure of length, and if we want to get an answer to the question, we must set the length limit at 2. This gives the following deduction:

at (pencil, y), at (y,county) $\rightarrow$ at (pencil,county)

at (pencil, y), at (y,county) → at (pencil,county)
*at (pencil,desk)

at (pencil, y), at (y,county) → at (pencil,county)
*at (pencil,desk)
at (pencil, y), at (y,z) → at (pencil, z)

at (pencil, y), at (y,county) → at (pencil,county)
*at (pencil,desk)
at (pencil, y), at (y,z) → at (pencil, z)
*at (pencil,desk)

at (pencil, y), at (y,county) → at (pencil,county)
*at (pencil,desk)
at (desk, z) → at (pencil, z)

at (pencil, y), at (y,county) → at (pencil,county)
*at (pencil,desk)
at (desk, z) → at (pencil, z)
*at (desk,home)

at (pencil, y), at (y,county) → at (pencil,county)
*at (pencil,desk)
*at (pencil,home)

at (pencil, y), at (y,county) → at (pencil,county)
*at (pencil,home)
at (desk,county) → at (pencil,county)

at (pencil, y),at (y,county) → at (pencil,county)
*at (pencil,home)
at (home,county) → at (pencil,county)

at (home,county) → at (pencil,county)
*at (home,county)

at (home,county) → at (pencil,county)
*at (home,county)
at (home, y),at (y,county) → at (home,county)

at (home,county) → at (pencil,county)
*at (home,county)
at (home, y),at (y,county) → at (home,county)
*at (home,county)

at (home,county) → at (pencil,county)
*at (home,county)
at (county,county) → at (home,county)

at (home,county) → at (pencil,county)
*at (home,county)

*at (pencil,county)

If we choose the second measure of length, we may set the length limit at 1, resulting in the following deduction:

at (pencil, *y*), at (*y*,county) → at (pencil,county)

at (pencil, *y*), at (*y*, county) → at (pencil,county)
*at (pencil,desk)

at (desk,county) → at (pencil,county)

at (desk,county) → at (pencil,county)
at (desk, *y*), at (*y*, county) → at (desk,county)

at (desk,county) → at (pencil,county)
at (desk, *y*), at (*y*, county) → at (desk,county)
*at (desk,home)

at (desk,county) → at (pencil,county)
at (home,county) → at (desk,county)

at (desk,county) → at (pencil,county)
at (home,county) → at (desk,county)
*at (home,county)

at (desk,county) → at (pencil,county)
*at (desk,county)

*at (pencil,county)

If we choose the third measure of length and set the length limit at 0, we get exactly the deduction that we get by choosing the second measure of length and setting the length limit at 1. But, counting each location list as a step in the deduction, we find that this deduction took only 9 steps, while the deduction we got using the first measure of length took 16 steps. In longer deductions, different choices of a measure of length may make an even greater difference in the length of the deduction.

The stopping points that prevent an endless deduction are determined by our choice of a measure of length of a location list. Which measure of length should we choose? In the examples given in this chapter, deductions are usually shorter when the second or third measures are chosen than when the first measure is chosen, but there is no choice that will guarantee shorter deductions for every possible corpus. Furthermore, there are many other measures of length of a location list that we might have taken, and there are ways of choosing stopping points that have nothing to do with the location list. We have just looked at three simple ways of choosing stopping points, which are all related to the length of the location list, to give an idea of how we might choose stopping points. For special corpuses, special ways of choosing stopping points might have to be found to keep deductions from getting too long.

6.5 Avoiding Endless Deduction

6.5.1 Stopping and Avoiding

In Section 6.4 we showed how to stop endless deductions, but stopping deductions may keep us from getting all the answers to a question. Suppose we are given the corpus

at (pencil,desk)
at (desk,home)
at (home,county)
at (x,y), at (y,z) → at (x,z)

and the question "at (pencil,county)" and further suppose we are using the first measure of the length of a location list. If we set the length limit at 2, then we get the answer "*at(pencil,county)," as shown in Part 6.4.4. But we don't know ahead of time how high to set the length limit: If we set it too high, the deduction will be too long; if we set it too low, we may not get all the answers. For example, if we set it at 1, we get the following deduction:

at (pencil, y), at (y,county) → at (pencil,county)

at (pencil, y), at (y,county) → at (pencil,county)
*at (pencil,desk)
at (desk,county) → at (pencil,county).

It ends without finding the answer. It would therefore be better if for some corpuses and questions we had a way of preventing endless deductions that would guarantee that we get all the answers to the questions. Preventing endless deduction without losing any of the answers to a question we call *avoiding* endless deduction.

There are two ways to avoid endless deduction: We can rewrite the corpus, or we can change the deductive process. When we ask a question and have to refuse to add a substatement because the location list is too long, we keep a record of the event and note that we may not have found all the answers to the original question. On the other hand, if we finish answering a question and no such event has occurred, then we know that we have found all the answers. Both ways are methods for keeping the length of the location list from reaching its limit.

6.5.2 Rewriting Statements

We can sometimes avoid an endless deduction by rewriting the statements in the corpus. The kind of endless deduction that can be avoided in this way is that which leads to a repeating subquestion rather than to a growing subquestion. The idea is to give the subquestion different names at different occurrences so that it doesn't repeat. For example consider the corpus and question of Part 6.5.1. As shown in Part 6.4.1, this leads to an endless deduction. But if we rewrite the corpus, giving

in (pencil,desk)
in (desk,home)
in (home,county)
in (x,y) → at (x,y)
in (x,y), at (y,z) → at (x,z)

then the deduction is no longer endless and we don't need to set a length limit. Rewriting the corpus in this way does not change the answers to any questions beginning with "at," although it does add answers to questions beginning with "in." With the new corpus and no length limit, the deduction of an answer to the question "at (pencil,county)" goes as follows:

in (pencil, y), at (y,county) → at (pencil,county)

in (pencil, y), at (y, county) → at (pencil,county)
*in (pencil,desk)

at (desk,county) → at (pencil,county)

at (desk,county) → at (pencil,county)
in (desk,county) → at (desk,county)

at (desk,county) → at(pencil,county)
in (desk, y), at (y, county) → at (desk,county)

at (desk,county) → at (pencil,county)
in (desk, y), at (y,county) → at (desk,county)
*in (desk,home)

at (desk,county) → at (pencil,county)
at (home,county) → at (desk,county)

at (desk,county) → at (pencil,county)
at (home,county) → at (desk,county)
in (home,county) → at (home,county)

at (desk,county) → at (pencil,county)
at (home,county) → at (desk,county)
in (home,county) → at (home,county)
*in (home,county)

at (desk,county) → at (pencil,county)
at (home,county) → at (desk, county)
*at (home,county)

at (desk,county) → at (pencil,county)
at (home,county) → at (desk,county)
*at (home,county)
in (home,x), at (x,county) → at (home,county)

at (desk,county) → at (pencil,county)
at (home,county) → at (desk,county)
*at (home,county)
in (home,x), at (x,county) → at (home,county)
*in (home,county)

at (desk,county) → at (pencil,county)
at (home,county) → at (desk,county)
*at (home,county)
at (county,county) → at (home,county)

at (desk,county) → at (pencil,county)
at (home,county) → at (desk,county)
*at (home,county)
at (county,county) → at (home,county)
in (county,county) → at (county,county)

at (desk,county) → at (pencil,county)
at (home,county) → at (desk,county)
*at (home,county)
at (county,county) → at (home,county)
in (county,x), at (x,county) → at (county,county)

at (desk,county) → at (pencil,county)
at (home,county) → at (desk,county)
*at (home,county)
at (county,county) → at (home,county)

at (home,county) → at (desk,county)
*at (home,county)

at (desk,county) → at (pencil,county)
*at (desk,county)

*at (pencil,county).

If we had rewritten the corpus as

in (pencil,desk)
in (desk,home)
in (home,county)

in $(x,y) \rightarrow$ at (x,y)
at (x,y), in $(y,z) \rightarrow$ at (x,z)

we would not have avoided the endless deduction.

6.5.3 Stopping on Repeated Subquestion

A second way to avoid endless deduction is to ask the question more than once, building up a special list of answers to repeated subquestions each time we ask the question. Each time a repeated subquestion is *asked,* answers are taken only from the special list. The question is not answered in the normal way. Each time a question that was repeated is *answered,* its answers are added to the special list.

If we have asked a question once, and if the special list is not empty, then we ask the question a second time. If more answers are added to the special list, we ask the question a third time. We continue asking the question until no new answers are added to the special list, or until the depth limit is reached. If we stop because no new answers were added to the special list, we know we have all the answers to the original question.

Each time we ask the original question, and for each subquestion that is asked, we go through the following steps:

1. Check the subquestion against all active questions. If it is identical (except for changes of variable) with any active question, mark the active question.
2. If the subquestion is a repeated subquestion, return any answers to it that may be on the special list. Do not answer it normally.
3. If the subquestion is not a repeated subquestion, answer it normally.

Each time a subquestion is answered, we go through the following step:

1. If the subquestion was marked, add all of its answers to the special list.

Thus we avoid certain endless deductions by saving the answers to repeated subquestions and by trying to answer the original question over and over until we no longer get new answers to repeated subquestions.

For example, suppose we are given the corpus

at (pencil,desk)
at (desk,home)
at (x,y), at $(y,z) \rightarrow$ at (x,z)

and we want to answer the question "at (pencil, x)." The progress of the deduction shows successive location lists and the successive states of the special list of answers to repeated questions. The special list will be indented to the right:

1. *at (pencil,desk)

   *at (pencil,desk)
   at (pencil, y), at (y,z) → at (pencil, z)

   *at (pencil,desk)

   at (pencil, x)
   *at (pencil,desk)

2. *at (pencil,desk)

   *at (pencil,desk)
   at (pencil, y), at (y,z) → at (pencil, z)

   *at (pencil,desk)
   at (pencil, y), at (y,z) → at (pencil, z)
   *at (pencil,desk)

   *at (pencil,desk)
   at (desk, z) → at (pencil, z)

   *at (pencil,desk)
   at (desk, z) → at (pencil, z)
   *at (desk,home)

   *at (pencil,desk)
   at (desk, z) → at (pencil, z)
   *at (desk,home)
   at (desk, y), at (y,z) → at (desk, z)

   *at (pencil,desk)
   at (desk, z) → at (pencil, z)
   *at (desk,home)

   at (pencil, x)
   *at (pencil,desk)
   at (desk, z)
   *at (desk,home)

   *at (pencil,desk)
   *at (pencil,home)

   at (pencil, x)
   *at (pencil,desk)
   *at (pencil,home)
   at (desk, z)
   *at (desk,home)

3. *at (pencil,desk)

   *at (pencil,desk)
   at (pencil, y), at (y,z) → at (pencil, z)

*at (pencil,desk)
at (pencil, y), at (y,z) → at (pencil, z)
*at (pencil,desk)
*at (pencil,home)

*at (pencil,desk)
at (pencil, y), at (y,z) → at (pencil, z)
*at (pencil,home)
at (desk, z) → at (pencil, z)

*at (pencil,desk)
at (pencil, y), at (y,z) → at (pencil, z)
*at (pencil,home)
at (desk, z) → at (pencil, z)
*at (desk,home)

*at (pencil,desk)
at (pencil, y), at (y,z) → at (pencil, z)
*at (pencil,home)
at (desk, z) → at (pencil, z)
*at (desk,home)
at (desk, y), at (y,z) → at (desk, z)

*at (pencil,desk)
at (pencil, y), at (y,z) → at (pencil, z)
*at (pencil,home)
at (desk, z) → at (pencil, z)
*at (desk,home)
at (desk, y), at (y,z) → at (desk, z)
*at (desk,home)

*at (pencil,desk)
at (pencil, y), at (y,z) → at (pencil, z)
*at (pencil,home)
at (desk, z) → at (pencil, z)
*at (desk,home)
at (home, z) → at (desk, z)

*at (pencil,desk)
at (pencil, y), at (y,z) → at (pencil, z)
*at (pencil,home)
at (desk, z) → at (pencil, z)
*at (desk,home)

*at (pencil,desk)
*at (pencil,home)
at (pencil, y), at (y,z) → at (pencil, z)

*at (pencil,home)

*at (pencil,desk)
*at (pencil,home)
at (home, z) → at (pencil, z)

*at (pencil,desk)
*at (pencil,home).

The third time we tried answering the question we found no new answers, and no new answers were added to the special list. So we stopped.

6.6 Examples

6.6.1 Not, And, Or

Denial is not a built-in part of the system. The question "smaller (pluto, mars)" has either the answer "*smaller (pluto,mars)" meaning "yes" or it has no answer at all. If it has no answer, then this means either that the answer is "no" or that the corpus doesn't have any information to base an answer on

To find out whether the answer to the question "smaller (pluto,mars)" is "no," we ask the question "not (smaller (pluto,mars))." If its answer is "*not (smaller (pluto,mars))," then the answer to the original question is "no." But in order to make this work, there must be some statements in the corpus specifically put there to handle denial. The corpus

smaller (pluto,mars)
smaller (mars,saturn)
smaller (saturn,jupiter)
smaller (x,y), smaller (y,z) → smaller (x,z)

cannot give a "no" answer to any question. To get "no" answers to the questions we expect to be asked (questions of the form "smaller(x,y)," where "x" is actually larger than "y"), we can add the statement "smaller (x,y) → not (smaller (y,x))" to the corpus.

If we want to be able to handle the denials of statements that already begin with "not," we can add the statement "x → not (not (x))." Similarly, conjunction and alternation are not built into the system. To give a general meaning to "and," we can add the statement "x,y → and (x,y)," and to give a general meaning to "or," we can add the statements

x → or (x,y)
y → or (x,y)

To give a general relation between "not" and "and," we can add the statements

not (x) → not (and (x,y))
not (y) → not (and (x,y))

and to give a general relation between "not" and "or," we can add the statement "not(x), not(y) → not(or(x,y))."

For every new kind of statement put in the corpus, special statements must be added to handle denials. For example, if the corpus contains the statements

rough (wool)
rough (linen)
smooth (silk)
smooth (nylon)

we might want to add the statements

rough (x) → not(smooth(x))
smooth (x) → not(rough(x))

Then, if we ask the question "rough (silk)," we get no answer, but if we ask the question "not(rough(silk))," we get the answer "*not(rough(silk))."

6.6.2 Logic Problem

The Logic Theorist (8) failed to prove at least one theorem in propositional calculus, which we can write "or(s, not(not(not(s))))." The detachment rule for propositional calculus can be written "implies (p,q), p → q," and the theorems needed to prove the theorem can be written

implies(implies(q,r), implies(or(p,q), or(p,r)))
or(p, not(p))
implies (p, not(not(p)))

Then if we think of the theorem to be proved as a question where "s" is a constant and not a variable, and if we consider finding an answer to the question the same as proving the theorem, then we can prove the theorem that the Logic Theorist could not prove. With the detachment rule and the three given theorems in the corpus, if we ask the question "or (s,not (not (not (s))))," we get the answer "*or(s,not(not(not(s))))."

6.6.3 Airport Problem

McCarthy (5) gave the Airport Problem as an example of a problem the "advice taker" ought to be able to solve. The advice taker is a deductive system that McCarthy thought should be written. Our deductive system is very much like the advice taker, except that the latter is not a question-answering system. McCarthy suggested that it contain rules for what statements to deduce, rather than having the statements to be deduced guided by a question that has been asked. The notation we have used for statements is that used by McCarthy for the advice taker.

We can take the statements McCarthy suggested for the Airport Problem, and write them in our system by changing them slightly. First, however, we had better explain what the words used in the Airport Problem mean. For each type of phrase given below, translations are given below the phrases and indented to the right:

at (x,y)

x is at y

walkable (x)

drivable (x)

x is a place where one can walk

x is a place where one can drive

implies $(x,\text{can}(y))$

implies $(\text{did}(y), z)$

when x is true, one can do y

when one has done y, z is true

go $(x,y,\text{walking})$

go $(x,y,\text{driving})$

walk from x to y

drive from x to y

canachult (x,y,z)

canachult $(x,\text{prog}(y,w),z)$

when x is true, by doing y one can make z true

when x is true, by doing y and w one can make z true

want (x)

do (x)

I want x to be true

I should do x

The word "canachult" stands for "can achieve ultimately." Using these phrases, the statements in the airport problem are as follows:

at (I,desk)

at (desk,home)

at (car,home)

at (home,county)

at (airport,county)

at (x,y), at (y,z) $\rightarrow$ at (x,z)

walkable (x), at (y,x), at (z,x) $\rightarrow$

implies(at(I, y),can(go(y,z, walking)))

drivable (x), at (y,x), at (z,x), at (car, y) $\rightarrow$

implies(at(I,car),can(go(y,z, driving)))

walkable (home)

drivable (county)

implies (did (go (x,y,z)),at(I, y))

want(at(I,airport))

implies $(x,\text{can}(y))$, implies $(\text{did}(y),z) \rightarrow$ canachult (x,y,z)

canachult (x,y,z), canachult (z,u,v) $\rightarrow$ canachult $(x, \text{prog}(y,u), v)$

at (I, v), canachult (at (I, v), prog (y,z), w), want (w) $\rightarrow$ do (y)

Then if we ask the question "do (x)," meaning "what should I do?" the system answers "*do(go(desk,car,walking))," meaning "first, walk from your desk to your car."

6.6.4 Monkey Problem

McCarthy (6) gives the Monkey Problem as another example of a sample problem for the "advice taker." Just as our deductive system can handle the Airport Problem when certain changes are made in the corpus, it can also handle the monkey problem when certain changes are made in the corpus.

The meanings of the phrases used in the monkey problem can be explained as follows:

place (u)

   u is a place

move (p,v,u)

   p moves v to the place u

climbs (p,v)
reach (p,v)
has (p,v)

   p climbs v
   p reaches v
   p has v

at (v,u)
on (p,v)

   v is at the place u
   p is on v

under (bananas)

   under the bunch of bananas

can (c,p,a)
can2 (p,a)

   under conditions c, p can do the action a
   under any conditions, p can do the action a

cause ($c1,a,c2$)
cause 2(a,c)

   under conditions $c1$, action a causes conditions $c2$
   under any conditions, action a causes conditions c

canult (p,c)

   by doing several things, p can ultimately cause conditions c

The statements in the corpus include, first of all, three general statements about causality:

can2(p,a), cause2(a,c) → canult (p,c)

can2(p,a), cause (c1,a,c2), canult (p,c1) → canult (p,c2)
can(c1,p,a), cause2(a,c2), canult (p,c1) → canult (p,c2)

The rest of the statements in the corpus have to do specifically with the monkey problem:

place (u) → can2(monkey, move(monkey,box,u))
cause2(move (p,v,u),at(v,u))
can2(monkey,climbs(monkey,box))
cause(at(v,u),climbs(p,v),and(at(v,u),on(p,v)))
place(under(bananas))
can(and(at(box,under(bananas)),on(monkey,box)),
    monkey,reach (monkey,bananas))
cause2(reach(p,x),has(p,x))

The general idea is that the bananas are too high for the monkey to reach. To get them he has to move a box under them, climb on the box, and reach for them. The question "canult(monkey,has(monkey,bananas))" means "can the monkey get the bananas?" And the answer "*canult(monkey,has(monkey, bananas))" means "the monkey can get the bananas."

In answering the question, the system also finds out what the monkey has to do to get the bananas.

6.6.5 Mikado Problem

Safier (13) formulated an advice-taker problem from the operetta "The Mikado." Again, our deductive system can handle the "Mikado Problem" when certain changes are made in the corpus, just as it can handle the Airport Problem and the Monkey Problem.

The meanings of the phrases used in the Mikado Problem are as follows:

married(x)
dead(x)
male(x)
female(x)
    x is married
    x is dead
    x is male
    x is female
marry(p1,p2)
accuses(p1,p2)
produce(p1,p2)
has(p1,claim,p2)
    p1 marries p2
    p1 accuses p2

*p*1 produces *p*2
*p*1 has a claim on *p*2

appear
continue(living)
continues(*p*, living)

appears
continues living
p continues living

thinks(*p*,*u*)

p thinks *u*

can(*c*,*p*,*a*)
can2(*p*,*a*)

under conditions *c*,*p* can do the action *a*
under any conditions, *p* can do the action *a*

cause(*c*1,*a*,*c*2)
cause2(*a*,*c*)
cause3(*c*1,*c*2)

under conditions *c*1 action *a* causes conditions *c*2
under any conditions action *a* causes conditions *c*
conditions *c*1 cause conditions *c*2

canult(*p*,*c*)

by doing several things, *p* can ultimately cause conditions *c*

The statements in the corpus include, first of all, three general statements about causality, two of which are the same as used in the Monkey Problem:

cause3 (*c*1,*c*2), canult (*p*,*c*1) → canult (*p*,*c*2)
can2 (*p*,*a*), cause2 (*a*,*c*) → canult (*p*,*c*)
can (*c*1,*p*,*a*), cause2 (*a*,*c*2), canult (*p*,*c*1) → canult (*p*,*c*2)

The rest of the statements in the corpus have to do specifically with the Mikado problem.

not (married (*p*1)), not (married (*p*2)), male (*p*1), female (*p*2) →
  can2(*p*1,marry (*p*1,*p*2))
cause2(marry (*p*1,*p*2),married (*p*1))
cause2(marry(*p*1, *p*2),married(*p*2))
not(married(Katisha))
not(married(Ko-Ko))
male(Ko-Ko)
female(Katisha)
cause3(married(Katisha),
  not(has(Katisha,claim,Nanki-Poo)))
cause3 (not (has (Katisha,claim,Nanki-Poo)),
  not(accuses(Katisha, Nanki-Poo)))

can(not(accuses(Katisha, Nanki-Poo)), Nanki-Poo,
    and(appear, continue(living)))
can (c,Nanki-Poo, and (appear,continue (living))) →
    can(c,Ko-Ko, produce(Ko-Ko,Nanki-Poo))
cause2(produce(p,Nanki-Poo),
    not(thinks(Mikado,dead(Nanki-Poo))))
cause3 (not (thinks (Mikado,dead (Nanki-Poo))),
    continues (Ko-Ko,living)).

The general idea is that if Ko-Ko doesn't watch out he will end up dead. When we ask the question "canult (Ko-Ko,continues (Ko-Ko,living))," which means "can Ko-Ko keep himself alive?" the system answers "*canult (Ko-Ko,continues (Ko-Ko,living))" which means "Ko-Ko can indeed keep himself alive," and finds out along the way just what Ko-Ko must do to keep himself alive.

6.6.6 Causality Principles

Similar statements were used in the Monkey Problem and the Mikado Problem to express general causality principles. We can collect those statements here and add another to give a complete set of causality principles that can be used on a variety of examples:

can($c1,p,a$), cause($c1,a,c2$), canult ($p,c1$) → canult ($p,c2$)
can($c1,p,a$), cause2($a,c2$), canult($p,c1$) → canult($p,c2$)
can2(p,a), cause($c1,a,c2$), canult($p,c1$) → canult($p,c2$)
can2(p,a), cause2(a,c) → canult(p,c)
cause3($c1,c2$), canult($p,c1$) → canult($p,c2$)

We might also want to add the statements

can2(p,a) → can(c,p,a)
cause2($a,c2$) → cause($c1,a,c2$)
cause3($c1,c2$) → cause($c1,a,c2$).

This set of statements, however, covers only the kind of causality where one person does something that sets up conditions permitting him to do something else. It does not cover the case where a person must do two things to set up conditions for doing a third thing and where the two things may interfere with one another. It does not cover the case where two or more people must cooperate to get something done, nor does it cover the case where people are competing.

The phrases used in these statements were translated in giving the monkey and Mikado examples. We can, however, give a sample translation of the first complete conditional statement in this section, as follows:

If under conditions $c1$ person p can do action a, and if under conditions $c1$ action a causes conditions $c2$, and if person p can bring about conditions $c1$, then person p can bring about conditions $c2$.

6.7 Efficiency

6.7.1 Making Deductions

When answering certain questions from a given corpus of statements takes longer than we can afford to wait, what do we do? The first thing is to make deductions once and for all, so they do not have to be made over and over each time a question is asked. We can replace a group of statements by all the statements that can be deduced from them. For example, if in the airport problem we replace the statements

at(I,desk)
at(desk,home)
at(car,home)
at(home,county)
at(airport,county)
at(x,y), at(y,z) → at(x,z)

by the statements

at(I,desk)
at(desk,home)
at(car,home)
at(home,county)
at(airport,county)
at(I,home)
at(I,county)
at(desk,county)
at(car,county)

Then the question "do(x)" is answered at least three times faster than it was before, depending on which version of the system we are using. Note that this is true in spite of the fact that there are more statements in the corpus. Every question must be matched against every statement in the corpus, and adding statements to the corpus is bound to slow down the answering of a single question. But the result of this change is that far fewer questions are asked; this more than makes up for the increased time required to answer each question.

6.7.2 Classifying

The second thing we can do to speed up question answering is to group together all questions with consequents that match a certain phrase, and put that phrase at the top of the group as a heading. Every question asked is matched first against the heading; only if it matches the heading of a group could it possibly match any of the statements in the group. For example, the expanded group of statement deduced in Part 6.7.1 might all be put under the heading "at(x,y)."

Furthermore, we can have subheadings of headings. We can have a whole hierarchy of headings and subheadings and subsubheadings, as elaborate as need be to speed up question answering. Once it gets too elaborate it will start slowing down. The expanded statements of Part 6.7.1, with heading and subheadings, might look like this:

at(x,y)
    at$(x,$desk)
        at(I,desk)
    at$(x,$home)
        at(I,home)
        at(desk,home)
        at(car,home)
    at$(x,$county)
        at(I,county)
        at(desk,county)
        at(car,county)
        at(home,county)
        at(airport,county)

6.7.3 Internal Deduction

The third thing we can do to speed up question answering is to combine the first two ideas, making deductions and classifying, and then let the system do the work. Suppose the corpus contains the statements

in(I,desk)
in(desk,home)
in(car,home)
in(home,county)
in(airport,county)
in$(x,y) \rightarrow$ at(x,y)

and suppose the system decides (or we tell it) to concentrate on eliminating the last statement. Suppose further that the only statements whose consequents begin with "in" are the ones that appear above. The system takes the first antecedent "in(x,y)" of the statement at which it is looking and matches it against the consequents of all the statements in the corpus. It matches the five other statements that appear above. Each of the statements matched is used, together with the statement to be eliminated, to make a deduction by the rules given in Section 6.2. Thus, from the statements given, the system can deduce the new statements

at(I,desk)
at(desk,home)
at(car,home)
at(home,county)
at(airport,county)

and add them to the corpus. But since every statement that matched the antecedent "in(x,y)" was used to make a deduction, the statement "in$(x,y) \rightarrow$ at(x,y)" is no longer needed, and the system can remove it from the corpus automatically. Furthermore, the system knows that every statement deduced must match the consequent "at(x,y)" of the statement that was removed, so the deduced statements can be formed into a group and the consequent of the statement that was removed can be used as a heading. All this can be done automatically by the system, and results in a much more efficient corpus. The corpus gets larger and larger as internal deductions are made, so the process must stop before the corpus gets larger than the space available for it in the machine.

6.7.4 Future Research

The main trouble with the system is that it is too slow in solving practical problems. The methods given in this section for increasing the speed of the system seem quite promising. Only the method given in Part 6.7.1 has been tried out; the other two methods can be elaborated and tested and should result in significant improvements. This seems to be the most promising direction for future research.

Appendix 6.1

Various versions of the system have been written as LISP programs (7). These programs have run successfully and all the ideas given in the first six sections of this chapter have been tested. Since the basic program is short, it will be reproduced here. First, however, let us see how statements, questions, and answers are represented as list structures.

A phrase is expressed as a list structure by changing all small letters to capital letters, removing commas, and interchanging each left parenthesis with the word to the left of it. Thus the phrase "want(at(I,airport))" becomes "(WANT (AT I AIRPORT))."

A statement is a list structure obtained by applying the function CONS to a list of antecedents and a consequent. Thus the statement "at(x,y), at$(y,z) \rightarrow$ at(x,z)" becomes "(((AT X Y) (AT Y Z)) AT X Z)."

A direct statement is a statement with an empty list of antecedents. Thus the direct statement "want (at (I,airport))" becomes "(NIL WANT (AT I AIRPORT))."

The translation of a phrase is different from that of the same phrase considered as a direct statement. The translation of a question or answer, however, is the same as that of a phrase.

The following is a complete deck for a basic version of the system plus the Monkey Problem. This version of the system does not have any provision for stopping or avoiding loops; therefore it cannot handle most of the other examples.

```
QUESTION ANSWERER N3070     FISCHER BLACK 2561
        DEBUG
DEFINE ((
(SOLUTION1 (LAMBDA (W) (PROG (Y Y1 V)
(COND ((MEMBER (CAR W) LIBRARY)
          (RETURN (EVALFORM W))))
(SETQ Y CORPUS)
A (COND ((NULL Y) (RETURN V)))
(SETQ Y1 (MATCH W (CAR Y)))
(SETQ Y (CDR Y))
(COND ((EQ Y1 (QUOTE NOMATCH)) (GO A)))
(SETQ V (CONC (SOLUTION2 Y1) V))
(GO A))))

(SOLUTION2 (LAMBDA (Y)
(PROG (W X W1 U Z V Z1 P)
(SETQ W (ANTECEDENT Y))
(SETQ X (CONSEQUENT Y))
(COND ((NULL W) (RETURN (LIST X))))
(SETQ W1 (CAR W))
(SETQ Y (CONS (CDR W) X))
(SETQ U (VARIABLES Y))
(SETQ Z (SOLUTION1 W1))
A (COND((NULL Z) (RETURN V)))
(SETQ Z1 (RELEASE U (CAR Z)))
(SETQ Z (CDR Z))
(SETQ P (SUBLIS (PAIRLIST W1 Z1) Y))
(SETQ V (CONC (SOLUTION2 P) V))
(GO A))))

(MATCH (LAMBDA (W V) (PROG (U)
(COND ((NOT (MATCH1 W (CONSEQUENT V)))
          (RETURN (QUOTE NOMATCH))))
(SETQ V (RELEASE (VARIABLES W) V))
(SETQ U (PAIRLIST (CONSEQUENT V) W))
(COND ((SMOOTH U) (RETURN (SUBLIS U V))))
(RETURN (QUOTE NOMATCH)))))
```

```
(MATCH1 (LAMBDA (W X) (COND
((AND (ATOM W) (ATOM X) (EQUAL W X)) T)
((ATOM W) (OR (VARIABLE W)
            (AND (ATOM X) (VARIABLE X)))))
((ATOM X) (VARIABLE X))
((NOT (MATCH1 (CAR W) (CAR X))) F)
(T (MATCH1 (CDR W) (CDR X))))))

(RELEASE (LAMBDA (W V) (PROG (Z Y X U)
(SETQ Z (VARIABLES V))
(SETQ Y (INTERSECTION W Z))
(SETQ X (APPEND W Z))
(SETQ U (NEWVARIABLES (LENGTH Y) X))
(RETURN (SUBLIS (PAIR Y U) V)))))

(VARIABLES (LAMBDA (X) (PROG (Y Z)
(COND ((VARIABLE X) (RETURN (LIST X)))
((ATOM X) (RETURN NIL)))
(SETQ Y (VARIABLES (CAR X)))
(SETQ Z (VARIABLES (CDR X)))
(RETURN (CONC Y Z)))))

(INTERSECTION (LAMBDA (X Y) (PROG (U)
A (COND ((NULL X) (RETURN U))
((MEMBER (CAR X) Y) (SETQ U (CONS (CAR X) U))))
(SETQ X (CDR X))
(GO A))))

(NEWVARIABLES (LAMBDA (X Y) (PROG (U Z)
(SETQ U VARIABLELIST)
A (COND ((ZEROP X) (RETURN Z)))
B (COND ((NOT (MEMBER (CAR U) Y)) (GO C)))
(SETQ U (CDR U))
(GO B)
C (SETQ Y (CONS (CAR U) Y))
(SETQ Z (CONS (CAR U) Z))
(SETQ X (SUB1 X))
(GO A))))
(PAIRLIST (LAMBDA (X Y) (PROG (Y1 Y2)
(COND ((AND) ATOM X) (ATOM Y) (EQUAL X Y)) (RETURN NIL))
((VARIABLE Y) (RETURN NIL))
((VARIABLE X) (RETURN (LIST (CONS X Y)))))
(SETQ Y1 (PAIRLIST (CAR X) (CAR Y)))
(SETQ Y2 (PAIRLIST (CDR X) (CDR Y)))
(RETURN (CONC Y1 Y2)))))
```

```
(SMOOTH (LAMBDA (X) (PROG (X1 Y)
A (COND ( (NULL X) (RETURN T) ) )
(SETQ X1 (CAR X) )
(SETQ X (CDR X) )
(SETQ Y (SASSOC (CAR X1) X
         (QUOTE (LAMBDA ( ) (QUOTE OK) ) ) ) )
(COND ( (EQ Y (QUOTE OK) ) (GO A ) )
( (EQUAL Y X1) (GO A) ) )
(RETURN F) ) ) )

(EVALFORM (LAMBDA (X) (PROG (X1 U)
(SETQ X (REVERSE X) )
A (COND ( (NULL X) (RETURN (EVAL U NIL) ) ) )
(SETQ X1 (CAR X ) )
(SETQ X (CDR X) )
(COND ( (NOT (NULL X) )
(SETQ X1 (LIST (QUOTE QUOTE) X1) ) ) )
(SETQ U (CONS X1 U) )
(GO A) ) ) )

(ANTECEDENT (LAMBDA (X) (CAR X) ) )

(CONSEQUENT (LAMBDA (X) (CDR X) ) )

(VARIABLE (LAMBDA (X) (AND (ATOM X)
(MEMBER X VARIABLELIST) ) ) )

) )

COMPILE ( (
SOLUTION1
SOLUTION2

MATCH
MATCH1
RELEASE
VARIABLES
INTERSECTION
NEWVARIABLES
PAIRLIST
SMOOTH
EVALFORM
ANTECEDENT
CONSEQUENT
VARIABLE
) )
```

```
EXCISE (*T*)
TRACE ( (
SOLUTION1
) )
CSET (LIBRARY NIL)
CSET (CORPUS (
( ( (PLACE U) ) CAN1 MONKEY  (MOVE MONKEY BOX U) )
( ( ) CAUSE1  (MOVE P V U)  (AT V U) )
( ( ) CAN1 MONKEY  (CLIMBS MONKEY BOX) )
( ( ) CAUSE  (AT V  U) (CLIMBS P V)  (AND (AT V U) (ON P V) ) )
( ( ) PLACE (UNDER BANANAS) )
( ( ) CAN (AND (AT BOX (UNDER BANANAS) ) (ON MONKEY BOX) )
        MONKEY (REACH MONKEY BANANAS) )
( ( ) CAUSE1 (REACH P  X)  (HAS P  X) )
( ( ( CAN1 P  A)  (CAUSE1  A  C) ) CANULT  P  C)
( ( ( CAN1 P A) (CAUSE C1 A C2) (CANULT P C1) ) CANULT P C2)
( ( ( CAN1 C1 P A) (CAUSE1 A C2) (CANULT P C1) ) CANULT P C2)
) )
(SET  (VARIABLELIST  (X Y Z U V P A C C1 C2) )
SOLUTION1  ( (CANULT  MONKEY  (HAS MONKEY BANANAS) ) )
        STOP  ) ) )  ) ) )  ) ) )  ) ) )  ) ) )
        FIN
```

Appendix 6.2

With the deductive rules given in Section 6.1, deducing a statement with no variables from a corpus is equivalent to proving a theorem from an elementary formal system as formulated by Smullyan (15, pp. 2-5). Thus, question-answering systems have the general properties of elementary formal systems, including unsolvability. To show this, we must give a mapping of elementary formal systems into question-answering systems such that every proof in an e.f.s. corresponds to a deduction in the mapped-into q.a.s., and vice versa. Unsolvability follows from noting that if we could decide whether a deduction exists in a q.a.s. then we could also decide whether a proof exists in an e.f.s. by finding the corresponding q.a.s. and the statement corresponding to the sentence to be proved, and deciding whether a deduction of the statement exists.

In this appendix we mean by a question-answering system the general question-answering system described in Section 6.2 plus a specific corpus. To map elementary formal systems into question-answering systems, we want to map "sequences of axioms" into corpuses, "sentences to be proved" into statements to be deduced, and "rules of inference" into deductive rules.

First we try the most straightforward mapping. "Signs," "variables," and "predicates" are carried over from the e.f.s. to the q.a.s. without change. A "term" that is a single sign or variable is also carried over without change. A term that contains two symbols (signs or variables) is mapped into the result of putting the symbols for "x" and "y" in "$f(x,y)$." A term that contains more than two symbols is more complex. We remove the last symbol from the term and find the mapping of the resulting term. Then we put the mapping for "x" and the last symbol for "y" in "$f(x,y)$" to get the mapping for the original term. For example, here is a term and its mapping:

axybya

$f(f(f(f(f(a,x),y),b),y),a)$.

Such a mapping of a term we will call the "f-image" of the term. Note that every term has a unique f-image and that no two terms have the same f-image. Thus the mapping of terms into f-images is reversible.

The mapping of an "atomic formula," consisting of a predicate followed by terms separated by commas, is obtained by mapping the terms into their f-images, and enclosing the sequence of terms in parentheses. Here is an atomic formula and its mapping:

Pabx, c, ya

$P(f(f(a,b),x), c, f(y,a))$

The mapping of a "well-formed formula," consisting of atomic formulas separated by arrows, is obtained by replacing every atomic formula by its mapping, and every arrow but the last by a comma. Here are a well-formed formula and its mapping:

Px → Py → Pxy

$P(x), P(y) \rightarrow P(f(x,y))$.

To complete this straightforward mapping, the "rules of inference" ("substitution" and "detachment") are carried over without change.

This mapping will not work, however, Suppose that we are given the e.f.s.

Pab

Px → Py → Pxy

and we want to prove the theorem "Pabab." The proof is obtained by putting "ab" for "x" and "y" and using the rule of detachment twice. But the corresponding q.a.s. is

$P(f(a,b))$

$P(x), P(y) \rightarrow P(f(x,y))$

and the corresponding statement is "$P(f(f(f(a,b),a),b))$." Putting "$f(a,b)$" for "x" and "y" and using the detachment rule twice, we get "$P(f(f(a,b), f(a,b)))$," which is not the statement we want.

To correct the mapping, we need a way to get phrases like "$f(f(a,b),f(a,b))$"

into a normal form in which they are f-images of terms. We need a list of statements defining a predicate "norm (x,y)," meaning "phrase x has normal form y." First we define a predicate "sign (x)" meaning "x is a sign." The exact statements we use will depend on just what signs are used in the e.f.s., but if they are the letters a-z, we can use the statements

sign (a)
sign (b)
.
.
.
sign (z).

Then the list of statements defining "norm(x,y)" is

1. sign (x) $\rightarrow$ norm(x,x)
2. norm(x,y), sign(z) $\rightarrow$ norm$(f(x,z),f(y,z))$
3. norm $(f(f(x,y),z),w) \rightarrow$ norm $(f(x,f(y,z)),w)$.

Given a phrase such as "$f(f(a,b),f(a,b))$," we can establish a procedure for deducing the statement of its normal form, which for this phrase would be "norm $(f(f(a,b),f(a,b)),f(f(f(a,b),a),b))$." Scan the phrase from left to right. Put the first sign encountered for "x" in statement 1 and detach the antecedent of the resulting statement. For each sign encountered after the first,

1. In statement 2, put the sign for "z", and put phrases for "x" and "y" that make "norm(x,y)" the same as the last statement deduced. Detach both antecedents of the resulting statement.
2. Count the right parentheses between the sign and the next comma. If the count is positive, subtract one. This gives the number of times statement 3 is to be used. For each use of statement 3, put for its variables phrases that make its antecedent the same as the last statement deduced. Detach its antecedent.

Now we can give the correct mapping of elementary formal systems into question-answering systems. The simple mapping is still used for signs, variables, predicates, terms, sentences to be proved, and the detachment rule. We must change the mappings for axioms and the substitution rule.

To find the correct mapping for an axiom, first find the simple mapping for the axiom. Every component but the first of every antecedent and the consequent of the resulting statement can be called an *element* of the statement. The elements of the statement "$P(x), P(y) \rightarrow P(f(x,y))$" are the phrases "$x$," "$y$," and "$f(x,y)$."

For every element that contains at least one variable but does not consist of a single variable, the *normalizer* of the element is obtained by putting the element for "x" and an entirely new variable not appearing in the statement for "y" in the phrase "norm(x,y)." The new variable chosen can be called the *free variable* of the element. No two elements of the same statement should have the same free variable. If we choose the free variable "z" for the element "f(x,y)" of the above statement, then its normalizer becomes "norm(f$(x,y),z)$."

For every element of the simple mapping of an axiom that has a normalizer, replace the element by its free variable and add the normalizer as an additional antecedent. Thus the axiom "Px → Py → Pxy" is correctly mapped into the statement "norm(f$(x,y),z)$, P(x), P(y) → P(z)." After all the axioms have been mapped into statements, add the statements defining "sign(x)" and "norm(x,y)" as given above. This completes the mapping of the axioms of an e.f.s. into statements of a q.a.s.

Finally, we must give the correct mapping of the substitution rule of inference. If we put words for variables in an axiom of the e.f.s., then we put the f-images of the words for the same variables in the corresponding statement of the q.a.s. Using the procedure given above for deducing the normal form of a phrase, we deduce normal forms for all the f-images substituted. Then we put normal forms for the free variables, and detach the normalizers of the statement.

Under the new mapping, the e.f.s.

Pab
Px → Py → Pxy

maps into the q.a.s.

$\mathrm{P}(\mathrm{f}(a,b))$
$\mathrm{norm}(\mathrm{f}(x,y),z), \mathrm{P}(x), \mathrm{P}(y) \rightarrow \mathrm{P}(z)$
$\mathrm{sign}(a)$
$\mathrm{sign}(b)$
$\mathrm{sign}(x) \rightarrow \mathrm{norm}(x,x)$
$\mathrm{norm}(x,y), \mathrm{sign}(z) \rightarrow \mathrm{norm}(\mathrm{f}(x,z), \mathrm{f}(y,z))$
$\mathrm{norm}(\mathrm{f}(\mathrm{f}(x,y),z),w) \rightarrow \mathrm{norm}(\mathrm{f}(x,\mathrm{f}(y,z)),w)$

and the deduction

Pab → Pab → Pabab
Pab → Pabab
Pabab

maps into the deduction (in outline form)

$\mathrm{norm}(\mathrm{f}(\mathrm{f}(a,b),\mathrm{f}(a,b)),z), \mathrm{P}(\mathrm{f}(a,b)), \mathrm{P}(\mathrm{f}(a,b)) \rightarrow \mathrm{P}(z).$
$\mathrm{norm}(a,a)$
$\mathrm{norm}(\mathrm{f}(a,b),\mathrm{f}(a,b))$
$\mathrm{norm}(\mathrm{f}(\mathrm{f}(a,b),a),\mathrm{f}(\mathrm{f}(a,b),a))$
$\mathrm{norm}(\mathrm{f}(\mathrm{f}(\mathrm{f}(a,b),a),b),\mathrm{f}(\mathrm{f}(\mathrm{f}(a,b),a),b))$
$\mathrm{norm}(\mathrm{f}(\mathrm{f}(a,b),\mathrm{f}(a,b)),\mathrm{f}(\mathrm{f}(\mathrm{f}(a,b),a),b))$
$\mathrm{norm}(\mathrm{f}(\mathrm{f}(a,b),\mathrm{f}(a,b)),\mathrm{f}(\mathrm{f}(\mathrm{f}(a,b),a),b)),$

$$P(f(a,b)), P(f(a,b)) \rightarrow P(f(f(f(a,b), a), b))$$

$$P(f(a,b)), P(f(a,b)) \rightarrow P(f(f(f(a,b), a), b))$$

$$P(f(a,b)) \rightarrow P(f(f(f(a,b), a), b))$$

$$P(f(f(f(a,b), a), b)).$$

The mapping from proofs to deductions is reversible. If we have a deduction we can get a corresponding proof by reversing the mapping. The steps of the deduction involving statements defining "sign(x)" or "norm(x,y)" are simply omitted in applying the reverse mapping.

Thus for every e.f.s. there is a q.a.s. such that a sentence can be proved in the e.f.s. if and only if the corresponding statement can be deduced in the q.a.s.

Bibliography

1. Artandi, S., and Hines, T. C., "Roles and Links–Or Forward to Cutter," *American Documentation,* Vol. 14, No. 1, 1963.
2. Cooper, W. S., "Fact Retrieval and Deductive Question-Answering Information Retrieval Systems," *J. Assn. for Computing Machinery,* Vol. 11, No. 2, 1964.
3. Gelernter, H. L., and Rochester, N., "Intelligent Behavior in Problem-Solving Machines," *IBM Journal,* Oct. 1958.
4. Green, Jr., B. F., et al., "Baseball: An Automatic Question-Answerer," *Proc. WJCC,* Vol. 19, 1961.
5. McCarthy, J., "Programs with Common Sense," *Proc. Symposium on Mechanisation of Thought Processes,* Her Majesty's Stationery Office, London, 1959 (Section 7.1 of the present volume).
6. McCarthy, J., "Situations, Actions, and Causal Laws," *Stanford Artificial Intelligence Project Memo* No. 2, July 1963 (Section 7.2 of the present volume).
7. McCarthy, J., et al., *LISP 1.5 Programmer's Manual,* The M.I.T. Press, Cambridge, Mass., 1963.
8. Newell, A., et al., "Empirical Explorations of the Logic Theory Machine: A Case Study in Heuristics," *Proc. WJCC, IRE,* 1957.
9. Quine, W. V., *Methods of Logic,* Henry Holt and Company, New York, 1950.
10. Raphael, B., "*SIR:* A Computer Program for Semantic Information Retrieval," Ph.D. Thesis, Mathematics Dept., M.I.T., Cambridge, Mass., 1964 (Chapter 2 of the present volume).
11. Reichenbach, H., *Elements of Symbolic Logic,* The Macmillan Co., New York, 1947.
12. Robinson, J. A., "Theorem Proving on the Computer," *J. Assn. for Computing Machinery,* Vol. 10, No. 2, 1963.
13. Safier, F., "'The Mikado' as an Advice Taker Problem," *Stanford Artificial* Intelligence Project Memo No. 3, 1963.
14. Simmons, R. F., et al., "Toward the Synthesis of Human Language Behavior," *Behavioral Science,* Vol. 7, No. 3, 1962.
15. Smullyan, R. M., "Theory of Formal Systems," *Annals of Mathematics Studies* No. 47, Princeton University Press, Princeton, N.J., 1961.

7. Programs with Common Sense

John McCarthy

7.1 The Advice Taker

The "Advice Taker" is a proposed program for solving problems by manipulating sentences in formal languages.* The main difference between it and other programs or proposed programs for manipulating formal languages, such as the Logic Theory Machine (6) and the Geometry Program of Gelernter (2), is that in the previous programs the formal system was the subject matter but the heuristics were all embodied in the program. In this program the procedures will be described as much as possible in the language itself and, in particular, the heuristics are all so described.

The main advantages we expect the advice taker to have is that its behavior will be improvable merely by making statements to it, telling it about its symbolic environment and what is wanted from it. To make these statements will require little if any knowledge of the program or the previous knowledge of the advice taker. One will be able to assume that the advice taker will have available to it a fairly wide class of immediate logical consequences of anything it is told and its previous knowledge. This property is expected to have much in common with what makes us describe certain humans as having common sense. We shall therefore say that a program has common sense if it automatically deduces for itself a sufficiently wide class of immediate consequences of anything it is told and what it already knows.

*Section 7.1 is a reprint of a paper taken from "Mechanisation of Thought Processes," Vol. 1, pp. 77-84, Proc. Symposium, National Physical Laboratory, London, November 24-27, 1958.

Before describing the advice taker in any detail, I would like to describe more fully our motivation for proceeding in this direction. Our ultimate objective is to make programs that learn from their experience as effectively as humans do. It may not be realized how far we are presently from this objective. It is not hard to make machines learn from experience how to make simple changes in their behavior of a kind which has been anticipated by the programmer. For example, Samuel has included in his checker program (8) facilities for improving the weights the machine assigns to various factors in evaluating positions. He has also included a scheme whereby the machine remembers games it has played previously and deviates from its previous play when it finds a position which it previously lost. Suppose, however, that we wanted an improvement in behavior corresponding, say, to the discovery by the machine of the principle of the opposition in checkers. No present or presently proposed schemes are capable of discovering phenomena as abstract as this.

If one wants a machine to be able to discover an abstraction, it seems most likely that the machine must be able to represent this abstraction in some relatively simple way.

There is one known way of making a machine capable of learning arbitrary behavior, and thus to anticipate every kind of behavior: This is to make it possible for the machine to simulate arbitrary behaviors and try them out. These behaviors may be represented either by nerve nets (5), by Turing machines (3), or by calculator programs (1). The difficulty is twofold. First, in any of these representations the density of interesting behaviors is incredibly low. Second, and even more important, small interesting changes in behavior expressed at a high level of abstraction do not have simple representations. It is as though the human genetic structure were represented by a set of blueprints: then a mutation would usually result in a wart, a failure of parts to meet, or even an ungrammatical blueprint which could not be translated into an animal at all. It is very difficult to see how the genetic representation scheme manages to be general enough to represent the great variety of animals observed and yet be such that so many interesting changes in the organism are represented by small genetic changes. The problem of how such a representation controls the development of a fertilized egg into a mature animal is even more difficult.

In our opinion, a system which is to evolve intelligence of human order should have at least the following features:

1. All behaviors must be representable in the system. Therefore, the system should either be able to construct arbitrary automata or to program in some general-purpose programming language.
2. Interesting changes in behavior must be expressible in a simple way.

3. All aspects of behavior except the most routine must be improvable. In particular, the improving mechanism should be improvable.
4. The machine must have or evolve concepts of partial success because on difficult problems decisive successes or failures come too infrequently.
5. The system must be able to create subroutines which can be included in procedures as units. The learning of subroutines is complicated by the fact that the effect of a subroutine is not usually good or bad in itself. Therefore, the mechanism that selects subroutines should have concepts of an interesting or powerful subroutine whose application may be good under suitable conditions.

Of the five points mentioned, our work concentrates mainly on the second. We base ourselves on the idea that in order for a program to be capable of learning something it must first be capable of being told it. In fact, in the early versions we shall concentrate entirely on this point and attempt to achieve a system which can be told to make a specific improvement in its behavior with no more knowledge of its internal structure or previous knowledge than is required in order to instruct a human. Once this is achieved, we may be able to tell the advice taker how to learn from experience.

The main distinction between the way one programs a computer and modifies the program and the way one instructs a human or will instruct the advice taker is this: A machine is instructed mainly in the form of a sequence of imperative sentences, while a human is instructed mainly in declarative sentences describing the situation in which action is required together with a few imperatives that say what is wanted. The advantages of imperative sentences are as follows:

1. A procedure described in imperatives is already laid out and is carried out faster.
2. One starts with a machine in a basic state and does not assume previous knowledge on the part of the machine.

The advantages of declarative sentences are as follows:

1. Advantage can be taken of previous knowledge.
2. Declarative sentences have logical consequences and it can be arranged that the machine will have available sufficiently simple logical consequences of what it is told and what it previously knew.
3. The meaning of declaratives is much less dependent on their order than is the case with imperatives. This makes it easier to have afterthoughts.
4. The effect of a declarative is less dependent on the previous state of the system so that less knowledge of this state is required on the part of the instructor.

The only way we know of expressing abstractions (such as the previous example of the opposition in checkers) is in language. That is why we have decided to program a system which reasons verbally.

7.1.1 The Construction of the Advice Taker

The advice taker system has the following main features:

1. There is a method of representing expressions in the computer. These expressions are defined recursively as follows: A class of entities called terms is defined and a term is an expression. A sequence of expressions is an expression. These expressions are represented in the machine by list structures (5).
2. Certain of these expressions may be regarded as declarative sentences in a certain logical system which will be analogous to a universal Post canonical system. The particular system chosen will depend on programming considerations but will probably have a single rule of inference which will combine substitution for variables with *modus ponens.* The purpose of the combination is to avoid choking the machine with special cases of general propositions already deduced.
3. There is an immediate deduction routine which when given a set of premises will deduce a set of immediate conclusions. Initially, the immediate deduction routine will simply write down all one-step consequences of the premises. Later this may be elaborated so that the routine will produce some other conclusions which may be of interest. However, this routine will not use semantic heuristics; i.e. heuristics which depend on the subject matter under discussion. The intelligence, if any, of the advice taker will not be embodied in the immediate deduction routine. This intelligence will be embodied in the procedures which choose the lists of premises to which the immediate deduction routine is to be applied. Of course, the program should never attempt to apply the immediate deduction routine simultaneously to the list of everything it knows. This would make the deduction routine take too long.
4. Not all expressions are interpreted by the system as declarative sentences. Some are the names of entities of various kinds. Certain formulas represent objects. For our purposes, an entity is an object if we have something to say about it other than the things which may be deduced from the form of its name. For example, to most people, the number 3812 is not an object: they have nothing to say about it except what can be deduced from its structure. On the other hand, to most Americans the number 1776 is an object because they have filed somewhere the fact that it represents the year when the American Revolution started. In the advice taker each object has a property list in which are listed the specific things we have to say about it. Some things which can be deduced from the name of the object may be included in the property list anyhow if the deduction was actually carried out and was difficult enough so that the system does not want to carry it out again.

5. Entities other than declarative sentences which can be represented by formulas in the system are individuals, functions, and programs.

6. The program is intended to operate cyclically as follows: The immediate deduction routine is applied to a list of premises and a list of individuals. Some of the conclusions have the form of imperative sentences. These are obeyed. Included in the set of imperatives which may be obeyed is the routine which deduces and obeys.

We shall illustrate the way the advice taker is supposed to act by means of an example. Assume that I am seated at my desk at home and I wish to go to the airport. My car is at my home also. The solution of the problem is to walk to the car and drive the car to the airport. First, we shall give a formal statement of the premises the advice taker uses to draw the conclusions. Then we shall discuss the heuristics which cause the advice taker to assemble these premises from the totality of facts it has available. The premises come in groups, and we shall explain the interpretation of each group.

1. First, we have a predicate "at." "at(x,y)" is a formalization of "x is at y." Under this heading we have the premises

   1. at (I, desk)
   2. at (desk, home)
   3. at (car, home)
   4. at (home, county)
   5. at (airport, county)

We shall need the fact that the relation "at" is transitive, which might be written directly as

   6. at (x,y), at (y,z) → at (x,z) .

or alternatively we might instead use the more abstract premises

   6′. transitive (at)

and

   7′. transitive (u) → (u (x,y), u (yz,z) → (u (x,z))

from which 6. can be deduced.

2. There are two rules concerning the feasibility of walking and driving.

   8. walkable (x), at (y,x), at (z,x), at (I,y)→can (go (y,z, walking))
   9. drivable (x), at (y,x), at (z,x), at (car,y), at (I,car)→can (go (y,z,driving))

There are also two specific facts.

   10. walkable (home)
   11. drivable (county)

3. Next we have a rule concerned with the properties of going.

   12. did (go (x,y,z)) → at (I,y)

4. The problem itself is posed by the premise:

   13. want (at (I,airport))

5. The above are all the premises concerned with the particular problem. The last group of premises are common to almost all problems of this sort. They are:

14. (x→can(y)), (did (y)→z)→canachult(x,y,z)

The predicate "canachult (x,y,z)" i.e., "can achieve ultimately," means that in a situation to which *x* applies, the action *y* can be performed and brings about a situation to which *z* applies. A sort of transitivity is described by

15. canachult (x,y,z), canachult (z,u,v)→ canachult (x,prog (y,u), v).

Here prog (*u,v*) is the program of first carrying out *u* and then *v*. (Some kind of identification of a single action *u* with the one step program prog (*u*) is obviously required, but the details of how this will fit into the formalism have not yet been worked out).

The final premise is the one which causes action to be taken.

16. x, canachult (x,prog (y,z), w), want (w)→do (y)

The argument the advice taker must produce in order to solve the problem deduces the following propositions in more or less the following order:

1. at (I,desk) → can (go (desk,car,walking))
2. at (I,car) → can (go (home,airport,driving))
3. did (go (desk,car,walking)) → at (I,car)
4. did (go (home,airport,driving)) → at (I,airport)
5. canachult (at (I,desk), go (desk,car,walking), at (I,car))
6. canachult (at (I,car), go (home,airport,driving), at (I,airport))
7. canachult (at (I,desk), program (go (desk,car,walking), go (home, airport, driving)), → at (I,airport))
8. do (go (desk,car,walking))

The deduction of the last proposition initiates action.

This reasoning raises two major questions of heuristics: The first is that of how the 16 premises are collected, and the second is that of how the deduction proceeds once they are found. We cannot give complete answers to either question in the present paper; they are obviously not completely separate since some of the deductions might be made before some of the premises are collected. Let us first consider the question of where the 16 premises come from.

First of all, we assert that except for the 13th premise (want (at (I,airport)) which sets the goal) add the 1st premise (at (I,desk) which we shall get from a routine which answers the question "where am I"), all the premises can reasonably be expected to be specifically present in the memory of a machine which has competence of human order in finding its way around. That is, none of them is so specific to the problem at hand that assuming its presence in memory constitutes an anticipation of this particular problem or of a class of problems narrower than those which any human can expect to have previously solved. We must impose this requirement if we are to be able to say that the advice taker exhibits common sense.

On the other hand, while we may reasonably assume that the premises are in memory, we still have to describe how they are assembled into a list by themselves to which the deduction routine may be applied. Tentatively, we expect the advice taker to proceed as follows: initially, the sentence "want (at (I,airport))" is on a certain list L, called the main list, all by itself. The program begins with an observation routine which looks at the main list and puts certain statements about the contents of this list on a list called "observations of the main list." We shall not specify at present what all the possible outputs of this observation routine are but merely say that in this case it will observe that "the only statement on L has the form 'want (u (x))'." (We write this out in English because we have not yet settled on a formalism for representing statements of this kind.) The "deduce and obey" routine is then applied to the combination of the "observations of the main list" list, and a list called the "standing orders list." This list is rather small and is never changed, or at least is only changed in major changes of the advice taker. The contents of the "standing orders" list has not been worked out, but what must be deduced is the extraction of certain statements from property lists. Namely, the program first looks at "want (at (I,airport))" and attempts to copy the statements on its property list. Let us assume that it fails in this attempt because "want (at (I,airport))" does not have the status of an object and hence has no property list. (One might expect that if the problem of going to the airport had arisen before, "want (at (I, airport))" would be an object, but this might depend on whether there were routines for generalizing previous experience that would allow something of general use to be filed under that heading.) Next in order of increasing generality the machine would see if anything were filed under "want (at (I,x)" which would deal with the general problem of getting somewhere. One would expect that premises 6 (or 6′ and 7′), 8, 9, 12 would be so filed. There would also be the formula

want (at (I,x)) → do (observe (where am I))

which would give us premise 1. There would also be a reference to the next higher level of abstraction in the goal statement which would cause a look at the property list of "want (x)". This would give us 14, 15, and 16.

We shall not try to follow the solution further except to remark that for "want(at (I,x))" there would be a rule that starts with the premises "at(I, y)" and "want (I,x)" and has as conclusion a search for the property list of "go (y,x,z)". This would presumably fail, and then there would have to be heuristics that would initiate a search for a *y* such that "at (I,y)" and "at ((airport,y)". This would be done by looking on the property lists of the origin and the destination and working up. Then premise 9 would be found which has as one of its premises "at (I,car)." A repetition of the above would find premise 8, which would complete the set of premises since the other "at" premises would have been found as by-products of previous searches.

We hope that the presence of the heuristic rules mentioned on the property lists where we have put them will seem plausible to the reader. It should be noticed that on the higher level of abstraction many of the statements are of the stimulus-response form. One might conjecture that division in man between conscious and unconscious thought occurs at the boundary between stimulus-response heuristics which do not have to be reasoned about but only obeyed, and the others which have to serve as premises in deductions.

7.2 Situations, Actions, and Causal Laws*

Although formalized theories have been devised to express the most important fields of mathematics and some progress has been made in formalizing certain empirical sciences, there is at present no formal theory in which one can express the kind of means-ends analysis used in ordinary life. The closest approach to such a theory of which I am aware is made by Freudenthal (2).

Our approach to the artificial-intelligence problem requires a formal theory. We believe that human intelligence depends essentially on the fact that we can represent in language facts about our situation, our goals, and the effects of the various actions we can perform. Moreover, we can draw conclusions from the facts to the effect that certain sequences of actions are likely to achieve our goals.

In Section 7.1 I discussed the advantages of having a computer program, the Advice Taker, that will reason from collections of facts about its problem and derive statements about what it can do. The name "advice taker" came from the hope that its behavior could be improved by giving it advice in the form of new facts rather than by rewriting the program. The reader is referred to Minsky (4) for a general introduction to the subject of artificial intelligence.

The first requirement for the advice taker is a formal system in which facts about situations, goals, and actions can be expressed and which contains general facts about means and ends as axioms. A start is made here on providing a system meeting the following specifications:

1. General properties of causality, and certain obvious but until now unformalized facts about the possibility and results of actions, are given as axioms.
2. It is a logical consequence of the facts of a situation and the general axioms that certain persons can achieve certain goals by taking certain actions.
3. The formal descriptions of situations should correspond as closely as possible to what people may reasonably be presumed to know about them when deciding what to do.

*Section 7.2 copies a memorandum originally distributed in 1963.

7.2.1 Situations and Fluents

One of the basic entities in our theory is the *situation.* Intuitively, a situation is the complete state of affairs at some instant of time. The laws of motion of a system determine all future situations from a given situation. Thus a situation corresponds to the notion of a point in phase space. In physics, laws are expressed in the form of differential equations which give the complete motion of the points of that space.

Our system is not intended to supply a complete description of situations nor the description of complete laws of motion. Instead, we deal with partial descriptions of situations and partial laws of motion. Moreover, the emphasis is on the simple qualitative laws of everyday life rather than on the quantitative laws of physics. As an example, take the fact that if it is raining and I go outside I will get wet.

Since a situation is defined as a complete state of affairs, we can never describe a situation fully; and we therefore provide no notation for doing so in our theory. Instead, we state facts about situations in the language of an extended predicate calculus. Examples of such facts are:

1. raining (s)
   meaning that it is raining in situation s
2. time $(s) = 1963.7205$
   giving the value of the time in situation s. It will usually prove convenient to regard the time as a function of the situation rather than vice versa, because the numerical value of the time is known and important only where the laws of physics are involved.
3. (at(I,home,s) or at(I,home)(s)
   meaning that I am at home in situation s. We shall use the second of the given notations that isolates the situation variable since in most, if not all, cases we will be able to suppress it completely.

We shall not describe here the logical system we intend to use. Basically, it is a predicate calculus, but we shall use the λ-notation and if necessary conditional expressions, as in LISP or ALGOL. We shall extend the meaning of the Boolean operators to operate on predicates. Thus by

$$\text{at(I,home)} \wedge \text{raining}$$

we mean the same as

$$\lambda s.\ \text{at(I,home)}(s) \wedge \text{raining}(s)$$

A predicate or function whose argument is a situation will be called a *fluent,* the predicate being called a *propositional fluent.* Thus, *raining, time,* and *at(I,home)* are all fluents, the first and last being propositional fluents. The term was used by Newton for a physical quantity that depends on time, and we therefore feel that the present use of the term is justified.

In our formulas we can usually use the fluents without explicitly writing variables that represent situations. This corresponds to the use of random variables in probability theory without using variables representing points in the sample space, even though random variables are supposed to be regarded as functions defined on a sample space. In fact, we shall go further and give an interpretation of our theory as a type of modal logic in which the fluents are not regarded as functions at all.

7.2.2 Causality

In order to express causal laws, we introduce the second-order predicate *cause.* The statement

$$\text{cause}(\pi)(s),$$

where π is a propositional fluent, is intended to mean that the situation s will lead in the future to a situation that satisfies the fluent π. Thus, cause (π) is itself a propositional fluent. As an example of its use we write

$$\forall s.\ \forall p.\ [\text{person}(p) \wedge \text{raining} \wedge \text{outside}(p) \supset \text{cause}(\text{wet}(p))]\ (s),$$

which asserts that a person who is outside when it is raining will get wet. We shall make the convention that, if π is a fluent, then $\forall\pi$ means the same as $\forall s\,.\,\pi(s)$.

With this convention we can write the previous statement as

$$\forall \forall p.\ \text{person}(p) \wedge \text{raining} \wedge \text{outside}(p) \supset \text{cause}(\text{wet}(p)),$$

thereby suppressing explicit mention of situations.

As a second example we discuss a special case of the law of falling bodies in the form:

$$\forall\forall t.\ \forall b.\ \forall t^1.\ \forall h\ \text{real}(t) \wedge \text{real}(t^1) \wedge \text{real}(h) \wedge \text{body}(b)$$
$$\wedge\ \text{unsupported}(b) \wedge [\text{height}(b) = h] \wedge [\tfrac{1}{2}gt^2 < h] \wedge$$
$$[\text{time} = t'] \supset \text{cause}(\text{height}(b) = h - \tfrac{1}{2}gt^2 \wedge \text{time} = t' = t).$$

The concept of causality is intended to satisfy the three following general laws, which may be considered as axioms:

C1. $\quad \forall.\ \text{cause}(\pi) \wedge [\forall.\pi \supset p] \supset \text{cause}(p)$

C2. $\quad \forall.\ \text{cause}(\text{cause}(\pi)) \supset \text{cause}(\pi)$

C3. $\quad \forall.\ \text{cause}(\pi_1) \vee \text{cause}(\pi_2) \supset \text{cause}(\pi_1 \vee \pi_2)$

The fact that we can suppress explicit mention of situations has the following interesting consequence: Instead of regarding the π's as predicates we may regard them as propositions and regard *cause* as a new modal operator. The operator $\forall$ seems then to be equivalent to the N (necessary) operator of ordinary modal logic. Conversely, it would appear that modal logic of necessity might be regarded as a monadic predicate calculus where all quantifiers are over situations.

In the present case of causality, we have a choice of how to proceed. Regarding the system as a modal logic seems to have the following two advantages:

1. If we use the predicate calculus interpretation, we require second-order predicate calculus in order to handle cause $(\pi)(s)$, whereas if we take the modal interpretation we can get by with first-order predicate calculus.
2. We shall want decision procedures or at least proof procedures for as much of our system as possible. If we use the modal approach, many problems will involve only substitution of constants for variables in universal statements and will therefore fall into a fairly readily decidable domain.

Another example of causality is given by a 2-bit binary counter that counts every second. In our formalism its behavior may be described by the statement:

$$\forall\forall t\, \forall x_0\, \forall x_1.\ \text{time} = t \wedge \text{bit0} = x_1 \supset \text{cause}\,($$
$$\text{time} = t{+}1 \wedge (\text{bit0} = x_0 \oplus 1) \wedge (\text{bit1} = x_1 \oplus (x_0 \wedge 1)))$$

In this example time, bit0, and bit1 are fluents, while t, x_0, and x_1 are numerical variables. The distinction is made clearer if we use the more long-winded statement

$$\forall s \forall t \forall x_0 \forall x_1.\text{time}\,(s) = t \wedge \text{bit0}\,(s) = x_0 \wedge \text{bit1}(s) = x_1 \supset$$
$$\text{cause}\,(\lambda s'.\text{time}\,(s') = t{+}1 \wedge (\text{bit0}(s') = x_0 \oplus 1) \wedge \text{bit1}\,(s') = x_1 \oplus (x_0 \wedge 1)))(s)$$

In this case, however, we can rewrite the statement in the form

$$\forall s.\text{cause}\,(\lambda s'.[\text{time}\,(s') = \text{time}\,(s) + 1] \wedge [\text{bit0}\,(s') = \text{bit0}(s) \oplus 1] \wedge$$
$$[\text{bit1}\,(s') = \text{bit1}\,(s) \oplus (\text{bit0}\,(s) \wedge 1)]\ )\,(s)$$

Thus we see that the suppression of explicit mention of the situations forced us to introduce the auxiliary quantities t, x_0, and x_1 which are required because we can no longer use functions of two different situations in the same formula. Nevertheless, the s-suppressed form may still be worthwhile because it admits the modal interpretation.

The time as a fluent satisfies certain axioms. The fact that there is only one situation corresponding to a given value of the time may be expressed by the axiom

T1. $\forall\forall\pi\forall\rho\forall t.$ cause $(\text{time} = t \wedge \pi) \wedge$ cause $(\text{time} = t \wedge \rho) \supset$ cause $(\text{time} = t \wedge \pi \wedge \rho)$

Another axiom is

T2. $\forall\forall t.\text{real}\,(t) \wedge t > \text{time} \supset \text{cause}\,(\text{time} = t)$

7.2.3 Actions and the Operator can

We shall regard the fact that a person performs a certain action in a situation as a propositional fluent. Thus

moves(person, object, location)(s)

is regarded as asserting that person moves object to location in the situation s. The effect of moving something is described by

$\forall\forall \rho \forall o \forall l.\text{moves}(\rho,o,l) \supset \text{cause}(\text{at } o,l))$

or in the long form

$\forall s \forall p \forall o \forall l.\text{moves}(p,o,l)(s) \supset \text{cause}(\lambda s'.\text{at}(o,l)(s'))(s)$

In order to discuss the ability of persons to achieve goals and to perform actions we introduce the operator *can.*

$\text{can}(p,\pi)(s)$

asserts that the person p can make the situation s satisfy π. We see that $\text{can}(p,\pi)$ is a propositional fluent and that like *cause, can* may be regarded either as a second-order predicate or a modal operator. Our most common use of *can* will be to assert that a person can perform a certain action. Thus we write

$\text{can}(p,\text{moves}(p,o,l))(s)$

to assert that in situation s, the person p can move the object o to location l.

The operator *can* satisfies the axioms

K1. $\forall\forall\pi\ \forall\rho\ \forall p.[\text{can}(p,\pi) \wedge (\pi \quad \rho) \supset (\text{can}(p,\rho)]$

K2. $\forall\forall\pi\ \forall p_1\ \forall p_2.[\sim \text{can}(p_1,\pi) \wedge \text{can}(p_1, \sim\pi)]$

K3. $\forall\forall p\ \forall\pi\ \forall\rho\ [\text{can}(p,\pi) \wedge \text{can}(p,\rho) \quad \text{can}(p,\pi \wedge \rho)]$

Using K1 and

$\text{can}(p, \text{moves}(p, o, l))$

and

$\forall\forall p \forall o \forall l.\text{moves}(p,o,l) \supset \text{cause}(\text{at}(o,l)),$

we can deduce

$\text{can}(p, \text{cause}(\text{at}(o,l))),$

which shows that the operators *can* and *cause* often show up in the same formula.

The ability of people to perform joint actions can be expressed by formulas like

$\text{can}(p_1, \text{can}(p_2, \text{marry}(p_1,p_2))),$

which suggests the commutative axiom

K4. $\forall\forall p_1\ \forall p_2\ \forall\pi.\text{can}(p_1,\text{can}(p_2,\pi)) \supset \text{can}(p_2,\text{can}(p_1,\pi))$

A kind of transitivity is empressed by the following

Theorem: From

1. $\text{can}(p, \text{cause}(\pi))$;

and

2. $\forall.\pi \supset \text{can}(p, \text{cause}(\rho))$;

it follows that

3. $\text{can}(p, \text{cause}(\text{can}(p, \text{cause}(\rho))))$.

Proof: Substitute $\text{can}(p, \text{cause}(\rho))$ for ρ in axiom C1 and substitute $\text{cause}(\pi)$ for π and $\text{cause}(\text{can}(p, \text{cause}(\rho)))$ for ρ in axiom K1. The conclusion then follows by propositional calculus.

In order to discuss the achievement of goals requiring several consecutive actions, we introduce *canult* (p,π) which is intended to mean that the person p can ultimately bring about a situation satisfying π. We connect it with *can* and *cause* by means of the axiom

KC1. $\forall.\forall p \forall \pi . \pi \vee \text{can}(p, \text{cause}(\text{canult}(p,\pi))) \supset \text{canult}(p,\pi)$

This axiom partially corresponds to the LISP-type recursive definition:

$\text{canult}(p,\pi) = \pi \vee \text{can}(p, \text{cause}(\text{canult}(p,\pi)))$

We also want the axiom

KC2. $\forall \forall p \forall \pi.\ \text{cause}(\text{canult}(p,\pi)) \supset \text{canult}(p,\pi)$

7.2.4 Examples

The first example we shall consider is a situation in which a monkey is in a room where a bunch of bananas is hanging from a ceiling too high to reach. In the corner of the room there is a box, and the solution to the monkey's problem is to move the box under the bananas and climb onto the box from which the bananas can be reached.

We shall describe the situation in such a way that it will follow from our axioms and the description that the monkey can get the bananas. We shall not discuss the heuristic problem of how monkeys might or even do solve the problem. Specifically, we shall prove that

canult(monkey, has(monkey, bananas)).

The situation is described in a very simplified way by the following statements:

H1. $\forall \forall u.$ place $(u) \supset$ can (monkey, move (monkey, box, u))

H2. $\forall \forall u \vee v \vee p$ move $(p,v,u) \supset$ cause (at (v,u))

H3. $\forall$ can (monkey,climbs (monkey,box))

H4. $\forall \forall u \forall v \vee p.$ at $(v,u) \wedge$ climbs $(p,v) \supset$ cause (at $(v,u) \wedge$ on (p,v))

H5. $\forall$ place (under (bananas))

H6. $\forall$ at (box, under (bananas)) $\wedge$ on (monkey, box) $\supset$ can (monkey,reach (monkey,bananas))

H7. $\forall \forall p \forall x$ reach $(p,x) \supset$ cause (has (p,x))

The reasoning proceeds as follows: From H1 and H5 by substitution of under (bananas) for u and by propositional calculus we get

1. can(monkey, move(box, under(bananas)))

Using 1, H2, and axiom C1, we get

2. can(monkey, cause(at(box, under(bananas))))

Similarly, H3, H4, and C1 give

3. at (box, under (bananas)) $\supset$ can (monkey,cause (at (box, under (bananas)) $\wedge$ on(monkey,box)))

Then H6 and H7 give

4. at (box, under (bananas)) $\wedge$ on (monkey,box) $\supset$ can (monkey,cause (has(monkey,bananas)))

Now, Theorem 1 is used to combine 2, 3, and 4, to result in

5. can(monkey,cause(can(monkey,cause(can(monkey,cause(has(monkey, bananas))))))

Using KC1, we reduce this to

canult(monkey, has(monkey, bananas)))

Another example concerns a two-person game where player p_1 has two moves, but whichever one he chooses, player p_2 has a move that will beat him. This situation may be described as follows:

1. $\text{can}\,(p_1, m_1) \wedge \text{can}\,(p_1, m_2) \wedge (m_1 \vee m_2)$
2. $[m_1 \supset \text{cause}\,(\pi_1)] \wedge [m_2 \supset \text{cause}\,(\pi_2)]$
3. $\forall . \pi_1 \vee \pi_2 \supset [\text{can}\,(p_2, n_1) \wedge \text{can}\,(p_2, n_2) \wedge (n_1 \vee n_2)]$
4. $\forall . (\pi_1 \wedge n_1) \vee (\pi_2 \wedge n_2) \supset \text{cause}\,(\text{win}\,(p_2))$

We would like to be able to draw the conclusion

3. $\text{canult}(p_2, \text{win}(p_2))$

We proceed as follows: From 1 and 2 we get

4. $\text{cause}\,(\pi_1) \vee \text{cause}\,(\pi_2)$

and we use Axiom C3 to get

5. $\text{cause}\,(\pi_1 \vee \pi_2)$

Next we weaken 3 to get

6. $\forall . \pi_1 \supset \text{can}\,(p_2, n_1)$ and
7. $\forall . \pi_2 \supset \text{can}\,(p_2, n_2)$

and then we use K1 to get

8. $\forall . \pi_1 \supset \text{can}\,(p_2, \pi_1 \wedge n_1)$ and
9. $\forall . \pi_2 \supset \text{can}\,(p_2, \pi_2 \wedge n_2)$

The propositional calculus gives

10. $\forall . \pi_1 \vee \pi_2 \supset \text{can}\,(p_2, \pi_1 \wedge n_1) \quad \text{can}(p_2, \pi_2 \wedge n_2)$

and using K3 we get

11. $\forall . \pi_1 \vee \pi_2 \supset \text{can}\,(p_2, (\pi_1 \wedge n_1) \quad (\pi_2 \wedge n_2))$

which together with 4 and K1 gives

12. $\forall . \pi_1 \vee \pi_2 \supset \text{can}\,(p_2, \quad \text{cause}\,(\text{win}\,(p_2)))$

which together with 5 and C1 gives

13. $\text{cause}(\text{can}(p_2, \text{cause}(\text{win}(p_2)))$

Using the axioms for *canult* we now get

14. $\text{canult}\,(p_2, \text{win}\,(p_2))$.

7.2.5 Note

After finishing the bulk of this investigation I came across the work of Prior (7). He defines modal operators P and F, where

P (π) means 'it has been the case that π' and

F (π) means 'it will be the case that π'

He subjects these operators to a number of axioms and rules of inference in close analogy to the well-known (9) modal logic of possibility, and also interprets this logic in a restricted predicate calculus where the variables range over times. This logic is then extended to include a somewhat undetermined future and he claims (unconvincingly) that it cannot be interpreted in predicate calculus.

I have not yet made a detailed comparison of our logic with Prior's, but here are some tentative conclusions:

1. The causality logic should be extended to allow inference about the past.
2. Causality logic should be extended to allow inference that certain propositional fluents will always hold.
3. cause(π) satisfies the axioms for his $F(\pi)$, which means that his futurity theory possesses, from his point of view, nonstandard models. Specifically, a collection of functions $p_1(t), p_2(t)$ may satisfy his futurity axioms and assign truth to $p(1) \wedge \sim (Fp)(0)$. In our system this is acceptable because something can happen without being caused to happen.
4. If we combine his past and futurity axioms, our system will no longer fit his axioms and

PF1. $p \quad \sim F(\sim P(p))$

PF2. $p \quad \sim P(\sim F(p))$

since we do not wish to say that whatever is was always inevitable.

Bibliography

1. Friedberg, R. A., "A Learning Machine," *IBM J. of Research and Development,* Part I: Vol. 2, No. 3, 1958; Part II: Vol. 3, No. 3, 1959.
2. Freudenthal, H. A., *Lincos: Design of a Language for Cosmic Intercourse,* North-Holland Press, Amsterdam, 1960.
3. McCarthy, J., "Inversion of Functions Defined by Turing Machines," *Automatic Studies,* Princeton, 1956.
4. Minsky, M., "Steps Toward Artificial Intelligence," *Proc. IRE,* Vol. 49, No. 1, 1961.
5. Minsky, M., "Neural Models for Memory," *Proc. Internatl. Congr. Physiological Sciences,* Vol. III, Leiden, 1962 (*Excerpta Medica* Internatl. Congr. Series 49).
6. Newell, A., et al., "Empirical Explorations of the Logic Theory Machine: A Case Study in Heuristics," *Proc. WJCC, IRE,* 1957.
7. Prior, A. N., *The Syntax of Time Distinctions,* Franciscan Studies, 1958
8. Samuel, A. L., "Some Studies in Machine Learning Using the Game of Checkers," *IBM J. of Research and Development,* Vol. 3, No. 3, 1959.

8. Descriptive Languages and Problem Solving*

Marvin L. Minsky

8.1 Introduction

Work on artificial intelligence is proceeding at a slow, apparently steady, rate. The complexity of problems being attacked is growing slowly, as is the complexity of the successful programs themselves. In the past it seems to have taken two or three years for each significant advance, and one may ask why progress is so slow. Much of this time has been spent on the development of programming languages and systems suitable for the symbol-manipulation processes involved. But much of the difficulty has been conceptual as well. Methods that worked quite well on easy problems did not extend smoothly to the difficult ones. Continued progress will require implementation of new ideas, for there are some very tough problems in our immediate path. It seems to us that solution of these problems will require the use of nontrivial formal and descriptive language systems. These are only beginning to appear as a working part of the problem-solving machinery, and it will take much ingenuity to bring current notions into usable form.

Our purpose here is to indicate a few of the considerations that seem to point toward the incorporation of complex linguistic processes into the next generation of heuristic programs. In another paper (1) I discussed the principles and mechanisms of a variety of problem-solving systems but did not dwell on the question of extending these to really complex problems. We assume the

*This is a slightly edited version of a paper published in the Proceedings of the 1961 Western Joint Computer Conference.

terminology of that paper. When one attempts to apply the techniques described there one discovers that

1. The search problems become very serious. One is faced not only with greatly enlarged problem trees but also with a greater variety of plausible methods.
2. The problem of learning from experience becomes qualitatively more difficult. To learn the lesson of a complex experience requires shrewd, deliberate analysis that cannot be approximated by any of the simple learning models based on averaging or on correlation.
3. The classification and pattern recognition methods must be on a descriptive level. Again, correlation or matching methods must be replaced by more sophisticated symbol-manipulation processes.
4. Planning methods, character and difference algebras, etc., threaten to collapse when the fixed sets of categories adequate for simple problems have to be replaced by the expressions of a descriptive language. The use of look-up tables for choosing methods will have to be supplemented by something more like reasoning.

When we call for the use of "reasoning," we intend no suggestion of giving up the game by invoking an intelligent subroutine. The program that administers the search will be just another heuristic program. Almost certainly it will be composed largely of the same sorts of objects and processes that will comprise the subject-domain programs. Almost certainly it will be recursively applied to itself so that the system can be finite. But it does seem clear that the basic (nonrecursive) part of the structure will have to be more complex than is any current system.

8.2 The Need for Analysis

The simplest problems, e.g., playing tic-tac-toe or proving the very simplest theorems of logic, can be solved by simple recursive application of all the available transformations to all the situations that occur, dealing with subproblems in the order of their generation. This becomes impractical in more complex problems as the search space grows larger and each trial becomes more expensive in time and effort. One can no longer afford a policy of simply leaving one unsuccessful attempt to go on to another. For, each attempt on a difficult problem will involve so much effort that one must be quite sure that, whatever the outcome, the effort will not be wasted entirely. One must become selective to the point that no trial is made without a compelling reason, just as expensive experiments must be carefully designed in any research. One must do a good deal of criticism and analysis between experiments so that each will be a critical test of a significant portion of the search space.

The ability to solve a difficult problem hinges on the ability to split or transform it into problems of a lower order of difficulty. To do this, without total reliance on luck, requires some understanding of the situation. One must be able to deduce, or guess, enough of the consequences of the problem statement to be able to set up simpler models of the problem situation. The models must have enough structure to make it likely that there will be a way to extend their solutions to the original problem.

The construction of less difficult subproblems will be useful, by definition, only if one has already a very good chance of solving *them* efficiently. Otherwise the search tree will grow beyond bounds. This means we must have already built up adequate solution methods for the lower order problems, e.g., as a set of more or less packaged subroutines. This entails some formidable requirements:

8.2.1 Training Sequences

The machine is presumed to have acquired its good subroutines through earlier solution of less complex problems. (We are not interested here in the case in which these methods are provided at the start.) Thus, the machine must have been exposed to a graded sequence of problems. To be sure, given time limits, a machine will select a graded subsequence from an unorganized variety of problems. But a careful arrangement will be necessary to insure that methods learned in the problems that the machine does manage to solve will be useful on more difficult problems met later. In any case one cannot rely on making large jumps, either in machines or in humans.

8.2.2 Refinement Phase

Solving simple problems is not enough. To make progress one needs also to "package" the successful method for effective later use. We are not interested in the trivial case of recognizing a problem solved once before, though this can be difficult enough when there is some disguise. The success must be generalized to cover a substantial variety of situations. To do this it would seem that there should be a phase of exploration and consolidation in which the successful method is refined–its central innovation (if any) isolated and packaged–in terms as general as possible. One must explore its range of application and construct an expression describing this range. This may involve inventing similar problems on which the method, or close variant, works and then constructing a plausible generalization.

Certainly people must go through such phases. One cannot usually solve hard problems with once-used but still unfamiliar methods. One must first "understand" the methods quite well; this means becoming able to recognize situations in which they are applicable. It is probably misleading to think of this as "practice" acquisition of facility through repetition. Exercise in, e.g., mathematical technique is probably very different from exercise in weightlifting. Its effect is not so much in reinforcing methods, or paths already weakly laid down, but rather to provide the necessary data for some inductive inference technique. The latter will replace the special method by one of somewhat greater generality.

Failure of the refinement phase to yield a precise, abstractly stated conclusion can be concealed to a point. One often encounters mathematical situations in which one can answer particular questions quickly, yet is unable to state a satisfactory formal generalization. This can happen through the assembly of a set of different models or examples which, as a group, show most or all of the features of the unformulated general theorem. One can answer some questions in the negative, by finding inconsistency with an example. Consistency with all leads one to the affirmative. Often the examples themselves are not formulated clearly, or entirely consciously. In such cases one will find that some statements seem "obvious" yet (because of the incomplete understanding which precludes giving any precise explanation) are also felt to be "intuitive." An incomplete formalization or conceptualization, e.g., such a set of examples, can be very powerful when used at or near the top level. But if not understood or "packaged," it could become a serious impediment later when, because of its informality, it cannot be used in deduction or in the construction of further abstractions.

8.2.3 Coding and Retrieval Problems

The compact representation of results of previous experience requires an adequate descriptive language, which must permit general statements about both problem-domain matters and problem-solving methods. It must also permit logical deductions to be made. This raises several problems.

One problem that has been a great nuisance to us arises in connection with nonmathematical problems in which actions affect the state of some subject domain. Thus a *move* affects the positions of pieces in a board game. When this happens, some statements formerly deduced about the situation cease to be true. (In a mathematical domain a theorem once proved remains true when one proves other theorems!) One must then deduce all the consequences of an action insofar as it affects propositions that one is planning to use. This might be done through some heuristic technique that can assess relevancy, or through a logic which takes such consequences into account. The trouble with the latter is that the antecedents of all the propositions must contain a condition about the state of the system, and for complex systems this becomes overwhelmingly cumbersome. Other systematic solutions to the problem seem about equally repellent. It is a problem that seems urgently to require a heuristic solution.

Our present proposal on this matter is to make the system plan ahead. Whenever an important deduction is made, the system is to try to discover which kinds of actions could affect its validity. Independent monitors are then set up to detect when such actions are proposed. The normal problem-solving exploration process goes on independently of these monitors and is interrupted when one of them detects a threat to the proposition it is defending. This model has a certain introspectively attractive character; it suggests a free conscious exploration with more or less subconscious trouble detectors. Unfortunately, its essentially parallel nature threatens to make its use in serial computer programming rather expensive. We hope someone will come up with a better idea.

In any case, the retrieval problem has to be faced. The problem of making useful deductions from a large body of statements (e.g., about the relevance of different methods to different kinds of problems) raises a new search problem. One must restrict the logical exploration to data likely to be relevant to the current problem. This selection function could hardly be completely built in at the start. It must develop along with other data accumulated by experience.

Another rather serious problem centers around abbreviations and proper names. The language must be used together with an abbreviative technique so that the most useful notions can be designated by reasonably convenient (short) representations. This is not only a matter of convenience and compactness; it is a more or less inescapable requirement of known inductive inference techniques and thus requisite for the formation of hypotheses or generalizations. Unfortunately an abbreviation cannot show all of the structure of the longer expression it designates. This seriously limits the possibilities of making formal logical deductions. Ultimately the machines will have to use mnemonic codings in their internal languages, just as we need to when we use their external languages.

The systematic solution to the abbreviation problem is, again, to revise the whole body of propositions in current use insofar as they are going to be used in the same deductive operations. All the alternatives to this that we can envision are of a somewhat stopgap nature. We content ourselves with the observation that it is equally a major problem for humans to make substantial changes in basic abstractions, ways of classifying or perceiving, and the like. Once one has built up a structure depending on a certain conceptual commitment, he will stave off a revision of its foundation as though the cost of changing it were high. Otherwise, perhaps, people would not argue so much. One may view that phenomenon, if one likes, as a matter of ego involvement. But it would be well to remember that being wrong (and having to change) involves a real intellectual cost and not merely a social cost.

8.3 Conclusion

The need to be able to make abstractions in symbolic language is already urgent in current attempts to make machines prove theorems, play games, etc. There are some very difficult problems to be faced in this area. We still maintain, with McCarthy, that "*in order for a program to be capable of learning something it must first be capable of being told it*" (2). Results on "self-organizing systems" without explicit provision for such abilities show very little promise to date, and systematic attempts in the direction of internal language processing should be promoted.

Bibliography

1. M. L. Minsky, "Steps Toward Artificial Intelligence," *Proc. IRE,* Vol. 49, 1961.
2. J. McCarthy, Section 7.1 of the present volume.

9. Matter, Mind, and Models*

Marvin L. Minsky

9.1 Introduction

This chapter attempts to explain why people become confused by questions about the relation between mental and physical events. When a question leads to confused, inconsistent answers, this may be because the question is ultimately meaningless or at least unanswerable, but it may also be because an adequate answer requires a powerful analytical apparatus. It is the author's view that many important questions about the relation between mind and brain are of this latter kind, and that some of the necessary technical and conceptual tools are becoming available as a result of work on the problems of making computer programs behave intelligently. We shall suggest a theory to explain why introspection does not give clear answers to these questions. Technical solutions to the questions will not be attempted, but there is probably some value in finding at least a clear explanation of why we are confused.

9.2 Knowledge and Models

If a creature can answer a question about a hypothetical experiment without actually performing it, then it has demonstrated some knowledge about the world. For, his answer to the question must be an encoded description of

*Published in Proc. International Federation of Information Processing Congress 1965, vol. 1, pp. 45-49. I do not regard this paper as "finished." It was repeatedly revised since about 1954 and published when further revision seemed unfruitful.

the behavior (inside the creature) of some sub-machine or "model" responding to an encoded description of the world situation described by the question.

We use the term "model" in the following sense: To an observer B, an object A* is a model of an object A to the extent that B can use A* to answer questions that interest him about A.

The model relation is inherently ternary. Any attempt to suppress the role of the intentions of the investigator B leads to circular definitions or to ambiguities about "essential features" and the like. It is understood that B's use of a model entails the use of encodings for input and output, both for A and for A*. If A is the world, questions for A are experiments. A* is a good model of A, in B's view, to the extent that A*'s answers agree with those of A's, on the whole, with respect to the questions important to B.

When a man M answers questions about the world, then (taking on ourselves the role of B) we attribute this ability to some internal mechanism W* inside of M. It would be most convenient if we could discern physically within M two separate regions, W* and M-W*, such that W* "really contains the knowledge" and M-W* contains only general-purpose machinery for coding questions, decoding answers, and general administrative work. However, one cannot really expect to find, in an intelligent machine, a clear separation between coding and knowledge structures, either anatomically or functionally, because (for example) some "knowledge" is likely to be used in the encoding and interpreting processes. What is important for our purposes is the intuitive notion of a model, not the technical ability to delineate a model's boundaries. Indeed, part of our argument hinges on the inherent difficulty of discerning such boundaries.

9.3 Models of Models

Questions about things in the world are answered by making statements about the behavior of corresponding structures in one's model W* of the world. For simple mechanical, physical, or geometric matters one can imagine, as did Craik (1), some machinery that does symbolic calculation but when read through proper codings has an apparently analogue character. But what about broader questions about the nature of the world? These have to be treated (by M) not as questions to be answered by W*, but as questions to be answered by making general statements about W*. If W* contains a model M* of M, then M* can contain a model W** of W*; and, going one step further, W** may contain a model M** of M*. Indeed, this must be the case if M is to answer general questions about himself. Ordinary questions about himself, e.g., how tall he is, are answered by M*, but very broad questions about his nature, e.g., what kind of a thing he is, etc., are answered, if at all, by descriptive statements made by M** about M*.

The reader may be anxious, at this point, for more details about the relation between W* and W**. How can he tell, for example, when a question is of the kind that requires reference to W** rather than to W*. Is W** a part of W*? (Certainly W*, like everything else, is part of W.) Unfortunately, I cannot supply these details yet, and I expect serious problems in eventually clarifying them. We must envision W** as including an interpretative mechanism that can make reference to W*, using it as a sort of computer-program subroutine, to a certain depth of recursion. In this sense W** must contain W*, but in another, more straightforward, sense W* can contain W**. This suggests first that the notion "contained in" is not sufficiently sophisticated to describe the kinds of relations between parts of programlike processes and second that the intuitive notion of "model" used herein is likewise too unsophisticated to support developing the theory in technical detail. It is clear that in this area one cannot describe intermodel relationships in terms of models as simple physical substructures. An adequate analysis will need much more advanced ideas about symbolic representation of information-processing structures.

9.4 Dimorphism of our World Models

A man's model of the world has a distinctly bipartite structure: One part is concerned with matters of mechanical, geometrical, physical character, while the other is associated with things like goals, meanings, social matters, and the like. This division of W* carries through the representations of many things in W*, especially to M itself. Hence, a man's model of himself is bipartite, one part concerning his body as a physical object and the other accounting for his social and psychological experience. When we see an object, we account for its mechanical support and coherence (we are amazed at levitations) and we also account, in different terms, for its teleology (who put it there and for what purpose). When something moves we find either a simple force or a purpose–rarely both–in the kind of ordinary common-sense explanation that concerns us here.

Why is this division so richly represented in language and thought? We recognize that a person's W* is not really two clearly disjoint parts but must have many overlapping, indistinctly bounded models. The bipartite structure proposed here is only an approximation, and we do not really want to suggest that the argument depends at all on a clear division into any particular number of parts.

The distinction between energetic and informational (or symbolic) explanations is another aspect of the same general dimorphism. In one sphere, mechanical-geometric constraints are powerful, e.g., impenetrability in the arrangement of physical objects, conservation in their transformation. In the other sphere, one finds symbolic constraints of (substantially) equal power. The two domains overlap in many complicated ways: a child discovers mechanical obstacles (in the form, e.g., of limitation of reach, mobility, strength, and precision) to its psychological goals; it discovers emotional symbols in the geometric arrangements of facial expressions, and intentions in postural attitudes. In explanations of complicated things the two models become inextricably involved–viz. the imagery of the preceding sentences. But this involvement reflects not so much any synthesis of the two kinds of explanation as it reflects the poverty of either model for description of complicated situations.

As for the genesis of such partitions, I suppose that they grow apart rather than together, on the whole. That is not to say that infantile, primitive models are more unitary, but rather that they are simply too indistinct to admit approximate boundaries. An infant is not a monist: It simply hasn't enough structure in M^{**} to be a dualist yet; it can hardly be said to have a position on the mind-body problem.

9.5 The Central Argument: Belief in Dualism

When a man is asked a general question about his own nature, he will try to give a general description of his model of himself. That is, the question will be answered by M^{**}. To the extent that M^* is divided as we have supposed and that the man has discovered this (that is, this fact is now represented in M^{**}), his reply will show this. *His statement (his belief) that he has a mind as well as a body is the conventional way to express the roughly bipartite appearance of his model of himself.*

Because the separation of the two parts of M^* is so indistinct and their interconnections are so complicated and difficult to describe, the man's further attempts to elaborate on the nature of this "mind-body" distinction are bound to be confused and unsatisfactory.

9.6 Heuristic Value of Quasi-Separate Models

From a scientific point of view, it is desirable to obtain a unitary model of the world comprising both mechanical and psychological phenomena. Such a theory would become available, for example, if the workers in artificial intelligence, cybernetics, and neurophysiology would all reach their goals. Still, such a success might have little effect on the over-all form of our personal world models. I maintain that for practical, heuristic reasons, these would still retain their form of quasi-separate parts. Even when a discipline is grossly transformed in techniques, bases, and concepts, it can maintain its identity if its problems and concerns remain grouped together for practical reasons. For example, Chemistry survives today as a science because the primitives of the quantum theory are a little too remote for direct application to practical problems; a hierarchy of intermediate concepts is necessary to apply the theory to everyday problems. The primitive notions of physics, or even of neurophysiology, will be far too remote to be useful in accounting directly for the mental events of everyday life.

Thus synthesis by direct theoretical reduction is unlikely to have a large effect on the over-all form of W^*. The heuristic need for approximately self-contained subtheories is too strong to resist in practical life and thought. Now one might hope for another kind of unity—parallel rather than hierarchical—in which the quasi-separate models are converted to basically similar structures and then merged by removal of redundancy, with coding for those differences that remain significant. It is doubtful that much can be done in this direction. The use of psychological explanations for physical processes runs exactly counter to the directions that have led to scientific progress. Similarly, there have long been available plenty of "reductions" of psychological explanations to analogies with simple physical systems, but these are recognized as inadequate and are giving way to information-processing models of more abstract character.

In everyday practical thought, physical analogy metaphors play a large role, presumably because one gets a large payoff for a model of apparently small complexity. (Actually, only the incremental complexity is small because most of the model is already there as part of the "physical" part of W^*.) It would be hard to give up such metaphors, even though they probably interfere with our further development, just because of this apparent high value-to-cost ratio. We cannot expect to get much more by extending the mechanical analogies, because they are so inflexible in character. Mental processes resemble more the kinds of processes found in computer programs: arbitrary symbol-associations, treelike storage schemes, conditional transfers, and the like. In short, we can expect the simpler useful mechanical analogies to survive, but it seems doubtful that they can grow to bring us usable ideas for the parallel unification of W^*.

Finally, we should note that in a creature with high intelligence one can expect to find a well-developed special model concerned with the creature's own problem-solving activity. In my view the key to any really advanced problem-solving technique must exploit some mechanism for planning—for breaking the problem into parts and shrewdly allocating the machine's effort and resources for the work ahead. This means the machine must have facilities for representing and analyzing its own goals and resources. One could hardly expect to find a useful way to merge this structure with that used for analyzing uncomplicated structures in the outer world, nor could one expect that anything much simpler would be of much power in analyzing the behavior of other creatures of the same character.

9.7 Interpreters

The notion of "part" is more complicated for things like computer programs than for ordinary physical objects. A single conditional branch makes it possible for a program to behave, functionally, like two very different machines in different circumstances, yet using almost (or exactly) the same sets of instructions.

The notion of a machine containing a model of itself is also complicated, and one might suspect potential logical paradoxes. There is no logical problem about the basic idea, for the internal model could be very much simplified, and *its* internal model could be vacuous. But, in fact, there is no paradox even in a machine's having a model of itself complete in all detail. For example, it is possible to construct a Turing machine that can print out an entire description of itself and also execute an arbitrarily complicated computation, so that the machine is not expending all its structure on its description. In particular, the machine can contain an "interpretative" program that can use the internal description to calculate what it itself would do under some hypothetical circumstance. Similarly, while it is impossible for a machine or mind to analyze from moment to moment precisely what it is doing at each step (for it would never get past the first step), there seems to be no logical limitation to the possibility of a machine understanding its own basic principles of operation or, given enough memory, examining all the details of its operation in some previously recorded state.

With interpretative operation ability, a program can use itself as its own model, and this can be repeated recursively to as many levels as desired, until the memory records of the state of the process get out of hand. With the possibility of this sort of "introspection," the boundaries between *parts, things,* and *models* become very hard to understand.

Does interpreted operation play an important role in our mental function? It is clear that one interprets memorized instructions in certain circumstances. One could memorize, for example, the rules for reading musical notation and then actually perform a piece of music, at a very slow tempo, by referring to these rules in executing each note. Eventually, with practice, one plays faster, and it seems clear that one is no longer interpreting the rules for each note, but that one has assembled special mechanisms for the task. This certainly suggests an analogy with the notion of "compiling" a previously interpreted program. Perhaps our level of consciousness is closely related to the extent to which the machine is functioning interpretatively rather than executing compiled programs. While interpreting, one has the opportunity of examining the next step in the task before doing it.

9.8 Free Will

If one thoroughly understands a machine or a program, he finds no urge to attribute "volition" to it. If one does not understand it so well, he must supply an incomplete model for explanation. Our everyday intuitive models of higher human activity are quite incomplete, and many notions in our informal explanations do not tolerate close examination. Free will or volition is one such notion: people are incapable of explaining how it differs from stochastic caprice but feel strongly that it does. I conjecture that this idea has its genesis in a strong primitive defense mechanism. Briefly, in childhood we learn to recognize various forms of aggression and compulsion and to dislike them, whether we submit or resist. Older, when told that our behavior is "controlled" by such and such a set of laws, we insert this fact in our model (inappropriately) along with other recognizers of compulsion. We resist "compulsion," no matter from "whom." Although resistance is logically futile, the resentment persists and is rationalized by defective explanations, since the alternative is emotionally unacceptable.

How is this reflected in M**? If one asks how one's mind works, he notices areas where it is (perhaps incorrectly) understood—that is, where one recognizes rules. One sees other areas where he lacks rules. One could fill this in by postulating chance or random activity. But this too, by another route, exposes the self to the same indignity of remote control. We resolve this unpleasant form of M** by postulating a *third part*, embodying a will or spirit or conscious agent. But there is no structure in this part; one can say nothing meaningful about it, because whenever a regularity is observed, its representation is transferred to the deterministic rule region. The will model is thus not formed from a legitimate need for a place to store definite information about one's self; it has the singular character of being forced into the model, willy-nilly, by formal but essentially content-free ideas of what the model must contain.

9.9 Conclusion

When intelligent machines are constructed, we should not be surprised to find them as confused and as stubborn as men in their convictions about mind-matter, consciousness, free will, and the like. For all such questions are pointed at explaining the complicated interactions between parts of the self-model. A man's or a machine's strength of conviction about such things tells us nothing about the man or about the machine except what it tells us about his model of himself.

The gross divisions of our models probably have much heuristic value to us. Indeed we identify (in children) some stages in delineating the distinctions between these models as associated with the growth of intelligence. The distinctions could be abandoned only at great cost in everyday practice. That is why, even if one accepts the conclusions of this essay, he is unlikely to note any serious effect on his way of thinking about most things.

Bibliography

1. Craik, K. J. W., *The Nature of Explanation,* Cambridge University Press, Cambridge, England, 1952.

Subject Index

Author Index